RCR ← "The Kid"

Best of luck

Robert C Smith DDS

5-13-83

HOST-PARASITE INTERACTIONS IN PERIODONTAL DISEASES

HOST-PARASITE INTERACTIONS
IN PERIODONTAL DISEASES

Proceedings of a symposium
held at Buffalo, New York
4–6 May 1981

EDITORS

Robert J. Genco
State University of New York at Buffalo
Buffalo, New York

Stephan E. Mergenhagen
National Institutes of Health
Bethesda, Maryland

American Society for Microbiology
Washington, D.C.
1982

Library of Congress Cataloging in Publication Data

Main entry under title:
Host-parasite interactions in periodontal diseases.

"Papers . . . delivered at a symposium on Host-Parasite Interactions in Periodontal Diseases, held in Buffalo, New York, 4–6 May 1981"—Pref.
Includes bibliographical references and index.
1. Periodontal disease—Etiology—Congresses. 2. Periodontal disease—Immunological aspects—Congresses. 3. Mouth—Microbiology—Congresses. 4. Bacterial diseases—Congresses. 5. Host-parasite relationships—Congresses. I. Genco, Robert J. II. Mergenhagen, Stephan E. [DNLM: 1. Host-parasite relations —Congresses. 2. Periodontal diseases—Microbiology—Congresses. WU 240 H831 1981]

RK361.A2H67   617.6′32   81-17656

ISBN 0-914826-37-9   AACR2

Contents

Preface   vii

Etiology and Microbial Specificity

Present Status of Studies on the Microbial Etiology of Periodontal
Diseases. SIGMUND S. SOCRANSKY, ANNE C. R. TANNER, ANNE D.
HAFFAJEE, JEFFREY D. HILLMAN, AND J. MAX GOODSON   1
Subgingival Microflora in Periodontal Disease: Cultural Studies.
W. E. C. MOORE, R. R. RANNEY, AND L. V. HOLDEMAN   13
Importance of Black-Pigmented *Bacteroides* in Human Periodontal
Disease. JØRGEN SLOTS   27
Capnocytophaga and *Actinobacillus actinomycetemcomitans:* Occur-
rence and Pathogenic Potential in Juvenile Periodontitis. B. F.
HAMMOND AND R. H. STEVENS   46
Role of Spirochetes in Periodontal Disease. WALTER J. LOESCHE AND
BARBARA E. LAUGHON   62
Physiological and Ecological Properties of the Oral Gram-Negative
Gliding Bacteria Capable of Attaching to Hydroxyapatite. JACK
LONDON, ROGER CELESK, AND PAUL KOLENBRANDER   76

Colonization by Periodontopathic Organisms

Colonization Mechanisms Involved in the Development of the Oral
Flora. JOHANNES VAN HOUTE   86
Oral Colonization by Gram-Positive Bacteria Significant to Periodontal
Disease. RICHARD P. ELLEN   98
Colonization of Subgingival Areas by Motile Rods and Spirochetes:
Clinical Implications. MAX A. LISTGARTEN   112
Coaggregation Reactions Between Oral Bacteria: Studies of Specific
Cell-to-Cell Adherence Mediated by Microbial Lectins. JOHN O.
CISAR   121
Age, Supragingival Plaque, and Steroid Hormones as Ecological Deter-
minants of the Subgingival Flora. KENNETH S. KORNMAN   132

Pathogenic and Virulence Factors
In Periodontal Diseases

Bacterial Surface Structures and Their Role in Periodontal Disease.
STANLEY C. HOLT   139
Bacterial Components Which Result in Bone Loss. ERNEST HAUSMANN,
BALA CHANDRAN NAIR, AND ROSEMARY DZIAK   151
Cellular Basis of Endotoxin Susceptibility. STEFANIE N. VOGEL AND
STEPHAN E. MERGENHAGEN   160
Pathogenicity of *Actinomyces* Species. HAROLD V. JORDAN   169
Noncytolytic Effects of *Actinobacillus actinomycetemcomitans* on
Leukocyte Functions. WILLIAM P. MCARTHUR, CHI-CHENG TSAI,
PIERRE BAEHNI, B. J. SHENKER, AND NORTON S. TAICHMAN   179
Bacterial Immunoglobulin A Proteases and Mucosal Diseases: Use of
Synthetic Peptide Analogs to Modify the Activity of These
Proteases. ANDREW G. PLAUT, JOANNE V. GILBERT, AND JAMES
BURTON   193

Cellular Aspects of Host Responses

Cellular Immunity in Periodontal Disease: an Overview. THOMAS
LEHNER 202
Lymphoid Cell Responsiveness and Human Periodontitis. ROY C.
PAGE 217
Mononuclear Cell-Mediated Alterations in Connective Tissue. SHARON
M. WAHL 225
Periodontal Diseases and Neutrophil Abnormalities.   T. E. VAN DYKE,
M. J. LEVINE, AND R. J. GENCO 235
Polymorphonuclear Leukocytes of the Human Gingival Crevice: Clinical
and Experimental Studies of Cellular Function in Humans and
Animals.   J. M. A. WILTON 246
Leukocidal Mechanisms of Actinobacillus actinomycetemcomitans.
N. S. TAICHMAN, W. P. MCARTHUR, C.-C. TSAI, P. C. BAEHNI, B. J.
SHENKER, P. BERTHOLD, C. EVIAN, AND R. STEVENS 261

Effector Systems — Specific and Nonspecific

Relation Between Periodontal Disease Activity and Serum Antibody
Titers to Oral Bacteria. KÅRE TOLO AND PER BRANDTZAEG 270
Association Between Systemic and Local Antibody and Periodontal
Diseases. M. A. TAUBMAN, J. L. EBERSOLE, AND D. J. SMITH 283
The Complement System in Periodontal Diseases. HARVEY A.
SCHENKEIN 299
Humoral and Cellular Mediation of Bone Resorption. ANN L. SANDBERG . 309
Roles of Lysozyme in the Host Response to Periodontopathic Micro-
organisms. VINCENT J. IACONO, BRUCE J. MACKAY, JERRY J.
POLLOCK, PAUL R. BOLDT, STEVEN LADENHEIM, BARBARA L. GROSS-
BARD, AND MARY L. ROCHON 318
Oxygen Radicals in Inflammation and Immunity. J. TERRELL
HOFFELD 343

Clinical Implications of Host—Parasite Interactions

Analogous Mechanisms of Tissue Destruction in Rheumatoid Arthritis
and Periodontal Disease. RALPH SNYDERMAN AND GALE A.
MCCARTY 354
Influence of Pharmacological Agents on Bone Resorption. PAUL
GOLDHABER AND LUKA RABADJIJA 363
Strategies in the Use of Antibacterial Agents in Periodontal Disease.
HARALD LÖE AND KENNETH KORNMAN 376
Treatment of Localized Juvenile Periodontitis. JAN LINDHE 382
Diagnosis of Creviculoradicular Infections: Disease-Associated Bacterial
Patterns in Periodontal Lesions. PAUL H. KEYES, MORRISON
ROGOSA, THOMAS E. RAMS, AND DAVID E. SARFATTI 395
Summary of Conference and Perspectives for the Future. IRWIN D.
MANDEL 404

Author Index 411
Subject Index 412

Preface

It is clear that periodontal diseases are initiated by bacteria. It is also evident that the host response plays a major role in the outcome of these infections. This volume addresses for the first time those unique host–parasite interactions which occur in periodontal diseases. It is organized to present an up-to-date summary of the microbiology and immunology of these diseases for scientists and students whose main interests are in infectious diseases or clinical periodontology. The chapters are written by recognized authorities who are actively engaged in research. Their contributed chapters are placed in six sections, each dealing with a distinct topic.

Section I deals with the etiology and microbial specificity of periodontal diseases. General reviews of studies of the subgingival microflora as well as specific reviews of the *Bacteriodes* species, *Capnocytophaga*, *Actinobacillus actinomycetemcomitans*, and spirochetes comprise this section. In Section II the chapters describe colonization of the oral cavity and its various ecological niches by periodontopathic organisms. Mechanisms of colonization by gram-negative and gram-positive organisms and the role of host factors in the ecology of the subgingival flora are described.

The chapters in Section III complete the bacteriology with discussion of pathogenic and virulence factors. Bacterial factors which cause bone resorption or kill neutrophils, differential virulence of *Actinomyces* species alone and in combination with associated organisms, and the genetic determinants of endotoxin susceptibility are presented. A chapter on bacterial immunoglobulin A proteases and mucosal diseases, which presents the concept of a bacterial product with the potential to neutralize a host defense mechanism, provides the transition from discussion of bacteria to discussion of host responses.

In Section IV, cellular aspects of the host response are discussed. An overview chapter on cellular immunity and regulation of the immune response is followed by chapters on mononuclear cell responsiveness in periodontal disease and on lymphocyte and macrophage mediators, which give a balanced view of the role of these cells in the disease process. Two chapters on the neutrophil detail recent findings on abnormalities of cell function in certain forms of periodontal disease that suggest a major protective role for this cell in the disease.

Section V provides a summary of data on effector mechanisms of importance in chronic infections. Chapters on antibodies and complement provide a background for understanding the role of these molecules in inflammation; they also provide a timely summary of recent findings on antibody titers and complement activation patterns characteristic in various forms of periodontal disease. A chapter follows which integrates and shows possible interaction between humoral and cellular immune mediation of bone resorption. The final chapters in this section describe those non-immunological factors which may be involved in the inflammatory response, such as lysozyme, lactoperoxidase, and reactive oxygen species including superoxide.

Section VI is comprised of chapters dealing with the clinical implications of studies of host–bacterium interactions. The opening chapter describes similarities between mechanisms of tissue destruction in rheumatic diseases and periodontal disease. Then follows a chapter on the influence of pharmacological agents on bone resorption. Chapters on antibacterial agents and periodontal disease present a strategy for treating the disease chemotherapeutically. The next chapter is a detailed description of a study comparing antibiotic treatment of juvenile and adult forms of periodontitis as an adjunct to conventional therapy. The final chapter presents a summary of the section and future research needs, put into an historical perspective.

The papers in this volume were delivered at a symposium on Host Bacterial Interactions in Periodontal Diseases, held in Buffalo, New York, 4–6 May 1981. The Symposium co-chairmen wish to acknowledge the National Institute of Dental Research and the State University of New York at Buffalo School of Dentistry for providing financial support for the symposium and its publication.

The diligent work and advice of the organizing committee, comprised of Joost J. Oppenheim, Jørgen Slots, and Russell Nisengard, were invaluable as a source of scientific expertise.

A special expression of the appreciation is extended to William Feagans whose constant encouragement and good judgement provided an environment conducive to both a productive meeting and this publication. We thank the extramural staff of the National Institute of Dental Research, including Samuel Kakehashi, Paul Parakkal, and Anthony Rizzo, for their efforts in identifying scientists active in the areas of research included in this volume.

We are pleased to acknowledge the excellent secretarial and administrative services provided by Rose Parkhill, Janice Hover, and Alfreida Haas. The assistance of Paula Mergenhagen in the editorial work is appreciated. Finally, we thank our wives, Sandra and Marjorie, who gave us support during the Symposium and in the preparation of this publication.

Robert J. Genco
Stephan E. Mergenhagen

ETIOLOGY AND MICROBIAL SPECIFICITY

Present Status of Studies on the Microbial Etiology of Periodontal Diseases

SIGMUND S. SOCRANSKY, ANNE C. R. TANNER, ANNE D. HAFFAJEE,
JEFFREY D. HILLMAN, AND J. MAX GOODSON

Forsyth Dental Center, Boston, Massachusetts 02115

HISTORICAL BACKGROUND

There may be individuals who wonder at the need for a continued consideration of the microbiology and immunology of periodontal disease since it has been reported that periodontal diseases can be effectively controlled by periodic scaling and a variety of mechanical and chemical home-care procedures (16, 23, 38, 43). Assuming that periodontal disease can be controlled by these procedures, one may still ask whether these are responsible approaches for the treatment of bacterial infections. The daily nonspecific removal of microorganisms as a means of treating a bacterial infection appears unique to periodontal disease. The fact that few, if any, other infections are treated in this manner should warn us that current therapy may not be optimal.

Envision, if you will, an individual 25 years of age who has the misfortune to be afflicted with some destructive form of periodontal disease. Following the old adage "once a periodontal patient, always a periodontal patient," for the next 50 years or so of his life this individual must have his teeth scraped at 3-month intervals and, in addition, brush, rub, or lavage all of the surfaces of his teeth on a daily basis. Available information suggests that emphasis on the maintenance phase of therapy is not misplaced. However, such therapy is clearly not optimal since it may be inaccurately directed and is certainly indiscriminately applied. Therapy generally lacks a defined endpoint and imposes an exceptional demand on patient motivation. A more acceptable approach for periodontal treatment would be the control or elimination of specific periodontal pathogens and their effects on the host. This could obviate the need for endless "maintenance" therapy. To achieve this goal, we must know more about the nature of periodontal infections, the characteristics of the pathogenic microorganisms which cause them, and the host's response to these organisms. Only with this information can therapy appropriate to the specific periodontal infections be rationally devised.

In the past decade, there has been significant progress in our understanding of the microbial etiology of periodontal diseases. Different destructive periodontal diseases have been distinguished, each apparently associated with a different microbial complex. For example, periodontosis, which at one time was thought to be a degenerative condition, has been recognized as being caused by microorganisms and can be successfully treated as an infectious disease. The nature of therapy is changing for periodontosis and other forms of advanced disease, and treatment is beginning to include antimocrobial therapy directed specifically at the subgingival microbial complexes associated with the different clinical entities. This recent progress in research, which has led to the clear association of different microbes with different forms of disease, as well as a

1

greater understanding of the host defense mechanisms and their role in the etiology and pathogenesis of periodontal diseases, has been encouraging. However, review of the earlier dental literature indicates that there have been similar periods of research into the specific microbial etiology of periodontal disease. Indeed, there appear to be distinct eras in the popularity of concepts of and approaches to understanding the etiology of periodontal diseases.

Cycles of emphasis on studies of the specific bacterial etiology of periodontal diseases appear to have an approximately 40-year period. From 1890 to 1930, there was an appreciation of the microbial etiology of periodontal diseases and a recognition that the diseases were probably caused by specific microorganisms. The research techniques employed seemed to influence the investigator's decision as to which microorganisms were significant in destructive forms of periodontal disease. Investigators employing stained-smear or wet-mount preparations often noted the presence of large proportions of amoebae in samples taken from sites of advanced destructive periodontal disease. One group of investigators (2, 21, 51) implicated amoebae as possible etiological agents, and several workers attempted to treat destructive forms of periodontal disease by using emitin hydrochloride to specifically eliminate amoebae from the individual. This form of therapy was reported to cause a dramatic improvement, particularly in the extent of gingival inflammation and suppuration. However, other investigators questioned the role of the amoebae because these organisms were found commonly in mouths of individuals without periodontal disease (12, 32, 33). They also cast doubt upon the specificity of the therapy employed because emitin hydrochloride is amoebicidal, hemostatic, and anti-inflammatory. It was suggested that the therapeutic effect observed was due to the anti-inflammatory activity of the drug rather than to its ability to eliminate this group of microorganisms.

Spirochetes were a second group of organisms implicated by virtue of their presence in wet-mount and stained-smear preparations of subgingival plaque samples. Spirochetes of different morphological types were found to be elevated in proportions in individuals with advanced forms of periodontal disease (17, 18, 20). Such observations led to the use of antimicrobial therapy directed at the elimination of the spirochetes from the periodontal pockets of diseased patients. The arsenical compound neosalvarsan, introduced by Ehrlich, had been used in the successful treatment of the spirochetal infection syphilis. It is not surprising that the efficacy of neosalvarsan in eliminating spirochetes from the human oral cavity was tested by workers attempting to control periodontal disease. For example, Kritchevsky and Séguin (18) used mechanical debridement coupled with systemically administered neosalvarsan in the treatment of advanced forms of periodontitis. These investigators and others (5, 6, 34, 58, 59) using salts of bismuth and mercury reported major successes which others were unable to repeat. Inconsistent therapeutic effects may have resulted from the use of mechanical debridement coupled with chemotherapeutic agents which may not have been appropriate in the treatment of all clinical conditions. Also, neosalvarsan, an agent found effective against spirochetes, may have been used to treat infections not associated with these organisms. The lack of consistent success in some of the therapies used in this and later eras may have been due to the treatment of quite different clinical conditions as if they were the same disease.

Streptococci were a third group of microorganisms implicated in the etiology of periodontal disease on the basis of culture techniques available at that time (8, 9). The high proportions of streptococci isolated undoubtedly reflected the low recoveries of viable organisms by the culture techniques employed. At that time, less than 15% of the microbiota enumerated by microscopic techniques could be cultured from samples taken from subgingival sites (8, 15). Since there did not appear to be any specific way of eliminating streptococci from periodontal pockets, investigators attempted to immunize patients by using vaccines derived from these microorganisms (32). Other investigators tested polyvalent vaccines derived from stock cultures of different subgingival species (3, 31) or from autogenous subgingival plaque (20, 29). They removed the microorganisms from the subgingival area by means of scalers, Pasteur pipettes, or other devices, killed the microorganisms by using iodine (19), and reinjected them either locally or systemically in an attempt to specifically combat gingival microorganisms associated with the disease. As might be expected, there were a number of individuals who reported quite remarkable successes with this form of therapy (3, 9, 29, 31, 32, 39) and other individuals who suggested that the therapy was completely ineffective (1, 11, 33). Once more, inconsistent results may have arisen because a single form of therapy was used to treat multiple forms of periodontal disease. More importantly, criteria of disease, and also the nature of "cures," were not defined. The unfortunate impression to be derived from studies in the 1890–1930 era is that, even if effective therapy for one or all forms of periodontal disease had been found, the lack of adequately controlled clinical trials and the enthusiastic endorsement by proponents of each of the therapeutic modalities proposed could not help but lead the skeptical reader to disregard all as mere anecdotal information. Almost every "trial" employed a combination of therapies so that it was unclear what contribution each form of therapy was making to the observed "success."

In time, investigators appear to have become disenchanted with the concept of specific microbial etiology, and as a result, the interest in the microorganisms resident in subgingival plaque as specific etiological agents of periodontal disease dwindled.

In the period from 1930 to approximately 1970, investigators seemed to suspect that periodontal infections were nonspecific or that complexes of microorganisms caused the infections. A great deal of emphasis was placed upon the study of mixed infections, such as the so-called fusospirochetal infections (19, 40, 41, 50) or the mixed anaerobic infections which were found to be associated, in many instances, with members of the *"Bacteroides melaninogenicus"* group (30, 53). The concept emerged that the differences observed between individuals in the nature and extent of periodontal disease were due in part to the amount of plaque which accumulated on tooth surfaces and in part to the effectiveness of the individual host's resistance. Using mainly direct microscopy of samples, Rosebury et al. (44) observed that most bacterial plaques were relatively similar in composition. Similar microbial forms were seen in almost all gingival or periodontal conditions although some sites exhibited a preponderance of certain morphological types. Thus, individuals with extensive periodontal disease were suspected of having inadequate home care or a weakened resistance to the accumulated microbiota, or both. Because it was unclear which of the organisms were pathogenic, therapy during this era was directed primarily at the suppression of all of the gingival microorganisms.

In the 1970s, attention was once more focused on the role of specific microorganisms in the etiology of periodontal diseases. Some of the changes which took place in the 1970s could be attributed in part to the demonstration by Keyes and Jordan (13, 14) of specificity in experimental periodontal disease in animals. It was also recognized that microbial plaques were not the same in composition and that rather major differences could be observed from site to site in the same individual as well as between individuals. This was contrary to the previous assumption that most plaques harbored similar microbial species but with some differences in their proportions. The observations of differences in microbial compositions of plaques led to the clinical question of whether there were differences in the microbiota between healthy sites and sites of periodontal disease in the same individual. The answer to this question (as will be reviewed in the following papers) was clearly, Yes, major differences do exist in the subgingival microbiota between healthy sites and sites with active destructive disease in the same individual. Initially, this question was investigated by sampling periodontosis patients (36, 37, 45). Elevated proportions of (at that time) unrecognized species were found in destructive disease sites as compared with healthy sites in the same patient. The next question was whether deep destructive lesions of periodontitis harbored the same microbiota as periodontosis lesions. Culture and microscopy studies indicated that a different microbiota existed in adult periodontitis lesions as compared with lesions of periodontosis, suggesting a possible specificity in etiology of these conditions (25, 46, 55). Further, it was demonstrated that lesions of gingivitis (27, 28, 49, 54) harbored microbial complexes different from those in lesions of periodontitis and periodontosis and in healthy conditions (35, 47). In electron microscopy studies of acute necrotizing ulcerative gingivitis lesions, a quite different microbial complex was observed, in which morphologically distinct spirochetes could be detected invading the underlying tissues (24, 26). This appears to be one of the few forms of periodontal disease in which invasion of the underlying connective tissues actually takes place. The only other report in humans of invasion by microorganisms into underlying tissues has been in terminal stages of advanced periodontitis, in which microorganisms were observed adjacent to the alveolar bone (7). Taken as a whole, the data presented in the past 10 years suggest that the microbial population of periodontal disease differs from that of health. What remains to be demonstrated is the significance of these differences and the identity of pathogenic species.

In reviewing studies of the microbiology of periodontal diseases over the past century, one cannot help but be struck by the awe in which the "complexity" of the plaque microbiota has been held. Investigators appear to have been overwhelmed by the array of morphological types observed and by the number of species which can be cultured from subgingival sites. But how large an array is there really? In one study reported in this volume, 84 different species or groups of organisms were recovered from the subgingival samples. W. E. C. Moore has estimated the existence of about 256 subgingival species. If we add uncultivated spirochetes and other uncultivated forms to this estimate, perhaps 300 or even 400 species may eventually be listed which can be found at least on some occasion in the subgingival area. Of these, perhaps 50 to 100 species will be regularly encountered in different states of health and disease. This number of species is surely not impossible to deal with. However, techniques must be devised to analyze and interpret microbiological data that take into account the range of species encountered and the variability in numbers of each from site to site and in different states of health and disease. Methods have been described that suggest an approach for the analysis of data of this type. The results described below suggest that patterns of microbiological differences can be recognized in data from studies of the predominant cultivable microbiota from sites with different forms of periodontal disease.

CURRENT RESEARCH APPROACHES

Using a gas-flushed sampling device, Newman and Socransky (36) sampled subgingival plaque from the apical region of 43 periodontal pockets in 15 patients. The samples were dispersed, diluted, and plated, and the predominant cultivable isolates were characterized and identified by previously described techniques (55). An average of 45 isolates was characterized in each of the samples. The most commonly detected species and their mean percentages in samples, when detected, are shown in Table 1. *Fusobacterium nucleatum* was the most commonly detected subgingival species. It was found in 86% of the sites and comprised 16.8% of the isolates when present. A group of slow-growing fusiform-shaped gram-negative rods which did not fit existing species descriptions was found in 60% of sites at a mean percentage of 10.5% when present. *Bacteroides gingivalis* and *Wolinella recta*, a group of gram-negative asaccharolytic vibrios, were also frequently isolated in high proportions from subgingival sites. *Actinobacillus actinomycetemcomitans*, though infrequently found in the sites of all patients examined, constituted an average of 24.8% of the site microbiota when present. A total of 84 groups of organisms were detected, of which 73 were found in at least two different sites. The organisms were not randomly distributed but in many instances appeared to be associated with the clinical conditions.

TABLE 1. *Most frequently detected species in 43 subgingival sites*

Species	% Incidence	Mean % (when present)
Fusobacterium nucleatum	86	16.8
"Fusiform" *Bacteroides*	60	10.5
Bacteroides gingivalis	53	22.6
Wolinella recta	53	9.0
Actinomyces naeslundii	44	5.0
Peptostreptococcus micros	33	7.6
Eikenella corrodens	30	5.6
Streptococcus sanguis type I	28	8.3
Streptococcus intermedius	28	5.3
Propionibacterium acnes	23	4.2
Actinobacillus actinomycetemcomitans	16	24.8

The microbiota found in lesions of adult periodontitis presented a range of microbial types that was rather difficult to interpret. In an attempt to investigate the degree to which periodontal microorganisms tended to associate, the data matrix of 43 sites and 73 species was tested for trends in population groupings. Cluster analysis was used to examine patterns of colonization of the subgingival isolates. A similarity coefficient, S_p, was defined to measure the degree of similarity of species between sites as follows:

$$S_p = \sum_{i=1}^{n} (\min x_i y_i)$$

where n is the number of species, x and y are individual sites, and min $x_i y_i$ is the lowest level of a species common to both sites. This coefficient provides a measure of the percentage of similar organisms which occur in each site in terms that are "biologically" meaningful to the investigator.

The defined coefficient is rather stringent since the summed minimum values of species present in sites are used, rather than the summed averages or maximum values. For this reason, the values of the coefficient are low. In addition, up to 25% of the organisms in certain samples could not be identified. Since no attempt was made to compensate for this factor, similarities between certain sites could only achieve a maximum of 75%. After determining the degree of similarity between species in individual sites, Sneath and Sokal (52) performed an average unweighted linkage sort to group the sites. Figure 1 is a trellis diagram demonstrating the degree of intersite similarity in microbial species. Eight clusters were defined. Cluster 1 included 4 samples from sites with advanced destructive periodontal disease but minimal clinical evidence of inflammation. Clusters 2 to 6 and site I2 included 31 samples taken from advanced lesions of adult subjects with periodontitis. All sites exhibited bone loss, pocketing greater than 5 mm, clinical evidence of inflammation, detectable plaque, and often calculus. Cluster 7 consisted of two sites from a periodontosis patient, and cluster 8 was the control sites sampled from patients in clusters 2 through 5. Median similarity values within clusters 2 through 6 were between 40 and 60%, which reflects a high degree of similarity in species recovered in these sites. Similarities in the percentages of microorganisms of the minimally inflamed, advanced disease sites and the control sites were less striking. This may have been a consequence of the more heterogeneous status of the sites included in the last two groups.

The Kruskal Wallis test was used to seek species which discriminated the sites in clusters 1 through 6. Table 2 summarizes the organisms which distinguished the clusters and exemplifies many of the predominant cultivable species which characterize different periodontal conditions. The minimally inflamed advanced disease sites harbored large proportions of B. melaninogenicus subsp. intermedius and Eikenella corrodens. High percentages of A. actinomycetemcomitans were cultured from periodontosis lesions. Subgingival samples from nondiseased sites harbored large proportions of Actinomyces species. The periodontitis clusters could be distinguished from other forms of disease and from each other on the basis of proportions of F. nucleatum, B. gingivalis, W. recta, fusiform Bacteroides, and Peptostreptococcus micros (Table 3). Sites dominated by F. nucleatum or by B. gingivalis could be differentiated into subclusters by the presence of different associated species.

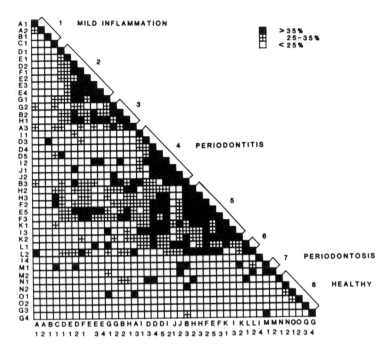

FIG. 1. Trellis diagram of cluster analysis of the similarity of microbial complexes in 43 subgingival sites. The similarity coefficient S_p was defined in the text, and an average unweighted linkage sort was performed. Eight clusters and one clearly different site were distinguished. The analysis grouped clinically similar sites as indicated by the labels along the hypotenuse of the trellis diagram.

TABLE 2. Organisms which discriminated clusters of sites
with different forms of periodontal disease

	Clusters			
Organism	1 Minimally inflamed periodontitis	2–6 Perio- dontitis	7 Perio- dontosis	8 Health
Bacteroides melaninogenicus subsp. intermedius	12[a]	0	0	0
Eikenella corrodens	6	0	0	0
Fusobacterium nucleatum	8	18	13	1
Bacteroides gingivalis	0	16	0	0
"Fusiform" Bacteroides	3	5	0	0
Actinobacillus actinomycetemcomitans . . .	0	0	58	0
Actinomyces sp.	2	0	1	27

[a]Median value within cluster. Significantly different on basis of Kruskal Wallis test, $P < 0.01$.

TABLE 3. *Organisms which discriminated periodontitis clusters*

Organism	Clusters			
	2	3	4	5
Fusobacterium nucleatum	31[a]	23	3	16
Wolinella recta	0	12	3	4
"Fusiform" *Bacteroides*	1	7	4	15
Peptostreptococcus micros	7	0	1	0
Bacteroides gingivalis	3	0	39	21

[a]Median value within cluster. Significantly different on basis of Kruskal Wallis test, $P < 0.01$.

These subsets of "periodontitis" could represent either different forms of periodontitis or various stages of disease activity. This analysis discriminated the clear microbiological differences between distinctly different forms of periodontal disease and presents an approach to subgrouping the complicated "periodontitis" category.

With the large numbers and types of potentially pathogenic organisms regularly found in both healthy sites and periodontal and gingival lesions, one wonders why all periodontal sites are not continuously undergoing destruction. For a destructive phase in periodontal disease to take place, it is probably necessary that certain prerequisites be fulfilled.

1. A pathogenic species must be transmitted from an individual harboring that species to a susceptible subject. If individuals fail to encounter a pathogen, there is no likelihood that they will develop disease.
2. Conditions in the subject's mouth must be suitable for initial colonization and subsequent growth of the microorganisms.
3. The pathogen must multiply to numbers that exceed some threshold level for initiation of pathology.
4. The species must be spatially located in the pocket so that the microorganism or its products can affect the attachment apparatus. A pathogenic species located on the occlusal surface of a tooth is unlikely to cause destructive periodontal disease.
5. A "triggering event" may be required to initiate a destructive phase. This might be a local factor such as the arrival or loss of an accessory species, food impaction, or trauma, or it might be a systemic factor such as some stressful event for the host.
6. Microbial species which are inhibitory to the pathogen or which would dilute or destroy its pathogenic determinant would have to be absent or be present only in low numbers.
7. Sufficient time would have to be available for completion of the pathological cycle. Interference, for example, by therapy, would preclude destruction.
8. The host must be susceptible. The nature of the host susceptibility will be examined in greater detail in subsequent papers, but factors such as age, compromised polymorphonuclear leukocyte function, and specific antibody responses, as well as endocrine and dietary factors, could play significant roles.

The multiplicity of events listed makes it clear that the combination necessary to lead to destructive disease must occur rather infrequently.

Since periodontal diseases are infectious diseases, approaches to their specific microbiological control is of considerable interest. One clinical condition, periodontosis, is now recognized as an infectious disease related to specific microorganisms. It seems worthwhile to examine some of the parameters which make this disease amenable to combined mechanical debridement and tetracycline therapy (22; R. J. Genco, L. J. Cianciola, and B. Roling, J. Dent. Res. Spec. Issue A **60**:527, 1981). The efficacy of tetracycline in the treatment of periodontosis may be related to at least three factors: the susceptibility of most *Actinobacillus* isolates to the antibiotic, the increased concentration of tetracycline in gingival crevice fluid, and the establishment of organisms which inhibit the growth of *A. actinomycetemcomitans* in pockets after therapy.

Slots et al. (48) found that all of 59 isolates of *A. actinomycetemcomitans* were susceptible to 1 μg of tetracycline per ml and suggested tetracycline to be the agent of choice in the treatment of *Actinobacillus* infections. This finding was similar to that of Walker et al. (57), who found few *Actinobacillus* strains resistant to tetracycline at levels of 2 μg/ml. Systemically administered tetracycline is concentrated in gingival crevice fluid at levels 2 to 10 times that found in the serum. Peak concentrations of tetracycline after single doses are achieved 5 to 7 h after the agent is administered, and levels of 1 μg/ml can be detected at 16 h (10). Multiple doses of tetracycline also result in increased concentrations of the agent in gingival crevice fluid (J. M. Gordon, C. B. Walker, J. C. Murphy, J. M. Goodson, and S. S. Socransky, J. Dent. Res. Spec. Issue A **59**:513, 1980). This property of concentration of the agent in gingival crevice fluid is shared by the tetracycline analog minocycline (4), but not by other antibiotics tested (56). Thus, most *A. actinomycetemcomitans* strains are susceptible to tetracycline, and the agent is concentrated at the site of the infection. This would explain an immediate efficacy of the agent, but would not explain the prolonged control of the disease.

J. D. Hillman and S. S. Socransky (J. Dent. Res. Spec. Issue A **60**:603, 1981) demonstrated the presence of organisms inhibitory to the growth of *A. actinomycetemcomitans* in samples taken from healthy sites or sites with other forms of periodontal disease. Species inhibitory to *A. actinomycetemcomitans* were usually not detected in periodontosis lesions. Inhibitory species included *Streptococcus sanguis* and *Streptococcus uberis*. It was shown that an inoculum of 10^6 cells would routinely implant *A. actinomycetemcomitans* in the oral cavities and gastrointestinal tract of germfree rats. However, repeated inoculation of 2×10^9 *A. actinomycetemcomitans* cells into gnotobiotic rats preinfected with *S. sanguis* failed to establish the actinobacillus. Further, implanting *S. sanguis* in animals previously infected with *A. actinomycetemcomitans* resulted in the elimination of *A. actinomycetemcomitans* from the oral cavities of the rats. The inhibition appears in part due to the formation of hydrogen peroxide by the streptococci, since incorporation of catalase into the test system abolished most of the inhibitory effect. It may be speculated that the prolonged efficacy of the tetracycline therapy for periodontosis is due to the posttherapy colonization of the lesion by a species inhibitory to *A. actinomycetemcomitans,* which prevents the re-establishment of this species and others which may also be pathogenic in the disease. If this is indeed the case, then a goal of effective therapy may be suggested, that is, to eliminate the pathogenic species and permit establishment of microbial species antagonistic to their return. The results from the therapy of periodontosis and also the prolonged efficacy of therapy for acute necrotizing ulcerative gingivitis suggest that such results can be achieved.

The recent microbiological and immunological evidence implicating certain microorganisms as etiological agents of specific periodontal diseases will provide an opportunity to systematically test a number of hypotheses related to disease etiology, mechanisms of pathogenicity, and host response. Further, elucidation of specific pathogens of different forms of periodontal disease should permit more accurate diagnosis and provide rational therapeutic endpoints for testing treatment modalities and preventive measures. Although periodontal therapy has been effective in the past, a shift in emphasis away from the continuous maintenance phase to specific elimination of pathogens would seem desirable.

ACKNOWLEDGMENTS

This work was supported by Public Health Service grants DE-04881-02 and DE-03488 from the National Institute for Dental Research.

LITERATURE CITED

1. **Appleton, J. L. T.** 1930. The use of vaccines, antivirus, bacteriophage and non-specific protein therapy in mouth infections. Dent. Cosmos **72:**1276–1288.
2. **Barrett, M. T.** 1914. Clinical report upon amoebic pyorrhea. Dent. Cosmos **56:**1345–1350.
3. **Casto, T. D.** 1925. The treatment of periodontoclosia with a polyvalent vaccine (Goldenberg's Inava Endocorps vaccine). Dent. Cosmos **67:**689–691.
4. **Ciancio, S. G., M. L. Mather, and J. A. McMullen.** 1980. An evaluation of minocycline in patients with periodontal disease. J. Periodontol. **51:**530–534.
5. **Cipes, L. R.** 1934. Bismuth therapy in periodontia. Dent. Cosmos **76:**697.
6. **Corby, A. E.** 1920. Mercuric cyanid in the treatment of Vincent's infection or so-called "trench-mouth." Dent. Cosmos. **62:**612–619.
7. **Frank, R. M., and J. C. Voegel.** 1978. Bacterial bone resorption in advanced cases of human periodontitis. J. Periodontal Res. **13:**251–261.
8. **Glynn, E. E.** 1923. The organisms found in the periodontal infections, and their relation to the 'toxaemia.' Br. Dent. J. **44:**601–619, 681–698.
9. **Goadby, K. W.** 1907. The Eramus Wilson Lecture on pyorrhea alveolaris. Lancet **i:**633–643.
10. **Gordon, J. M., C. B. Walker, J. M. Goodson, and S. S. Socranksy.** 1980. Sensitive assay for measuring tetracycline levels in gingival crevice fluid. Antimicrob. Agents Chemother. **17:**193–198.
11. **Hirschfeld, I.** 1926. An investigation of inava endocorps vaccine. J. Am. Dent. Assoc. **13:**1613–1624.
12. **Howe, P. R.** 1916. The endamoebae and pyorrhea alveolaris. Dent. Cosmos **58:**369–374.
13. **Jordan, H. V., and P. H. Keyes.** 1964. Aerobic, gram-positive, filamentous bacteria as etiologic agents of experimental periodontal disease in hamsters. Arch. Oral Biol. **9:**401–414.
14. **Keyes, P. H., and H. V. Jordan.** 1964. Periodontal lesions in the syrian hamster. III. Findings related to an infectious and transmissible component. Arch. Oral Biol. **9:**377–400.
15. **Kligler, I. J.** 1915. A biochemical study and differentiation of oral bacteria with special reference to dental caries. II. Experimental. J. Allied Dent. Soc. **10:**282–330.
16. **Knowles, J. W., F. G. Burgett, R. R. Nissle, R. A. Schick, E. C. Morrison, and S. P. Ramfjord.** 1979. Results of periodontal treatment related to pocket depth and attachment level: eight years. J. Periodontol. **50:**225–233.
17. **Kolle, W.** 1917. Spirochatenbefunde und Salvarsan bei Alveolar-pyorrhoe. Med. Klin. **3:**59–60.
18. **Kritchevsky, B., and P. Séguin.** 1918. The pathogenesis and treatment of pyorrhea alveolaris. Dent. Cosmos **60:**781–784.
19. **Kritchevsky, B., and P. Séguin.** 1921. Local and general spirochaetosis. Dent. Cosmos **63:**888–892.
20. **Kritchevsky, B., and P. Séguin.** 1924. The unity of spirochetoses in the mouth. Dent. Cosmos **66:**511–520.
21. **Le Clear, T.** 1915. Method of identification of Endamoebae in dry smears. Dent. Cosmos **57:**1313.
22. **Liljenberg, B., and J. Lindhe.** 1980. Juvenile periodontitis. Some microbiological, histopathological and clinical characteristics. J. Clin. Periodontol. **7:**48–61.

23. **Lindhe, J., and S. Nyman.** 1975. The effect of plaque control and surgical pocket elimination on the establishment and maintenance of periodontal health. A longitudinal study of periodontal therapy in cases of advanced periodontitis. J. Clin. Periodontol. **2:**67–79.

24. **Listgarten, M. A.** 1965. Electron microscopic observations of the bacterial flora of acute necrotizing ulcerative gingivitis. J. Periodontol. **36:**328–339.

25. **Listgarten, M. A.** 1976. Structure of the microbial flora associated with periodontal health and disease in man. A light and electron microscopic study. J. Periodontol. **47:**1–18.

26. **Listgarten, M. A., and D. W. Lewis.** 1967. The distribution of spirochetes in the lesion of acute necrotizing ulcerative gingivitis: an electron microscopic and statistical survey. J. Periodontol. **38:**379–386.

27. **Listgarten, M. A., H. E. Mayo, and R. Tremblay.** 1975. Development of dental plaque on epoxy resin crowns in man. A light and electron microscopic study. J. Periodontol. **46:**10–26.

28. **Loesche, W. J., and S. A. Syed.** 1978. Bacteriology of human experimental gingivitis: effect of plaque and gingivitis score. Infect. Immun. **21:**830–839.

29. **Lose, G. D., and J. R. Fouré.** 1935. Observations on periodontoclasia, with special reference to the use of autogenous vaccine and surgical intervention. Dent. Cosmos **77:**868–877.

30. **Macdonald, J. B., R. M. Sutton, M. L. Knoll, E. M. Madlener, and R. M. Grainger.** 1956. The pathogenic components of an experimental mixed infection. J. Infect. Dis. **98:**15–20.

31. **McGehee, W. H. O.** 1912. Stock vaccines in the treatment of pyorrhea alveolaris. Dent. Cosmos **54:**997–1002.

32. **Medalia, L. S.** 1916. The present status of alveolar osteomyelitis pyorrhea alveolaris. Its causes, and treatment and vaccines. Dent. Cosmos **58:**1000–1012.

33. **Merritt, A.** 1916. The irrationality of bacterial vaccines in the treatment of pyorrhea alveolaris. Dent. Cosmos **58:**62–69.

34. **Miller, T. S.** 1934. Bismuth therapy in periodontia. Dent. Cosmos **76:**999.

35. **Newman, M. G., V. Grinenco, M. Weiner, I. Angel, H. Karge, and R. Nisengard.** 1978. Predominant microbiota associated with periodontal health in the aged. J. Periodontol. **49:**553–559.

36. **Newman, M. G., and S. S. Socransky.** 1977. Predominant cultivable microbiota in periodontosis. J. Periodontal Res. **12:**120–128.

37. **Newman, M. G., S. S. Socransky, E. D. Savitt, D. A. Propas, and A. Crawford.** 1976. Studies of the microbiology of periodontosis. J. Periodontol. **47:**373–379.

38. **Nyman, S., and J. Lindhe.** 1979. A longitudinal study of combined periodontal and prosthetic treatment of patients with advanced periodontal disease. J. Periodontol. **50:**163–169.

39. **Patterson, T. B.** 1928. Presidential address. Br. Dent. J. **49:**459–460.

40. **Proske, H. O., and R. R. Sayers.** 1934. Pulmonary infections in pneumoconiosis. I. A bacteriologic and experimental study. Public Health Rep. **29:**839–858.

41. **Proske, H. O., and R. R. Sayers.** 1934. Pulmonary infection in pneumoconiosis. II. Fuso-spirochetal infection. Experiments in guinea pigs. Public Health Rep. **29:**1212–1217.

42. **Ramfjord, S. P., J. W. Knowles, E. C. Morrison, F. G. Burgett, and R. R. Nissle.** 1980. Results of periodontal therapy related to tooth type. J. Periodontol. **51:**270–273.

43. **Ramfjord, S. P., J. W. Knowles, R. R. Nissle, R. A. Schick, and F. G. Burgett.** 1973. Longitudinal study of periodontal therapy. J. Periodontol. **44:**66–77.

44. **Rosebury, T., J. B. Macdonald, and A. R. Clarke.** 1950. A bacteriologic survey of gingival scrapings from periodontal infections by direct examination, guinea pig inoculation, and anaerobic cultivation. J. Dent. Res. **29:**718–731.

45. **Slots, J.** 1976. The predominant cultivable organisms in juvenile periodontitis. Scand. J. Dent. Res. **84:**1–10.

46. **Slots, J.** 1977. The predominant cultivable microflora of advanced periodontitis. Scand. J. Dent. Res. **85:**114–121.

47. **Slots, J.** 1977. Microflora in the healthy gingival sulcus in man. Scand. J. Dent. Res. **85:**247–254.

48. **Slots, J., R. T. Evans, P. M. Lobbins, and R. J. Genco.** 1980. In vitro antimicrobial susceptibility of *Actinobacillus actinomycetemcomitans.* Antimicrob. Agents Chemother. **18:**9–12.

49. **Slots, J., D. Moenbo, J. Langebaek, and A. Frandsen.** 1978. Microbiota of gingivitis in man. Scand. J. Dent. Res. **86:**174–181.

50. **Smith, D. T.** 1930. Fusospirochetal disease of the lungs produced with cultures from Vincent's angina. J. Infect. Dis. **46:**303–310.

51. **Smith, T. S.** 1915. The emetin hydrochloride question in the treatment of pyorrhea alveolaris. Dent. Cosmos **57:**1313.

52. **Sneath, P. H. A., and R. R. Sokal.** 1973. Numerical taxonomy. The principles and practice of numerical classification. W. H. Freeman and Co., San Francisco.

53. **Socransky, S. S., and R. J. Gibbons.** 1965. Required role of *Bacteroides melaninogenicus* in mixed anaerobic infections. J. Infect. Dis. **115:**247–253.

54. **Syed, S. A., and W. J. Loesche.** 1978. Bacteriology of human experimental gingivitis: effect of plaque age. Infect. Immun. **21:**821–829.

55. **Tanner, A. C. R., C. Haffer, G. T. Bratthall, R. A. Visconti, and S. S. Socransky.** 1979. A study of the bacteria associated with advancing periodontal disease in man. J. Clin. Periodontol. **6:**278–307.
56. **Walker, C. B., J. M. Gordon, H. A. Cornwall, J. C. Murphy, and S. S. Socransky.** 1981. Gingival crevicular fluid levels of clindamycin compared with its minimal inhibitory concentrations for periodontal bacteria. Antimicrob. Agents Chemother. **19:**867–871.
57. **Walker, C. B., T. A. Niebloom, J. M. Gordon, and S. S. Socransky.** 1980. In vitro susceptibilities of bacteria from human periodontal pockets to 13 antimicrobial agents, p. 508–511. *In* J. D. Nelson and C. Grassi (ed.), Current chemotherapy and infectious disease, vol. 1. American Society for Microbiology, Washington, D.C.
58. **White, P. G.** 1915. Deep muscular injections of succinimid of mercury in pyorrhea alveolaris. Dent. Cosmos **57:**405–408.
59. **Wright, B. L.** 1915. The treatment of pyorrhea alveolaris and its secondary systemic infections by deep muscular injections of mercury. Dent. Cosmos **57:**1003–1009.

Subgingival Microflora in Periodontal Disease: Cultural Studies

W. E. C. MOORE, R. R. RANNEY, AND L. V. HOLDEMAN

Virginia Commonwealth University Clinical Research Center for Periodontal Diseases: Department of Anaerobic Microbiology, Virginia Polytechnic Institute and State University, Blacksburg, Virginia 24061, and Department of Periodontics, School of Dentistry, Medical College of Virginia, Virginia Commonwealth University, Richmond, Virginia 23298

In spite of several decades of intensive investigation in several laboratories, the floras associated with periodontal disease remain poorly defined. Microscopic analyses of the floras associated with diseased sites conclusively demonstrate that the proportion of gram-negative bacteria and spirochetes is increased and the proportion of gram-positive cocci and rods is decreased. These observations do not tell us much about the benign, destructive, or protective properties of the species that increase or decrease during the transition from health to disease. Determination of the composition of the flora and the role of different bacteria currently is a major effort in several laboratories where a variety of procedures are being used to sample diseased sites and to culture and identify the isolates. Comparative data indicate that relatively minor differences in these techniques can influence the results and subsequent correlations between various components of the flora and different states or stages of periodontal disease. Some of our observations on the technical problems encountered in this work, and possible solutions to some of those problems, are presented here.

The complexity of the flora is a major barrier to understanding the microbial changes that lead to tissue and bone destruction or to the determination of specific etiologies. In our recent work, 264 morphologically and biochemically distinct bacterial groups or species of bacteria have been seen among 6,800 isolates from sites affected with periodontitis or gingivitis. There were 78 described species and 186 undescribed groups in at least 28 genera with a wide range of metabolic activities and cultural requirements. There is evidence that some additional species could not grow on the isolation media or did not survive isolation to allow a complete analysis.

SAMPLING

Several different procedures are used in different laboratories to obtain samples from the gingival sulcus, and each procedure may affect the results differently.

One method, described by Newman et al. (11), uses a broach in a gas-flushed cannula that is capped with aluminum foil for insertion into the sulcus. The cap and the surrounding cannula are designed to protect the broach from contamination during insertion and removal from the gingival sulcus. The anaerobic gas is used to protect the specimen from air. There are several technical problems with this procedure. Chromium in stainless-steel cannulas and broaches catalytically oxidizes moist samples; thus, the protective effect of the oxygen-free gas flushing the cannula may be lost. Calcium alginate fibers that are used to wrap the broach are inhibitory for some anaerobes. The

13

relatively large diameter of the capped cannula may serve to force material from the gingival margin into the depths of the sulcus before sampling, and the equipment is somewhat bulky and decreases tactile sensitivity for sampling.

Samples can be taken with paper points that are inserted into the crevice or sulcus after supragingival deposits are removed. The points are usually left in place for a short time to absorb exudate and bacteria before they are aseptically transferred to the dispersion fluid (15). Although the paper may carry oxygen into the sulcus, there is no catalytic oxidizing action. Serum and exudates in specimens are known to protect anaerobes from the deleterious effects of oxygen for reasonable lengths of time. Paper points may be selective for bacterial species that are primarily free in the exudates as compared with those that are attached to the tooth root or tissue surface.

Samples also are taken by irrigation of the site and retrieval of the sample through syringe needles. This procedure might be least likely to recover species in plaque attached to the tooth. Again, the moist samples may be subject to some oxidizing action of stainless steel.

Samples also have been obtained after tooth extractions (12) or a coronally reflected flap (13). Both approaches carry risks of mechanically dislocating significant portions of the plaque and introduce bleeding which may affect the composition of the samples. Obviously, these methods are not universally applicable in that surgical procedures are required.

Probably the most frequent approach has been to use a curette or scaler after cleaning the supragingival area. Our standard procedure has been a slight modification of this technique in which we use Morse detachable-tip 00 scalers that are nickel-plated to prevent oxidation of the specimens. As a control specimen for possible contamination by the supragingival flora at the gingival margin, we take a first sample of the supragingival area after the superficial cleaning. The subgingival sulcus flora is then sampled with a second sterile scaler. The scaler tips are detached with sterile forceps and placed in CO_2-flushed tubes of dilution broth within 5 s of sampling. The striking difference in the bacterial composition of the supra- and subgingival samples suggests that contamination of the sulcus sample is minimal. The scaler probably samples more of the flora that is attached to the tooth root or that might be associated with the sulcular epithelial surface than do the other methods. Results with the scaler sampling method indicate that *Capnocytophaga* species and *Eubacterium saburreum*, reported in high numbers from subgingival specimens that were taken by other methods, are much more prevalent supragingivally than in the diseased sulcus. In our experience curettes were more satisfactory than broaches. The broaches produced bleeding as often as the curettes, and the stainless-steel broaches, which did oxidize dilution fluids, became smooth and ineffective when they were nickel-plated.

Data for an adequate comparison of sampling methods are not available. Even if the same site could be sampled simultaneously by two methods, analysis of an adequate number of isolates for a valid comparison would be costly. For any of the methods, we do not know how well each sample actually represents the flora in a given site or how reproducible each sample is. The magnitude of sample variance, which has not been determined, might significantly affect interpretations of site-to-site or time-to-time variations in the composition of the flora.

SAMPLE DISPERSION

The clumps of filamentous bacteria commonly associated with periodontal samples must be dispersed for accurate dilution, colony counts, and isolation of pure cultures. It is generally believed that simple agitation of samples with vortex mixers is not adequate.

Most commonly, the sampling instrument or irrigation fluid is placed in chemically reduced dilution fluid and treated with a sonic probe to dislodge and separate organisms in the sample. A technical problem with this procedure is that it produces a selective change in the composition of the flora by destroying greater numbers of some spirochetes and other fragile bacteria than of other species.

We have attempted to avoid this problem by placing the sampling instrument in 1.5 ml of reduced sterile dilution fluid with about 0.05 g of glass beads (110 to 150 μm in diameter) in a CO_2-filled stoppered tube (12 by 75 mm). This mixture is agitated on a vortex mixer for 10 s. Some bacterial cells may be killed if they are trapped between two colliding surfaces, but there is little if any selective killing of individual species. Cultural recovery of spirochetes is equal to or greater than the dark-field count of the preparation, and over 90% of the single colonies of *Actinomyces* are pure by serological tests. Thus, the procedure appears to be effective in dispersing the tangled clumps of bacteria without selectively killing fragile species.

ANAEROBIC ENVIRONMENT

The anaerobic count in cultures of subgingival samples is usually several logs higher than the aerobic count, but the precautions used to provide a highly reduced environment vary from laboratory to laboratory. Roll tubes, anaerobic jars, or glove boxes are commonly used. Each of these methods can give different results in different laboratories, and each has been claimed to be superior. There are many technical details that could be responsible for the reported differences.

We made a comparison of isolations with plates and roll tubes, using similar media in both. The freshly prepared plates were stored in anaerobic jars until use. Duplicate dilutions of periodontal specimens were spread on the plates aerobically on the bench top (as is done where glove boxes are not used), and the plates were then returned to anaerobic jars which were made anaerobic by the evacuation–replacement method using 80% N_2–10% CO_2–10% H_2 and fresh catalyst pellets. The roll tubes at 53°C were inoculated under 80% N_2–12% CO_2–3% H_2 and spun immediately. After incubation for 5 days at 37°C, both tubes and plates were counted under $10\times$ magnification. Overlapping colonies of the same morphotype on plates were counted as one. Likewise, bifoliate or multifoliate colonies in roll tubes were counted as one. The cultural counts for each method were derived from the average of two plates or tubes containing 30 to 300 colonies.

The major differences between the conditions in the plates and tubes were a 3% difference in concentrations of H_2 and CO_2, whole blood (in plates) or serum (in roll tubes), exposure of the plates to air during inoculation, and the higher temperature of the roll tube medium for 2 to 3 min after inoculation.

On the basis of total counts, each method was superior to the other for some specimens (Table 1). The flora of the sulcus of affected sites in patients with moderate or severe periodontitis was generally the most sensitive to culture on the plates. The distribution of the differences also suggests that the flora may become less able to survive culture on plates inoculated in air, as the flora becomes more complex during extended periods without tooth brushing in experimental gingivitis studies.

The sensitivity of the floras to these minor differences in culture technique is further indicated by differences in the relative proportions of various species that were represented among colonies. In 83 samples for which the plate counts and tube counts were similar, equal numbers of colonies were picked from each, in random order without selection by following spiral lines drawn around the tubes or bottoms of the plates. Among 1,423 isolates from tubes and 1,430 from plates, many species were detected with about equal frequency by the two methods; other species were not. Some apparently sensitive species are shown in Table 2.

Because the total colony counts were similar for these 83 samples, there is no evidence that either procedure yields "more representative" results than the other. However, with samples in which the total count differed greatly, the method that gave the highest colony count can be assumed to produce the more representative result. On this basis, neither method was consistently superior. To obtain the least bias in results, one must select isolates from both plates and tubes for each sample unless the colony counts differ significantly. Different media and culture techniques also affect the recovery of spirochetes from these samples (R. M. Smibert, J. Dent. Res. Spec. Issue A **60**:485, abstr. 702, 1981).

TABLE 1. *Highest tube or plate total colony counts in 213 samples*

Samples from	Supragingival		Subgingival	
	Tube	Plate	Tube	Plate
Healthy controls	1[a]	2	0	3
Healthy sites (JP)	1	4	0	5
Expt'l. gingivitis[b]				
Day 4	—	—	10	14
Day 11	—	—	12	20
Day 26	—	—	16	16
Periodontitis				
Moderate	6	6	7	3
Severe	15	12	25	6
Juvenile (JP)	5	7	8	9

[a]Number of samples with higher cultural count. Sixty-three percent of the higher colony counts were within 150% of the respective lower counts, 18 percent were within 150 to 250%, and 18 percent differed by more than 250%. — = not analyzed.

[b]26 days without tooth brushing.

MEDIA

No single medium can provide optimal conditions for the isolation of all species from complex floras. Bacteria in such floras often depend upon the products of other bacterial species. If not used by the species that require them, the products may be toxic to other organisms. The medium for the plate and roll tube study was chosen after comparisons of several formulas on the basis of highest total colony counts from the same specimens. No single medium tested produced the highest counts from all specimens. To date we have obtained the highest counts with medium D-4, which is prereduced supplemented brain heart infusion agar (4) with 0.5% ammonium formate and 10% (vol/vol) of a mixture of serum–fresh yeast extract–cocarboxylase (50 ml of filter-sterilized [final filter, 0.2-μm pore size] nonhemolyzed rabbit serum [Pelfreeze]; 50 ml of extract of fresh yeast [1 oz of Fleishman's yeast powder incubated in 100 ml of distilled water at 56°C for 4 days and then filtered through cheesecloth and through filters of decreasing pore size down to 0.2 μm]; 0.5 ml of filter-sterilized cocarboxylase solution [25 mg of cocarboxylase in 100 ml of distilled water]). The serum–fresh yeast–cocarboxylase is added to tubes of sterile molten agar at 55°C. On the basis of total colony counts from several specimens for each comparison, this isolation medium was superior to chopped-meat broth or Trypticase soy broth base. Added combinations of rumen fluid, sodium or ammonium fumarate, sodium formate, sodium pyruvate, or mucin were not consistently helpful with any of the base media.

TABLE 2. *Examples of species that appear to be sensitive to plate or tube isolation techniques*

Species	No. of isolates	
	Tube	Plate
F. nucleatum	82	25
C. ochracea	24	11
Selenomonas D-12	19	6
E. saburreum	11	5
E. alactolyticum	8	3
Eubacterium D-4	10	1
Fusobacterium D-2	6	0
S. sanguis II	15	40
B. intermedius[a]	7	19
Homology group NCTC 9336[b]	3	19
B. gingivalis	1	10
P. acnes	7	44
Actinomyces serogroup 963	9	24
Facultative gram-neg. rod D-6	0	15

[a]Formerly *B. melaninogenicus* subsp. *intermedius.*

[b]Phenotypically similar to *B. intermedius.*

INCUBATION

If plates or roll tubes were counted after 5 days of incubation and again at 13 days, the total counts increased by 0 to 20%. If the colonies are not picked until the maximum count is reached, instead of at 5 days, an increased proportion of the original colonies may fail to subculture. At 5 days, 331 of 6,848 colonies (4.8%) failed to subculture in broth media. Agar subcultures of colonies similar to those that failed to grow in broth revealed at least three distinct types that grow poorly in broth, but these still do not account for all of the missing isolates. A. C. R. Tanner, S. S. Socransky, and C. M. Smith (J. Dent. Res. Spec. Issue A **60**:485, abstr. 703, 1981) recently photographed and reincubated plates to detect slow-growing colonies. They detected an organism that could be grown in broth only after the broth had been "detoxified" by exposure to 6% (final concentration) powdered agar at 37°C for 1 h. The agar is removed by filtration before the broth is sterilized. The presence of this fusiform-shaped *Bacteroides* species correlated well with certain clinical disease states in that study.

DIRECT MICROSCOPIC COUNTS

The ideal way to determine how much of the flora is detected by the isolation medium would be to compare the cultural count with the direct microscopic count of the specimen, as is done with many other types of specimens. However, debris (especially in specimens taken with curettes) precludes an accurate microscopic count. Our cultural recoveries have ranged from 15 to 185% of the direct microscopic count in Petroff-Hausser chambers. Gram-stained preparations and preparations stained with acridine orange examined under ultraviolet microscopy had even less precision. These observations indicate that different culture procedures can be compared only by parallel cultural analysis of identical dilutions from the same specimens.

SAMPLE SIZE

Because of the similarity of colonies produced by many species, one cannot assume that all similar colonies are of the same species. For accurate statistical analysis of the bacterial composition of specimens, or groups of specimens, it is necessary to obtain a representative cross section of the cultivable flora by picking a predetermined number of colonies in an unbiased manner. The number of colonies to be picked from each sample is dictated by the purpose of the study and the available resources. We chose to pick 30 colonies from each specimen on the basis of three factors:

1. *Available personnel.* If primary isolates are stored for later analysis, many fastidious gram-positive and gram-negative species may be lost. The most reliable results are produced only if the necessary growth conditions and identification are determined before the isolates are stored. The number of primary isolates that can be handled simultaneously is limited by the number of personnel available.

2. *Our initial interest in patient populations (rather than specific patients or sites).* Because of the need for a more complete description of the periodontal microflora (17), our primary interest is in the microbiology of patient populations rather than in a more detailed analysis of a few specific patients or sites. On a statistical basis, and for the same total effort, analysis of fewer

isolates per specimen from more sites and patients will provide a more representative analysis of the microflora in populations of patients with periodontal disease.

3. *Coverage values from initial specimens.* Good's formula H_9 (2) for "coverage" provides a useful indication of the complexity of the flora in specimens and is helpful for determining the number of isolates to be analyzed. The simple form of this estimate is [1 − (number of species seen once/number of isolates analyzed)] × 100 = % coverage. In an example specimen, 13 species were found among 30 isolates; 7 of these species occurred only once. The coverage was [1 − (7/30)] × 100 = 77%. This estimate indicates that the 13 observed species account for about 77% of the total colonies in the sample. The 23% of the colonies that were not represented by these species might include dozens of additional species that occur in lower numbers. With 30 colonies from each of 77 specimens from subgingival sites with moderate, severe, or juvenile periodontitis, an average of 12 species was detected per specimen (range, 1 to 25). The average coverage was 77% (range, 30 to 99%).

The coverage analysis also can be used with summations of data from many specimens. From all 77 subgingival samples there were 2,305 isolates, and 178 species were detected, 51 of the species being detected only once. The 178 species represented an estimated 97.8% of the cultivable flora from the diseased sites in these patients. A refined version of the coverage estimate also includes consideration of the frequencies of species that are observed more than once (2). The validity of the coverage analysis is heavily dependent upon the care with which each isolate is identified and distinguished from all other isolates.

SPECIES IDENTIFICATION

Identification of bacterial isolates from periodontal specimens is difficult and expensive, and many investigators do not attempt it. But accurate identification is necessary for determination of the physiological properties of species that may play key roles in the initiation or progression of disease.

There are numerous problems with procedures to identify isolates. Reference information and reported differential characteristics may not be repeatable under conditions used in different laboratories. With many species the results of biochemical tests are greatly influenced by the size and age of the inoculum and the degree of anaerobiosis maintained in the medium. Results of "rapid" tests, which may depend on preformed enzymes, often do not correspond to results from tests that require the growth of the organism in the substrate being tested. Frequently, there is a temptation to identify isolates as members of known species because biochemical test results are similar to reported results, but when direct comparisons are made with authentic strains, such isolates often are found to be distinct species.

Since the advent of deoxyribonucleic acid (DNA)−DNA homology analysis, which in effect compares nearly all properties of the organisms, including those that cannot be measured with available phenotypic tests, it has become evident that most species have fewer variable characteristics than was believed. Genetically distinct species that cannot be differentiated by any common phenotypic tests have been detected from periodontal specimens (L. V. Holdeman, J. L. Johnson, and W. E. C. Moore, J. Dent. Res. Spec. Issue A **60**:414, abstr. 415, 1981). It is important to recognize these genetically distinct organisms, because they may play very different roles in the disease process.

Examination of phenotypic characteristics of strains that have high DNA–DNA homology values has shown that almost any given phenotypic test may have great or little differential value for different species. For example, if weighted computer identifications are used, fermentation of mannose might be considered a "minor" characteristic for many species, but it is the only common phenotypic test that differentiates *Fusobacterium varium* from an equally common, and genetically distinct (unnamed) species. Conversely, indole production is usually considered an important or major characteristic. It does correlate with genetically homologous *Bacteroides* species, but in some genetically homologous *Fusobacterium* species it is variable and therefore a "minor" characteristic. Until many more DNA–DNA homology data are available, it will be difficult to determine which biochemical tests are most useful for precise identification of many periodontal species.

Recently, polyacrylamide gel electrophoresis (PAGE) of soluble cellular proteins (10) has provided a rapid way to compare isolates with one another and with reference or type strains. With careful direct comparison of the protein patterns, the precision of this method may sometimes exceed that of DNA–DNA homology in that serotypes of some genetically homologous species may be distinguished. Identical electrophoretic protein patterns are produced by different cultures of the same strain, and identical or nearly identical patterns are produced by strains that have 80% or greater DNA–DNA homology. PAGE can be used to detect identical organisms among multiple isolates that were picked from a specimen in a randomized manner, and when patterns are compared directly with those of reference strains, it adds a new dimension of precision to the identification of many species.

SPECIES FROM PERIODONTAL SAMPLES

Although the incidence of several different species correlates with various stages of gingivitis or periodontitis, no single species has shown complete correlation. This strongly suggests that more than one bacterial species may cause clinical signs of periodontal disease. The amount of correlation shown by any species, isolated by any method, can provide important clues to the etiology of disease, to interrelationships with other species that might be required to initiate the disease, or to properties that may be held in common by different species that can cause destruction of tissue attachment and its associated loss of bone. For these reasons all correlations must be carefully considered, but they are not proof of causal relationships. The organisms could be benign "indicator" organisms that are favored by the same conditions that favor the etiological agents.

Among the potential etiological agents, it is reasonable to consider species that are frequently encountered and also species that are common pathogens of other sites in the body. The gingival crevice and sulcus appear to be the major natural habitat of commonly encountered pathogens in several genera.

The information on the composition of the flora of diseased sites summarized below is from 2,305 isolates picked in a randomized manner from 77 subgingival samples of sites with moderate, severe, or juvenile periodontitis. The healthy flora (for comparative purposes) was from a smaller set of samples with only 316 isolates representing the predominant flora of 11 sites in four people over 60 years of age with no periodontal disease.

Actinomyces. Dental plaque is the major natural habitat of *Actinomyces*. In samples from diseased sites, we have differentiated 22 groups or serotypes in this genus. Serotypes were determined by fluorescent-antibody reactions with labeled conjugates. Strains that reacted with both *A. viscosus* II and *A. naeslundii* (usually serogroup I) conjugates were encountered rather frequently and are designated "NV." Electrophoretic protein patterns suggest that these cross-reacting strains represent a distinct entity. Strains that did not react with available antisera were designated "NR" and assigned to the species of serologically positive strains they most nearly resembled according to their phenotypic characteristics and electrophoretic patterns. Strains of *A. naeslundii, A. viscosus,* and, to a lesser extent, *A. israelii* are sometimes difficult to differentiate on the basis of phenotypic characteristics. Examination of phenotypic characteristics of serologically positive strains showed that catalase production often was not reliable for differentiation among these species.

In decreasing order of frequency, the groups were *A. naeslundii* (serotype III), *A. naeslundii* NR, *A. israelii* I, *A. viscosus* II, *Actinomyces* serotype 963 (W. VA strain 963), *A. meyeri* NR, serogroup NV, *A. israelii* NR, *A. naeslundii* I, *A. israelii* II, *A. meyeri, A. odontolyticus* I, *A. odontolyticus* NR, and *A. naeslundii* II. Eight groups that appeared to be different from one another and from described species were generally isolated less frequently. *Actinomyces* species comprised 10.5% of all the isolates from diseased sulci.

Although *A. meyeri* (at 1% of the flora) is less numerous than either *A. israelii* (NR and serotypes I and II) at 2.3% of the flora and *A. naeslundii* (NR and serotypes I, II, and III) at 3.6% of the flora, it may be a significant organism. *A. meyeri* was the most common "unidentified actinomyces" referred to us from clinical specimens from other body sites (43 referred clinical isolates, of which 10 were from brain abscesses). Although this species is relatively easy to identify, its real incidence in clinical specimens is not known because it usually is not recognized. However, it appears to equal or exceed *A. israelii* (27 referred clinical isolates, none from brain abscesses) as a pathogen in other body sites.

Actinomyces species represented 35% of all isolates from periodontal samples taken from healthy individuals. Twelve groups or serotypes of *Actinomyces* were observed. The most frequent groups were *Actinomyces* serogroup NV, *A. naeslundii* NR, *A. viscosus* II, *A. naeslundii* III, *A. naeslundii* I, *A. odontolyticus* NR and II, *A. viscosus* NR, *Actinomyces* serotype 963, and *A. odontolyticus* I. These observations suggest that these species may not, in themselves, be responsible for periodontal disease, although a proportional numerical increase of *Actinomyces* has been associated with the development of gingivitis (5) and can cause periodontal bone loss in animal models (9).

Fusobacterium. *F. nucleatum* comprised 8.2% (the most common species) of all 2,305 isolates from diseased sites and occurred at least once in 52% of these specimens. This organism is a common pathogen in other body sites. It produces collagenase and large quantities of butyric acid, and is a reasonable suspect for contributions to the etiology of periodontal disease. *F. nucleatum* is relatively easy to identify by typical morphology, failure to ferment carbohydrates, production of indole, and cultures that have a typical odor of "bad breath." There are several different electrophoretic protein patterns among different strains (even those from the same mouth), and very few strains have greater than 70 or 75% DNA–DNA homology (Y. Selin and J. L. Johnson, J. Dent. Res. Spec. Issue A **60:**415, abstr. 420, 1981; T. V. Potts, L. V. Holdeman, and J. Slots, J. Dent. Res. Spec. Issue A **60:**327, abstr. 65, 1981).

The only other described species of *Fusobacterium* in diseased sites was *F. naviforme*. Phenotypically, *F. naviforme* is similar to *F. nucleatum,* but the two species are genetically unrelated. Cells of *F. naviforme* usually show more pleomorphism than *F. nucleatum,* and *F. naviforme* does not convert threonine to propionate, a test that requires quantitative determination of propionate from cultures in basal medium with and without added threonine. Some strains of *F. nucleatum* do not convert much threonine to propionate, and these strains are difficult to distinguish from *F. naviforme*. However, *F. naviforme* has a distinctive electrophoretic pattern of proteins that shows little strain-to-strain variation.

Ten additional groups or species have been differentiated on the basis of morphology, hydrogen production, fermentation of some carbohydrates, esculin hydrolysis, threonine and lactate conversion to propionate, indole production, and electrophoretic protein patterns. Designation of these less common organisms as species must await either DNA–DNA homology studies to confirm their species status or confirmation that distinctive protein patterns that are uniform among different phenotypically similar strains always correlate with DNA homology results. Several isolates might have been classified as *F. russii* on the basis of phenotypic characteristics, but their cellular protein pattern is very distinct from the type and reference strains of *F. russii*.

Eubacterium. From the subgingival diseased sites we detected 19 species of *Eubacterium,* which together represent 12.1% of the isolates. *E. nodatum* (3) was the most common of these and was the second most common isolate from diseased sites (6.5% of all isolates). It was not detected among the 316 isolates from healthy periodontia. The species is easily recognized. Morphologically, it is similar to *Actinomyces* species, but it is less aerotolerant, is nonfermentative, and produces butyric acid as a major product. Although we have isolated it with similar frequency from plates (35 times) and roll tubes (46 times), it is not mentioned in previous reports. This suggests that it might be part of the flora attached to the tooth root or tissue that could be more readily obtained with scalers than with other methods.

E. brachy (3) represented 2.4% of the total isolates from diseased sites but was not detected in samples from older people with healthy periodontia. This species might be confused with *Peptostreptococcus anaerobius* in that it is a short (but definite) rod (rather than coccus) in chains, has similar biochemical reactions, and produces similar straight- and branched-chain fatty acids and large amounts of hydrogen. However, *E. brachy* is not inhibited by sodium polyanethol sulfonate and has an electrophoretic protein pattern that is not at all like that of *P. anaerobius*. *E. brachy* was detected with similar frequency from plates and tubes.

E. timidum (3) was the third most common of all species from diseased sites (2.5% of 2,305 isolates). In broth it grows slowly and poorly in small tight clumps or small white balls. The cells are like very small actinomyces cells, and cultures are nonreactive in our usual biochemical tests (4). It was isolated from both plates (29 times) and tubes (42 times).

E. alactolyticum is another pathogen of other body sites. The incidence of this species was limited entirely to the subgingival flora of diseased sites, where it represented 0.9% of all isolates. *E. alactolyticum* is easily recognized by its "diphtheroid" morphology and strong fermentation of glucose and fructose and sometimes sorbitol or weak fermentation of mannitol. In these respects it could be mistaken for *P. acnes,* but it is both indole and nitrate negative, and produces the two-, four-, six-, and eight-carbon normal fatty acids. It is catalase negative but cannot be distinguished from propionibacteria on this basis because catalase production is variable in species of *Propionibacterium.*

E. saburreum represented 0.09% of the isolates from diseased subgingival sites, but occurred over seven times as frequently in the corresponding supragingival areas. We have found that strains of *E. saburreum* often tend to stain gram negative. These could be mistaken for undescribed fermentative species of *Fusobacterium* unless Gram stains were made from young cultures in carbohydrate-free medium.

There were 14 undescribed species of *Eubacterium.* Of most interest is *Eubacterium* D-8, which comprised 3.5% of the flora from diseased subgingival sites but was not seen in samples from healthy sites. This gram-variable rod of various lengths, in short chains, grows poorly and is negative for all of the biochemical tests we usually run (4). It produces very small amounts of acetic acid and may produce traces of formic, succinic, or butyric acids as well, but no detectable gas or hydrogen.

It appears that the presence of several species of *Eubacterium* correlates with periodontal disease about as well as the correlations suggested for many other species.

Capnocytophaga. Several reports have suggested that *C. gingivalis, C. ochracea,* and *C. sputigena* are important agents in the etiology of periodontal disease, and significance has been attached to the ability of these species to "glide" or swarm on the surface of certain commercial agar plates (and by "gliding" possibly carry other agents into the gingival crevice).

Our data indicate that there is little reason to believe that these species are of more significance in periodontal disease than are many other species. They were present in greater concentrations in samples from healthy sites than in samples from sulci of diseased sites (Table 3). The greater number of *C. ochracea* in the supragingival areas of diseased sites suggests that this aerotolerant organism is stimulated by increased gingival exudates or the products of other bacteria. In moist areas even nonmotile bacteria can spread at rates of centimeters per day and there is no requirement for them to be carried by "gliding" bacteria.

Some strains of these genetically distinct species (8, 16) are difficult to separate on the basis of phenotypic tests. Their protein patterns are quite similar but are helpful for differentiation.

TABLE 3. *Capnocytophaga species as percent of total isolates*

Species	Sites		
	Healthy	Diseased	
		Sulci	Supragingival
C. gingivalis	0.96%	0.30%	0.69%
C. ochracea	0.32%	0.74%	3.74%
C. sputigena	0.32%	0.22%	0.30%

Bacteroides. Twenty-five species of *Bacteroides* were found in the samples from the sulci of diseased sites. Only seven of these were described species, but several others were frequent isolates and, in at least two laboratories, manuscripts are being prepared to describe them. Those that produce black pigment on blood agar have received much attention by different investigators, but their true significance in the disease process has not been determined, primarily because the group includes at least nine genetically distinct species that can produce black or dark-brown colonies (caused by porphyrin accumulation) on blood agar. Unfortunately, within several of these species, not all of the genetically homologous strains produced pigment, even with additional heme in the medium.

Among the saccharolytic "pigmenting" species of bacteroides, the characteristics given in Table 4 appeared to separate the genetically distinct species that we plan to propose in a separate publication. The most frequent of these species in the sulcus of diseased sites was *B. intermedius* at 3.5% of the total flora (over twice its incidence in the adjacent supragingival samples). It was detected in 26% of the sulcus samples, but was not isolated from healthy sites or in any of 81 experimental gingivitis samples, even after 26 days without tooth brushing.

TABLE 4. *Differentiation of saccharolytic pigmenting Bacteroides[a]*

Characteristic	Species (strain)[b]
Lactose +	
Esculin hydrolysis +	
Cellobiose +	*B. loescheii* (ATCC 15930*)
Cellobiose −	*B. socranskii* (ATCC 33185*)
Esculin hydrolysis −	*B. melaninogenicus* (ATCC 25845)
Lactose −	
Indole +	*B. intermedius* (ATCC 25611*) and Homology group 8944 (NCTC 9336)[c]
Indole −	*B. corporis* (VPI 9342)

[a]These species ferment glucose, digest gelatin, and are inhibited by 20% bile. None ferments arabinose or xylose, or produces catalase.

[b]Type or proposed type strains are followed by an asterisk (*); others are reference strains.

[c]We do not now know of any phenotypic characteristics that can differentiate these two homology groups; however, there appear to be slight differences in their PAGE protein patterns.

Coykendall et al. (1) showed that *B. gingivalis* is a species genetically distinct from *B. asaccharolyticus,* which is phenotypically similar. *B. gingivalis* can be distinguished serologically and by its production of phenylacetic acid (6), which is readily detected by chromatography of methylated culture broth. Several laboratories have reported a very high incidence of *B. gingivalis* in specimens from advanced and inflamed severe periodontitis (14). There are some indications (7, 17) that this species may increase after major tissue destruction has occurred. With the exception of one site, the incidence of *B. gingivalis* in our specimens was comparatively low (0.6% of all sulcus isolates), but our patient populations have been purposely selected to avoid severely advanced periodontitis in people over 30 years of age.

Other species. Within the scope of this presentation, it is not possible to discuss all of the observed species that might play contributing roles in periodontal disease and that deserve equal consideration. A number of species in *Selenomonas, Wolinella* (Tanner et al., description submitted to Int. J. Syst. Bacteriol.), and *Actinobacillus,* as well as several genera of cocci, are certainly worthy of mention. Some of these species confuse the issue of etiology by appearing in only one or two of the diseased sites, where they represented 50 to 100% of the isolates both on plates and in roll tubes. These species might represent the elusive etiological agent, but only of the disease in those sites. They are certainly not representative of periodontal disease in our human population. Such occurrences serve to weaken our statistical analyses, which attempt to evaluate the significance of various species in periodontitis, and strengthen the need to determine the accuracy and statistical variance of our sampling procedures to ascertain whether they reliably can be removed from our statistical analyses as special populations.

SUMMARY

Comparative data indicate that sample, culture, and identification methods can influence the results of microbial analyses of the floras associated with periodontal disease. Correlation of the incidence of a number of bacterial species with periodontitis suggests that several species are potential etiological agents.

ACKNOWLEDGMENTS

We thank the California Department of Public Health for the *Actinomyces* serological conjugates used in this work, and E. P. Cato, P. C. Atkins, R. Z. Beyer, J. A. Cooke, A. P. Donnelly, D. E. Hash, L. S. Fabrycky, J. L. Hungate, L. L. Long, A. C. Mitchell, D. B. Sinsabaugh, S. C. Smith, S. E. Stevens, and D. M. Wall for their contributions to these studies.

Parts of the projects from which these observations were made were financed by The Commonwealth of Virginia and by Public Health Service grants DE-05139 and DE-05054 from the National Institute of Dental Research and AI-15244 from the National Institute of Allergy and Infectious Diseases.

LITERATURE CITED

1. **Coykendall, A. L., F. S. Kaczmarek, and J. Slots.** 1980. Genetic heterogeneity in *Bacteroides asaccharolyticus* (Holdeman and Moore 1970) Finegold and Barnes 1977 (approved lists, 1980) and proposal of *Bacteroides gingivalis* sp. nov. and *Bacteroides macacae* (Slots and Genco) comb. nov. Int. J. Syst. Bacteriol. **30:**559–564.
2. **Good, I. J.** 1953. The population frequencies of species and the estimation of population parameters. Biometrica **40:**237–264.
3. **Holdeman, L. V., E. P. Cato, J. A. Burmeister, and W. E. C. Moore.** 1980. Descriptions of *Eubacterium timidum* sp. nov., *Eubacterium brachy* sp. nov., and *Eubacterium nodatum* sp. nov. isolated from human periodontitis. Int. J. Syst. Bacteriol. **30:**163–169.

4. **Holdeman, L. V., E. P. Cato, and W. E. C. Moore (ed.).** 1977. Anaerobe laboratory manual, 4th ed., p. 1–156. Department of Anaerobic Microbiology, Virginia Polytechnic Institute and State University, Blacksburg.
5. **Jordan, H. V., P. H. Keyes, and B. Vellock.** 1972. Periodontal lesions in hamsters and gnotobiotic rats infected with *Actinomyces* of human origin. J. Periodontal Res. **7:**21–25.
6. **Kaczmarek, F. S., and A. L. Coykendall.** 1980. Production of phenylacetic acid by strains of *Bacteroides asaccharolyticus* and *Bacteroides gingivalis* (sp. nov.). J. Clin. Microbiol. **12:**288–290.
7. **Kagan, J. M.** 1980. Local immunity to *Bacteroides gingivalis* in periodontal disease. J. Dent. Res. Spec. Issue **59**(DI):1750–1756.
8. **Leadbetter, E. R., S. C. Holt, and S. S. Socransky.** 1979. *Capnocytophaga:* new genus of gram-negative gliding bacteria. I. General characteristics, taxonomic considerations and significance. Arch. Microbiol. **122:**9–16.
9. **Loesche, W. J., and S. A. Syed.** 1978. Bacteriology of human experimental gingivitis: effect of plaque and gingivitis score. Infect. Immun. **21:**830–839.
10. **Moore, W. E. C., D. E. Hash, L. V. Holdeman, and E. P. Cato.** 1980. Polyacrylamide slab gel electrophoresis of soluble proteins for studies of bacterial floras. Appl. Environ. Microbiol. **39:**900–907.
11. **Newman, M. G., S. S. Socransky, E. D. Savitt, D. A. Propas, and A. Crawford.** 1976. Studies on the microbiology of periodontosis. J. Periodontol. **47:**373–379.
12. **Sabiston, C. B., Jr., and W. R. Grigsby.** 1972. Anaerobic bacteria from the advanced periodontal lesion. J. Periodontol. **43:**199–201.
13. **Slots, J.** 1976. The predominant cultivable organisms in juvenile periodontitis. Scand. J. Dent. Res. **83:**274–278.
14. **Slots, J.** 1979. Subgingival microflora and periodontal disease. J. Clin. Periodontol. **6:**351–382.
15. **Slots, J., P. Mashimo, M. J. Levine, and R. J. Genco.** 1979. Periodontal therapy in humans. I. Microbiological and clinical effects of a single course of periodontal scaling and root planing and of adjunctive tetracycline therapy. J. Periodontol. **50:**495–509.
16. **Socransky, S. S., S. C. Holt, E. R. Leadbetter, A. C. R. Tanner, E. Savitt, and B. F. Hammond.** 1979. *Capnocytophaga:* a new genus of gram-negative gliding bacteria. III. Physiological characterization. Arch. Microbiol. **122:**29–34.
17. **Tanner, A. C. R., C. Haffer, G. T. Bratthall, R. A. Visconti, and S. S. Socransky.** 1979. A study of the bacteria associated with advancing periodontitis in man. J. Clin. Periodontol. **6:**278–307.

Importance of Black-Pigmented
Bacteroides in Human Periodontal Disease

JØRGEN SLOTS

*Department of Oral Biology and Periodontal Disease Clinical Research Center,
State University of New York at Buffalo, Buffalo, New York 14226*

INTRODUCTION

Human periodontal disease is associated with a complex microflora in which more than 250 bacterial species can be encountered. It is likely that many periodontal species are capable of initiating chronic gingival inflammation if bacterial cells are present in sufficiently high numbers. On the other hand, relatively few species may be responsible for the conversion of a gingivitis lesion into a progressive periodontitis lesion with periodontal fiber destruction and loss of alveolar bone. Recent studies show that the proportion of gram-negative anaerobic organisms increases markedly in the subgingival microflora with increasing severity of periodontal disease (85, 96, 122). It has also been shown that many of the gram-negative isolates from periodontitis lesions belong to the black-pigmented *Bacteroides* group of organisms. These bacteria may play an important role in the etiology and pathogenesis of periodontal disease because of their high prevalence in diseased periodontal pockets and their well-established pathogenic potential.

The purpose of this communication is to review data that may help to clarify the importance of black-pigmented *Bacteroides* in human periodontal disease. Consideration is given to taxonomy, serology, association with periodontal disease, host response, experimental periodontal disease in animals, pathogenicity and potentially pathogenic products, and the effect of elimination.

TAXONOMY

Identification and characterization of the nonmotile, nonsporeforming, gram-negative, anaerobic rods that produce black pigment when grown on blood agar has been a particular problem since the discovery of these bacteria. Oliver and Wherry in 1921 (72) named the organisms *Bacterium melaninogenicum,* but they provided little information on the biochemical characteristics of the species. Gibbons and co-workers (8, 79) demonstrated that the black-pigmented *Bacteroides* group of organisms could be divided into nonfermenters, weak fermenters, and strong fermenters. For these three subgroups, Holdeman and Moore (29) respectively assigned the names *Bacteroides melaninogenicus* subsp. *asaccharolyticus, Bacteroides melaninogenicus* subsp. *intermedius,* and *Bacteroides melaninogenicus* subsp. *melaninogenicus.*

Early genetic studies (13, 124) found that the guanine-plus-cytosine $(G+C)$ content of the deoxyribonucleic acid (DNA) of asaccharolytic *B. melaninogenicus* strains was 50 to 54 mol% and that of saccharolytic *B. melaninogenicus* strains was 40 to 45 mol%. Because of the marked genetic and metabolic difference, the asaccharolytic members of *B. melaninogenicus* were transferred in 1977 to the separate species *Bacteroides asaccharolyticus* (13).

27

B. asaccharolyticus itself, however, was genetically heterogeneous, as demonstrated by Coykendall et al. (10). Human oral isolates of the species had between 46.7 and 49.1 mol% G+C, and human nonoral isolates had between 51.6 and 53.4 mol% G+C. In addition, the DNAs of the oral and nonoral isolates hybridized at very low levels. The oral genotype was established as a new species, *Bacteroides gingivalis*. The nonoral isolates, which in fact may consist of more than one genotype, were retained in the species *B. asaccharolyticus*. Common biochemical tests in taxonomy (18, 28) cannot distinguish between *B. gingivalis* and *B. asaccharolyticus;* however, phenylacetic acid production (34, 59), trypsin-like activity (85a), agglutination of sheep erythrocytes (68, 86), and serological assays (78; C. Mouton, P. G. Hammond, J. Slots, M. J. Reed, and R. J. Genco, Ann. Microbiol. [Inst. Pasteur], in press) appear useful in separating the two species, as shown in Table 1. The polypeptide patterns (102, 110), cellular fatty acids (62, 80; K. P. Ferguson, D. W. Lambe, Jr., and W. R. Mayberry, Abstr. Annu. Meet. Am. Soc. Microbiol. 1981, C59, p. 272), mucopeptide composition (81, 124), electrophoretic mobility of malate dehydrogenase (81), and antibiotic susceptibility patterns (81) may also be valuable distin-

TABLE 1. *Biochemical, serological, and genetic characteristics of black-pigmented* Bacteroides[a]

Species/subspecies	Glucose fermentation	Metabolic acid end products	Indole production	Catalase production	Esculin hydrolysis	Lactose fermentation
B. gingivalis	−	APIbBIvPh	+	−	−	−
B. asaccharolyticus	−	APIbBIv	+	−	−	−
B. melaninogenicus subsp. *intermedius*		AIbIvS		−		
Homology group A	+		+		−	−
Homology group B	+		+		−	−
Homology group C	+		−		−	−
B. melaninogenicus subsp. *melaninogenicus*		AIbIvS		−		
Homology group A	+		−		−	+.
Homology group B	+		−		+	+
Homology group C	+		−		+	+
B. melaninogenicus subsp. *levii*	+	APIbBIvS	−	−		
B. macacae	+	APIbBIv	+	+	−	+
Canine *Bacteroides*	(−)	APIbBIv	+	+	ND	ND

[a]Sign: A, acetic acid; P, propionic acid; Ib, isobutyric acid; B, buytric acid; Iv, isovaleric acid; S, succinic acid; Ph, phenylactic acid; +, 90% or more positive reactions; −, 90% or more negative reactions; v, variable (11 to 89% positive reactions); ND, no data available.

guishing characteristics.

The saccharolytic black-pigmented bacteroides are listed in the 8th edition of *Bergey's Manual* (4) as two subspecies, *B. melaninogenicus* subsp. *intermedius* and *B. melaninogenicus* subsp. *melaninogenicus*. Although these organisms phenotypically are quite similar (28), Johnson (33) recently found that *B. melaninogenicus* subsp. *intermedius* contains 41 to 44 mol% G + C and *B. melaninogenicus* subsp. *melaninogenicus* contains 41 to 50 mol% G + C, and that three distinct DNA–DNA homology groups exist within each subspecies. Johnson also showed that at least five of the six genotypes can be identified on the basis of variable indole production, esculin hydrolysis, and cellobiose, lactose, and sucrose fermentation (Table 1).

Black-pigmented *Bacteroides* organisms have also been recovered from monkeys, dogs, cattle, horses, sheep, pigs, rabbits, guinea pigs, and hamsters (6, 22). Studies on these organisms are limited, but distinct genotypes appear to exist for macaque strains *(Bacteroides macacae)* (10), bovine strains *(B. melaninogenicus* subsp. *levii)* (101), and dog strains (10). Distinguishing phenotypic characteristics for these animal strains are listed in Table 1.

Sucrose fermenta-tion	Cellobiose fermenta-tion	Hemagglu-tination of sheep erythrocytes	Trypsin-like activity	Serology	% G + C	Site of isolation
−	−	+	+	1 serogroup	48	Oral cavity of humans and *M. arctoides*
−	−	−	−	2 serogroups	52	Nonoral sites of humans
		−	−	2 serogroups		Oral and nonoral sites of humans and animals
v	−				43	
v	−				41	
−	−				44	
		−	−	1 serogroup		Oral and nonoral sites of humans and animals
+	−				41	
+	−				50	
+	+				47	
		−	v	1 serogroup	48	Cattle, oral and nonoral sites of humans?
−	−	−	v	1 serogroup	43	Oral cavity of *M. arctoides*
ND	ND	ND	v	1 serogroup	42	Oral cavity of beagle dog

SEROLOGY

Black-pigmented *Bacteroides* is an example of a group of organisms for which progress in taxonomy has stimulated progress in serology and vice versa. These organisms exhibit little or no cross-reaction with antisera to numerous nonrelated aerobic and anaerobic species (38, 76, 78, 121), and early studies showed a relationship between their biochemical and serological profiles (8, 76). In a series of studies by Lambe (40–42), who used fluorescent-antibody reagents to representative nonoral strains of *B. asaccharolyticus* and *B. melaninogenicus* subspecies, it was established that *B. asaccharolyticus*, *B. melaninogenicus* subsp. *melaninogenicus,* and *B. melaninogenicus* subsp. *levii* each contain one serogroup and *B. melaninogenicus* subsp. *intermedius* contains two serogroups.

The antigenic composition of oral black-pigmented *Bacteroides* has been investigated in my laboratory by double immunodiffusion and immuno-electrophoresis (78, 87) and by direct (63) and indirect (90; Mouton et al., submitted for publication) immunofluorescence techniques. A main finding in these studies was that *B. gingivalis* does not share major antigens with the nonoral *B. asaccharolyticus* or with oral and nonoral *B. melaninogenicus* subsp. *intermedius* or *B. melaninogenicus* subsp. *melaninogenicus*. The antigen components of strains of *B. melaninogenicus* subsp. *intermedius* and *B. melaninogenicus* subsp. *melaninogenicus* do not appear to be site specific, as numerous cross-reactions were observed between oral and nonoral isolates. At least one antigen was found to be shared by strains of *B. melaninogenicus* subsp. *intermedius* and strains of *B. melaninogenicus* subsp. *melaninogenicus,* but subspecies-specific antigens were also found. *B. macacae, B. melaninogenicus* subsp. *levii,* and the catalase-positive beagle dog strains each comprise antigenically distinct groups of organisms. The number of currently recognized serogroups of black-pigmented *Bacteroides* is listed in Table 1.

Some information is available about the antigenic components of black-pigmented *Bacteroides*. Capsular antigens appear to be species and subspecies specific (52, 53) and are present on most if not all fresh clinical isolates (125; K. Okuda, J. Slots, and R. J. Genco, J. Dent. Res. Spec. Issue A **59**:386, abstr. 475, 1980). Other components found in *Bacteroides* which might be antigenic are the pili or fimbriae (69), lipopolysaccharide (25, 55), and some proteins (120). Clearly, more work is necessary to identify the antigens of these organisms, to characterize them chemically, and to study their biological properties in an attempt to elucidate the molecular basis for the pathogenesis of the infections caused by these species.

The recognition of the possession of unique sets of antigens by the various species and subspecies of black-pigmented *Bacteroides* is imperative in investigations of host–bacterium interactions. The results obtained in such studies may be representative only for the species or subspecies examined, and referring to the study organisms merely as *B. melaninogenicus* appears to be highly inadequate.

ASSOCIATION WITH HUMAN PERIODONTAL DISEASE

Historically, black-pigmented *Bacteroides* organisms have been regarded as important bacteria in the pathogenesis of periodontal disease. As early as 1928, Burdon (6) mentioned that, although the organisms were present in all mouths, a long and careful search was required to detect them in healthy individuals. On the other hand, their number increased markedly with the development of purulent periodontitis. Burdon also used the quantitative recovery of the organisms as an index of the severity of the disease and to monitor the effect of periodontal treatment.

The results of recent studies using improved anaerobic culture techniques to detect *Bacteroides* are presented in Table 2. All investigators agree that black-pigmented *Bacteroides* organisms are present infrequently and in low numbers in subgingival plaque associated with minimal periodontal disease. They are also rarely recovered from the oral cavity of children (2, 3, 37, 127), who, interestingly, often exhibit little periodontal disease despite large plaque accumulations (9, 51). In contrast, in 75% or more of advanced periodontitis lesions in adults, these organisms average 20 to 30% of the cultivable microflora.

The correlation between *B. gingivalis* and rapidly progressing alveolar bone destruction is relatively well documented. This organism has not been reported to be present in high numbers in chronic gingivitis lesions. On the other hand, its close association with advancing periodontitis lesions with severe gingivitis has been established in several microbiological studies (Table 2). *B. gingivalis* can also be present in high proportions in generalized juvenile periodontitis lesions (48).

The relationship between *B. melaninogenicus* subsp. *intermedius* and periodontal disease is not as clear. This organism is the predominant black-pigmented *Bacteroides* in long-standing gingivitis with little or no alveolar bone loss (Table 2), and it appears to be involved in the development of experimental gingivitis (47) and pregnancy gingivitis (39). Data from our laboratory (J. Slots and J. J. Zambon) further show that *B. melaninogenicus* subsp. *intermedius* constitutes a significant segment of the microflora in acute necrotizing ulcerative gingivitis (Table 3). Information is also available on *B. melaninogenicus* subsp. *intermedius* as a major isolate from advanced periodontitis with severe gingival inflammation (127). Although these findings point to the ability of *B. melaninogenicus* subsp. *intermedius* to induce gingival inflammation, the organism has also been recovered from deep periodontal pockets with minimal gingivitis (117). Differences in clinical features of infections associated with *B. melaninogenicus* subsp. *intermedius* may be explained in at least three ways. (i) The three newly discovered genotypes of *B. melaninogenicus* subsp. *intermedius* may differ significantly in periodontopathic potential; some strains may be capable of inducing gingivitis but have a low bone-destroying potential, whereas other strains may be able to initiate alveolar bone breakdown. (ii) The host response may vary. (iii) Another unidentified organism may modify the periodontopathic potential of *B. melaninogenicus* subsp. *intermedius* or even be responsible for the periodontal diseases studied.

B. melaninogenicus subsp. *melaninogenicus* is not frequently isolated from periodontal pockets and appears not to be related to any specific periodontal condition. One report noted that the organism is present in high numbers in the "normal" gingival microflora of young adults (11). Organisms which biochemically and serologically resemble *B. melaninogenicus* subsp. *levii* can be recovered from humans (41), but they seem to be rare periodontal isolates (127; P. G. Hammond, J. Slots, and R. J. Genco, Abstr. Annu. Meet. Am. Soc. Microbiol. 1980, C66, p. 285).

Immunofluorescence studies of histological specimens showed that black-

TABLE 2. *Occurrence of black-pigmented* Bacteroides
in periodontal health and disease

Disease state	Sites infected with *Bacteroides*/total sites studied	% *Bacteroides* of the total viable flora at infected sites	Predominant *Bacteroides* species	Reference
Normal gingiva/ minimal disease	3/5	3	No data	Gibbons et al. (17)
	5/9	8	No data	Williams et al. (123)
	3/7	4	*B. melaninogenicus* subsp. *intermedius*	Slots (84)
	17/30	5	*B. melaninogenicus* subsp. *intermedius*	Spiegel et al. (100)
	1/5	6	*B. melaninogenicus* subsp. *intermedius*	Tanner et al. (117)
	1/20	1	*B. melaninogenicus* subsp. *intermedius*	Zambon et al. (127)
	7/11	8	*B. melaninogenicus* subsp. *intermedius*	White and Mayrand (122)
Gingivitis/early periodontitis	6/9	11	*B. melaninogenicus* subsp. *intermedius*	Slots et al. (92)
	4/6	2	*B. melaninogenicus* subsp. *intermedius*	Spiegel et al. (100)
	30/38[a]	15	*B. melaninogenicus* subsp. *intermedius*; *B. gingivalis*	White and Mayrand (122)
Advanced periodon- titis in adults	5/5	8	No data	Gibbons et al. (17)
	5/8	6	No data	Williams et al. (123)
	7/8	36	*B. gingivalis*; *B. melanino- genicus* subsp. *intermedius*	Slots (83)
	29/29[b]	18	*B. gingivalis*; B. melanino- *genicus* subsp. *intermedius*	Spiegel et al. (100)
	13/16	28	*B. gingivalis*; *B. melanino- genicus* subsp. *intermedius*	Tanner et al. (117)
	19/40	23	*B. melaninogenicus* subsp. *intermedius*	Zambon et al. (127)
	No data/27	35	*B. gingivalis*; *B. melanino- genicus* subsp. *intermedius*	White and Mayrand (122)

[a]Data are combined for gingival indices 1 and 2.
[b]Data are combined for periodontal classes 3 and 4.

TABLE 3. *Black-pigmented* Bacteroides *in acute necrotizing ulcerative gingivitis*

Patient	No. of sample sites	Small spirochetes[a]	Intermediate spirochetes[a]	Large spirochetes[a]	B. melaninogenicus subsp. intermedius[b]	B. gingivalis[b]
1	11	6 (0–22)[c]	10 (0–45)	0 (0–1)	13 (0–32)	2 (0–8)
2	8	10 (0–20)	27 (0–50)	1 (0–3)	8 (0–28)	1 (0–6)
3	1	14	8	3	15	0
4	5	12 (3–30)	24 (17–30)	35 (9–60)	15 (9–23)	1 (0–3)

[a]The spirochete counts were obtained from wet-mount preparations by phase-contrast microscopy.
[b]Data were obtained with an indirect fluorescent-antibody staining procedure. The antisera against *B. gingivalis* (immunosorbed with strains of *B. melaninogenicus* subsp. *intermedius*) and *B. melaninogenicus* subsp. *intermedius* (immunosorbed with strains of *B. gingivalis*) were used at a dilution of 1:800. Goat antibodies monospecific for rabbit IgG, conjugated with fluorescein isothiocyanate, were used at a dilution of 1:100. Cultures showed that virtually all strains detected with the reagent for *B. melaninogenicus* were of the subspecies *B. melaninogenicus* subsp. *intermedius*.
[c]Data for spirochetes and black-pigmented *Bacteroides* are expressed as percentages of the total cell counts. The mean percentage is shown with the range in parentheses.

pigmented *Bacteroides* organisms and their products are present on the surface of the pocket epithelium and in the subepithelial connective tissues of inflamed periodontal pockets (7, 116). Studies in humans on the humoral and cellular immune response to *B. gingivalis* and *B. melaninogenicus* subspecies further suggest that these bacteria and the host response they evoke are associated with periodontal destruction (see Host Response in this paper).

It is worth emphasizing that *B. gingivalis* and *B. melaninogenicus* subspecies are not recoverable from all advanced periodontitis lesions. The dominant organisms in localized juvenile periodontitis are *Actinobacillus actinomycetemcomitans* (93) and *Capnocytophaga* (66, 82), species with recognized pathogenic potential. Also, some adult periodontitis lesions are free from black-pigmented *Bacteroides*. In these adults, bacteria other than black-pigmented *Bacteroides* likely have caused the periodontal destruction. It is also theoretically possible that these lesions were in remission at the time of examination because of prior suppression of the causative bacteria of the *B. gingivalis–B. melaninogenicus* group of organisms. A "spontaneous" resolution of periodontal disease appears to be a relatively common phenomenon (J. M. Goodson, A. C. R. Tanner, A. D. Haffajee, and S. S. Socransky, J. Dent. Res. Spec. Issue A **60**:387, abstr. 305, 1981; K. R. McHenry, E. Hausmann, R. J. Genco, and J. Slots, J. Dent. Res. Spec. Issue A **60**:387, abstr. 306, 1981). Testing of these possibilities depends on the development of more sensitive clinical methods for measuring the rate of periodontal disease progression at a given moment.

HOST RESPONSE

The first report of antibody production in response to oral infections caused by black-pigmented *Bacteroides* was that of Courant and Gibbons (8). These authors found antibodies against a mixture of lipopolysaccharide extracted from eight *Bacteroides* strains and from autologous *Bacteroides* strains in serum from each of 16 individuals. Hofstad (27) examined 120 serum samples for antibodies reacting with purified lipopolysaccharide of *B. melaninogenicus* (presumably *B. melaninogenicus* subsp. *intermedius*) and demonstrated specific antibodies in most children more than 1 year of age and in adults. That serum antibodies to

B. melaninogenicus subsp. *intermedius* commonly can be found in children and adults, dentulous or edentulous, was recently confirmed with a sensitive enzyme-linked immunosorbent assay (C. Mouton, J. Slots, and R. J. Genco, Abstr. Annu. Meet. Am. Soc. Microbiol. 1979, E(H)8, p. 79). The widespread occurrence of serum antibodies against *B. melaninogenicus* subsp. *intermedius* despite this organism's sporadic occurrence in dental plaque may indicate that serologically closely related *B. melaninogenicus* strains of tonsillar, intestinal, vaginal, or other nonoral origin contribute to the antibody production. That antibody formation has been induced by unidentified, cross-reacting bacterial or food antigens is also a possibility.

Because of the unique antigenic composition of *B. gingivalis,* serum antibodies reactive with *B. gingivalis* are likely induced by the oral organisms. Mashimo et al. (58) examined serum from 95 adults for precipitating antibodies to soluble antigens of *B. gingivalis* and found 15 positive sera. Using a capsular antigen-containing extract of *B. gingivalis* and an enzyme-linked immunosorbent assay, Mouton et al. (64) studied the level of serum antibodies against *B. gingivalis* in various age groups and in relation to periodontal disease. More than 80% of normal adults had detectable specific immunoglobulin G (IgG) antibodies, whereas only 45% of children 6 to 12 years of age and no children less than 6 months of age demonstrated specific IgG antibodies (Fig. 1). The active synthesis of IgG antibodies directed to *B. gingivalis* is thus strongly enhanced concomitant with eruption of the permanent teeth and colonization of the organism in the oral cavity. The presence of high mean IgG antibodies in

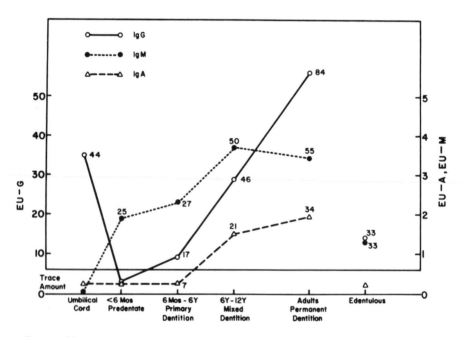

FIG. 1. *Changes with age of serum immunoglobulins reactive with* B. gingivalis. *The curves connect the mean values expressed as EU-G, EU-A, and EU-M obtained for each age group. Numbers adjacent to each point indicate the percentage of positive individuals in each group. Reprinted with permission from reference 64.*

umbilical cord sera is consistent with maternal–fetal transfer. Specific IgM and IgA antibodies were found in some individuals, but the activities of these antibodies were generally low.

Mouton et al. (64) detected IgG serum antibodies to *B. gingivalis* in all five periodontal categories studied (Fig. 2). The observation that the mean IgG antibody levels in the localized juvenile periodontitis and the acute necrotizing ulcerative gingivitis groups were as low as that of the normal adult group agrees with the small numbers of *B. gingivalis* isolates found in these diseases.

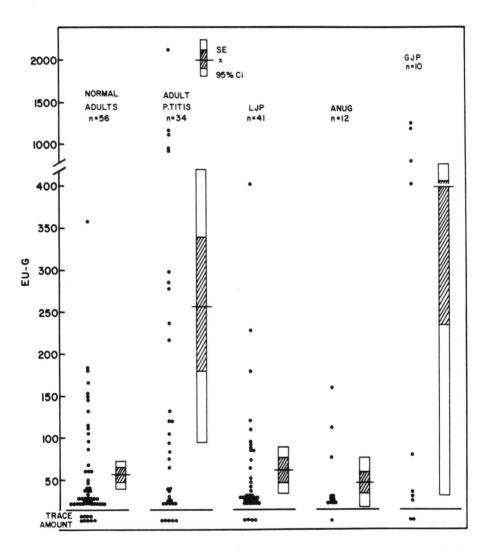

FIG. 2. *Levels of IgG specific for* B. gingivalis *in various periodontal conditions. Each point represents the antibody activity level of an individual serum sample expressed as EU-G. Shown for each group is the mean ± standard error (SE, □) and ± the 95% confidence interval (Ci, □). ANUG, Acute necrotizing ulcerative gingivitis; P.titis, periodontitis. Reprinted with permission from reference 64.*

In contrast, the mean IgG antibody level was fivefold higher in the adult periodontitis group and eightfold higher in the generalized juvenile periodontitis group than that of control groups of normal adults. *Bacteroides* species in serious nonoral infections can evoke a significant antibody response (99), and a similar immunological response appears to occur in periodontal disease. Mouton et al. (64) also found that 17 of 34 adult periodontitis patients had low levels of specific IgG. Because no culture was performed, it was not assessed whether the low IgG levels reflected the absence, or the presence only in small numbers, of *B. gingivalis* cells or whether immunological unresponsiveness might have occurred in patients infected with the organism.

Mansheim et al. (57), using an enzyme-linked immunoassay (54), also demonstrated that the level of serum anticapsule IgG antibodies to *B. gingivalis* increased with age. In eight adult periodontitis patients, aged 29 to 38 years, the specific serum IgG antibody levels were not significantly different from those of the healthy population of the same age (57). Their finding of no association between severity of adult periodontitis and specific antibody level may be due to the small number of patients examined.

The local immune response to *B. gingivalis* at the site of a gingival lesion has also been investigated. Kagan (35), using an immunofluorescence technique to determine the specificity of gingival plasma cells for *B. gingivalis* antigens, found that 32% of plasma cells in the advanced periodontitis lesion bound cells of *B. gingivalis* compared with only 3% of the plasma cells in the early lesion. These results indicate that *B. gingivalis* can evoke a strong local immune response in advanced periodontitis lesions, and they provide additional evidence that this bacterium is an important periodontopathic organism.

Several workers have related the tissue damage of periodontal disease to features of the cellular immune response. Utilization of black-pigmented *Bacteroides* of unknown species or subspecies and differences in methodology and patient populations, however, makes a comparison of many of these studies difficult. Ivanyi and Lehner (31), using a sonic extract of *B. melaninogenicus*, found an increased response to this organism in patients with moderate periodontitis and a decreased response in patients with severe periodontitis. Other investigators also reported a cellular unresponsiveness to black-pigmented *Bacteroides* in advanced periodontal disease (5). In contrast, Patters and co-workers (74, 75) and Lang and Smith (43) showed that lymphocyte stimulation by *B. gingivalis* sonic extract was increased in adult periodontitis patients. Significantly weaker responses were found in gingivitis, mild-to-moderate periodontitis, and edentulous patient groups. These authors concluded that the specificity of the lymphocyte blastogenic response to *B. gingivalis* correlates with the presence of the organism in the subgingival microflora during various disease states.

Study on the cellular response to plaque bacteria has revealed that polymorphonuclear leukocytes comprise more than 90% of the cells in the crevicular fluid of hosts with periodontitis lesions (1). In vitro (44, 104, 105) and in vivo (104, 106) experiments have shown that *B. gingivalis* and *B. melaninogenicus* subsp. *intermedius* clearly can attract polymorphonuclear leukocytes, presumably by complement activation (71) and possibly by bacterial chemotactic products, but not to a larger degree than that of various reference strains. Hence, the pyogenic nature of infections caused by black-pigmented *Bacteroides* cannot be explained solely on the basis of chemotactic capacity.

EXPERIMENTAL PERIODONTITIS IN ANIMALS

Unavailability of adequate animal models has hampered the search for specific organisms in periodontal disease. Black-pigmented *Bacteroides* fail to colonize germfree rodents (16). In beagle dogs, catalase-positive, black-pigmented *Bacteroides* (111) have been related to periodontal destruction (112). However, study of spontaneous animal periodontal disease faces problems similar to those of human studies, including complexity in microflora and host response and assessment of disease activity.

A *Macaca arctoides* periodontitis model, in which alveolar bone breakdown in 2 to 4 weeks can be induced by a subgingivally placed ligature, has been developed in our laboratory (20, 89, 90). Antibacterial therapy before and after insertion of the ligature prevented bone loss (20), indicating that bacterial action and not mechanical trauma of the ligature is responsible for the bone destruction. Strains of *B. macacae* (87) and *B. gingivalis* increased in proportion from a few percent to about 66% of the total isolates concomitant with a significant loss of alveolar bone mass. A suppression of *Bacteroides* by antibacterial therapy resulted in remineralization of the alveolar bone. These data and similar data obtained by Kornman and co-workers with beagle dogs (B. Siegrist, K. S. Kornman, K. Nuki, and A. Soskolne, J. Dent. Res. Spec. Issue A **59**:387, abstr. 478, 1980) and *Macaca fascicularis* (K. S. Kornman, S. C. Holt, and P. B. Robertson, J. Dent. Res. Spec. Issue A **59**:388, abstr. 483, 1980) strongly implicate *B. gingivalis* and closely related strains as important pathogens in certain types of actively destructive periodontal disease.

PATHOGENICITY AND POTENTIALLY PATHOGENIC PRODUCTS

Pathogenic properties of black-pigmented *Bacteroides* which may be relevant to periodontal disease are listed in Table 4.

Black-pigmented *Bacteroides* organisms have many characteristics of an overt pathogenic bacterium. They are often isolated from various types of serious mixed anaerobic infections: appendicitis, infected surgical wounds, uterus and blood in patients with puerperal infections, and abscesses of the lungs, brain, skin, liver, and peritoneal cavities (reviewed in 12, 40). *B. asaccharolyticus* and *B. melaninogenicus* subsp. *intermedius* occur more commonly in clinical specimens than *B. melaninogenicus* subsp. *melaninogenicus* and *B. melaninogenicus* subsp. *levii* (41). *B. gingivalis* has been recovered in our laboratory from lung infections. The asaccharolytic species and *B. melaninogenicus* subsp. *intermedius* are the most common black-pigmented *Bacteroides* in the normal flora of the intestinal tract, the vaginal tract, and the mouth, and they therefore may be most likely to cause infection of usually sterile sites. An alternative explanation is that these species are the most virulent black-pigmented *Bacteroides* species.

Synergistic anaerobic infections are the most extensively studied model system of the pathogenicity of black-pigmented *Bacteroides* (23, 50, 113). Studies have demonstrated that the addition of a strain of *B. melaninogenicus* to an avirulent mixture of oral bacteria can make the bacterial complex uniformly infective, resulting in severe abscess formation in experimental animals (49, 98). Pure cultures of black-pigmented *Bacteroides* were not infective (49, 113); however, the other organisms of the infectious mixture did not appear to possess important pathogenic properties. Their presence was necessary merely to

TABLE 4. *Potential pathogenic mechanisms of black-pigmented* Bacteroides *in periodontal disease*

Bacterial products or action	Effect
Abscess formation	Destruction of tissue
Capsule	Inhibition of phagocytosis
Lipopolysaccharide	Bone resorption
Enzymes	Destruction of tissue
Collagenase *(B. gingivalis)*	
Trypsin *(B. gingivalis)*	
Fibrinolysin	
Hyaluronidase	
Heparinase	
Ribonuclease	
Deoxyribonuclease	
Cytotoxic substances	Destruction of tissue
Indole	
Ammonia	
Hydrogen sulfide	
Methylmercaptan	
Fatty acids	
Immunopathology	Destruction of tissue
Humoral	
Cellular	

provide required growth factors such as menadione, vitamin K_1, or succinate for the *Bacteroides* strain (49, 60).

Recently, Mayrand et al. (61) showed that *B. gingivalis* isolates in combination with five other species were uniformly infective in the animal infection assay, producing either a localized lesion or a rapidly spreading infection. In contrast, all *B. melaninogenicus* isolates tested were unable to produce infection (61). Other combinations of bacteria have demonstrated the virulence of *B. melaninogenicus* subsp. *intermedius* (103). These findings point to the necessity of considering the accompanying microflora when evaluating the pathogenicity of black-pigmented *Bacteroides*.

The observation that black-pigmented *Bacteroides* can survive in periodontal pockets and in experimental abscesses (103) despite a massive migration of polymorphonuclear leukocytes to the site of infection is of interest. The apparent ability to resist phagocytosis, which may be an important virulence factor (70, 115), may be due to the capsular layer of the organisms (45, 56, 70, 114, 125) or to an impaired function of the polymorphonuclear leukocytes induced by the microorganisms (30).

The lipopolysaccharides of black-pigmented *Bacteroides* are atypical. They do not contain heptose and 2-keto-3-deoxyoctonate (26, 55), and they exhibit only weak endotoxic activity (24, 55, 107, 108). Lipopolysaccharide preparation of *B. melaninogenicus* can, however, stimulate bone resorption in bone culture assays (21, 109).

Strains of *B. gingivalis–B. melaninogenicus* subspecies produce an array of lytic enzymes, including collagenase (15, 19, 61, 79, 126) and other proteases

(32, 61, 85a), plasma clotting and fibrinolytic activities (77, 119), heparinase (65), and hyaluronidase, ribonuclease, and deoxyribonuclease (49, 95). *B. gingivalis,* being the only species which routinely produces collagenase (61) and trypsin-like enzyme (85a), particularly appears to be a highly proteolytic organism. The role of bacterium-derived enzymes in the infectious process is unclear. Fusobacterial infections have been enhanced by cell-free extracts of *B. melaninogenicus* possessing collagenolytic activity (36). On the other hand, *B. melaninogenicus* strains which produce no collagenase can also show infectivity (R. C. Kestenbaum, J. Massing, and S. Weiss, J. Dent. Res. Suppl. **43:**747, abstr. 9, 1964). Polymorphonuclear leukocytes and other host cells, moreover, produce several enzymes with activity similar to that of bacterial enzymes (94), and the relative importance of host-derived enzymes has not been established.

Black-pigmented *Bacteroides* organisms also elaborate potentially cytotoxic products such as indole, ammonia, hydrogen sulfide, methylmercaptan, and fatty acids (95). Again, the harmful effect, if any, of these toxic substances in periodontal disease remains unknown.

Manifestation of the pathogenic potential of black-pigmented *Bacteroides* indirectly through the host's immune response must also be considered. The organisms can, via complement or antibody (or both), stimulate extracellular release of potential tissue-damaging lysosomal enzymes from polymorpho-nuclear leukocytes. Other immunopathological mechanisms of interest for periodontal disease include anaphylactic reactions, immune complex-mediated reactions, and cell-mediated hypersensitivity reactions. Recent reviews of this extensive research area have been presented by Nisengard (67), Taubman and Smith (118), and Genco (14).

EFFECT OF ELIMINATION

Slots and Gibbons (88) proposed that the oral colonization of *B. gingivalis* and other gram-negative species is dependent in part on the presence of gram-positive bacteria to serve as attachment sites for the *Bacteroides* species. Kinetic studies of establishment of the subgingival microflora furthermore have revealed that the total number of subgingival microorganisms and the proportions of gram-negative motile and nonmotile bacteria can remain suppressed for 3 to 6 months or even longer after successful periodontal therapy (46, 91).

Study on the subgingival recolonization after therapy of specifically black-pigmented *Bacteroides* has been carried out by Österberg et al. (73). They found that conventional periodontal debridement combined with systemic tetracycline therapy could suppress the subgingival proportion of *B. gingivalis* for more than 6 months after cessation of therapy. Loesche and co-workers (48) treated five advanced periodontitis patients with systemic metronidazole (750 mg per day for 7 days), an antibacterial agent which has a unique spectrum of activity against anaerobic microorganisms. Isolates of *B. gingivalis* comprised from 35 to 41% of the subgingival microflora prior to treatment and decreased to 0.1% of the flora immediately after treatment. At 6 months after treatment, the proportions of *B. gingivalis* had still not returned to pretreatment levels. Many periodontal pockets greater than 5 mm deep showed a reduction of 2 to 4 mm in depth and a significant increase in periodontal attachment area. Although spirochetes and probably other organisms also decreased in numbers after the metronidazole therapy, these data do incriminate *B. gingivalis* as an important periodontopathic organism. They also point to the potential usefulness of treating periodontal diseases as specific infections by using appropriate antimicrobial agents.

CONCLUDING COMMENTS

Socransky (97) summarized some of the unique problems which confront the investigator attempting to determine the etiological role of specific microorganisms in human periodontal disease. He also presented an alternative to Koch's postulates which takes into account association, elimination, host response, animal pathogenicity, and potentially pathogenic mediators for determination of etiological significance. On the basis of the information presented here, it appears that *B. gingivalis* and possibly *B. melaninogenicus* subsp. *intermedius* fulfill most, if not all, of the criteria for pathogenic importance. Even though it cannot be fully excluded that the presence of black-pigmented *Bacteroides* may be secondary to pathological changes caused by other bacteria, it seems valid, at least as a working hypothesis, to regard these bacteria as important pathogens in human periodontal diseases. This hypothesis does not exclude that species other than black-pigmented *Bacteroides* can be involved in periodontal disease. Nor does it mean that all periodontal pockets infected with black-pigmented *Bacteroides* are breaking down or inevitably will experience periodontal destruction. However, the concept of the black-pigmented *Bacteroides* species as important microorganisms in the development of human periodontal disease provides researchers and clinicians with a useful tool upon which to base their continuing study and management of periodontal disease.

ACKNOWLEDGMENT

This work was supported by Public Health Service grant DE 04898 from the National Institute of Dental Research.

LITERATURE CITED

1. **Attström, R.** 1975. The roles of gingival epithelium and phagocytosing leukocytes in gingival defence. J. Clin. Periodontol. 2:25–32.
2. **Bailit, H. L., D. C. Baldwin, and E. E. Hunt, Jr.** 1964. Increasing prevalence of gingival *Bacteroides melaninogenicus* with age in children. Arch. Oral Biol. 9:435–438.
3. **Berger, V., M. Kapovits, and G. Pfeiffer.** 1959. Zur Besiedlung der kindlichen Mundhöhle mit anaeroben Mikroorganismen. Z. Hyg. Infektionskr. 145:564–573.
4. **Buchanan, R. E., and N. E. Gibbons (ed.)** 1974. Bergey's manual of determinative bacteriology, 8th ed. The Williams & Wilkins Co., Baltimore.
5. **Budtz-Jörgensen, E., J. Kelstrup, K. Funder-Nielsen, and A. M. Knudsen.** 1977. Leukocyte migration inhibition by bacterial antigens in patients with periodontal disease. J. Periodontal Res. 12:21–29.
6. **Burdon, K. L.** 1928. Bacterium melaninogenicum from normal and pathologic tissues. J. Infect. Dis. 42:161–171.
7. **Courant, P. R., and H. Bader.** 1966. *Bacteroides melaninogenicus* and its products in the gingiva of man. Periodontics 4:131–136.
8. **Courant, P. R., and R. J. Gibbons.** 1967. Biochemical and immunological heterogeneity of *Bacteroides melaninogenicus.* Arch. Oral Biol. 12:1605–1613.
9. **Cox, M. O., J. J. Crawford, R. L. Lundblad, and W. T. McFall, Jr.** 1974. Oral leukocytes and gingivitis in the primary dentition. J. Periodontal Res. 9:23–28.
10. **Coykendall, A. L., F. S. Kaczmarek, and J. Slots.** 1980. Genetic heterogeneity in *Bacteroides asaccharolyticus* (Holdeman and Moore 1970) Finegold and Barnes 1977 (approved lists, 1980) and proposal of *Bacteroides gingivalis* sp. nov. and *Bacteroides macacae* (Slots and Genco) comb. nov. Int. J. Syst. Bacteriol. 30:559–564.
11. **Duerden, B. I.** 1980. The isolation and identification of *Bacteroides* spp. from the normal human gingival flora. J. Med. Microbiol. 13:89–101.

12. **Finegold, S. M.** 1977. Anaerobic bacteria in human disease. Academic Press, Inc., New York.
13. **Finegold, S. M., and E. M. Barnes.** 1977. Report of the ICSB taxonomic subcommittee on gram-negative anaerobic rods. Proposal that the saccharolytic and asaccharolytic strains at present classified in the species *Bacteroides melaninogenicus* (Oliver and Wherry) be reclassified in two species as *Bacteroides melaninogenicus* and *Bacteroides asaccharolyticus.* Int. J. Syst. Bacteriol. **27:**388–391.
14. **Genco, R. J.** 1979. Immunobiology and immunopathology of the oral cavity. *In* H. C. Slavkin and D. W. Cohen (ed.), Monographs of oral sciences, vol. 1, no. 6. Distribution Systems Inc., Bristol, Pa.
15. **Gibbons, R. J., and J. B. MacDonald.** 1961. Degradation of collagenous substrates by *Bacteroides melaninogenicus.* J. Bacteriol. **81:**614–621.
16. **Gibbons, R. J., S. S. Socransky, and B. Kapsimalis.** 1964. Establishment of human indigenous bacteria in germ-free mice. J. Bacteriol. **88:**1316–1323.
17. **Gibbons, R. J., S. S. Socransky, S. Sawyer, B. Kapsimalis, and J. B. MacDonald.** 1963. The microbiota of the gingival crevice area of man. II. The predominant cultivable organisms. Arch. Oral Biol. **8:**281–289.
18. **Harding, G. K. M., V. L. Sutter, S. M. Finegold, and K. S. Bricknell.** 1976. Characterization of *Bacteroides melaninogenicus.* J. Clin. Microbiol. **4:**354–359.
19. **Hausmann, E., and E. Kaufman.** 1969. Collagenase activity in a particulate fraction from *Bacteroides melaninogenicus.* Biochim. Biophys. Acta **194:**612–615.
20. **Hausmann, E., L. F. Ortman, and N. Sedransk.** 1979. Experimental alveolar bone loss in the monkey evaluated by ^{125}I absorptiometry. Calcif. Tissue Int. **29:**133–139.
21. **Hausmann, E., L. G. Raisz, and W. A. Miller.** 1970. Endotoxin: stimulation of bone resorption in tissue culture. Science **168:**862–864.
22. **Heinrich, S., G. Pulverer, and U. Hanf.** 1959. Über das physiologische Vorkommen des Bacteroides melaninogenicus bei Mensch und Tier. Schweiz. Z. Pathol. Bakteriol. **22:**861–870.
23. **Hite, K. E., M. Locke, and H. C. Hesseltine.** 1949. Synergism in experimental infection with nonsporulating anaerobic bacteria. J. Infect. Dis. **84:**1–9.
24. **Hofstad, T.** 1970. Biological activities of endotoxins from *Bacteroides melaninogenicus.* Arch. Oral Biol. **15:**343–348.
25. **Hofstad, T.** 1969. Serological properties of lipopolysaccharide from oral strains of *Bacteroides melaninogenicus.* J. Bacteriol. **97:**1078–1082.
26. **Hofstad, T.** 1974. The distribution of heptose and 2-keto-3-deoxy-octonate in Bacteroidaceae. J. Gen. Microbiol. **85:**314–320.
27. **Hofstad, T.** 1974. Antibodies reacting with lipopolysaccharides from *Bacteroides melaninogenicus, Bacteroides fragilis, Fusobacterium nucleatum* in serum from normal human subjects. J. Infect. Dis. **129:**349–352.
28. **Holdeman, L. V., E. P. Cato, and W. E. C. Moore.** 1977. Anaerobic laboratory manual, 4th ed. Virginia Polytechnic Institute and State University, Blacksburg.
29. **Holdeman, L. V., and W. E. C. Moore.** 1970. Outline of clinical methods in anaerobic bacteriology, 2nd revision. Virginia Polytechnic Institute and State University Anaerobe Laboratory, Blacksburg.
30. **Ingham, H. R., P. R. Sisson, D. Tharagonnet, J. B. Selkon, and A. A. Codd.** 1977. Inhibition of phagocytosis *in vitro* by obligate anaerobes. Lancet **ii:**1252–1254.
31. **Ivanyi, L., and T. Lehner.** 1970. Stimulation of lymphocyte transformation by bacterial antigens in patients with periodontal disease. Arch. Oral Biol. **15:**1089–1096.
32. **Iwata, K.** 1965. A study on the anaerobic bacteria of periodontal disease. Shikwa Gakuho **65:**72–90.
33. **Johnson, J.** 1980. Classification of anaerobic bacteria, p. 19–29. *In* N. Kosakai (ed.), Proceedings of International Symposium on Anaerobes. Japan Convention Services, Inc., Tokyo.
34. **Kaczmarek, F. S., and A. L. Coykendall.** 1980. Production of phenylacetic acid by strains of *Bacteroides asaccharolyticus* and *Bacteroides gingivalis* (sp. nov.). J. Clin. Microbiol. **12:**288–290.
35. **Kagan, J. M.** 1980. Local immunity to *Bacteroides gingivalis* in periodontal disease. J. Dent. Res. **59**(Special Issue D, part 1):1750–1756.
36. **Kaufman, E. J., P. A. Mashimo, E. Hausmann, C. T. Hanks, and S. A. Ellison.** 1972. Fusobacterial infection: enhancement by cell-free extracts of *Bacteroides melaninogenicus* possessing collagenolytic activity. Arch. Oral Biol. **17:**577–580.
37. **Kelstrup, J.** 1966. The incidence of *Bacteroides melaninogenicus* in human gingival sulci, and its prevalence in the oral cavity at different ages. Periodontics **4:**14–18.
38. **Ko, H. L., and G. Pulverer.** 1974. Serologishe Untersuchungen an Bacteroides melaninogenicus. Zentralbl. Bakteriol. Parsitenkd. Infektionskr. Hyg. Abt. 1 Orig. Reihe A **228:**94–99.
39. **Kornman, K. S., and W. J. Loesche.** 1980. The subgingival microbial flora during pregnancy. J. Periodontal Res. **15:**111–122.
40. **Lambe, D. W., Jr.** 1974. Determination of *Bacteroides melaninogenicus* serogroups by fluorescent antibody staining. Appl. Microbiol. **28:**561–567.
41. **Lambe, D. W., Jr.** 1980. Serology of *Bacteroidaceae,* p. 141–153. *In* D. W. Lambe, Jr., R. J. Genco, and K. J. Mayberry-Carson (ed.), Anaerobic bacteria: selected topics. Plenum Publishing Corp., New York.

42. **Lambe, D. W., Jr., and R. C. Jerris.** 1976. Description of a polyvalent conjugate and a new serogroup of *Bacteroides melaninogenicus* by fluorescent antibody staining. J. Clin. Microbiol. 3:506–512.

43. **Lang, N. P., and F. N. Smith.** 1977. Lymphocyte blastogenesis to plaque antigens in human periodontal disease. I. Populations of varying severity of disease. J. Periodontal Res. 12:298–309.

44. **Lindhe, J., and S. S. Socransky.** 1979. Chemotaxis and vascular permeability produced by human periodontopathic bacteria. J. Periodontal Res. 14:138–146.

45. **Listgarten, M. A., and C.-H. Lai.** 1979. Comparative ultrastructure of *Bacteroides melaninogenicus* subspecies. J. Periodontal Res. 14:332–340.

46. **Listgarten, M. A., J. Lindhe, and L. Helldén.** 1978. Effect of tetracycline and/or scaling on human periodontal disease. J. Clin. Periodontol. 5:246–271.

47. **Loesche, W. J., and S. A. Syed.** 1978. Bacteriology of human experimental gingivitis: effect of plaque and gingivitis score. Infect. Immun. 21:830–839.

48. **Loesche, W. J., S. A. Syed, E. C. Morrison, B. Laughon, and N. S. Grossman.** 1981. Treatment of periodontal infections due to anaerobic bacteria with short-term treatment with metronidazole. J. Clin. Periodontol. 8:29–44.

49. **Macdonald, J. B., S. S. Socransky, and R. J. Gibbons.** 1963. Aspects of the pathogenesis of mixed anaerobic infections of mucous membranes. J. Dent. Res. 42:529–544.

50. **Macdonald, J. B., R. M. Sutton, M. L. Knoll, E. M. Madlener, and R. M. Grainger.** 1956. The pathogenic components of an experimental fusospirochetal infection. J. Infect. Dis. 98:15–20.

51. **Mackler. S. B.** 1973. Plaque development and gingivitis in the primary dentition. J. Periodontol. 44:18–24.

52. **Mansheim, B. J., and S. E. Coleman.** 1980. Immunochemical differences between oral and nonoral strains of *Bacteroides asaccharolyticus*. Infect. Immun. 27:589–596.

53. **Mansheim, B. J., and D. L. Kasper.** 1977. Purification and immunochemical characterization of the outer membrane complex of *Bacteroides melaninogenicus* subspecies *asaccharolyticus*. J. Infect. Dis. 135:787–799.

54. **Mansheim, B. J., and D. L. Kasper.** 1979. Detection of anticapsular antibodies to *Bacteroides asaccharolyticus* in serum from rabbits and humans by use of an enzyme-linked immunosorbent assay. J. Infect. Dis. 140:945–951.

55. **Mansheim, B. J., A. B. Onderdonk, and D. L. Kasper.** 1978. Immunochemical and biologic studies of the lipopolysaccharide of *Bacteroides melaninogenicus* subspecies *asaccharolyticus*. J. Immunol. 120:72–78.

56. **Mansheim, B. J., C. A. Solstad, and D. L. Kasper.** 1978. Identification of a subspecies-specific capsular antigen from *Bacteroides melaninogenicus* subspecies *asaccharolyticus* by immunofluorescence and electron microscopy. J. Infect. Dis. 138:736–741.

57. **Mansheim, B. J., M. L. Stenstrom, S. B. Low, and W. B. Clark.** 1980. Measurement of serum and salivary antibodies to the oral pathogen *Bacteroides asaccharolyticus* in human subjects. Arch. Oral Biol. 25:553–557.

58. **Mashimo, P. A., R. J. Genco, and S. A. Ellison.** 1976. Antibodies reactive with *Leptotrichia buccalis* in human serum from infancy to adulthood. Arch. Oral Biol. 21:277–283.

59. **Mayrand, D.** 1979. Identification of clinical isolates of selected species of *Bacteroides:* production of phenylacetic acid. Can. J. Microbiol. 25:927–928.

60. **Mayrand, D., and B. C. McBride.** 1980. Ecological relationships of bacteria involved in a simple, mixed anaerobic infection. Infect. Immun. 27:44–50.

61. **Mayrand, D., B. C. McBride, T. Edwards, and S. Jensen.** 1980. Characterization of *Bacteroides asaccharolyticus* and *B. melaninogenicus* oral isolates. Can. J. Microbiol. 26:1178–1183.

62. **Miyagawa, E., R. Azuma, and T. Suto.** 1979. Cellular fatty acid composition in gram-negative obligately anaerobic rods. J. Gen. Appl. Microbiol. 25:41–51.

63. **Mouton, C., P. Hammond, J. Slots, and R. J. Genco.** 1980. Evaluation of Fluoretec-M for detection of oral strains of *Bacteroides asaccharolyticus* and *Bacteroides melaninogenicus*. J. Clin. Microbiol. 11:682–686.

64. **Mouton, C., P. G. Hammond, J. Slots, and R. J. Genco.** 1981. Serum antibodies to oral *Bacteroides asaccharolyticus (Bacteroides gingivalis):* relationship to age and periodontal disease. Infect. Immun. 31:182–192.

65. **Nakamura, T., Y. Suginaka, and I. Takazoe.** 1976. Heparinase activity in lesion of periodontal diseases. Bull. Tokyo Dent. Coll. 17:147–155.

66. **Newman, M. G., S. S. Socransky, E. D. Savitt, D. A. Propas, and A. Crawford.** 1976. Studies on the microflora of periodontosis. J. Periodontol. 47:373–379.

67. **Nisengard, R. J.** 1977. The role of immunology in periodontal disease. J. Periodontol. 48:505–516.

68. **Okuda, K., J. Slots, and R. J. Genco.** 1981. *Bacteroides gingivalis, Bacteroides asaccharolyticus* and *Bacteroides melaninogenicus* subspecies: cell surface morphology and adherence to erythrocytes and human buccal epithelial cells. Curr. Microbiol. 6:7–12.

69. **Okuda, K., and I. Takazoe.** 1978. Immunological study of the pili of *Bacteroides melaninogenicus*. Bull. Tokyo Dent. Coll. 19:93–95.

70. **Okuda, K., and I. Takazoe.** 1973. Antiphagocytic effects of the capsular structure of a pathogenic strain of *Bacteroides melaninogenicus.* Bull. Tokyo Dent. Coll. **14:**99–104.
71. **Okuda, K., K. Yanagi, and I. Takazoe.** 1978. Complement activation by *Propionibacterium acnes* and *Bacteroides melaninogenicus.* Arch. Oral Biol. **23:**911–915.
72. **Oliver, W. W., and W. B. Wherry.** 1921. Notes on some bacterial parasites of the human mucous membranes. J. Infect. Dis. **28:**341–345.
73. **Österberg, S. K.-Å., B. L. Williams, and J. Jorgensen.** 1979. Long-term effects of tetracycline on the subgingival microflora. J. Clin. Periodontol. **6:**133–140.
74. **Patters, M. R., P. Chen, J. McKenna, and R. J. Genco.** 1980. Lymphoproliferative responses to oral bacteria in humans with varying severities of periodontal disease. Infect. Immun. **28:**777–784.
75. **Patters, M. R., R. J. Genco, M. J. Reed, and P. A. Mashimo.** 1976. Blastogenic response of human lymphocytes to oral bacterial antigens: comparison of individuals with periodontal disease to normal and edentulous subjects. Infect. Immun. **14:**1213–1220.
76. **Pulverer, G.** 1958. Zur Morphologie, Biochemie und Serologie des Bacteriodes melaninogenicus. Z. Hyg. Infektionskr. **145:**293–303.
77. **Pulverer, G., H. L. Ko, Z. Wegrzynowicz, and J. Jeljaszewicz.** 1977. Clotting and fibrinolytic activities of Bacteroides melaninogenicus. Zentralbl. Bakteriol. Parsitenkd. Infektionskr. Hyg. Abt. 1 Orig. Reihe A. **239:**510–513.
78. **Reed, M. J., J. Slots, C. Mouton, and R. J. Genco.** 1980. Antigenic studies of oral and nonoral black-pigmented *Bacteroides* strains. Infect. Immun. **29:**564–574.
79. **Sawyer, S. J., J. B. Macdonald, and R. J. Gibbons.** 1962. Biochemical characteristics of *Bacteroides melaninogenicus.* Arch. Oral Biol. **7:**685–691.
80. **Shah, H. N., and M. D. Collins.** 1980. Fatty acid and isoprenoid quinone composition in the classification of *Bacteroides melaninogenicus* and related taxa. J. Appl. Bacteriol. **48:**75–87.
81. **Shah, H. N., R. A. D. Williams, G. H. Bowden, and J. M. Hardie.** 1976. Comparison of the biochemical properties of *Bacteroides melaninogenicus* from human dental plaque and other sites. J. Appl. Microbiol. **41:**473–492.
82. **Slots, J.** 1976. The predominant cultivable organisms in juvenile periodontitis. Scand. J. Dent. Res. **84:**1–10.
83. **Slots, J.** 1977. The predominant cultivable microflora of advanced periodontitis. Scand. J. Dent. Res. **85:**114–121.
84. **Slots, J.** 1977. Microflora in the healthy gingival sulcus in man. Scand. J. Dent. Res. **85:**247–254.
85. **Slots, J.** 1979. Subgingival microflora and periodontal disease. J. Clin. Periodontol. **6:**351–382.
85a. **Slots, J.** 1981. Enzymatic characterization of some oral and nonoral gram-negative bacteria with the API ZYM system. J. Clin. Microbiol. **14:**288–294.
86. **Slots, J., and R. J. Genco.** 1979. Direct hemagglutination technique for differentiating *Bacteroides asaccharolyticus* oral strains from nonoral strains. J. Clin. Microbiol. **10:**371–373.
87. **Slots, J., and R. J. Genco.** 1980. *Bacteroides melaninogenicus* subsp. *macacae,* a new subspecies from monkey periodontopathic indigenous microflora. Int. J. Syst. Bacteriol. **30:**82–85.
88. **Slots, J., and R. J. Gibbons.** 1978. Attachment of *Bacteroides melaninogenicus* subsp. *asaccharolyticus* to oral surfaces and its possible role in colonization of the mouth and of periodontal pockets. Infect. Immun. **19:**254–264.
89. **Slots, J., and E. Hausmann.** 1979. Longitudinal study of experimentally induced periodontal disease in *Macaca arctoides:* relationship between microflora and alveolar bone loss. Infect. Immun. **23:**260–269.
90. **Slots, J., E. Hausmann, C. Mouton, L. F. Ortman, P. G. Hammond, and R. J. Genco.** 1980. The relationship between periodontal microflora and alevolar bone loss in *Macaca arctoides,* p. 109–121. *In* D. W. Lambe, Jr., R. J. Genco, and K. J. Mayberry-Carson (ed.), Anaerobic bacteria: selected topics. Plenum Publishing Corp., New York.
91. **Slots, J., P. Mashimo, M. J. Levine, and R. J. Genco.** 1979. Periodontal therapy in humans. I. Microbiological and clinical effects of a single course of periodontal scaling and root planing, and of adjunctive tetracycline therapy. J. Periodontol. **50:**495–509.
92. **Slots, J., D. Möenbo, J. Langebaek, and A. Frandsen.** 1978. Microbiota of gingivitis in man. Scand. J. Dent. Res. **86:**174–181.
93. **Slots, J., H. S. Reynolds, and R. J. Genco.** 1980. *Actinobacillus actinomycetemcomitans* in human periodontal disease: a cross-sectional microbiological investigation. Infect. Immun. **29:**1013–1020.
94. **Smolen, J. E., and G. Weissmann.** 1978. The granulocyte: metabolic properties and mechanisms of lysosomal enzyme release, p. 56–76. *In* K. Havemann and A. Janoff (ed.), Neutral proteases of human polymorphonuclear leukocytes. Biochemistry, physiology and clinical significance. Urban and Schwarzenberg, Baltimore.
95. **Socransky, S. S.** 1970. Relationship of bacteria to the etiology of periodontal disease. J. Dent. Res. **49:**203–222.
96. **Socransky, S. S.** 1977. Microbiology of periodontal disease—present status and future considerations. J. Periodontol. **48:**497–504.
97. **Socransky, S. S.** 1979. Criteria for the infectious agents in dental caries and periodontal disease. J. Clin. Periodontol. **6:**16–21.

44   ETIOLOGY AND MICROBIAL SPECIFICITY

98. **Socransky, S. S., and R. J. Gibbons.** 1965. Required role of *Bacteroides melaninogenicus* in mixed anaerobic infections. J. Infect. Dis. **115**:247–253.
99. **Sonnenwirth, A. C.** 1979. Antibody response to anaerobic bacteria. Rev. Infect. Dis. **1**:337–341.
100. **Spiegel, C. A., S. E. Hayduk, G. E. Minah, and G. N. Krywolap.** 1979. Black-pigmented *Bacteroides* from clinically characterized periodontal sites. J. Periodontal Res. **14**:376–382.
101. **Steenbergen, T. J. M. van, J. J. De Soet, and J. De Graaff.** 1979. DNA base composition of various strains of *Bacteroides melaninogenicus*. FEMS Microbiol. Lett. **5**:127–130.
102. **Strom, A., J. K. Dyer, C. Marsh, and J. L. Tribble.** 1976. Identification and characterization of species of the family *Bacteroidaceae* by polyacrylamide gel electrophoresis. J. Dent. Res. **55**:252–256.
103. **Sundqvist, G. K., M. I. Eckerbom, A. P. Larsson, and U. T. Sjögren.** 1979. Capacity of anaerobic bacteria from necrotic dental pulps to induce purulent infections. Infect. Immun. **25**:685–693.
104. **Sundqvist, G., and E. Johansson.** 1980. Neutrophil chemotaxis induced by anaerobic bacteria isolated from necrotic dental pulps. Scand. J. Dent. Res. **88**:113–121.
105. **Sveen, K.** 1977. Rabbit polymorphonuclear leukocyte migration *in vitro* in response to lipopolysaccharides from *Bacteroides, Fusobacterium* and *Veillonella*. Acta Pathol. Microbiol. Scand. Sect. B **85**:374–380.
106. **Sveen, K.** 1977. Rabbit polymorphonuclear leukocyte migration *in vivo* in response to lipopolysaccharides from *Bacteroides, Fusobacterium* and *Veillonella*. Acta Pathol. Microbiol. Scand. Sect. B **85**:381–387.
107. **Sveen, K.** 1977. The capacity of lipopolysaccharides from *Bacteroides, Fusobacterium* and *Veillonella* to produce skin inflammation and the local and generalized Schwartzman reaction in rabbits. J. Periodontal Res. **12**:340–350.
108. **Sveen, K., T. Hofstad, and K. C. Milner.** 1977. Lethality for mice and chick embryos, pyrogenicity in rabbits and ability to gelate lysate from amoebocytes of *Limulus polyphemus* by lipopolysaccharides from *Bacteroides, Fusobacterium* and *Veillonella*. Acta Pathol. Microbiol. Scand. Sect. B **85**:388–396.
109. **Sveen, K., and N. Skaug.** 1980. Bone resorption stimulated by lipopolysaccharides from *Bacteroides, Fusobacterium,* and *Veillonella*, and by the lipid A and the polysaccharide part of *Fusobacterium* lipopolysaccharide. Scand. J. Dent. Res. **88**:535–542.
110. **Swindlehurst, C. A., H. N. Shah, C. W. Parr, and R. A. D. Williams.** 1977. Sodium dodecyl sulphate-polyacrylamide gel electrophoresis of polypeptides from *Bacteroides melaninogenicus*. J. Appl. Bacteriol. **43**:319–324.
111. **Syed, S. A.** 1980. Characteristics of *Bacteroides asaccharolyticus* from dental plaques of beagle dogs. J. Clin. Microbiol. **11**:522–526.
112. **Syed, S. A., M. Svanberg, and G. Svanberg.** 1981. The predominant cultivable dental plaque flora of beagle dogs with periodontitis. J. Clin. Periodontol. **8**:45–56.
113. **Takazoe, I., and T. Nakamura.** 1971. Experimental mixed infection by human gingival crevice material. Bull. Tokyo Dent. Coll. **12**:85–93.
114. **Takazoe, I., K. Okuda, and A. Yamamoto.** 1975. Distribution of a K-antigen among oral strains of *Bacteroides melaninogenicus*. Bull. Tokyo Dent. Coll. **16**:1–5.
115. **Takazoe, I., M. Tanaka, and T. Homma.** 1971. A pathogenic strain of *Bacteroides melaninogenicus*. Arch. Oral Biol. **16**:817–822.
116. **Takeuchi, H., M. Sumitani, K. Tsubakimoto, and M. Tsutsui.** 1974. Oral microorganisms in the gingiva of individuals with periodontal disease. J. Dent. Res. **53**:132–136.
117. **Tanner, A. C. R., C. Haffer, G. T. Bratthall, R. A. Visconti, and S. S. Socransky.** 1979. A study of the bacteria associated with advancing periodontitis in man. J. Clin. Periodontol. **6**:278–307.
118. **Taubman, M. A., and D. J. Smith.** 1978. Aspects of immunology relevant to periodontal diseases. *In* J. H. Shaw, E. A. Sweeney, C. C. Cappuccino, and S. M. Meller (ed.), Textbook of oral biology. W. B. Saunders Co., Philadelphia.
119. **Wegrzynowicz, Z., H. L. Ko, G. Pulverer, and J. Jeljaszewicz.** 1978. The nature of clotting and fibrinolytic activities of Bacteroides melaninogenicus. Zentralbl. Bakteriol. Parasitenkd. Infektionskr. Hyg. Abt. 1 Orig. Reihe A **240**:106–111.
120. **Weiss, C.** 1937. Observations on *Bacterium melaninogenicum:* demonstration of fibrinolysin, pathogenicity and serological types. Proc. Soc. Exp. Biol. **37**:473–476.
121. **Werner, H., and M. Sebald.** 1968. Étude sérologique d'anaérobies gram-négatifs asporulés, et particulièrement de *Bacteroides convexus* et *Bacteroides melaninogenicus*. Ann. Inst. Pasteur Paris **115**:350–366.
122. **White, D., and D. Mayrand.** 1981. Association of oral Bacteroides with gingivitis and adult periodontitis. J. Periodontal Res. **16**:259–265.
123. **Williams, B. L., R. M. Pantalone, and J. C. Sherris.** 1976. Subgingival microflora and periodontitis. J. Periodontal Res. **11**:1–18.
124. **Williams, R. A. D., G. H. Bowden, J. M. Hardie, and H. Shah.** 1975. Biochemical properties of *Bacteroides melaninogenicus* subspecies. Int. J. Syst. Bacteriol. **25**:298–300.

125. **Woo, D. D. L., S. C. Holt, and E. R. Leadbetter.** 1979. Ultrastructure of *Bacteroides* species:
    Bacteroides asaccharolyticus, Bacteroides fragilis, Bacteroides melaninogenicus subspecies
    melaninogenicus, and *B. melaninogenicus* subspecies *intermedius.* J. Infect. Dis. **139:**534–546.
126. **Yamamoto, A., and I. Takazoe.** 1976. Efficient fractionation of collagenolytic sample from oral
    Bacteroides melaninogenicus. Bull. Tokyo Dent. Coll. **17:**123–130.
127. **Zambon, J. J., H. S. Reynolds, and J. Slots.** 1981. Black-pigmented *Bacteroides* spp. in the
    human oral cavity. Infect. Immun. **32:**198–203.

Capnocytophaga and Actinobacillus actinomycetemcomitans: Occurrence and Pathogenic Potential in Juvenile Periodontitis

B. F. HAMMOND AND R. H. STEVENS

University of Pennsylvania School of Dental Medicine and Center for Oral Health Research, Philadelphia, Pennsylvania 19104

The crevicular microbiota associated with the lesions of localized juvenile periodontitis (LJP) has been studied by several investigators (14, 15, 19, 20). Although many details remain to be clarified, a couple of valid generalizations about the microbiota can now be made. First, the total numbers of bacteria in the lesions of LJP are lower than in most forms of destructive periodontal disease (7). The quantitative estimations (10^5 to 10^6 organisms per periodontal pocket) are two to three orders of magnitude below the numbers ordinarily found in comparable lesions of adult periodontitis. The correspondingly minimal amount of bacterial plaque is predictably associated with a minimal amount of inflammation. In contrast, the massive amounts of plaque produced by gram-positive organisms, e.g., *Actinomyces viscosus* in marginal gingivitis, are accompanied by severe inflammatory changes in the gingival area. Because of the rapid bone loss characteristically observed in LJP patients, it has often been assumed that the reduced size of the bacterial component is compensated for by a series of highly potent mediators of bone and soft tissue destruction.

Second, there are several levels of specificity that exist regarding the nature and activities of the flora. The proportions and the kinds of bacteria regularly isolable from the crevices of LJP are quite characteristic. We are not dealing with the anecdotal "schmutz pyorrhea" described in the early literature but with a specific infectious disease, having an identifiable "microbial fingerprint." Each of the major populations making up this "fingerprint" is, in turn, controlled or regulated by one property or, more often than not, by an array of specific properties. This hypothesis of bacteriological specificity can be demonstrated quite easily if one examines two of the most important bacterial populations associated with the LJP microflora, *Actinobacillus actinomycetemcomitans* and members of the genus *Capnocytophaga*, notably *C. sputigena.*

A. ACTINOMYCETEMCOMITANS

General

A. actinomycetemcomitans was named in 1912 by Klinger (10) because of its association with *Actinomyces israelii* infections. The organism is a small, nonmotile, gram-negative coccobacillus requiring CO_2 and usually producing granular growth in broth (unless Tween 80 or some surfactant is added to the medium). Although its nutritional requirements are fastidious, the organism is metabolically quite versatile, producing a variety of end products from carbohydrate substrates. The laboratory identification of the organism is based on the scheme outlined below.

I. Biochemical tests
  A. Sugar fermentations
    1. Uniformly positive: glucose, fructose, mannose
    2. Uniformly negative: adonitol, amygdalin, arabinose, cellobiose, sucrose, glycerol, inositol, lactose, melibiose, rhamnose, ribose, salicin, sorbitol
    3. Variable: mannitol, dextrin, maltose, xylose
  B. Other
    1. Peroxide breakdown, positive
    2. Nitrate reduction, positive
    3. Oxidase reaction, negative
    4. Proteolysis, negative
    5. Requirement for hemin, negative
    6. Requirement for nicotinamide adenine dinucleotide, negative
    7. Resistance to NaF, positive
    8. Gaseous requirements: air + CO_2 = good growth; air − CO_2 = little or no growth; anaerobic + CO_2 = growth variable

II. Molecular taxonomy and comparison with known strains
  A. Guanine plus cytosine (G + C) ratio
    1. Unknown strains, 40.1 to 40.6 mol%
    2. ATCC 29524, 41.8 to 42.6 mol%
  B. Deoxyribonucleic acid (DNA) homology: 97% with ATCC 29524 as reference strain
  C. Protein profiles and immunodiffusion patterns of clinical isolates are remarkably similar to those of ATCC type strains 29524 or 29523

III. Morphological: Both are observed by electron microscopy to be short gram-negative rods (1.5 to 1.7 μm long, 0.55 μm in diameter) with typical membrane vesicles ("blebs")

As indicated above, all strains ferment anaerobically glucose, fructose, and mannose, fail to ferment a large number of other sugars, and depending on the strain, exhibit variable fermentation of mannitol, dextrin, maltose, and xylose. Most strains decompose hydrogen peroxide, reduce nitrate, and are resistant to NaF (10 μg/ml). Most strains are not proteolytic, lack oxidase, and do not require hemin or nicotinamide adenine dinucleotide. They have a G + C ratio of approximately 40 mol%, and most strains isolated thus far show high levels of DNA sequence homology with ATCC strains 29524 and 29522. The serological profiles are also quite characteristic and will be reviewed in a later section.

Occurrence in LJP

Numerous reports in the literature have demonstrated directly or indirectly the almost invariable presence of A. actinomycetemcomitans in the gingival crevices of LJP patients, and many of these reports are often cited as evidence for an etiological role of this organism in LJP. Most of these studies followed the early discovery by Irving et al. (7) that an organism designated Y4 was able to produce massive bone loss and overall periodontal destruction in monocontaminated gnotobiotic rats. Although the organism was not identified by genus or species designation, it was clear that the disease produced in these animals was quite different from those previously demonstrated in similar animals monocontaminated with gram-positive organisms. Specifically, there was little or no plaque, and "inflammatory reactions as evidenced by leukocytic infiltration were minimal." This strain, Y4, was originally isolated from an LJP lesion, and Newman, Socransky, and co-workers (14, 15) included it in categories labeled groups III and IV on the basis of certain biochemical properties. These biochemical properties do not conform exactly to those of the type strains of A. actinomycetemcomitans (ATCC 29523, 29522, or 29524).

However, when the same strain was tested by other investigators recently (2, 20), it was clear that Y4 is the same capnophilic, facultative, gram-negative rod described in *Bergey's Manual* as *A. actinomycetemcomitans*. At about the same time, Slots (19) also reported that the predominant cultivable organisms in juvenile periodontitis were gram-negative anaerobes, but here again they were not identified. The first published identification of Y4 as *A. actinomycetemcomitans* derived from our laboratory, where serological data, immunoelectrophoresis, and Ouchterlony techniques were coupled with biochemical tests and DNA studies in comparing known strains of *A. actinomycetemcomitans* (2). S. S. Socransky and A. C. R. Tanner (personal communication) had previously arrived at this same conclusion on the basis of metabolic and other studies (see Baehni et al. [2] for discussion).

Serological studies

Furthermore, recent serological studies have demonstrated a significant host response in LJP patients to whole cells of *A. actinomycetemcomitans* and various subcellular fractions. One study using the enzyme-linked immunosorbent assay technique concluded that isotype-specific serum antibody responses to Y4 were related to the occurrence of LJP (J. L. Ebersole, D. E. Frey, M. A. Taubman, D. J. Smith, and R. J. Genco, J. Dent. Res. Spec. Issue A **59**:330, abstr. 249, 1980). Details of this sensitive assay system have recently been published by Ebersole et al. (4). Another report indicated that precipitins to *A. actinomycetemcomitans* are common in patients with LJP but not in normal subjects or in patients with other periodontal diseases (R. Genco, N. A. Taichman, and C. A. Sadowski, J. Dent. Res. Spec. Issue A **59**:329, abstr. 246, 1980). Antibody responses to isolated antigens of *A. actinomycetemcomitans* have also been checked by the enzyme-linked immunosorbent assay technique (J. L. Ebersole, D. E. Frey, M. A. Taubman, D. J. Smith, R. J. Genco, and B. F. Hammond, J. Dent. Res. Spec Issue A **59**:339, abstr. 255, 1980). These investigators showed that immunoglobulin G antibody to two soluble *A. actinomycetemcomitans* antigens (the partially purified leukotoxin, LT, and the purified leukotoxin-associated carbohydrate antigen, LG) were greatly increased in LJP patients (70%) as compared with edentulous patients, normal subjects, and patients with other kinds of periodontal disease. Antibodies to a partially purified preparation of *A. actinomycetemcomitans* (strain Y4) endotoxins were also detected in sera of LJP patients but to a lesser extent. The results suggested that these three antigen preparations may comprise a major portion of the human response to the Y4 organism.

Considerable attention has been given recently to the characterization of the LG antigen after we noted that any strain possessing the LG antigen was invariably leukotoxic. Furthermore, most of the leukotoxic strains thus far examined, including strains Y4 and ATCC 29522 and 29524, possess the LG antigen. The LG antigen, although nontoxic itself, therefore appears to be a serotype-specific antigen whose presence might be useful as a serological monitor for the Y4/ATCC 29524 biotype. Some of the following specific information about this antigen is presented because it is the only one of the antigenic fractions which has been isolated, purified, and, in part, characterized chemically.

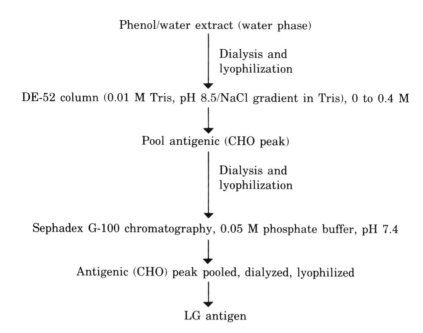

FIG. 1. *Scheme for the isolation of the LT-associated antigen (LG) of* A. actinomycetemcomitans *(Y4). Tris = Tris(hydroxymethyl)aminomethane.*

Figure 1 represents an outline of the procedures used in the isolation of LG. Y4 cells from 50-liter batches of fluid thioglycolate broth (Difco) were harvested, washed, and extracted with hot phenol/water by the Westphal procedure as modified by Knox and Parker (11). The water-phase supernatant contained a soluble antigen which reacted in immunodiffusion plates with most of the clinical isolates and type collection strains. The material was put through a diethylaminoethyl-cellulose column (2.5 by 60 cm) eluted with 0.01 M tris(hydroxymethyl)aminomethane buffer (pH 8.5) against a 0 to 0.4 M NaCl gradient. This antigen came out near the void volume in a carbohydrate peak but was grossly contaminated with other macromolecules. The pooled peak fractions were dialyzed, lyophilized, and subjected to a Sephadex G-100 column (2.5 by 100 cm) eluted with 0.05 M phosphate buffer (pH 7.4). Figure 2 shows the elution profile of the material as monitored for carbohydrate and protein. Note that there is a rather sharp carbohydrate peak starting around fraction 40 and finishing near fraction 90 with very little detectable protein. Serological monitoring showed a similar profile, with the antigen being found first around fraction 42 and finishing near fraction 84–90. These fractions in the carbohydrate peak were pooled, and a single cationic antigen was revealed (Fig. 3).

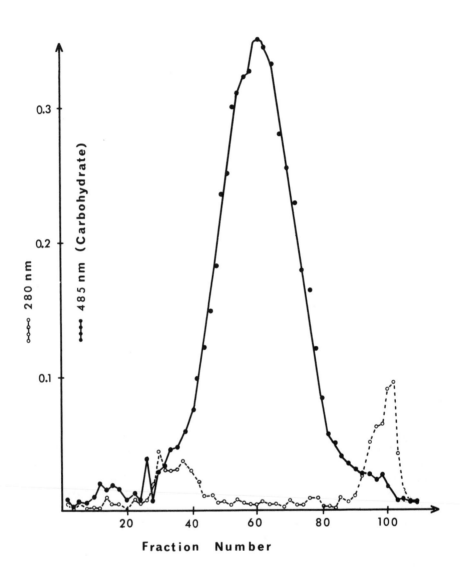

FIG. 2. *Elution profile of an extract of* A. actinomycetemcomitans *(strain Y4) on Sephadex G-100. The extract was previously put through a column of diethylaminoethyl-cellulose (DE-52) as indicated in Fig. 1. The Sephadex G-100 column (2.5 by 100 cm) was eluted with 0.05 M phosphate buffer, pH 7.4. The solid line (closed circle) represents carbohydrate monitoring and the broken line (open circles) represents protein as determined by absorption at 280 nm.*

a

LG Antigen Monitoring of Sephadex G-100 Fractions
(Water Phase/Phenol-Water Extract)
A. actinomycetemcomitans (Y4)

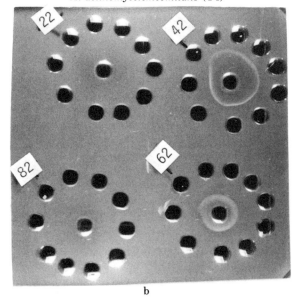

b

Pooled Fractions (42–90)

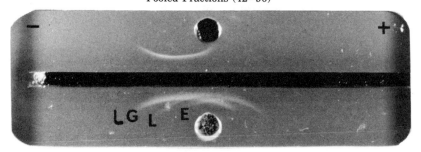

Y4 Sonic Extract

FIG. 3. *LG antigen monitoring of Sephadex G-100 fractions described in Fig. 1. (a) Monitoring of individual fractions by Ouchterlony method. The center wells in each of the four quadrants contained antiserum prepared against whole cells of A. actinomycetemcomitans (Y4), and the peripheral wells contained 0.1 ml of a dialyzed and lyophilized fraction (originally 2 ml) reconstituted to 0.5 ml (fractions 22 through 100 were examined). (b) An immunoelectropherogram showing pooled fraction 42–90 containing the carbohydrate (LG) antigen (top well) and a sonic extract of Y4 containing three antigens (LG, the leukotoxin-associated carbohydrate antigen; L or the leukotoxin-associated protein antigen and E, the endotoxin). The center trough contains antiserum prepared against whole cells of strain Y4.*

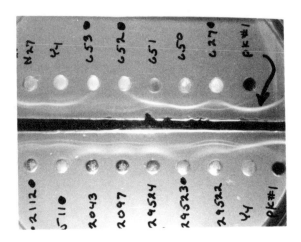

FIG. 4. *Ouchterlony plate comparing the antigens present in sonic extracts of various* A. actinomycetemcomitans *strains (small circular wells). The antiserum in the central trough was prepared against whole cells of strain Y4. Note that several strains (653, 652, 627, 29523, 511, and 2112) lack the LG antigen, peak 1 and also identified by the arrow.*

Chemical analysis of the material revealed that the material was carbohydrate containing 78% methylpentose, 6.9% galactose, and 4.4% glucosamine, with trace amounts of heptose, glucose, and phosphorus. Ketodeoxyoctonate was not detected, but 5.8% protein was demonstrated. The molecular weight (as estimated by comparing average elution volumes of our material with dextran standards) indicated a value of 74,000. Artificially high values for molecular weight are obtained if care is not taken to prevent aggregation.

The frequency of this antigen in known strains of *A. actinomycetemcomitans* was examined by the Ouchterlony technique. Figure 4 shows an Ouchterlony plate with the sonic extracts of 14 such strains and the purified antigen (LG) against an antiserum to whole cells of strain Y4. The LG antigen gave a reaction of identity with a band present in some but not all strains. The several strains which lacked the LG antigen shared several other characteristics. LG-negative strains are generally nonleukotoxic or have low to variable levels of leukotoxicity. Subsequent studies by C. H. Lai, M. A. Listgarten, and B. F. Hammond (J. Periodontal Res., in press) showed that these strains did not produce significant numbers of membrane vesicles (these structures are described below in the section on pathogenicity). In contrast, LG-positive strains are invariably leukotoxic and produce huge numbers of vesicles. Moreover, the LG antigen is unique to *A. actinomycetemcomitans* and has not been detected serologically or chemically in a large number of oral gram-negative bacteria, including the following:

Most nonleukotoxic strains of *A. actinomycetemcomitans*
Haemophilus aphrophilus strains
Haemophilus paraphrophilus
Bacteroides melaninogenicus
Bacteroides asaccharolyticus

Bacteroides oralis
Eikenella corrodens
Capnocytophaga sputigena
Capnocytophaga ochracea
Capnocytophaga gingivalis

The antigen has also been detected in a human strain of *A. actinomycetemcomitans* (strain KB) isolated from the blood stream of a patient with subacute bacterial endocarditis. This organism was virtually identical to strain Y4 by all of the criteria outlined at the beginning of this paper. It is also probable that this antigen is responsible for the specificity of the Y4 group antigen described in a recent paper by P. Baehni et al. (J. Periodontal Res., in press) and identified as part of the "membrane-binding component." As indicated previously, antibodies to LG are also found in 70% of LJP patient sera.

The properties of *A. actinomycetemcomitans* LG antigen can be summarized as follows:

1. It is a soluble carbohydrate antigen with a high percentage of methylpentose. The approximate molecular weight is 74,000.
2. It is found only in leukotoxic strains and is absent in most nonleukotoxic strains and other oral gram-negative bacteria.
3. It is serologically and chemically distinct from the leukotoxin and the endotoxin.
4. Antibodies to the LG antigen are found in the sera of patients with localized juvenile periodontitis.
5. The antigen is characteristically seen in membrane vesicles of the Y4 group of leukotoxic *A. actinomycetemcomitans* strains (see below).

Other aspects of the serology of *A. actinomycetemcomitans* have been presented at recent meetings, and the reader is referred to these reports for further descriptions of antigenic analysis (see J. Dent. Res. Spec. Issue A **60**:523, abstr. 852, 855, 856, 1981). It is important to remember that a definitive statement cannot yet be made about the group and type antigens of this species.

Pathogenic Potential
The pathogenic potential of *A. actinomycetemcomitans* has been recognized for many years. Apart from the initial reports by Klinger (10) and others (3, 5) implicating this organism in the pathology of actinomycosis, several other investigators have isolated the organism from many nonoral disease sites. Convincing evidence that it is the sole etiological agent in certain cases of subacute bacterial endocarditis has been available since 1964. Mitchell and Gillespie (13) and a recent review by Affias et al. (1) indicate that there have been over 37 cases reported of endocarditis induced by *A. actinomycetemcomitans* since its isolation and identification as a valid taxonomic entity. The only report that links endocarditis caused by *A. actinomycetemcomitans* with a rapidly destructive periodontal lesion in children is now in press (R. Anolick, J. Campos, R. J. Berkowitz, and A. Friedman, Clin. Pediatr. [Philadelphia], in press) and the clinical isolate (strain KB), as described previously, is known to possess the LG antigen. Several other kinds of infectious disease processes including septicemia, facial abscesses, and pleural abscesses have also been attributed to *A. actinomycetemcomitans* (see 16 for a review).

In spite of this wealth of information demonstrating the pathogenic capacities of this organism, almost nothing was known of the pathogenic mechanisms involved until dental researchers discovered its role in periodontal disease. In the past few years, several important findings have been reported which provide extremely plausible explanations for the unusual pattern of tissue damage associated with *A. actinomycetemcomitans*-induced periodontal disease. The following section reviews these advances.

LT. Although LTs were among the first of the classical virulence factors to be described for bacteria, there had been no report of such a factor for any plaque-associated bacteria prior to the work of Baehni et al. (2). Given the extraordinary diversity of the crevicular flora, it is indeed suprising that very little has been reported about any aspect of specific cytotoxic factors of such bacteria. Since most crevicular bacteria do not penetrate the crevicular epithelium, it has always been assumed that subcellular fractions (endotoxins, cell wall components, etc.) would be able to penetrate the crevicular barrier. The detection of the *A. actinomycetemcomitans* LT represented an important confirmation of this idea. The LT is a soluble, heat-labile, protease-sensitive protein that is cytotoxic for human peripheral blood polymorphonuclear leukocytes (PMNs) and monocytes but not for leukocytes of other animals (26), with the possible exception of monkeys (unpublished data). Leukotoxicity is independent of phagocytosis but is enhanced by serum.

Some of the details of LT are presented in a later paper (N. S. Taichman et al., this volume), but it is appropriate at this point to reflect on the possible significance of this material in the pathogenesis of LJP. Not only do LJP patients have antibodies to this material, but leukotoxic strains are regularly isolable from LJP lesions.

What is less clear is the *essentiality* of this property in LJP pathogenesis. Certainly, the specificity of LT for human leukocytes underlines the non-essentiality of the property in the Sprague-Dawley rat model of periodontal disease. Since rat PMNs and other leukocytes are not susceptible to LT action, one might be tempted to conclude that LT is irrelevant in the rat model. Unfortunately, gnotobiotic studies with LT-negative *A. actinomycetemcomitans* strains have not yet been reported so that the net effect of LT in the *A. actinomycetemcomitans*-induced disease in rats cannot be assessed in unequivocal terms at this time. It is possible that LT activity could be coupled synergistically with some other properties to produce a more severe disease. One may also argue that the human and rat forms of the disease are different in the manner and extent to which specific virulence factors are involved.

Second, the proportion of leukotoxic and nonleukotoxic *A. actino-mycetemcomitans* isolates from LJP lesions has not yet been fully documented. Some of the data from a recent report by Slots et al. (20) can be interpreted as showing that certain biotypes occur more frequently than others in LJP lesions. Our studies confirm the finding of Slots et al. that the biotypes (represented by ATCC 29523 or strain 627) which occur most frequently are the nonleukotoxic strains. In preliminary screening of human clinical isolates using the immunotargeting procedure described in a recent abstract (N. Taichman, R. Stevens, B. F. Hammond, C. Tsai, P. Baehni, and W. McArthur, J. Dent. Res. Spec. Issue A **60:**523, abstr. 855, 1981), we have shown once again that nonleukotoxic colonies predominate on such plates. The important question about host response in these patients to the various biotypes reveals an interesting phenomenon: antibody response still appears to be directed against antigens unique to leukotoxic strains (the LT and to a lesser extent the LG antigen). It is, therefore, apparent that the cultural findings do not necessarily reflect host response. It is possible to have a crevicular microflora dominated by one biotype but an antibody response directed primarily at *another* biotype. On balance, it seems reasonable to say that although (i) the serological data indicate a penetration of the crevicular epithelium by this LT and (ii) the theoretical implications of a compromised host defense both point to a role for LT in human disease, it must be admitted that direct proof of the importance of this factor in disease is still lacking.

Endotoxin (LPS). A second major virulence factor proposed for *A. actinomycetemcomitans* is the endotoxic lipopolysaccharide (LPS). Kiley and Holt (9) recently isolated the LPS and showed that the partially purified material was generally quite similar in its chemical composition to the classic LPS of gram-negative bacteria, i.e., a polysaccharide side chain and a hydrophobic lipid (lipid A) covalently joined by an inner or core polysaccharide containing ketodeoxyoctonate and heptose. The smaller amounts of ketodeoxyoctonate and heptose in this endotoxin were the only differences from the usual LPS structure although similar findings have been reported for other oral gram-negative bacteria, including *C. sputigena* (23). The reasons for this peculiarity in structure of the LPS molecule are not clear, nor is it possible at this time to relate structure to function in a context of oral ecology or pathogenic potential.

What is abundantly clear is that this antigenic macromolecule has a great capacity for interacting with eucaryotic cells in ways that could account for some of the destructive manifestations of periodontal disease. In their quite comprehensive report, Kiley and Holt showed that the LPS fractions from two human oral isolates of *A. actinomycetemcomitans* had the capacity to be reactive in many biological assay systems. In addition to giving positive reactions in the Shwartzman skin test and mouse lethality experiments, the endotoxins were extremely potent in assays more directly relevant to human periodontal disease, i.e., bone resorption, macrophage cytotoxicity, and platelet aggregation. In all of these in vitro studies, the LPS was highly reactive, especially in bone resorption studies, where resorptive ability (as measured by ^{45}Ca release) was of the same order of magnitude as for prostaglandins. Although the in vitro systems involved nonhuman cells and cell systems (mouse macrophages, rabbit platelets, fetal rat long bones), it is still impressive to see such a variety of biological activities attributable to one rather accessible surface macromolecule.

Membrane vesicles. The accessibility of LPS as part of the outer membrane was assumed initially. The demonstration that LPS could probably occur free in the external environment was indicated in the early ultrastructural studies of Holt and colleagues (6) and subsequently by Lai, Listgarten, and Hammond (J. Periodontal Res., in press) in their recognition of membrane vesicles being shed from the cells during growth (Fig. 5). These spheric evaginations of the outer membrane are quite small (40 nm in diameter—about the size of a phage head) and are often cited as the explanation of the "free endotoxin" concept (17). Since whole bacterial cells do not appear to penetrate the crevicular epithelium, it is quite conceivable that these very small particles could serve as the vehicles by which endotoxins and other pharmacologically active toxins of bacterial origin gain access into the periodontal tissues.

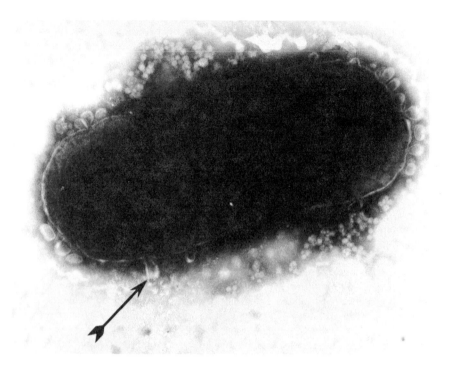

FIG. 5. *Transmission electron micrograph of* A. actinomycetemcomitans *(ATCC strain 29522) (negatively stained with phosphotungstic acid) showing numerous extracellular vesicles of various sizes (indicated by arrow). (Magnification,* ×86,000.) *Photograph kindly supplied by C. Lai.*

We have investigated this possibility in some detail and showed that these membrane vesicles not only contain endotoxin (LPS) but also other non-LPS, heat-sensitive, protease-sensitive bone-resorptive factors as well as the LT and the LT-associated carbohydrate antigen (LG).

The vesicles ("blebs") were easily isolated from the culture fluid supernatants by differential centrifugation over a cushion of 35 to 40% sucrose at 100,000 × *g*. The growth phase was not very important since blebs were produced during all phases of growth. Electron microscopy of the 100,000 × *g* pellet revealed an essentially homogeneous mass of small membrane-bound vesicles (Fig. 6). Tests for endotoxic activity of these blebs showed them to be positive in the *Limulus* amoebocyte lysate clotting assay, chick embryo lethality test (lethal dose 50% was less than 0.01 µg), Shwartzman skin test, and pyrogenicity tests in rabbits. Moreover, the bleb preparations showed a very marked ability to resorb bone as measured by ^{45}Ca release from fetal rat long bones (A. Nowotny, U. Behling, B. F. Hammond, P. Pham, and F. Sanavi, J. Dent. Res. Spec. Issue A **60**:522, abstr. 851, 1981). There also appears to be a concentration of the bone-resorbing activity in blebs since greater than 50 times the dry weight of whole cells of Y4 is required to give a comparable response in the same system. As indicated previously, there appear to be at least two such bone-resorptive factors, of which one is endotoxin and the other is heat-labile, protease-sensitive factor whose activity is distinct from the endotoxin (A. Nowotny, personal communication).

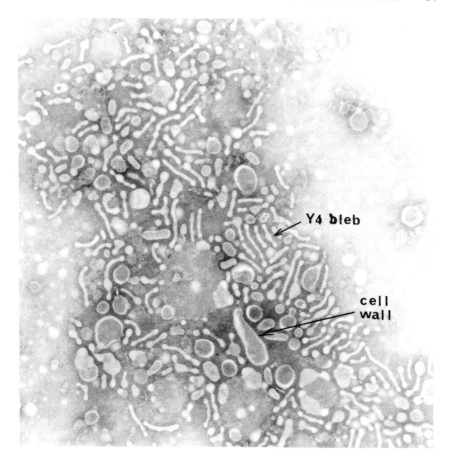

FIG. 6. *Negatively stained transmission electron micrograph of a preparation of* A. actinomycetemcomitans *(strain Y4) membrane vesicles. The vesicles were obtained by differential centrifugation of supernatant fluid from a 72-h broth culture at 100,000 × g. Blebs assume spherical and tubular configurations. (Magnification, × 68,000.) Photograph kindly supplied by Max Listgarten.*

The vesicles also contain significant amounts of detectable LT. The evidence for vesicle leukotoxicity derives from several sources. First, there is the observation of Lai, Listgarten, and Hammond (J. Periodontal Res., in press) that leukotoxic strains have numerous extracellular membrane vesicles (mean number of vesicles for nine strains was $127 \pm 57/\mu m^3$), whereas nonleukotoxic strains demonstrated few or no vesicles (mean number of vesicles for five strains was $4.7 \pm 4.2/\mu m^3$). Second, there was the more direct demonstration of leukotoxicity by demonstration of lactic dehydrogenase release from human PMNs in which it was shown that both vesicles and sonic extracts of vesicles were as active as whole-cell sonic extracts of strain Y4. Table 1 illustrates these findings. A companion ultrastructural study of PMNs exposed to blebs revealed the same kinds of PMN cellular disorganization and membrane destruction as described for whole-cell sonic extracts. Finally, it was possible to show in slab gel electrophoresis that these vesicles contain a protein of the same

TABLE 1. *Leukotoxicity of membrane vesicles ("blebs") of strain Y4*

Prepn	% LDH release[a] (50 blebs/PMN)
Bleb (100,000 × g pellet)	45
Bleb sonic extract	61
Y4 whole-cell sonic extract	63
Triton X (positive control)	100
PMNs alone (negative control)	0

[a]Percent lactic dehydrogenase as determined previously (2).

electrophoretic properties as a known leukotoxic protein. If the slab gel protein (from bleb) was cut out and subsequently eluted, the resulting eluate was able to bind antibody to the toxin. It was therefore possible to inhibit toxin neutralization with bleb protein (presumably the LT). We have also shown that the LT-associated carbohydrate antigen (LG) is present in these blebs, confirming our earlier finding that wherever LG is present the leukotoxin can also be demonstrated.

Our original notion that the LT did not occur in culture filtrates, i.e., was cell-bound, is therefore not substantiated. The demonstration of leukotoxic vesicles in such filtrates and in cell-free supernatants (16,000 × g supernatants) provides a means by which leukotoxic and other cytotoxic factors are free in the external environment.

The overall assessment of the vesicles is therefore based on the demonstration that they contain several virulence-associated factors whose potential for interaction with host cells is enhanced because they occur free in the crevicular milieu. The total amount of surface area provided by these vesicles as they are produced over the life span of a bacterium is much greater than could be provided by a single bacterium in their absence. Since there is an increased surface area and a more widespread distribution of that surface area, the potential for tissue destruction by cytotoxic surface factors is multiplied accordingly.

TABLE 2. *Specificity of* A. actinomycetemcomitans *strains*

Character	Strain		
	Y4	ATCC 29523	627
Leukotoxicity[a]	+	−/+	−
Surface LG[b] antigen[c]	+	−	−
Leukotoxic protein (LT)	+	−/+	−
Surface appendages	+	−	−
Endotoxin-mediated bone loss[d]	+	?	?
Membrane vesicles ("blebs")[e]	+	−/+	−

[a]Baehni et al. (2).

[b]LG = methylpentose antigen.

[c]B. F. Hammond, M. Darkes, and C.-C. Tsai, J. Dent. Res. Spec. Issue A 59:512, abstr. 973, 1980.

[d]Kiley and Holt (9).

[e]C. H. Lai, M. Listgarten, and B. F. Hammond (J. Periodontal Res., in press).

These series of experiments describing the properties of various strains of *A. actinomycetemcomitans* reemphasize and confirm the previously described concept of bacteriological specificity associated with the crevicular microflora and disease. Certain of the strains share an array of specific properties, e.g., leukotoxicity, serotype antigen (LG), and membrane vesicle formation; others (strain 627) lack all of these properties. An intermediate group (ATCC 29523, 511, 2112) generally lack these properties or they are variable with respect to leukotoxicity. This variability is currently being investigated in light of the recent discovery of a mitomycin-inducible bacteriophage (R. H. Stevens, C. Lai, and B. F. Hammond, J. Dent. Res. Spec. Issue A **60**:523, abstr. 854, 1981). A summary of the findings related to the specificity of the strains is listed in Table 2.

CAPNOCYTOPHAGA

Although they have not received the same kind of concerted attention as *A. actinomycetemcomitans,* members of the genus *Capnocytophaga* still occupy an important position in the crevicular microflora of LJP patients. Several investigators have shown significant numbers of these organisms in gingival crevices in LJP patients (15, 19, 27), and related studies using *Capnocytophaga*-monocontaminated animals (8) have indicated clear periodontopathic potential. The animal experiments showed "complete removal of the periodontium." These studies and others prompted a number of investigations that led to the establishment of the new genus *Capnocytophaga,* a group of gram-negative, flexible rods with a gliding motility and a fermentative-type metabolism that requires CO_2 (6, 12, 21, 28).

It is clear that a considerable amount of heterogeneity exists within the genus. DNA studies (base composition and sequence homology relationships) (28) show at least three different groups consistent with the naming of three different species: *C. ochracea* (formerly *Bacteroides ochraceus*), *C. gingivalis,* and *C. sputigena.* Not a great deal is known about the relative pathogenicity of the three species or about pathogenic mechanisms in general.

C. sputigena has perhaps been studied in somewhat greater detail, probably as the result of the early study of Irving, Socransky, and Tanner (8) indicating that this species (strain 4) caused almost complete destruction of the periodontium in 42 days and was the most pathogenic of the several gram-negative species studied in animal model systems. An endotoxin has been isolated from this strain, but tests for numerous biological activities (pyrogenicity, chick and mouse embryo lethality, leukotoxicity, mitogenicity, and macrophage activation) failed to reveal anything remarkable in terms of pathogenic potential (23). More interest seems to be generated in this species as a result of the detection of a factor which inhibits the proliferation of human fibroblasts (24). The inhibition was dose related and not due to cultural conditions or the LPS of this organism. The full significance of this observation cannot be assessed at this time because the factor has not been purified and no information is available on its in vivo occurrence in human disease. However, it is quite possible that such a factor could compromise the integrity of the gingivo–crevicular barrier and result in impaired healing after a microbial challenge or some other traumatic experience. A type-specific carbohydrate antigen has also been isolated and purified (22) and could be used in epidemiological monitoring studies.

The other major finding for *C. sputigena,* also involving strain 4, was the ability of sonic extracts and culture fluids of this organism to produce defects in the locomotion, ability to adhere to glass, and the morphology of neutrophils (18). Distinctive abnormalities in PMN morphology and function were first observed in two patients with *Capnocytophaga* infections, and these abnormalities disappeared after eradication of the infection. These findings presage the activity of yet another exotoxin since the dialyzable *Capnocytophaga* factor was found in culture fluids and in peripheral blood, i.e., sites remote from intact bacterial cells. The other study involving strain C4 showed that this organism, along with several other gram-negative crevicular bacteria, was able to cause the release of lysosomal enzymes from PMNs. Some of these enzymes could presumably mediate tissue damage in the periodontium after their release from PMNs.

C. ochracea is currently being studied as an etiological factor in severe periodontitis of juvenile diabetics (P. Mashimo, R. Genco, Y. Yamamoto, and B. Park, Abstr. Annu. Meet. Am. Soc. Microbiol. 1980, abstr. I139, p. 107). A knowledge of this organism assumes importance since there may be systemic effects (leukotoxicity?) of the periodontal infection which could trigger a diabetic crisis.

Some of these findings are summarized in Table 3.

TABLE 3. *Specificity of* C. sputigena

Factor	*C. sputigena*	*C. ochracea*	*C. gingivalis*
Bone loss in experimental animals	Rapid and severe	Slow and moderate	Minimal or none
Disorder in "leukocyte" migration (18)[a]	+	?/−	?/−
Surface appendages (6)	+	−	−
Type-specific antigen (22)	+	−	−
DNA homology group (28)	4	25	27
Inhibition of fibroblast growth (24)	+	?	?

[a]Numbers in parentheses refer to the Literature Cited section.

LITERATURE CITED

1. **Affias, S., A. West, J. W. Stewart, and E. V. Haldane.** 1978. *Actinobacillus actinomycetemcomitans* endocarditis. Can. Med. Assoc. J. **118:**1256–1260.
2. **Baehni, P., C.-C. Tsai, W. P. McArthur, B. F. Hammond, and N. S. Taichman.** 1979. Interaction of inflammatory cells and oral microorganisms. VIII. Detection of leukotoxic activity of a plaque-derived gram-negative microorganism. Infect. Immun. **24:**233–243.
3. **Brede, H. D.** 1959. Zur Aitiologie und Microbiologie der Aktinomykose. I. *In-Vitro* Versuche zur Frage der fermentativen Unterstutzung des *Actinomyces israeli* durch Begleitbakterien. Zentralbl. Bakteriol. Parasitenkd. Infektionskr. Hyg. Abt. 1 Orig. **174:**110–122.
4. **Ebersole, J. L., D. E. Frey, M. A. Taubman, and D. J. Smith.** 1980. An ELISA for measuring serum antibodies to *Actinobacillus actinomycetemcomitans.* J. Periodontal Res. **15:**621–632.
5. **Heinrich, S., and G. Pulverer.** 1959. Zur Atiologie und Mikrobiologie der Aktinomykose. III. Die pathgene Bedeutung des *Actinobacillus actinomycetemcomitans* unter den "Begleitbakterien" des *Actinomyces israeli.* Zentralbl. Bakteriol. Parsitenkd. Infektionskr. Hyg. Abt. 1 Orig. **176:**91–101.
6. **Holt, S. C., E. R. Leadbetter, and S. S. Socransky.** 1979. *Capnocytophaga:* new genus of gram-negative gliding bacteria. II. Morphology and ultrastructure. Arch. Microbiol. **122:**17–27.
7. **Irving, J. T., M. G. Newman, S. S. Socransky, and J. D. Heeley.** 1975. Histological changes in experimental periodontal disease in rats monoinfected with a gram-negative organism. Arch. Oral Biol. **20:**219–220.

8. **Irving, J. T., S. S. Socransky, and A. C. R. Tanner.** 1978. Histological changes in experimental periodontal disease in rats monoinfected with gram-negative organisms. J. Periodontal Res. **13**:326–332.

9. **Kiley, P., and S. C. Holt.** 1980. Characterization of the lipopolysaccharide from *Actinobacillus actinomycetemcomitans* Y4 and N27. Infect. Immun. **30**:862–873.

10. **Klinger, R.** 1912. Untersuchungen uber menschliche Aktinomycose. Zentralbl. Bakteriol. **62**:191.

11. **Knox, K. W., and R. B. Parker.** 1973. Isolation of a phenol soluble endotoxin from *Leptotrichia buccalis.* Arch. Oral Biol. **18**:85–93.

12. **Leadbetter, E. R., S. C. Holt and S. S. Socransky.** 1979. *Capnocytophaga:* new genus of gram-negative gliding bacteria. I. General characteristics, taxonomic considerations, and significance. Arch. Microbiol. **122**:9–16.

13. **Mitchell, M., and W. Gillespie.** 1964. Bacterial endocarditis due to an *Actinobacillus.* J. Clin. Pathol. **17**:511.

14. **Newman, M. G., and S. S. Socransky.** 1977. Predominant cultivable microbiota in periodontosis. J. Periodontal Res. **12**:120–128.

15. **Newman, M., S. S. Socransky, E. D. Savitt, D. A. Propos, and A. Crawford.** 1976. Studies on the microbiology of periodontosis. J. Periodontol. **47**:373–379.

16. **Page, M. I., and E. O. King.** 1966. Infections due to *Actinobacillus actinomycetemcomitans* and *Haemophilus aphrophilus.* N. Engl. J. Med. **275**:181–188.

17. **Russell, R. R. B.** 1976. Free endotoxin—a review. Microbios Lett. **2**:125–135.

18. **Shurin, S. B., S. S. Socransky, E. Sweeney, and T. P. Stossel.** 1979. A neutrophil disorder induced by *Capnocytophaga,* a dental microorganism. N. Engl. J. Med. **301**:849–854.

19. **Slots, J.** 1976. The predominant cultivable organisms in juvenile periodontitis. Scand. J. Dent. Res. **84**:1–10.

20. **Slots, J., H. S. Reynolds, and R. J. Genco.** 1980. *Actinobacillus actinomycetemcomitans* in human periodontal disease: a cross-sectional microbiological investigation. Infect. Immun. **29**:1013–1020.

21. **Socransky, S. S., S. C. Holt, E. R. Leadbetter, A. C. R. Tanner, E. Savitt, and B. F. Hammond.** 1979. *Capnocytophaga:* new genus of gram-negative gliding bacteria. III. Physiological characterization. Arch. Microbiol. **122**:29–33.

22. **Stevens, R. H., B. F. Hammond, and C. H. Lai.** 1979. Group and type antigens of *Capnocytophaga.* Infect. Immun. **23**:532–539.

23. **Stevens, R. H., M. N. Sela, W. P. McArthur, A. Nowotny, and B. F. Hammond.** 1980. Biological and chemical characterization of endotoxin from *Capnocytophaga sputigena.* Infect. Immun. **27**:246–254.

24. **Stevens, R. H., M. N. Sela, J. Shapira, and B. F. Hammond.** 1980. Detection of a fibroblast proliferation inhibitory factor from *Capnocytophaga sputigena.* Infect. Immun. **27**:271–275.

25. **Tsai, C.-C., B. F. Hammond, P. Baehni, W. P. McArthur and N. S. Taichman.** 1978. Interaction of inflammatory cells and oral microorganisms. VI. Exocytosis of PMN lysosomes in response to gram-negative plaque bacteria. J. Periodontal Res. **13**:504–512.

26. **Tsai, C.-C., W. P. McArthur, P. C. Baehni, B. F. Hammond, and N. S. Taichman.** 1979. Extraction and partial characterization of a leukotoxin from a plaque-derived gram-negative microoganism. Infect. Immun. **25**:427–439.

27. **van Palenstein Helderman, W. H.** 1975. Total viable counts and differential count of *Vibrio (Campylobacter) sputorum, Fusobacterium nucleatum, Selenomonas sputigena, Bacteroides ochraceus* and *Veillonella* in the inflamed and non-inflamed human gingival crevice. J. Periodontal Res. **10**:294–305.

28. **Williams, B. L., and B. F. Hammond.** 1979. *Capnocytophaga:* new genus of gram-negative gliding bacteria. IV. DNA base composition and sequence homology. Arch. Microbiol. **122**:35–39.

Role of Spirochetes in Periodontal Disease

WALTER J. LOESCHE AND BARBARA E. LAUGHON

University of Michigan School of Dentistry, Ann Arbor, Michigan 48109

INTRODUCTION

Spirochetes are ubiquitous in those plaques (the microbial mat adhering to the tooth surfaces) associated with gingivitis and periodontitis. This ancient observation has never been given the authority of either a pathognomic or even a diagnostic characteristic in periodontal disease. This stems from the inability of investigators to reliably culture these organisms in vitro so as to validate pathogenicity by animal experiments or to demonstrate virulence factors in vitro. An argument can be made that the ascendancy of the spirochetes in the periodontal plaque is secondary to periodontal inflammation. In the microenvironment of the pocket, the spirochetes would be selected for as they could capitalize on the low Eh present therein (18), the availability of serum components which serve as nutrients (35), and their motility. Yet even if the spirochetes are opportunistic, this in no way detracts from their ability to contribute to or potentiate the microbial assault on the periodontium.

The literature related to the oral spirochetes has been reviewed by Rosebury (44) and Loesche (35). Smibert has reviewed the taxonomy of spirochetes (50), and Canale-Parola, their physiology (6, 7). Holt has described their ultrastructural characteristics and chemical composition (15). The availability of these comprehensive treatises permits the following review to address these issues briefly and then to focus on recent clinical and microscopic studies which make a cogent, albeit circumstantial, case for the etiological role of spirochetes in periodontal disease.

MORPHOLOGY AND TAXONOMY

Spirochetes are morphologically unique, gram-negative bacteria characterized by flexible cell walls and internal flagella. Listgarten and Socransky (32) differentiated the oral spirochetes on the basis of cellular diameter and number of axial filaments (endoflagella). The small spirochetes are 0.1 to 0.25 μm in diameter, possess 1 or 2 flagella at each end of the cell, and comprise the cultivable species *Treponema denticola, T. macrodentium,* and *T. orale.* The intermediate spirochetes are 0.2 to 0.5 μm in diameter, possess from 3 to 20 flagella at each end, and are represented by *T. vincentii* (which has 3 to 6 flagella). The large spirochetes are 0.5 μm or more in diameter, contain 12 to more than 20 flagella originating at each end, and possess a structurally distinct outer membrane. There is presently no cultivable representative of this last group, although E. G. Hampp (J. Dent. Res. **33**:660, abstr. 43, 1954) reported the isolation of a large spirochete which he termed *Borrelia buccale* and which is no longer extant.

The taxonomy of the cultivable oral spirochetes is summarized in Table 1. All isolates are classified in the genus *Treponema* and are obligate anaerobes. They are differentiated on the basis of their metabolic activities and number of axial

TABLE 1. *Differentiating characteristics of cultivable oral spirochetes*[a]

Species	Filaments	Glucose	Lactate	NH$_3$	Indole	Trypsin	Products
T. denticola	2-4-2	–	–	+	+	+[b]	ApL[c]
T. macrodentium	1-2-1	+	–	–	–	–	AfL
T. orale	1-2-1	–	+	–	+	?	Ap
T. vincentii	5-10-5	+	–	+	+	–	AB

[a] Summary of information from references 14 and 51.

[b] Indicates hydrolysis of the trypsin substrate *N*-benzoyl-arginine-naphthylamide.

[c] Acid end products: A, major acetic; p, moderate propionic; f, moderate formic; L, major lactic; and B, major butyric.

filaments. *T. denticola* is the valid name for organisms previously called *Spirochaeta dentium, T. microdentium, T. ambiguum,* and *T. comandonii* (51). *T. macrodentium* is a small spirochete which does not require serum but does require fermentable carbohydrate and isobutyric acid for growth (56). *T. orale* is the proper specific epithet for *T. oralis,* and *Treponema vincentii* is more appropriate than *Borrelia vincentii* (51).

ISOLATION AND CULTIVATION

The cultivable oral spirochetes grow best under anaerobic conditions in complex media containing peptones and serum, but their growth rate is quite slow compared with that of other oral bacteria. On primary isolation plates, therefore, acidic end products diffusing from rapidly metabolizing streptococcal colonies (for example) may prevent spirochetes from initiating growth at all. This plus other problems with sensitivity to oxygen (34) and to sonication have given oral spirochetes a not-entirely-deserved reputation for being extremely difficult to cultivate.

Noguchi in 1912 observed the ability of spirochetes to migrate through agar away from the site of inoculation, forming hazes of growth (42). This motile behavior, which is most likely due to some form of chemotaxis (7), has been the basis of all isolation procedures until very recently. Pure spirochetes, let alone pure cultures, are not assured since several kinds of spirochetes may co-migrate, and contamination of the agar surface with other bacteria complicates the isolation procedure. In 1961, Loesche and Socransky (36) reported that small spirochetes were able to penetrate membrane filters on the surface of agar plates and form hazes below that resembled individual colonies. This procedure is quite useful for small spirochetes with a cellular diameter of approximately 0.3 μm or less, but the intermediate and large spirochetes require filter pore sizes which permit the penetration of motile bacteria such as *Vibrio, Selenomonas,* and *Capnocytophaga*. The membrane procedure does not lend itself to the quantitative isolation of spirochetes. Leschine and Canale-Parola (23) recently reported the use of the antibiotic rifampin as a selective agent for the isolation of oral spirochetes. Using an agar dilution technique, they were able to isolate and clone one intermediate and three small oral spirochetes. The use of rifampin and polymyxin B in a selective medium has also been suggested (R. M. Smibert, J. Dent. Res. Spec. Issue A **60**:485, abstr. 702, 1981). The incorporation of antibiotics into culture media will greatly facilitate the enumeration of certain spirochetes in subgingival plaque during treatment evaluation and should stimulate more interest in the basic biology of these organisms.

Most of the information available on the growth requirements of oral spirochetes concerns the small-sized species (4, 6, 16, 55, 56). *T. denticola* has been shown to be sensitive to O_2 (34), and since the Eh of the periodontal pocket has been estimated to be about -100 mV (18), all other spirochetes inhabiting this niche are assumed to be at least equally anaerobic. *T. denticola, T. macrodentium,* and *T. vincentii* require thiamine pyrophosphate (cocarboxylase) for growth, and extracts of *T. denticola* require this cofactor for acetyl-phosphate formation from pyruvate (13). The addition of 10% serum or ascitic fluid to cultures of *T. vincentii* and *T. denticola* stimulates maximal growth (50). The identity of this host factor(s) is not known, but *T. denticola* can be cultured in a serum-free medium containing bovine serum albumin saturated with oleic and palmitic acids (33). The replacement of serum by α_2 globulins (53) or long-chain fatty acids could not be duplicated by other workers (13) and may be dependent on the method of preparation or the commercial source of α_2 globulin. *T. macrodentium* does not require serum or similar animal products, but growth is dependent upon isobutyric acid, polyamines, and glucose (11, 55). In our laboratory, we are able to culture *T. denticola* and *T. vincentii* to cell densities of 10^9/ml and harvest cell pellets of 2 g (wet weight) per liter using a Trypticase-yeast extract-serum medium incubated anaerobically at 34°C.

Quantification of spirochetes in periodontal plaques has been hampered by their extreme sensitivity to sonication. Gram-negative bacteria, especially *Fusobacterium nucleatum,* are killed exponentially over time by sonic treatment with a Branson Sonifier (43). A more gentle method of plaque dispersal with a Kontes sonicator has been described (S. A. Syed and W. J. Loesche, J. Dent. Res. **57:**320, abstr. 982, 1978), but spirochetes remain exquisitely sensitive (Fig. 1). The use of the Tekmar homogenizer (Tekmar Co., Cincinnati, Ohio) as an alternative procedure is presently under evaluation in our laboratory. As can be seen in Fig. 1, 20 s of homogenization does not adversely affect the viability of pure cultures of *T. denticola.* Preliminary results with subgingival plaque indicate that homogenization compares favorably with sonication in efficiency of dispersal as judged by percentage recovery of viable organisms. Therefore, by the use of a more gentle dispersal method, a medium containing rifampin, anaerobic sample processing, and incubation of 2 weeks' duration, we have obtained pure colonies of small spirochetes plated directly from periodontal plaque. The rifampin medium is not strictly selective for spirochetes, however, as *Fusobacterium, Capnocytophaga,* and *Eikenella corrodens* colonies are also resistant to 2µg of rifampin per ml.

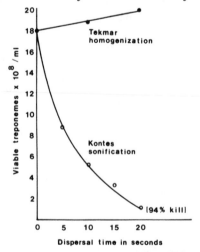

FIG. 1. *Effect of dispersal by a Tekmar homogenizer or a Kontes sonicator on viable counts of* T. denticola.

TABLE 2. *Metabolic activities of* T. denticola

Substrate	Enzyme(s)	Products
Glucose	Embden-Meyerhof	Lactate
Pyruvate	Clostridial-type	Acetate, ethanol, CO_2
Cysteine, Serine, Alanine	Deaminase, etc.	Pyruvate, NH_3, H_2S
Arginine	Iminohydrolase	Proline, NH_3, CO_2, putrescine
Fibrin	—	—
Benzoyl-arginine-naphthylamide	Trypsin-like protease	Peptides or free amino acids

PHYSIOLOGY

Among the oral spirochetes, the physiology of *T. denticola* has been the most thoroughly studied. The metabolic versatility of this organism (Table 2) probably contributes to its survival in the competitive environment of the gingival sulcus (6). *T. denticola* seems able to obtain energy from glucose by the Embden-Meyerhof-Parnas pathway; from pyruvate, serine, cysteine, and alanine by a clostridial-type phosphoclastic system; and from arginine by an arginine iminohydrolase pathway which includes carbamate kinase (3, 13). The organism is also proteolytic, as it hydrolyzes gelatin (14), dissolves fibrin (41), and possesses a trypsin-like activity against benzoyl-arginine-naphthylamide (manuscript in preparation). Treponemes cannot synthesize or elongate fatty acids and rely upon those present in media or tissue for growth (16, 33).

The cultivable oral spirochetes as a group produce a large array of potentially toxic substances as end products of their metabolism. The list includes ammonia, indole, hydrogen sulfide, butyric acid, and putrescine. In addition, *T. vincentii* exhibits an acetylglucosamidase activity which may play a role in the destruction of tissue ground substance. The trypsin-like activity of *T. denticola* is a potentially pathogenic mechanism. Proteolytic activity may have a direct effect upon the junctional epithelium, as trypsin has been shown in vitro to disrupt cell–cell and cell–substratum adhesions (5). Trypsin has been reported to activate latent gingival tissue collagenase by destruction of a collagenase inhibitor in serum (2) and to activate the alternate pathway of complement fixation, causing release of leukotactic factors (61). These activities, singly or in concert, could be responsible for significant pathology in the periodontium.

MICROBIAL SPECIFICITY IN PERIODONTAL DISEASE

Early bacteriological investigations in periodontal disease were unable to demonstrate the presence of a unique periodontopathic flora. Although "spirochetes were invariably far more numerous [in pathological conditions] than in any of the normal samples, they were still present" (45). Accordingly, Rosebury et al. (45) and others (52) concluded that periodontal disease was not characterized by a unique flora but rather by a nonspecific overgrowth of the indigenous flora on the dentogingival surfaces. Microbial specificity did not reappear as a concept until about 1970 when animal studies demonstrated the pathogenic potential of *Actinomyces viscosus* (17) and *A. naeslundii* (54) for periodontal tissues, and immunological investigations showed that T lymphocytes obtained from periodontal patients, but not those from healthy subjects, were uniquely stimulated by sonic extracts of *A. viscosus* (22). About this time, bacteriologists began to culture plaque from single tooth sites and observed significant quantitative differences in the proportions or levels of certain species when healthy and diseased gingival sites (37, 59) and periodontal pockets (48) were compared. Momentum with regard to bacterial specificity was fully achieved when Newman and Socransky (40) isolated a characteristic flora containing *Capnocytophaga* sp., *Actinobacillus actinomycetemcomitans,* and *Eikenella corrodens* from deep pockets in patients diagnosed as having localized juvenile periodontitis. Subsequent investigations have implicated *Bacteroides gingivalis* in active periodontitis (38, 48) and *B. melaninogenicus* subsp. *intermedius* in pregnancy gingivitis (21).

Concurrent with these developments were a series of dark-field and electron microscopic studies by Listgarten and his colleagues (27, 28, 31) and phase-contrast microscopic observations by Keyes et al. (19) which made an impressive argument that spirochetes are pathognomic in periodontal disease. These studies have not generated subsequent animal and in vitro testing because of the difficulties associated with the cultivation of spirochetes and the inability to establish anaerobes in germfree or other animal systems. Accordingly, spirochetes have not received the attention that the clinical studies warrant. In the sections which follow, evidence in support of the role of spirochetes in periodontal disease will be presented under the headings of association studies and response-to-treatment studies (Table 3).

TABLE 3. *Application of causation criteria to the role of spirochetes in periodontal disease*

Type of study	Findings
Association	Abundance of morphological evidence which demonstrates spirochetes in plaques associated with periodontal disease.
Animal models	None described. Difficulties with isolation and in vitro cultivation of many types of spirochetes.
Longitudinal studies	Few performed.
Response to treatment	Spirochetes among first to disappear. Also first to reappear.

ASSOCIATION STUDIES

Gingivitis. The characteristic morphology and motility of the spirochetes enables them to be readily identified by dark-field or phase microscopy. Leeuwenhoek in his original description of the microscope described spirochetes in tooth scrapings (9), and Vincent some 80 years ago implicated, on microscopic evidence, spirochetes as etiological in acute necrotizing ulcerative gingivitis (ANUG) (44). More recent observations demonstrate a clear relationship between periodontal disease and proportions of spirochetes in the microscopic count (Table 4).

TABLE 4. *Evidence which associates spirochetes with periodontal disease*

Diagnosis	Light microscopic (% of count)	Electron microscopic
Health	0.6 (46),[a] 1.8 (28)	Not observed (27)
Gingivitis		
Experimental, 3 wk	Appear at 8-12 days (58)	
Experimental, 2 mo		Surface of plaque (31)
Naturally occurring	17 (46)	Surface of plaque (27)
ANUG	30[b]	Invade tissue (26)
Periodontitis		
Juvenile	6.8 (24), few (40)	Surface of plaque (62)
		Not observed (27)
Post-juvenile	56 (24)	High proportions (surface) (27)
Active	56 (24), 38 (28)	High proportions (surface) (27)
		Invade tissue (10)
Maintained pockets	<3[c]	

[a] Numbers in parentheses give reference.
[b] Unpublished data of Loesche et al.
[c] Unpublished data of Syed et al.

In gingival and periodontal health, spirochetes can be observed, but comprise a small percentage of the microscopic count (28, 46). As the plaque volume is minimal in health, the absolute levels of spirochetes may be so low that they often cannot be detected by light microscopy and have yet to be observed by electron microscopy (27). It is assumed that the spirochetes are present at undetectable levels in most, if not all, of these plaques associated with health because of findings obtained with experimental gingivitis models.

In these studies volunteers were brought to a state of optimal gingival health by frequent dental cleanings and meticulous oral hygiene procedures. At zero time, minimal plaque was present and no spirochetes could be detected microscopically (58). Oral hygiene procedures were then suspended for 2 to 3 weeks, and within 4 to 18 days all subjects had detectable spirochetes in their plaques. These spirochetes most likely represented progeny of organisms which survived the original mechanical debridement and were subsequently selected for by the stagnant conditions on the dentogingival surfaces that exist in the absence of oral hygiene. This is a more attractive hypothesis than to assume that each reappearance of spirochetes represented a separate colonization from exogenous sources. If the former is so, then spirochetes, once established, apparently are extremely difficult to eradicate from the dentogingival surfaces.

In an extension of the no-hygiene model, Listgarten et al. (31) placed epoxy resin crowns on five or more teeth in volunteers and asked these subjects to avoid as much as possible the cleaning of these teeth during the stay of the crowns in the mouth. At appropriate intervals, the crowns were removed without disturbing the accumulated plaque and were prepared for electron microscopic examination. At the outset, none of the involved teeth had plaque or gingivitis scores which exceeded a value of one. After 2 months of minimal oral hygiene, there was a bleeding gingivitis around all of the crowns (gingivitis index = 2.4). At that time, there was a prominent spirochete-rich layer on the plaque surface that would be in contact with the inflamed gingiva. The plaques on teeth that were extracted for clinical reasons were also examined by electron microscopic procedures (27). Those plaques associated with naturally occurring gingivitis also had spirochetes confined to the surface layer in that portion of the plaque which approximated the gingival tissue. This increase of spirochetes in gingivitis agrees with an earlier light microscopic study of subgingival plaques which showed that, in the presence of gingivitis, the spirochetes accounted for 17% of the microscopic count (46).

The close approximation of the spirochete layer to the gingival tissues suggests a role for the spirochetes in gingival inflammation. If these spirochetes possess an array of enzymes comparable to that found in *T. denticola* (Table 2), then their metabolic by-products could elicit an inflammatory response, if they are capable of diffusing into the gingival tissue. The low molecular weight of many of these products, combined with the decreased barrier functions of inflamed tissues, makes this diffusion quite probable.

The electron microscopic evidence places the spirochetes in a favored position to enter the tissue. If the spirochetes take this alignment in order to better sequester host-derived nutrients, then it is conceivable that more adventuresome cells are continually attempting to penetrate the gingival lining in response to a nutrient gradient. This chemotactic response would be aided by the spirochetes' motility and small size, which would enable them to penetrate the spaces between the gingival epithelial cells more easily than the other plaque species. Thus, it should be no surprise that spirochetes have been found invading the tissue in ANUG (26) and in periodontitis (10).

In ANUG, microscopic studies show that spirochetes account for about 30% of the count (Table 4; W. J. Loesche et al., unpublished data). Ultrastructural studies have demonstrated spirochetes in the connective tissue and margin of the lesion well in advance of other plaque bacteria (26). Listgarten and Lewis (29) have quantified the proportions of small, intermediate, and large spirochetes in superficial and deep plaque layers taken from the ANUG lesions. All types of spirochetes were uninformly distributed in the two layers, intermediate spirochetes with seven or more axial filaments being significantly more numerous in the deeper layers. These spirochetes have yet to be cultivated. If these spirochetes are surviving in viable tissue, they most likely are not as oxygen sensitive as the small cultivable *Treponema* spp. (34). Thus, the invasiveness of spirochetes could reflect the survival of foraging, moderately anaerobic organisms in tissues made relatively ischemic because of stress, smoking, and malnutrition (35).

Periodontitis. The preceding investigations showed that as the gingivitis increased in severity, so too did the proportions of spirochetes in the plaque. This same relationship held, with one exception, for periodontitis (Table 4). The exception is localized juvenile periodontitis, in which spirochetes appear to account for less than 10% of the scant flora that is present in these pockets (Table 4). When present, they apparently are still confined to the surface layer of the plaque (62).

In post-juvenile periodontitis (rapidly progressive periodontitis, generalized juvenile periodontitis) the spirochetes comprised between 35 and 56% of the microscopic count and dominated in those surface layers of the plaque which approximate the tissue (24, 27; Table 4). The same high range of proportions has been found in active periodontitis (Table 4). Again, the spirochete-rich layer is confined to the surface of the plaque (27), and there is electron microscopic evidence that some spirochetes invade the tissue (10).

The microscopic profile of the percentage of spirochetes (Table 4) and the cultural profile of the percentage of *B. gingivalis* (>25% of the cultural count) (38, 48, 57) are so similar in post-juvenile periodontitis and active periodontitis that these diseases appear to represent the same type of specific infection in the individual pockets. These clinical entities appear to differ only with regard to the number of infected pockets and the age of the patient. In contrast, plaques taken from stabilized pockets, i.e., pockets that have remained at a 3- to 5-mm depth for 1 or more years, had undetectable to low proportions of spirochetes (Table 4) and about 4% *B. gingivalis* (S. A. Syed et al., unpublished data). Bacteriological differences of this magnitude which coincide with clinical observations have great etiological significance as well as diagnostic value. When the percentage of spirochetes is plotted as a function of the severity of the clinical diagnosis, a striking correlation is apparent (Fig. 2). This relationship indicates that the percentage of spirochetes can provide diagnostic information concerning the clinical status of the pocket in all instances except localized juvenile periodontitis. If this is so, then we have an objective parameter with which we can monitor treatment efficacy and, accordingly, increase or decrease the magnitude of our antimicrobial efforts.

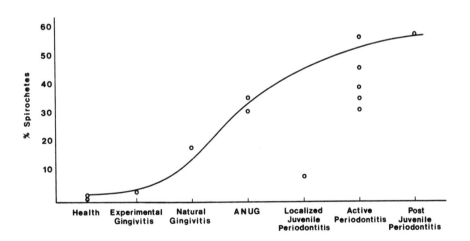

FIG. 2. *Relationship between percent spirochetes in microscopic count and severity of periodontal diagnosis. Diagnosis arranged according to the extent of clinical involvement. The data on percent spirochetes are taken from references cited in Tables 4 and 5.*

RESPONSE-TO-TREATMENT STUDIES

If spirochetes and organisms such as *B. gingivalis* and *A. actinomy-cetemcomitans* (49) are of etiological significance in periodontal disease, then their demise in the subgingival plaque should coincide with the restoration of periodontal health. The studies listed in Table 5 indicate that this is so in the case of spirochetes and, in addition, provide a means of evaluating various treatment modalities and schedules in terms of their efficacy in controlling the proportions of spirochetes in the plaque.

Mechanical debridement of the tooth surfaces is a valid means of controlling the amount of plaque, and thereby the levels of spirochetes, in subgingival sites. However, as observed in the experimental gingivitis model, it apparently did not eliminate the spirochetes from these surfaces, as judged by their quick return after cessation of oral hygiene (Table 4). When the teeth were scaled and oral hygiene was reintroduced, the spirochetes became undetectable within 1 day (Table 5).

This illustrates the efficacy of the mechanical approach in suppressing the spirochetes when access is good, as is the situation with gingivitis. When deep pockets exist, mechanical access is diminished, and it becomes most difficult to completely eliminate plaque from the root surfaces and furcations (60). Thus, a residual infection remains which can repopulate the pocket plaque and perpetuate the periodontal inflammatory response. This infection can be controlled by rescaling the root surfaces at intervals of 2 to 3 months (1, 20), as

TABLE 5. *Response-to-treatment studies which demonstrate role of spirochetes in periodontal disease*

Diagnosis	Spirochetes in samples (%)			Change in pocket depth (mm)[a]
	Before treatment	Treatment	After treatment	
Gingivitis				
Experimental (58)[b]	2	Scaling	0 (1 day[c])	GI − 0
ANUG[d]	35	Metronidazole	2.4 (7 days)	GI − 0
Periodontitis				
Listgarten	39	No treatment	45 (25 wk)	0.8
et al. (30)	35	Scaling (3×)	6 (25 wk)	1.8
	40	Tetracycline	24 (25 wk)	1.8
	36	Tetracycline + scaling (3×)	7 (25 wk)	2.2
Lindhe	46	Oral hygiene	54 (14 days)	0.0
et al. (25)	45	Scaling	4 (14 days)	1.2
	44	Topical tetracycline	27 (14 days)	0.6
Mousques et al. (39)	34	Scaling	21 (42 days)	1.4

[a] GI = gingivitis index.
[b] Numbers in parentheses give reference.
[c] Time after treatment.
[d] Unpublished data of Loesche et al.

is shown in Table 4 under the diagnosis of maintained pockets. This ability of mechanical debridement to reduce the proportions of spirochetes in plaque and to improve periodontal health has been investigated by Listgarten, Lindhe, and their colleagues (25, 30, 39; Table 5).

In one series of experiments (12, 30), six periodontitis patients were given systemic tetracycline (1 g per day) during the first and second weeks and the seventh and eighth weeks of the trial, whereas six other patients received no antibiotic. In each patient the teeth in one-half of each arch were scaled and root planed, whereas the teeth in the contralateral half were not treated. The study thus included four treatment groups in each of whom the spirochetes comprised about 40% of the microscopic flora before treatment (Table 5). There was no change in the proportions of spirochetes in the no-treatment group in the plaque samples obtained after 25 weeks of the trial. For those teeth which were scaled three times during this interval, the spirochetal proportions decreased to about 6%, and the pocket depths were reduced 1 mm or more compared with the no-treatment group (Table 5). The tetracycline alone caused a moderate reduction in spirochetes and did not seem to enhance the antispirochetal effect of the scaling. However, the greatest reduction in pocket depth was achieved when the tetracycline was combined with the scaling.

In a second clinical trial (25), the tetracycline was delivered locally for 2 days to the pocket via hollow fiber devices, whereas other pockets in the same mouth were either scaled or left untreated. All pockets were 6 mm or more in depth and harbored about 45% spirochetes in their plaques. Oral hygiene instructions, in the absence of scaling or tetracycline, had no effect on the proportions of spirochetes or the pocket depth (Table 5). The tetracycline reduced the proportions of spirochetes about 40% and caused a 0.6-mm reduction of pocket depth. The scaling was even more effective in reducing both the spirochetes and the pocket depth (Table 5). This study, performed with matched pockets within the same mouth, demonstrated that the efficacy of treatment, as measured clinically, corresponded with the reduction in spirochetal proportions. If the demise of the spirochetes was not causally related to the improvement in periodontal health, it at least documented this event.

In a third study (39), 14 patients were given a single full-mouth scaling and root-planing session. At base line a single diseased site in each subject was assessed for probing depth and for the percentage of spirochetes in the pocket plaque. These measurements were repeated at weekly intervals after the scaling. The proportions of spirochetes decreased significantly from the base-line value of 34% to a low of 2% on day 7. Thereafter, their proportions increased, but it was not until day 42 that they were no longer significantly reduced compared with the base-line values. At that time, the pockets showed an average reduction of 1.4 mm.

Mechanical debridement is directed against plaque bulk and does not specifically discriminate against spirochetes. Likewise, tetracyclines are broad spectrum in their antimicrobial activity. Thus, the improvement in pocket health that was coincident with the decrease in proportions in spirochetes could be related to the decline of the total plaque flora, as well as to the decline of other specific bacterial types. It is not likely that an agent with an antimicrobial spectrum limited to spirochetes will ever exist. However, metronidazole, an antiprotozoan compound, has a spectrum of activity that is restricted to anaerobes and will inhibit oral spirochetes in vitro at levels of less than 1 μg/ml

(8). Metronidazole has been used with clinical success for almost 20 years in the treatment of ANUG (47). We have treated six ANUG patients with metronidazole, 250 mg three times daily for 7 days. Before treatment, the spirochetes averaged 35% of the microscopic count, whereas 1 week after treatment they accounted for about 2% of the flora (Table 5). This significant reduction was associated with a prompt disappearance of clinical symptoms.

We have observed significant reductions of spirochetes and *B. gingivalis* in periodontitis patients after 1 week of metronidazole treatment (38). The most profound reduction occurred when the metronidazole was combined with scaling, as was also observed when the tetracycline was combined with the scaling (12, 30; Table 5). The reduction in the proportion of spirochetes that resulted when we performed full-mouth scaling during the week that the patients were on metronidazole is shown in Table 6 for 19 pockets found in six patients with active periodontitis and for 13 pockets found in four patients with post-juvenile or generalized juvenile periodontitis. This treatment significantly suppressed the spirochetal proportions for at least 12 to 14 weeks in both clinical entities. Of particular interest was the finding that in four of the six periodontitis patients 10 of the 12 sampled pockets had not become detectably recolonized by the spirochetes some 90 days after the completion of treatment. The patients' periodontal status at 90 days was superior to that of the two patients in whom all seven sampled sites had become recolonized by spirochetes (Loesche et al., unpublished data). The metronidazole–scaling treatment was less able to eliminate the spirochetes from the pockets of the generalized juvenile periodontitis patients (Table 6).

These response-to-treatment studies make a strong argument for the involvement of spirochetes in all forms of periodontal disease except possibly localized juvenile periodontitis. When an organism comprises 34 to 46% of the flora before treatment and then drops significantly to below 10% as a result of treatment which restores periodontal health, this organism must be considered a periodontopathic organism. This is not synonomous with declaring that the spirochetes are the only periodontopathic organisms which were suppressed, because our data make an equally convincing case for *B. gingivalis*. The ease and speed with which spirochetes can be diagnosed in subgingival plaques, as opposed to the difficulty, the delay, and the cost of anaerobic culturing for the

TABLE 6. *Effect of systemic metronidazole treatment plus scaling on proportions and frequency of spirochetes in subgingival plaque*

Time	Periodontitis		Generalized juvenile periodontitis	
	% Spirochetes	Frequency[a]	% Spirochetes	Frequency[a]
Before treatment	32 ± 20^b	19/19	$34 \pm {}^{\,b}$	10/13
After treatment				
1–3 weeks	4 ± 12	1/17	0.9 ± 1.4	4/13
12–14 weeks	13 ± 18	$9/19^c$	9 ± 9	11/13

[a] Number of sites positive for spirochetes per number sampled.

[b] Significantly higher than other values in column (paired t test, $P < 0.05$).

[c] Combined frequency for two subgroups of patients with frequencies of 7/7 and 2/12 (see text for details).

detection of *B. gingivalis,* make it likely that in the future the clinical progress of most forms of periodontal disease will be monitored by microscopic examination of the spirochetes in subgingival plaques.

SUMMARY

Spirochetes manifest themselves in plaques associated with periodontal disease, where they account for 35 to 55% of the microscopically detectable flora. They localize on the outer surface of the plaque, where they are in intimate contact with the sulcular or pocket epithelium, or both. The physiological characteristics of the few species that can be cultured indicate that their products could be cytotoxic if they enter the host. This possibility is quite likely given the fact that the spirochetes themselves have been observed to invade the tissue in ANUG and in periodontitis. Mechanical and chemical treatments which cause pocket reduction also significantly reduce the proportions of the spirochetes in plaque. Metronidazole, which has a spectrum of activity against anaerobes, is curative in ANUG and markedly improves periodontal health in cases of periodontitis and generalized juvenile periodontitis. This improvement is coincident with a significant reduction in spirochetes. Taken as a whole, these observations indicate that the spirochetes, if not pathogens in periodontal disease, are at least diagnostic of periodontal status.

ACKNOWLEDGMENTS

This work was supported by Public Health Service grants DE 03011, DE 02731, and F32 DE 05172 from the National Institute of Dental Research.

LITERATURE CITED

1. **Axelsson, P., and J. Lindhe.** Effect of controlled oral hygiene procedures on caries and periodontal disease in adults. J. Clin. Periodontol. 5:133–151.
2. **Birkedal-Hansen, H., C. M. Coob, R. E. Taylor, and H. M. Fullmer.** 1975. Trypsin activation of latent collagenase from several mammalian sources. Scand. J. Dent. Res. 83:302–305.
3. **Blakemore, R. P., and E. Canale-Parola.** 1976. Arginine catabolism by *Treponema denticola.* J. Bacteriol. 128:616–622.
4. **Breznak, J. A.** 1973. Biology of nonpathogenic, host associated spirochetes. Crit. Rev. Microbiol. 2:457–489.
5. **Britch, M., and T. D. Allen.** 1980. The modulation of cellular contractility and adhesion of trypsin and EGTA. Exp. Cell Res. 125:221–231.
6. **Canale-Parola, E.** 1977. Physiology and evolution of spirochetes. Bacteriol. Rev. 41:181–204.
7. **Canale-Parola, E.** 1978. Motility and chemotaxis of spirochetes. Annu. Rev. Microbiol. 32:69–99.
8. **Davies, R. M.** 1970. The *in vitro* sensitivity of oral spirochaetes to metronidazole. J. Periodontal Res. 5:183–186.
9. **Dobell, C.** 1960. Antony von Leeuwenhoek and his "Little Animals." Dover, New York.
10. **Frank, R.** 1980. Bacterial penetration in the apical wall of advanced human periodontitis. J. Periodontal Res. 15:563–573.
11. **Hardy, P. H., Jr., and C. O. Munro.** 1966. Nutritional requirements of anaerobic spirochetes. I. Demonstration of isobutyrate and bicarbonate as growth factors for a strain of *Treponema microdentium.* J. Bacteriol. 91:27–32.
12. **Hellden, L. B., M. A. Listgarten, and J. Lindhe.** 1979. The effect of tetracycline and/or scaling on human periodontal disease. J. Clin. Periodontol. 6:222–230.
13. **Hespell, R. B., and E. Canale-Parola.** 1971. Amino acid and glucose fermentation by *Treponema denticola.* Arch. Mikrobiol. 78:234–251.
14. **Holdeman, L. V., E. P. Cato, and W. E. C. Moore (ed.).** 1977. Anaerobe laboratory manual, 4th ed. Virginia Polytechnic Institute and State University, Blacksburg.
15. **Holt, S. C.** 1978. Anatomy and chemistry of spirochetes. Microbiol. Rev. 42:114–160.
16. **Johnson, R. C.** 1977. The spirochetes. Annu. Rev. Microbiol. 31:89–106.
17. **Jordan, H. V., and P. H. Keyes.** 1964. Aerobic gram-positive, filamentous bacteria as etiologic agents of experimental periodontal disease in hamsters. Arch. Oral Biol. 9:401–411.
18. **Kenney, E. B., and M. M. Ash.** 1969. Oxidation reduction potential of developing plaque, periodontal pockets and gingival sulci. J. Periodontol. 40:630–633.

19. **Keyes, P., W. E. Wright, and S. A. Howard.** 1978. The use of phase-contrast microscopy and chemotherapy in the diagnosis and treatment of periodontal lesions. An initial report. Quintessence Int. **1:**51–76.
20. **Knowles, J. W., F. G. Burgett, R. R. Nissle, R. A. Shick, E. C. Morrison, and S. P. Ramfjord.** 1979. Results of periodontal treatment related to pocket depth and attachment level. Eight years. J. Periodontol. **50:**225–233.
21. **Kornman, K. S., and W. J. Loesche.** 1980. The subgingival microbial flora during pregnancy. J. Periodontal Res. **15:**111–122.
22. **Lehner, T.** 1972. Cell-mediated immune responses in oral disease. A review. J. Oral Pathol. **1:**39–58.
23. **Leschine, S. B., and E. Canale-Parola.** 1980. Rifampin as a selective agent for isolation of oral spirochetes. J. Clin. Microbiol. **12:**792–795.
24. **Liljenberg, B., and J. Lindhe.** 1980. Juvenile periodontitis. Some microbiological, histopathological and clinical characteristics. J. Clin. Periodontol. **7:**48–61.
25. **Lindhe, J., L. Heijl, J. M. Goodson, and S. S. Socransky.** 1979. Local tetracycline delivery using hollow fiber devices in periodontal therapy. J. Clin. Periodontol. **6:**141–149.
26. **Listgarten, M. A.** 1965. Electron microscopic observations of the bacterial flora of acute necrotizing ulcerative gingivitis. J. Periodontol. **36:**328–339.
27. **Listgarten, M. A.** 1976. Structure of the microbial flora associated with periodontal health and disease in man. A light and electron microscopic study. J. Periodontol. **57:**1–18.
28. **Listgarten, M. A., and L. Hellden.** 1978. Relative distribution of bacteria at clinically healthy and periodontally diseased sites in humans. J. Clin. Periodontol. **5:**115–132.
29. **Listgarten, M. A., and D. W. Lewis.** 1967. The distribution of spirochetes in the lesion of acute necrotizing elcerative gingivitis. An electron microscopic and statistical survey. J. Periodontol. **38:**379–386.
30. **Listgarten, M. A., J. Lindhe, and L. Hellden.** 1978. Effect of tetracycline and/or scaling on human periodontal disease. J. Clin. Periodontol. **5:**246–271.
31. **Listgarten, M. A., H. E. Mayo, and R. Tremblay.** 1975. Development of dental plaque on epoxy resin crowns in man. J. Periodontol. **46:**10–26.
32. **Listgarten, M. A., and S. S. Socransky.** 1965. Electron microscopy as an aid in the taxonomic differenciation of oral spirochetes. Arch. Oral Biol. **10:**127–138.
33. **Livermore, B. P., and R. C. Johnson.** 1974. Lipids of the *Spirochaetales:* comparison of the lipids of several members of the genera *Spirochaeta, Treponema,* and *Leptospira.* J. Bacteriol. **120:**1268–1273.
34. **Loesche, W. J.** 1969. Oxygen sensitivity of various anaerobic bacteria. Appl. Microbiol. **18:**723–727.
35. **Loesche, W. J.** 1976. Periodontal disease and the treponemes, p. 261–275. *In* R. C. Johnson (ed.), The biology of the parasitic spirochetes. Academic Press, Inc., New York.
36. **Loesche, W. J., and S. S. Socransky.** 1961. Defect in small millipore filters as disclosed by a new technique for isolating oral treponemes. Science **138:**134–149.
37. **Loesche, W. J., and S. A. Syed.** 1978. Bacteriology of human experimental gingivitis: effect of plaque and gingivitis score. Infect. Immun. **21:**830–839.
38. **Loesche, W. J., S. A. Syed, E. C. Morrison, B. Laughon, and N. S. Grossman.** 1981. Treatment of periodontal infections due to anaerobic bacteria with short-term treatment with metronidazole. Case reports of five patients. J. Clin. Periodontol. **8:**29–44.
39. **Mousques, T., M. A. Listgarten, and R. W. Phillips.** 1980. Effect of scaling and root planing on the composition of the human subgingival microbial flora. J. Periodontal Res. **15:**144–151.
40. **Newman, M. G., and S. S. Socransky.** 1977. Predominant cultivable microbiota in periodontosis. J. Periodontal Res. **12:**120–128.
41. **Nitzan, D., J. F. Sperry, and T. D. Wilkins.** 1978. Fibrinolytic activity of oral anaerobic bacteria. Arch. Oral Biol. **23:**465–470.
42. **Noguchi, H.** 1912. Cultural studies on mouth spirochaetae *(Treponema microdentium* and *macrodentium)* J. Exp. Med. **15:**81–89.
43. **Robrish, S. A., S. B. Grove, R. S. Bernstein, P. T. Marucha, S. S. Socransky, and B. Amdur.** 1976. Effect of sonic treatment on pure cultures and aggregates of bacteria. J. Clin. Microbiol. **3:**474–479.
44. **Rosebury, T.** 1962. Microorganisms indigenous to man. McGraw-Hill Book Co., Inc., New York.
45. **Rosebury, T., J. B. MacDonald, and A. R. Clark.** 1950. A bacteriologic survey of gingival scrapings from periodontal infections by direct examination, guinea pig inoculation, and anaerobic cultivation. J. Dent. Res. **29:**718–731.
46. **Schultz-Haudt, S. D., M. A. Bruce, and B. G. Bibby.** 1954. Bacterial factors in nonspecific gingivitis. J. Dent. Res. **33:**454–458.
47. **Shinn, D. L.** 1977. Vincent's disease and its treatment. *In* S. M. Finegold (ed.), Metronidazole. Excerpta Medica, New York.
48. **Slots, J.** 1979. Subgingival microflora and periodontal disease. J. Clin. Periodontol. **6:**351–382.
49. **Slots, J., H. S. Reynolds, and R. J. Genco.** 1980. *Actinobacillus actinomycetemcomitans* in human periodontal disease: a cross-sectional microbiological investigation. Infect. Immun. **29:**1013–1020.

50. **Smibert, R. M.** 1973. Spirochaetales, a review. Crit. Rev. Microbiol. **2**:491–552.
51. **Smibert, R. M.** 1974. The genus *Treponema*, p. 175–184. *In* R. E. Buchanan and N. E. Gibbons (ed.), Bergey's manual of determinative bacteriology, 8th ed. The Williams and Wilkins Co., Baltimore.
52. **Socransky, S. S., R. J. Gibbons, A. C. Bortnick, E. Rosenthal, and J. B. MacDonald.** 1963. The microbiota of the gingival crevice area of man. I. Total microscopic and viable counts and counts of specific organisms. Arch. Oral Biol. **8**:275–280.
53. **Socransky, S. S., and C. Hubersak.** 1967. Replacement of ascitic fluid or rabbit serum requirement of *Treponema dentium* by α-globulin. J. Bacteriol. **94**:1795–1796.
54. **Socransky, S. S., C. Hubersak, and D. Propas.** 1970. Induction of periodontal destruction in gnotobiotic rats by a human oral strain of *Actinomyces naeslundii*. Arch. Oral Biol. **15**:993–995.
55. **Socransky, S. S., W. J. Loesche, C. Hubersak, and J. B. MacDonald.** 1964. Dependency of *Treponema microdentium* on other oral organisms for isobutyrate, polyamines, and a controlled oxidation-reduction potential. J. Bacteriol. **88**:200–209.
56. **Socransky, S. S., M. Listgarten, C. Hubersak, J. Cotmore, and A. Clark.** 1969. Morphological and biochemical differentiation of three types of small oral spirochetes. J. Bacteriol. **98**:878–882.
57. **Tanner, A. C. R., C. Haffer, G. T. Bratthall, R. A. Visconti, and S. S. Socransky.** 1979. A study of the bacteria associated with advancing periodontitis in man. J. Clin. Periodontol. **6**:278–307.
58. **Theilade, E., W. H. Wright, S. B. Jensen, and H. Loe.** 1966. Experimental gingivitis in man. II. A longitudinal clinical and bacteriological investigation. J. Periodontal Res. **1**:1–13.
59. **van Palenstein-Helderman, W. H.** 1975. Total viable count and differential count of *Vibrio (Campylobacter) sputorum*, *Fusobacterium nucleatum*, *Selenomonas sputigena*, *Bacteroides ochraceus*, and *Veillonella* in the inflamed and healthy human gingival crevice. J. Periodontal Res. **10**:294–306.
60. **Waerhaug, J.** 1978. Healing of the dento-epithelial junction following subgingival plaque control. J. Periodontol. **49**:119–134.
61. **Ward, P. A., J. Chapitis, M. C. Conroy, and I. H. Lepow.** 1973. Generation by bacterial proteinases of leukotactic factors from human serum, and human C3 and C5. J. Immunol. **110**:1003–1009.
62. **Westergaard, J., A. Frandsen, and J. Slots.** 1978. Ultrastructure of the subgingival microflora in juvenile periodontitis. Scand. J. Dent. Res. **86**:421–429.

Physiological and Ecological Properties of the Oral Gram-Negative Gliding Bacteria Capable of Attaching to Hydroxyapatite

JACK LONDON, ROGER CELESK, AND PAUL KOLENBRANDER

Laboratory of Microbiology and Immunology, National Institute of Dental Research, National Institutes of Health, Bethesda, Maryland 20205, and Department of Biology, University of Dayton, Dayton, Ohio 45409

INTRODUCTION

A number of surveys have established that a significant fraction of the bacterial flora associated with periodontal plaque is composed of gram-negative microorganisms (8, 16, 18, 19, 21). More recently, concerted efforts to cultivate, identify, and ultimately determine the pathogenic potential of these organisms have led to a better understanding of the ecology of this complex habitat. During a survey of the periodontal plaque flora, we isolated a group of flexuous gram-negative gliding bacteria whose members resemble the nonfruiting members of the *Myxobacteriales*. These isolates differ from representatives of the recently created genus *Capnocytophaga* (10, 20) in that they do not exhibit a strictly fermentative metabolism or an absolute requirement for CO_2 when grown in complex (5) or defined media (Eagles, BBL Microbiology Systems). Thus, they have been designated *Cytophaga* sp. until they are assigned species epithets. This paper summarizes a series of published and unpublished investigations, the purpose of which was to characterize these organisms nutritionally and biochemically and to define those properties which permit their integration into and survival in a highly specialized and densely populated environment.

METABOLIC PROPERTIES

Nutrition. Twenty-one strains of gliding bacteria were isolated from dispersed periodontal plaque samples obtained by Paul Keyes and cultured on either freshly prepared Columbia blood agar plates (BBL) or modified Schaedler agar supplemented with 5% (vol/vol) defibrinated horse blood. Modified Schaedler agar contains, per liter: Trypticase (BBL), 5.68 g; proteose peptone no. 3, 1 g; polypeptone, 5 g; yeast extract, 5 g; NaCl, 1.7 g; K_2HPO_4, 1.5 g; KH_2PO_4, 1 g; L-cysteine HCl, 0.52 g; hemin, 10 mg; dextrose, 2.5 g; pH to 6.9. Because the periodontal plaque flora is predominantly anaerobic or facultatively anaerobic, the blood agar plates were incubated in GasPaks (BBL) under an atmosphere of H_2/CO_2 at 37°C. On freshly prepared blood agar plates (moist) or plates containing less than 1.5% agar, these flexuous bacteria produced spreading colonies that were distinct from colonies formed by other microorganisms found in the plaque samples (Fig. 1A). If older media were used, a smooth refractile colony was produced (Fig. 1B). Isolates were cloned and maintained in screw-cap tubes containing 10 ml of Schaedler broth. It was subsequently found that neither a CO_2-laden atmosphere nor anaerobiosis was essential for growth, and thereafter static cultures were incubated in air at 37°C with weekly or bimonthly transfer. Essentially, all strains grew at the expense of glucose,

76

mannose, sucrose, and maltose. Sixty percent also utilized fructose, and between 30 and 50% grew on raffinose, lactose, dextrin, or starch. Several strains could also utilize one or more of the following carbohydrates: galactose, salicin, trehalose, inulin, and cellobiose. Anaerobically, these carbohydrates were fermented to acid end products, the pH of the medium being lowered from 7.1 to 5.2 when substrate was added to a final concentration of 20 to 30 mM.

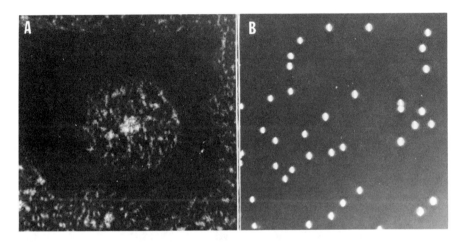

FIG. 1. *Differences in colonial morphology of* Cytophaga *sp. strain DR2002 produced by the presence or absence of gliding motility. (A) Diffuse or spreading colony produced by expression of motility on a freshly prepared Columbia blood agar plate. (B) Compact, refractile colonies formed on a 4-week-old (dry) Columbia blood agar plate where motility is not expressed.*

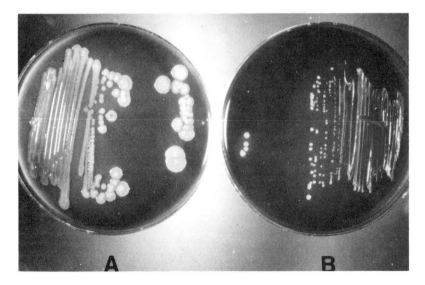

FIG. 2. *Enhancement of colony size of* Cytophaga *sp. strain DR2001 by growth in air. (A) Schaedler blood agar plate incubated in air; (B) Schaedler blood agar plate incubated in an H_2/CO_2 atmosphere.*

TABLE 1. *Metabolic alterations produced by the transition from anaerobic growth to aerobic growth of the oral* Cytophaga *species*

Organism	Gas phase	Growth yield[a]	Final pH	End products[b]		Tricarboxylic acid cycle enzymes[c]			
				Succinate	Acetate	Isocitrate DH	α-Ketoglutarate DH	Succinic DH	Malate DH
Cytophaga sp. DR2001	H₂/CO₂ Air	12.2 24	5.5 7.4	11.1 0	5.6 6.5	0.29 0.66	0.024 0.20	2.2 4.9	79 39
Cytophaga sp. DR2002	H₂/CO₂ Air	14 35	5.3 7.0	15 3.2	4.2 4.1	0.96 1.41	0.04 0.48	3.4 5.0	62 65

[a]Reported as milligrams of cells (dry weight) per mole of glucose.
[b]Reported as millimoles of end products formed per mole of glucose.
[c]Specific activities reported as micromoles of substrate oxidized per minute per milligram of protein. DH, dehydrogenase.

Metabolic alterations resulting from aerobic growth. *Cytophaga* sp. strains DR2001, DR2002, and DR2021 were adapted to aerobic growth by transferring the respective organisms from a static culture to a flask containing a shallow layer (2 to 3 mm) of Schaedler broth supplemented with 20 mM glucose. After 24 h of incubation at 37°C, a few drops of flask culture were used to inoculate similar flasks that were gently rocked or shaken. If these cultures were streaked onto duplicate Schaedler blood agar plates and were incubated in either H_2/CO_2 or air, the colonies produced under the latter conditions were significantly larger after 5 days of growth at 37°C (Fig. 2). This observation prompted a quantitative comparison of the metabolic differences between aerobic and anaerobic growth. Aerobically and anaerobically grown liquid cultures were compared after 48 h of growth at 37°C for total cell yield, final pH, end products, and levels of tricarboxylic acid cycle enzymes. The results are summarized in Table 1. Anaerobic growth was characterized by a production of succinic acid from glucose and a sharp decrease in pH of the culture medium. Aerobic growth resulted in a significantly greater final cell yield, an increase in pH, and a reduction or complete absence of the fermentation product, succinic acid. The levels of isocitrate dehydrogenase, succinic dehydrogenase, and malate dehydrogenase were not signally affected during the transition from anaerobic to aerobic growth. However, α-ketoglutarate dehydrogenase levels rose almost 10-fold when the organisms were grown in air. The cultural and metabolic changes that occurred when *Cytophaga* strains DR2001 and DR2002 underwent a shift from anaerobic to aerobic growth are consonant with a change from a fermentative to a respirational metabolism. The demonstration of cytochrome (unpublished data) in these isolates lends additional credence to the notion that the oral *Cytophaga* strains are capable of synthesizing a functional respiratory system under the appropriate conditions of growth.

ECOLOGICAL CONSIDERATIONS

Colonization of the tooth root surfaces. An in vitro plaque assay (12) showed that freshly isolated cultures of *Cytophaga* sp., strains DR2001, DR2002, and DR2021, were capable of colonizing the surface of intact tooth roots (4). These bacteria were shown to preferentially colonize the cementum surface of cleaned and sterilized teeth that had been suspended in Schaedler broth

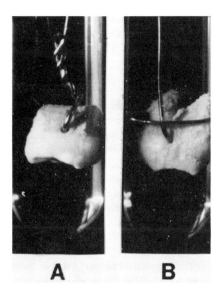

FIG. 3. *In vitro deposition of plaque on the cementum surface of the tooth root by (A) Cytophaga sp. strain DR2001 and (B) Cytophaga sp. strain DR2002.*

supplemented with either 15 mM sucrose or 25 mM glucose (Fig. 3). A heavy amber-colored plaque deposit which differed chemically from plaque produced by *Streptococcus mutans* began to accumulate after 3 to 4 days of incubation. In contrast to the *S. mutans* plaque, endodextranase did not disperse the *Cytophaga* sp. plaque deposit. The production of succinic acid by bacteria immobilized within the plaque deposit was most likely responsible for the extensive demineralization of the underlying cementum matrix.

Adherence to hydroxyapatite-containing surfaces. Continuous cultivation of the three strains in laboratory media produced variants that had lost the ability to effectively form plaque deposits on root surfaces. They did, however, retain the ability to attach firmly to shards of human tooth enamel and produce microcolonies (Fig. 4). The adherent properties of the *Cytophaga* sp. isolates were studied by using mechanically powdered root material, hydrazine (deproteinized)-treated root powder, and spheroidal hydroxyapatite beads (SHA) (4) as model systems. Plotting the ratio of unbound cells (C) to bound cells (Q) against unbound cells produced a linear function which fulfilled the requirements of the Langmuir isotherm equation [$C/Q = 1/KN + C/N$ (7)]. From the equation the maximum number of binding sites (N) and the affinity constants (K_a) were calculated for the adsorption of *Cytophaga* sp. strains DR2001 and DR2002 to their respective substrates.

FIG. 4. *Section of a microcolony of Cytophaga sp. strain DR2002 on a piece of human enamel produced in vitro after 48 h of incubation in Schaedler broth. Note the hydroxyapatite spicules below the colony. Bar = 1 μm.*

Values of approximately 1.3×10^7 (cells per mg of SHA) and 1.5×10^{-9} (ml per cell) were obtained for N and K_a, respectively, for both *Cytophaga* strains with SHA as a substrate (Table 2). Experiments with hydrazine-treated root powder yielded N and K_a values that were essentially identical to those with SHA. However, using native root powder as a substrate resulted in N values that were roughly one-half those observed with SHA, whereas the K_a values remained unchanged. This latter observation suggests that the protein matrix of the tooth root is not as effective a substrate as hydroxyapatite. Table 2 shows that a unit weight of SHA contains roughly the same number of binding sites for *Cytophaga* sp. as it does for *Actinomyces viscosus* and *Streptococcus sanguis*; these numbers are higher than that observed with *S. salivarius*. Coating the surface of the substrate with saliva reduced the number of binding sites for the gram-negative bacteria, whereas it increased both the number of sites *(N)* and the affinity *(K_a)* for the two latter organisms. Although the number of binding sites for the *Cytophaga* strains was reduced by saliva treatment, the affinity between bacteria and substrate was increased. This property distinguishes the gliding bacteria from *A. naeslundii* and *S. salivarius,* both of which exhibited lower N and K_a values when tested with saliva-coated SHA (6). Among the few representatives of oral gram-negative bacteria tested for their ability to adhere to hydroxyapatite, the *Cytophaga* sp. strains appear to be the only group capable of effectively binding to this substrate. Cells of *Bacteroides melaninogenicus* (16) and *Capnocytophaga ochracea* (2) bound to SHA in numbers that were 50- to 100-fold lower than the control organism, *S. sanguis.* A more extensive survey is needed to discover whether the oral *Cytophaga* strains are unique in their ability to bind to hard surfaces of the exposed periodontium.

The surfaces of the *Cytophaga* sp. cells are covered with tubular and spherical vesicles (Fig. 5) that are shed in copious quantities during growth. These structures were isolated free from contaminating intact cells to determine whether they carried receptor sites for the SHA. Preincubation of the root powder or SHA with vesicle preparations prevented *Cytophaga* sp. cells from attaching to either substrate. The interaction between vesicles and substrate was strong enough to withstand vigorous and extensive washing. Purified outer

TABLE 2. *Comparison of the parameters defining the adsorption of certain oral bacteria to hydroxyapatite*

Organism	Untreated surfaces		Saliva-coated surfaces		Reference
	No. of binding sites $(N)^a$	Affinity constant $(K_a)^b$	No. of binding sites (N)	Affinity constant (K_a)	
A. viscosus	6.0×10^5	2.0×10^{-7}	8.2×10^5	1.0×10^{-7}	22
	1.8×10^6	9.7×10^{-8}	4.5×10^6	12.5×10^{-8}	6
A. naeslundii	2.9×10^6	48×10^{-8}	1.6×10^6	9.0×10^{-8}	6
S. sanguis	2.0×10^6	3.5×10^{-8}	4.5×10^6	12×10^{-8}	6
S. mitis	1.1×10^6	87×10^{-8}	2.4×10^6	26×10^{-8}	6
S. salivarius	6.0×10^5	65×10^{-8}	1.3×10^5	3.0×10^{-8}	6
Cytophaga sp. DR2001 ..	1.4×10^7	17×10^{-8}	8.6×10^6	37×10^{-8}	5
Cytophaga sp. DR2002 ..	1.2×10^7	15×10^{-8}	2.6×10^6	20×10^{-8}	5

$^a N$ = number of binding sites per milligram of substrate as calculated from the Langmuir isotherm equation.

$^b K_a$ = affinity constant reported as milliliters per cell as calculated from the Langmuir isotherm equation.

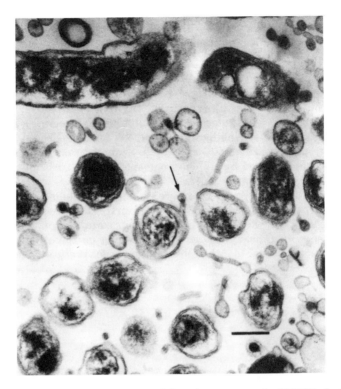

FIG. 5. *Negatively stained preparation of* Cytophaga *sp. strain DR2002 depicting the extensive network of vesicles associated with the cell's outer membrane. Bar = 1 μm. Arrow indicates attached vesicle.*

membrane components such as lipopolysaccharide or endotoxin were also effective in preventing attachment.

Altering the outer membrane of intact bacteria with various enzyme or heat treatments affected the cells' ability to bind to SHA. For example, if cell suspensions were heated at 100°C for 15 min, the adsorptive capacity of the cells was reduced by 50%. Incubating cell suspensions in the presence of 0.1 M ethylenediaminetetraacetic acid, neuraminidase, pronase, or phospholipase A_2 for various periods of time up to 6 h had no effect on their ability to adhere to SHA. In contrast, proteinase K, phospholipase C, and phospholipase D reduced the cells' ability to attach to SHA by at least 50%. It appeared, therefore, that the specific proteins and phospholipids or phospholipoproteins are associated with adherence. Whether the three enzymes affected the same receptor sites is not yet known. It is noteworthy that only those phospholipases that catalyze the hydrolysis of the lipid polar "head groups" (C and D), such as serine, choline, or ethanolamine, effectively reduced the organisms' ability to adsorb to hydroxyapatite. The loss of the positively charged molecule could reduce the ionic interactions between positively charged membrane components and the negatively charged phosphate groups in phosphate-rich regions of hydroxyapatite. It should be recognized, however, that the actions of proteinase K and the phospholipases may not be affecting specific receptor sites at all, but may instead be causing regional conformational changes that produce a blocking or masking of the receptors.

MICROBIAL INTERACTIONS

Those microorganisms capable of participating in the formation of stable heterogeneous aggregates in natural environments often confer upon themselves selective advantages not available to the general population. Two notable benefits are the ability (i) to adhere to and subsequently colonize surfaces in specialized habitats and (ii) to synergistically share nutrients or metabolites not provided by the environment. Several such interactions have already been demonstrated between oral gram-positive and gram-negative bacteria (3, 4). With special reference to the oral gliding bacteria, it was reported recently (P. Kolenbrander and S. Hurst-Calderone, Int. Assoc. Dent. Res. Proc. J. Dent. Res. **60**:333, 1981) that certain strains of *A. israelii* coaggregated with *Capnocytophaga* sp. Depending on the strain of *A. israelii* used, the coaggregation, like that observed between *A. viscosus* and *S. sanguis*,

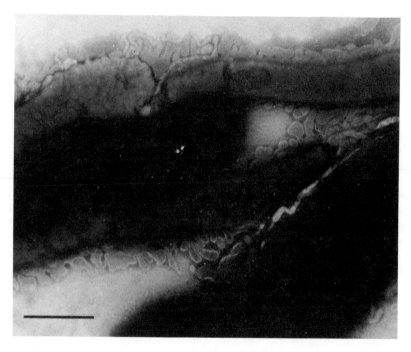

FIG. 6. *Negatively stained coaggregate containing* Cytophaga *sp. strain DR2002 (lighter cells) and* Actinomyces israelii *ATCC 23860 (darkly stained cells).*

was reversed by the addition of lactose. *Cytophaga* sp. strains DR2001 and DR2002 were tested for their ability to coaggregate with over 50 strains of *A. viscosus* or *A. naeslundii* and 5 strains of *A. israelii* (P. Kolenbrander and R. Celesk, unpublished data). Strain DR2001 failed to aggregate with any of the actinomycetes tested, whereas DR2002 formed aggregates with *A. israelii* strains ATCC 23860 and CROB2051. In neither case was the reaction reversed by lactose, and the heat-sensitive partner of the pair was the *Cytophaga* sp. Electron microscopy revealed that the association of the two organisms in the aggregate involved intimate cell-to-cell contact (Fig. 6). Neither strain appeared to aggregate with strains of *S. sanguis*.

ANIMAL STUDIES

To determine whether the oral *Cytophaga* isolates were capable of producing the symptomatology usually associated with periodontal disease, we performed studies with monoinfected germfree rats in collaboration with Robert Fitzgerald and Paul Keyes. Nineteen-day-old Sprague-Dawley rats maintained on Diet 2000 were infected with strain DR2001, strain DR2002, or the combination of strain DR2002 and *S. sanguis* strain F90A. Strain DR2002 persisted in the oral cavity of all the rats tested for 60 days and could be recovered from oral swabs in significant numbers, whereas strain DR2001 appeared to be lost rapidly over a 30-day period. Coimplantation with *S. sanguis* permitted higher numbers of strain DR2002 to be recovered from the oral cavity and feces of all test animals, when compared with the monoinfected animals described above. Examination of the hard tissue of the rat heads revealed that no bone loss had occurred, and the gingivae showed no pocketing or tissue destruction. It appears, therefore, that if the *Cytophaga* species studied here possess any special pathogenic potential, it is not expressed in the absence of the complex microflora that normally produces or inhabits the periodontal pocket. The studies contrast with those of Irving et al. (9), in which *Capnocytophaga sputigena* (strain 4) produced significant bone loss when implanted in germfree rats.

SUMMARY

The non-carbon dioxide-requiring oral gliding bacteria represent the first group of gram-negative bacteria capable of attaching to hydroxyapatite with the same efficiency as *S. sanguis* and *A. viscosus*. Experiments performed in vitro have demonstrated that these bacteria colonize the cementum surface of the tooth root in a fashion mechanically different from that of *S. mutans* (5). Experiments using an SHA model system have shown that the attachment of *Cytophaga* sp. to hydroxyapatite is inhibited by pretreatment of the substrate with saliva or human serum. In this respect, these gram-negative bacteria resemble *S. salivarius* and *A. naeslundii* (6). However, coating substrates with excess amounts of either fluid only reduces the extent of attachment and has no apparent effect on the affinity with which these organisms attach to hydroxyapatite-containing substrates (5). Thus, the *Cytophaga* sp. may still be able to adhere to cementum root surfaces bathed in crevicular fluid and subsequently colonize this area in vivo. The attachment of gram-negative bacteria such as these to root surfaces may account for the detection of tightly bound endotoxin-like molecules on the cementum surfaces of teeth extracted from patients with periodontal disease (1). Localized endotoxin depositions probably contribute to the chronic inflammatory response associated with the physical manifestations of periodontal disease (14).

The ability of *A. israelii* to coaggregate with the gram-negative gliding bacteria adds a new dimension to the ecology of plaque deposits in the periodontal pocket. Descriptions of highly specific interactions between diverse members of the oral microflora are appearing in the literature with a greater frequency, and these have been summarized in detail in this volume by John Cisar. Such studies are just beginning to provide a molecular basis for the ordered structure of plaque deposits that have been observed and described by electron microscopists (11, 12). Both the *Cytophaga* sp. and *A. israelii* (unpublished data) attach to hydroxyapatite surfaces; however, the order in which the two organisms might aggregate in vivo is not yet certain. The sequence can be established experimentally in future studies. It is clear, however, that the potential for these two bacterial species to aggregate and colonize the cementum surfaces adjacent to the periodontal pocket exists. Critical studies of the receptor sites on either organism will be necessary to establish the biochemical nature of the interaction and to ascertain whether *Cytophaga* sp. and *A. israelii* actually do form microcolonies in periodontal plaque.

LITERATURE CITED

1. **Aleo, J. J., F. A. DeRenzis, P. O. Farber, and A. P. Varboncoreur.** 1974. The presence of biologic activity of cementum-bound endotoxin. J. Periodontol. **45:**672–674.
2. **Appelbaum, B., E. Golub, S. C. Holt, and B. Rosan.** 1979. In vitro studies of dental plaque formation: adsorption of oral streptococci to hydroxyapatite. Infect. Immun. **25:**717–728.
3. **Bladen, H., G. Hageage, F. Pollack, and R. Harr.** 1970. Plaque formation *in vitro* on wires by Gram negative oral microorganisms (Veillonella). Arch. Oral Biol. **15:**127–133.
4. **Celesk, R. A., and J. London.** 1980. Attachment of oral *Cytophaga* species to hydroxyapatite-containing surfaces. Infect. Immun. **29:**768–777.
5. **Celesk, R. A., R. M. McCabe, and J. London.** 1979. Colonization of the cementum surface of teeth by oral gram-negative bacteria. Infect. Immun. **26:**15–18.
6. **Clark, W. B., L. L. Bammann, and R. J. Gibbons.** 1978. Comparative estimates of bacterial affinities and adsorption sites on hydroxyapatite surfaces. Infect. Immun. **19:**846–853.
7. **Gibbons, R. J., E. C. Moreno, and D. M. Spinell.** 1976. Model delineating the effects of a salivary pellicle on the adsorption of *Streptococcus miteor* onto hydroxyapatite. Infect. Immun. **14:**1109–1112.
8. **Gibbons, R., S. S. Socransky, S. Sawyer, B. Kapsimalis, and J. B. McDonald.** 1968. The microbiota of the gingival crevice area of man. II. The predominant cultivable organisms. Arch. Oral Biol. **8:**281–289.
9. **Irving, J. T., S. S. Socransky, and A. C. R. Tanner.** 1978. Histological changes in experimental periodontal disease with rats monoinfected with Gram negative organisms. J. Periodontal Res. **13:**326–332.
10. **Leadbetter, E. R., S. C. Holt, and S. S. Socransky.** 1979. *Capnocytophaga;* new genus of Gram negative gliding bacteria. I. General characteristics, taxonomic considerations and significance. Arch. Microbiol. **122:**9–16.
11. **Listgarten, M. A.** 1976. Structure of the microbial flora associated with periodontal health and disease in man. J. Periodontol. **47:**1–18.
12. **Listgarten, M. A., H. E. Mayo, and R. Tremblay.** 1975. Development of dental plaque on epoxy resin crowns in man. A light and electron microscopic study. J. Periodontol. **46:**10–26.
13. **McCabe, R. M., P. H. Keyes, and A. Howell, Jr.** 1967. An *in vitro* method of assessing the plaque forming ability of oral bacteria. Arch. Oral Biol. **12:**1653–1656.
14. **Mergenhagen, S. E., D. L. Rosenstreich, M. Wilton, S. M. Wahl, and L. M. Wahl.** 1976. Interaction of endotoxin with lymphocytes and macrophages. *In* R. F. Beers, Jr., and E. G. Basset (ed.), The role of immunological factors in infectious allergic and autoimmune processes. Raven Press, New York.
15. **Mouton, C., H. S. Reynolds, E. A. Gasiecki, and R. Genco.** 1979. *In vitro* adhesion of tufted oral streptococci to *Bacterionema matruchotii*. Curr. Microbiol. **3:**181–186.
16. **Slots, J.** 1979. Subgingival microflora and periodontal disease. J. Clin. Periodontol. **6:**351–382.
17. **Slots, J., and R. J. Gibbons.** 1978. Attachment of *Bacteroides melaninogenicus* subsp. *assacharolyticus* to oral surfaces and its possible role in colonization of the mouth and of periodontal pockets. Infect. Immun. **19:**254–264.

18. **Socransky, S. S.** 1977. Microbiology of periodontal disease. Present status and future conditions. J. Periodontol. **48:**497–504.
19. **Socransky, S. S., R. J. Gibbons, A. C. Dale, L. Bortnick, E. Rosenthal, and J. B. McDonald.** 1963. The microbiota of the gingival crevice of man. I. Total microscopic and viable counts of specific organisms. Arch. Oral Biol. **8:**275–280.
20. **Socransky, S. S., S. C. Holt, E. R. Leadbetter, A. C. R. Tanner, E. Savitt, and B. F. Hammond.** 1979. *Capnocytophaga:* new genus of Gram negative gliding bacteria. III. Physiological characterization. Arch. Microbiol. **122:**29–33.
21. **Tanner, A. C. R., C. Haffer, G. T. Brathall, R. A. Visconti, and S. S. Socransky.** 1979. A study of the bacteria associated with advancing periodontitis in man. J. Clin. Periodontol. **6:**278–307.
22. **Wheeler, T. T., W. B. Clark, and D. C. Birdsell.** 1979. Adherence of *Actinomyces viscosus* T14V and T14AV to hydroxyapatite surfaces in vitro and human teeth in vivo. Infect. Immun. **25:**1066–1074.

Colonization Mechanisms Involved in the Development of the Oral Flora

JOHANNES van HOUTE

Forsyth Dental Center, Boston, Massachusetts 02115

INTRODUCTION

Interactions between bacteria and the human host leading to the development and maintenance of a characteristic oral flora have received a great deal of attention in recent years. This is due mainly to the recognition of the bacterial etiology of dental caries and periodontal disease and the prospect of exploiting knowledge of the ecology of causative bacterial agents to prevent or cure these infectious diseases.

The following discussion will deal only with certain aspects of oral bacterial ecology. Furthermore, only an outline of some current concepts will be given; a more in-depth analysis of many details of the material discussed, as well as other aspects of the topic, can be found in numerous recent reviews (7, 9–11, 23, 24, 34, 38–40) and elsewhere in this volume.

Major intraoral colonization factors. Cellular adherence and growth are the two major parameters which govern the formation of bacterial masses on teeth (dental plaques) and bacterial colonization on the oral mucosal surfaces. The fundamental importance of the process of bacterial adherence for the colonization of oral bacteria was not realized until the early 1970s and evolved from studies of plaque formation by *Streptococcus mutans*. It is now clearly recognized that in an open system such as the mouth bacterial colonization requires first that cells become sufficiently attached to the tissues so that they can withstand the powerful prevailing cleansing forces; next, of course, attached bacteria should be able to proliferate.

Adherence as a bacterial ecological determinant. In vitro and in vivo studies of the attachment of oral bacteria to various oral surfaces have firmly established the importance of adherence per se as an ecological determinant (7, 9–11, 38, 39). Oral bacteria vary widely in their ability to attach to oral surfaces. The relative adherence of a number of bacterial species has been found to correlate positively with their natural intraoral distribution. Clearly, the extent to which an organism can attach to a particular surface will influence the extent to which it can colonize. This influence may vary depending on the type of surface. Thus, vestibular or palatinal mucosal surfaces are sparsely populated by bacteria and few epithelial cells have regions with confluent bacterial layers; continuous cell desquamation appears to prevent large bacterial accumulations by reducing the time during which cell proliferation can occur. Consequently, the proportions of different organisms on these mucosal surfaces probably reflect largely their innate ability to attach to the surface as well as their cell numbers in saliva or on contacting oral surfaces which are available for attachment.

86

Tooth surfaces, on the other hand, are often covered by thick bacterial accumulations. Initially adhering organisms, once firmly attached, may persist for long periods; as a result, changes in the proportions of different organisms may occur over time as a result of differences in individual growth rate.

Acquisition of oral bacteria. Although a large variety of organisms will enter the mouth after birth, only certain types will become part of the indigenous oral flora. Many indigenous oral bacteria do not appear to be free living in nature and are not found in foods or on other human tissues. This suggests that they originate from the mouths of other people; not surprisingly, family members, because they ordinarily have the most intensive contact with the infant, have especially been implicated (38). For example, no important habitats or sources of *S. mutans* other than humans have been found; the mouth appears to be its natural habitat. Tracing of the organism via bacteriocin typing suggests that the mother is frequently the source of infection. A mother–child link has also been suggested by studies demonstrating that *S. mutans* is much more frequently detectable in infants with a developing dentition who have mothers with a high oral *S. mutans* level than in infants who have mothers with negligible levels (1); a positive correlation between the *S. mutans* levels of young school children and their mothers (but not their fathers) has also been found (41).

The acquisition of oral bacteria from the outer environment after birth, as indicated above, is a highly selective process; organisms such as *Escherichia coli,* characteristic of the intestinal flora, are only transient oral contaminants (34). Furthermore, many of the different indigenous bacterial species in the mouth have a clear preference for certain locations (10, 39). For example, *S. mutans, S. sanguis,* and *Actinomyces viscosus* preferentially colonize the teeth, lactobacilli are mainly found in caries lesions, and *S. salivarius* and *A. naeslundii* colonize especially the dorsum of the tongue, whereas many gram-negative organisms and spirochetes are virtually exclusively found in the gingival crevice. Generally, bacteria are known to exhibit distinct host as well as tissue tropisms resulting in many different microcosms, each with a characteristic microflora, in different hosts or on different host tissues. Bacteria in such a microcosm appear particularly skilled in colonizing the tissue of their preference, presumably as a result of favorable adaptive changes in their cell surface receptors involved in adherence or in their growth characteristics.

FACTORS INFLUENCING THE ACQUISITION OF ORAL BACTERIA AND DENTAL PLAQUE FORMATION

A number of factors which affect either the adherence or the growth of bacteria are presently considered to play a role in the establishment of bacteria in the mouth of the infant, in the intraoral distribution of indigenous bacteria, in the formation of supra- and subgingival plaque, or in the colonization of the oral mucosal surfaces. These include the ability of the bacterial cell to attach to oral surfaces, the number of bacterial cells available for attachment, the retentiveness of the oral surfaces, saliva (flow rate, antibody, mucinous and other glycoproteins, lysozyme, lactoperoxidase, lactoferrin), gingival fluid, oxidation–reduction potential, diet, and host bacterial flora (competition for binding sites, bacteriocins, influence on pH) (9–11, 23, 24, 30, 34, 39). Most of these can be discussed in relation to the initial intraoral establishment of bacteria or the process of plaque formation.

Acquisition of oral bacteria. Findings from a variety of studies indicate that different species of oral bacteria do not all appear simultaneously in the infant's mouth. Many anaerobic bacteria do not implant until after tooth eruption, and in adults many species are virtually exclusively associated with the gingival crevice (10, 34). It seems reasonable to assume that their presence there is made possible by the low oxidation–reduction potential that prevails.

The emergence of teeth also appears to be required for the establishment of facultative organisms such as *S. sanguis, S. mutans, A. viscosus,* and lactobacilli; organisms such as *S. salivarius* and *A. naeslundii* appear prior to tooth eruption (10, 39). Extraction of teeth leads to the disappearance of *S. sanguis, S. mutans,* and lactobacilli, but does not affect *S. salivarius.* This pattern is consistent with the preferential intraoral habitat of these organisms. Studies of these organisms suggest that their predilection for oral surfaces is directly related to their relative ability to attach to the surfaces (10, 31, 39).

Lactobacilli constitute a somewhat special case since they predominate in caries lesions but are only infrequently isolated in appreciable numbers from sound tooth surfaces; filling of cavities leads to their disappearance from the mouth in many cases (40). Their localization may be due to their low ability to attach to teeth coupled with their highly acid-tolerant character (40). The lactobacilli in the lesions would be relatively well protected from the oral cleansing forces and would have a selective growth advantage over many less acid-tolerant plaque organisms under the highly acidic conditions that frequently prevail in the lesions.

Various studies also suggest that even those bacterial species whose colonization is uniquely associated with tooth eruption vary widely with respect to the onset of their intraoral establishment. Quantitative implantation of *S. sanguis* apparently precedes that of *S. mutans,* whereas *Bacteroides melaninogenicus* and spirochetes are not consistently isolated from most people until late adolescence or adulthood (38). In the case of the streptococci it has been found that, as a general rule, *S. sanguis* has a relatively greater ability to attach to the teeth and some mucosal surfaces that does *S. mutans* (10). This difference likely accounts for the generally localized colonization of *S. mutans* on the tooth surface and the more ubiquitous distribution on the teeth of *S. sanguis,* which results in generally much higher salivary concentrations of *S. sanguis* (10). If infants do indeed become infected via contact with the saliva of other humans, the earlier appearance of *S. sanguis* on the infant's teeth could be due to its greater ability to attach to the tooth surface coupled with its presence in high numbers in the donor's saliva. The importance of the latter factor is supported by the above-mentioned study in which the detection of *S. mutans* on the teeth of infants was found to be directly related to its concentration in the saliva of their mothers (1).

The low numbers of *B. melaninogenicus* cells and spirochetes in many gingival crevice areas even of adults suggest that these organisms are much less talented oral colonizers than many other indigenous organisms. The availability of nutrients such as hemin or vitamin K in the gingival crevice area (34), a nutritional effect of sex hormones (K. S. Kornman and W. J. Loesche, Int. Assoc. Dent. Res. Prepr. Abstr., 57th Gen. Meet. 1979, abstr. 58), or the presence of

Actinomyces and certain gram-positive organisms in dental plaque to which *B. melaninogenicus* may attach (11) have all been speculated to be of significance for subgingival colonization by this organism.

A question of interest is whether odontopathogens such as *S. mutans* or certain gram-negative organisms, implicated in the etiology of dental caries or periodontal diseases, can become established only early in life or can be acquired throughout life. Obviously, from a standpoint of acceptability of specific antibacterial therapy as a general measure, changes in the degree of host susceptibility or of natural contact between infected and uninfected individuals which would allow natural infection to occur only in the young or very young would be highly desirable.

Animal experiments suggest age-related changes in host susceptibility to infection by *S. mutans, A. viscosus,* and *Lactobacillus salivarius* (38), but the significance of the findings for the human situation is not clear. Studies of the infection by *S. mutans* of erupting teeth in children aged 6 or 12 to 14 years (38), the spread of this organism in the adult mouth from inserted devices to other teeth (38), and its implantation in the adult mouth after intraoral inoculation with high cell numbers (38) do not suggest an appreciable decrease in bacterial susceptibility with age or the impossibility of primary infection as an adult. However, data which would make possible a comparison with very young children are lacking. Likewise, the level of contact which is necessary for successful bacterial transfer between the infant and donors and the frequency of occurrence of this level of contact later in life are unknown; moreover, both will vary considerably from one situation to another. Direct evidence supporting regular natural transfer of oral bacteria between adults is unavailable. Tracing of *S. mutans* in families via bacteriocin typing (N. Masuda, T. Shimamoto, S. Sobue, and S. Hamada, Int. Assoc. Dent. Res. Prepr. Abstr., 58th Gen. Meet. 1980, abstr. 784) and the frequent finding that one parent is heavily infected with *S. mutans* whereas the organism is undetectable in the other (41) do not support this possibility.

Initiation of supragingival plaque formation. Studies of the initial phase of plaque formation on cleaned teeth have shown that bacteria adhere initially as well-separated cells or cell aggregates in areas prone to infection (11, 17). The latter include fissures, areas near the gingiva, or areas with imperfections (roughness, cracks) which are relatively sheltered from the oral cleansing forces. The presence of cell aggregates may be due to attachment of single cells or doublets followed by apposition of other such cells or by adherence of preformed cell aggregates. Limited aggregation of bacteria, for example via salivary mucinous glycoproteins or immunoglobulin A, may actually promote adherence, whereas adherence will be decreased when the aggregates are larger (18). Analysis of adsorption isotherms which permits differentiation between the number of binding sites on the surface of attachment and the strength of the adsorption bond (11) suggests that bacteria vary with respect to the aggregate sizes which enhance or limit their adherence.

The affinity of different bacteria for the tooth surface as influenced by the two above-mentioned parameters will determine whether they can adhere only in the most retentive, protected tooth surface areas or whether they can also attach and persist in less retentive areas; it will not only influence the degree of their localization but also the size of their populations on the teeth.

The types and numbers of different bacteria found initially on a tooth surface are also influenced by the number of cells available for attachment (39). Furthermore, in vivo studies of bacterial adherence suggest that the concentrations of bacteria in saliva need to exceed a certain threshold level before they can be detected on exposed tooth surfaces (39). In the case of *S. mutans* these concentrations have been estimated to be in the order of 10^3 and 10^4 colony-forming units per ml for fissures and less retentive tooth surfaces, respectively; the critical levels of other organisms can be higher or lower than these figures, depending on their affinity. Other studies suggest that most bacteria initially present on the surface are only loosely associated and that only a small proportion of the cells with which the oral surfaces come in contact become firmly attached (39).

The formation of dental plaque on the coronal tooth surfaces in principle involves two types of processes. The first entails initial adherence of organisms present in saliva or on contacting surfaces to the acquired pellicle which is generally present except for a short period after tooth eruption. The second involves bacterial accumulation via proliferation of attached cells and adherence of unattached cells to bacteria attached to the tooth surface.

The acquired pellicle is thought to form mainly by selective adsorption of different salivary glycoproteins; immunoglobulins A, G, and M, enzymes (e.g., lysozyme), blood group-reactive substance, or bacterial extracellular polysaccharides may also be present (11, 39).

Electron microscopic observations indicate that many oral bacteria possess a fibrillar coating or fimbriae on their cell surface; distinct differences exist with respect to the density, morphology, and location of the fimbriae of various organisms (12, 13, 16, 17, 28, 38). Electron microscopic studies also suggest that fimbriae are important mediators of bacterial attachment to the tooth surface or to oral epithelial surfaces. Oral bacteria also synthesize a variety of extracellular polysaccharides which may influence their attachment. In addition, salivary components such as high-molecular-weight mucinous glycoproteins, immunoglobulins, or lysozyme have been shown to induce aggregation of various oral bacteria (3, 5, 22, 39). Since bacterial attachment to the pellicle or plaque periphery involves bacteria suspended in saliva or present on contacting surfaces, it seems likely that cell-bound salivary components also influence this process.

Extracellular glucans (dextran, mutan) synthesized specifically from sucrose by *S. mutans* are known to play a role in the plaque-forming ability of this organism. The name *S. mutans* actually represents different organisms which are separable on the basis of the composition of their deoxyribonucleic acid, their serology, or biochemical (fermentation) reactions (11). At present, there is no conclusive evidence that glucan is essential for, or even enhances, the initial attachment of the most commonly present *S. mutans* types to the acquired pellicle (39). Some recent evidence suggests that their initial adherence involves in part lectin (carbohydrate-binding protein)-like cell surface receptors and exposed α-galactoside residues of salivary glycoprotein in the pellicle (8). As discussed below, glucans appear to be involved in the accumulation of *S. mutans* cells on the tooth surface. Extracellular glucans are also synthesized by other streptococci such as *S. sanguis*, *S. mitis*, and *S. salivarius*. However, these organisms generally lack the ability to bind these glucans to the extent that *S. mutans* does, and there is no evidence that glucans play a major role in promoting the binding of these organisms to the tooth surface (39).

Plaque bacteria are known to synthesize many other extracellular polysaccharides besides glucans. *S. mutans, S. salivarius,* and *A. viscosus* produce fructans from sucrose (39). In contrast to the relatively slowly degradable glucans, fructans can be hydrolyzed rapidly by plaque bacteria (26, 39). Evidence that these polysaccharides can enhance the initial adherence of the bacteria which produce them is lacking; rather, they may serve as readily available bacterial energy reserves. *A. viscosus* is also known to synthesize a heteropolysaccharide slime consisting of large amounts of N-acetylglucosamine and smaller amounts of glucose and galactose (39). However, various studies suggest that this polysaccharide may impair the organism's attachment to the pellicle by coating receptors on cell surface fibrils (39).

Bacterial interactions with salivary components appear to be very complex. Bacteria have been shown in vitro to adhere with varying efficiencies to hydroxyapatite (39). Treatment of apatite with saliva prior to the addition of bacteria to mimic a pellicle-coated tooth surface may increase or decrease their attachment depending on the strains tested; this influence may be in part attributed to immunoglobulin A (14, 19, 39).

In vitro studies have also shown that the adherence of various oral bacteria to saliva-coated hydroxyapatite is often impaired when cells are suspended in saliva instead of buffer (4, 39). Exposure of bacteria to high-molecular-weight mucinous salivary glycoproteins or immunoglobulin A can also inhibit their adherence to oral epithelial cells (39). Other in vitro studies indicate a similarity between the salivary components involved in bacterial aggregation and those present in the acquired pellicle; some salivary glycoproteins also appear to have bacterial binding sites in common with epithelial cells (36, 39).

Unattached bacteria are suspended in saliva in vivo and the in vitro findings therefore suggest that high-molecular-weight mucinous glycoproteins or immunogobulins which are bound to the bacterial cell surface may impair cellular adherence by blocking cell surface binding receptors or by cellular aggregation. Generalizations with respect to the impact of these interactions on the colonization of different species of oral bacteria appear difficult also because evidence indicates that differences among bacteria may be strain rather than species specific, that laboratory maintenance of test organisms can change their adherence, and that saliva from different people differs quantitatively and qualitatively with respect to adherence-associated components.

Accumulation of supragingival plaque. Adherence of bacteria in the initial phase of plaque formation on a cleaned tooth surface coupled with subsequent proliferation of attached cells in a lateral direction will eventually lead to a continuum of different bacterial cells, aggregates, and "colonies." Also, cell accumulation will lead to an increase in thickness of the bacterial layer, which can become hundreds of micrometers thick in sheltered tooth surface areas before its formation is limited by the oral cleansing forces. The increased cell density on the tooth surface will lead to adhesive interactions between bacteria of similar or dissimilar type which should be of sufficient strength to allow buildup of plaque; it will also lead to growth-enhancing or inhibitory influences of the bacteria upon one another.

Sucrose-mediated extracellular glucan synthesis by *S. mutans* appears to favor the organism's accumulation (11, 39). Intercellular binding via glucan molecules interacting with glucan-binding receptors on the cell surface as well as entrapment of cells in the glucan matrix surrounding the cells have been proposed as mechanisms (M. L. Freedman, J. M. Tanzer, and A. L. Coykendall, Symposium and workshop on animal models in cariology, 1980). Insoluble glucans rich in α-1,3 linkages (mutan) are thought to play a more important role in the accumulation of *S. mutans* cells than more soluble glucans rich in α-1,6 linkages (6, 11; Freedman et al., Symposium and workshop on animal models in cariology, 1980).

Some evidence suggests that extracellular glucans synthesized by *S. sanguis* and *S. salivarius* may favor the colonization of some strains of these species (39). However, these polysaccharides do not appear to have a generally favorable effect on the accumulation of these organisms as they do in the case of *S. mutans*. Dextrans isolated from *S. mutans* or *S. sanguis* can also bind to cells of certain *A. viscosus* strains, leading to their aggregation; *A. viscosus* is not known to synthesize glucans (39). *A. viscosus* cells can also coaggregate with sucrose-grown *S. mutans* or *S. sanguis* cells (39). However, these interactions may occur only with *A. viscosus* strains of animal but not of human origin. Some strains of lactobacilli are similar to *S. mutans* or *A. viscosus* in exhibiting dextran-induced aggregation, and it is known that some *Lactobacillus* sp. can synthesize dextran (39). However, concrete evidence concerning a role of glucan synthesis in the colonization of lactobacilli is lacking.

A variety of plaque bacteria can form plaques in vitro when incubated with sucrose and preparations of enzymes (glucosyltransferases) involved in the conversion of sucrose to glucan molecules (39). However, the binding of these enzymes to their cell surface is in most cases weak and they can be easily washed away; in the case of some strains, the enzymes can become strongly absorbed, and such strains are then capable of glucan synthesis and plaque formation. It is unclear whether this process is of significance in vivo and whether, for example, cells of other bacterial species adjacent to aggregates or colonies of *S. mutans* which are synthesizing glucans can become entrapped in them and be retained on the tooth surface.

A favorable effect of earlier-mentioned polysaccharides, other than extracellular glucans, on bacterial accumulation has not been established. Lipoteichoic acid has been proposed to play a major role in plaque formation by oral streptococci by increasing their negative charge; in the case of *S. mutans* lipoteichoic acid has been visualized to become entrapped in the synthesized glucans. The role of electrostatic forces and of lipoteichoic acid in bacterial attachment to and accumulation on teeth is a controversial subject and needs further clarification (2, 7, 11, 39).

As discussed earlier, salivary components, including high-molecular-weight mucins, immunoglobulins, or lysozyme, are known to bind to the surface of many plaque bacteria and to induce their aggregation. The interbacterial plaque matrix which is responsible for the structural integrity of plaque has also been shown to contain immunoglobulins and lysozyme and most likely also contains similar high-molecular-weight mucins (11, 39). Thus, such components may become bound to bacteria proliferating at the plaque periphery or can be carried on the tooth surface by unattached bacteria when these become attached. Both processes should therefore contribute to plaque matrix formation and bacterial accumulation.

In vitro studies which have demonstrated bacterial coaggregation of mixtures of oral bacteria as well as electron microscopic pictures of plaque indicate that interbacterial binding of similar or dissimilar organisms can also occur via direct cell-to-cell interactions instead of by binding via host products or bacterial extracellular polysaccharides (11, 39). Such interactions are well illustrated by the "corncob" structures, some of which appear to consist of a central filament identified as *Bacterionema matruchotii* covered by streptococci. It seems likely that these interactions contribute to bacterial accumulation and to the structural integrity of plaque.

Bacterial accumulation via proliferation of attached cells is probably supplemented to a varying extent by the attachment of bacteria to the plaque periphery. Electron microscopic studies of sections of plaque showing "columns" of similar bacteria extending from the inside of plaque toward its periphery suggest, however, that proliferation of attached bacteria rather than bacterial adherence is the major contributor to plaque mass (9).

There is evidence that the presence of plaque on the teeth may enhance or limit colonization by unattached bacteria. Studies with *S. mutans* have shown that it readily colonizes artificial Mylar fissures inserted in teeth in vivo when they are sterile but not when they are precolonized by indigenous bacteria; cleaning of teeth also promotes the persistence of artificially introduced cells as compared with plaque-covered teeth; also, rodents naturally infected with *S. mutans* generally resist infection by other subsequently introduced *S. mutans* strains, whereas prior inoculation of germfree rats with *A. viscosus* and *S. sanguis* may have the same effect (38). These observations may be partly a result of the fact that bacteria located on the outer surface of plaque are more easily removed by the cleansing forces than bacteria located deeper in plaque; moreover, plaque growth from within and away from the tooth surface will cause continuous loss of peripheral cells. Other contributing factors may include a lesser adherence of the cells to the plaque periphery or growth-inhibiting substances such as bacteriocins elaborated by peripheral plaque bacteria (32, 33, 37).

Various studies also suggest that the presence of plaque may favor the colonization of some bacteria. *B. melaninogenicus* subsp. *asaccharolyticus,* when suspended in buffer, attaches to saliva-treated hydroxyapatite and certain gram-positive bacteria; when suspended in saliva, significant attachment occurs only to the gram-positive bacteria (11). In vivo the organism attaches well to dental plaque but not to cleaned teeth or various mucosal surfaces (11). Thus, the organism's colonization in vivo may require the prior presence of a gram-positive flora on the teeth.

The close proximity of accumulating plaque organisms may also lead to interactions which affect bacterial growth. An increase in the thickness and age of plaque may lead to a proportional shift toward a more anaerobic flora. Bacteriocin production by certain plaque bacteria has been postulated to influence the distribution of different organisms within plaque (32, 33, 37). Considerable evidence indicates that changes in dietary carbohydrate also cause population shifts (40). A higher carbohydrate intake may lead to a selection of organisms such as *S. mutans,* lactobacilli, and yeasts. In the case of *S. mutans,* this effect may be partly related to the favorable effect of sucrose-mediated glucan synthesis; other factors could be the more frequent acidification of plaque which favors *S. mutans* because of its relatively high acid tolerance (35) or its dependence on readily fermentable dietary carbohydrates for optimal growth. Especially the second factor has been traditionally favored to explain the effect of dietary carbohydrate on the highly acid-tolerant lactobacilli. Plaque bacteria may also be stimulated in their growth by products of other bacteria. For example, acid end products such as lactate produced by a variety of bacteria can be utilized by *Veillonella* species which are unable to ferment simple carbohydrates or by *Neisseria* species (10).

Specificity of bacterial adherence to oral surfaces. Various observations indicate that the attachment of bacteria to oral surfaces occurs via a variety of different mechanisms. In hindsight, this not surprising in view of the marked differences in physical, chemical, and other characteristics of bacterial cell surfaces as well as oral surfaces. The remarkable degree of specificity which characterizes bacterial attachment is shown by competition studies indicating that different streptococci interact with different receptor sites on the pellicle (10, 15, 39). It is also suggested by experiments involving pretreatment of epithelial cells with particular antisera, which inhibits the adherence of one type of organism but not of another (39), by studies indicating that separate aggregating factors are present in saliva for different organisms which also differ in their affinity for the organisms as well as for hydroxyapatite (39), by studies of bacterial coaggregation which may occur with mixtures of only certain dissimilar organisms (39), and by studies which have shown that "corncobs" can be reproduced in vitro only with certain organisms (39), as well as by the difference in the distribution of cell surface-associated extracellar glucan-binding receptors among oral organisms (10, 39).

Bacteria therefore appear to possess a recognition system which can identify and react with specific surface components on oral surfaces, salivary components, or other bacteria. Recent studies suggest that lectin receptor-type interactions can be involved (39). As mentioned earlier, many oral bacteria possess fimbriae which are known to have lectin-like properties; the cell surface also possesses sugar-binding proteins as well as enzymes. The attachment of *S. mutans* to saliva-coated hyroxyapatite may, as noted earlier, involve α-galactoside residues of salivary glycoproteins in the pellicle (8). *S. mutans* and possibly also *A. viscosus* possess a dextran-binding lectin involved in dextran-induced agglutination (39). The attachment of *Leptotrichia buccalis* is strongly inhibited by lactose and *N*-acetyl-D-galactosamine, whereas raffinose, melibiose, D-galactose, and D-galactosamine appear less effective (39). The adherence of *A. naeslundii* to saliva-coated hydroxyapatite is inhibited by lactose, galactose, glucose, and sucrose (39). In addition, coaggregation between a strain of *A. viscosus* and a strain of *S. sanguis* can be inhibited by lactose, D-galactose, and β-methyl-D-galactoside but is little affected by α-methyl-D-galactoside, melibiose, or maltose; other evidence suggests that this coaggregation involves a lectin on the cell surface of *A. viscosus* and a carbohydrate on the *S. sanguis* cell surface (39). Lectin receptor-type interactions also appear to be involved in saliva-induced bacterial aggregation (25, 27, 39).

Studies of the attachment of oral bacteria also indicate that each may possess multiple binding receptors. *A. viscosus* and *A. naeslundii* aggregate in the presence of saliva and bind to saliva-coated hydroxyapatite; they also coaggregate with various organisms (39). *S. mutans* strains possess glucan-binding sites (glucosyltransferase(s) and nonenzyme protein), as well as receptors involved in adherence to saliva-coated hydroxyapatite (39). Possession of multiple instead of single binding sites should be expected to promote bacterial persistence and survival in a particular habitat by diminishing the influence of unfavorable cell surface changes due to mutation or other factors.

Formation of subgingival plaque. Bacterial accumulations in the gingival sulcus or pathologically deepened sulcus (pocket) associated with gingivitis, periodontitis, or periodontosis (juvenile periodontitis) appear to differ in structure and bacterial composition from supragingival plaque (20, 21). They frequently contain relatively more gram-negative organisms, which are located preferentially at the sulcus bottom in gingivitis or as a loosely adherent zone on top of a layer of gram-positive and gram-negative organisms which are attached to the root surface in periodontitis; the subgingival flora in periodontosis consists of more sparsely distributed, predominantly gram-negative organisms embedded in an amorphous matrix without an adherent zone of gram-positive bacteria.

The conditions under which subgingival plaque is formed are characterized by the presence of gingival fluid and little or no presence of saliva, relative protection from oral cleansing forces, unique growth conditions, e.g., special nutrients in gingival fluid, a low oxidation–reduction potential, the lack of a direct effect of diet, and a different tooth surface, i.e., cementum.

Subgingival plaques probably form predominantly by extension of supragingival plaques via growth along the tooth surface in an apical direction; the numerous motile organisms may gain entrance by active movement. In view of the unidirectional flow of gingival fluid and the slow rate at which the gingival sulcus deepens in periodontal disease, it seems likely that reattachment of dislodged bacterial cells in the gingival crevice to clean tooth surface areas located deeper contributes little to subgingival plaque formation. Nonmotile, gram-negative organisms may become attached to certain gram-positive organisms in supragingival plaque, as discussed earlier in the case of *B. melaninogenicus* (11), and, provided that they are located in an area near or in the sulcus with the proper growth conditions, may begin to flourish (29). A transitional flora consisting of gram-positive organisms characteristic for supragingival plaque and gram-negative organisms predominantly in subgingival plaque which separates both can generally be detected.

There is a paucity of information about the factors which influence the formation of the adherent plaque, how and how long motile and "loosely adherent" organisms persist, and many other aspects. Although gingival fluid should be expected to play a pivotal role, practical problems, e.g., obtaining sufficient quantities for studies, have prevented studies so far.

SUMMARY

Bacterial adherence and growth are discussed in relation to the acquisition, intraoral localization, and colonization of oral bacteria on the teeth and mucosal surfaces. The adherence of bacteria to oral surfaces is required for their successful colonization; it exhibits a high degree of specificity and may involve lectin-like interactions. Adherence and growth factors both play a role in the selective acquisition of oral bacteria as well as in their intraoral localization. Adherence probably exerts a relatively greater influence on the proportions in which different species colonize the continually shedding mucosal surfaces than on their proportions in supragingival plaques. Adhesive interactions in supragingival plaque formation may involve bacterial extracellular polymers, salivary components (e.g., high-molecular-weight glycoproteins, immuno-globulins), or direct cell-to-cell binding. Salivary components may supplement the mechanical cleansing activity of saliva by inhibiting bacterial adherence. Little is known about the factors which influence subgingival plaque formation.

LITERATURE CITED

1. **Berkowitz, R. J., J. Turner, and P. Green.** 1981. Maternal salivary levels of *Streptococcus mutans* and primary oral infection of infants. Arch. Oral Biol. **26**:147–149.
2. **Bolton, R. W.** 1980. Adherence of oral streptococci to hydroxyapatite *in vitro* via glycerol-teichoic acid. Arch. Oral Biol. **25**:111–114.
3. **Bratthall, D., and A. Carlen.** 1978. Salivary agglutinin and secretory IGA reactions with oral streptococci. Scand. J. Dent. Res. **86**:430–443.
4. **Celesk, R. A., and J. London.** 1980. Attachment of oral *Cytophaga* species to hydroxyapatite-containing surfaces. Infect. Immun. **29**:768–777.
5. **Everhart, D. L., M. Shreck, and N. Seltizer.** 1980. Salivary agglutinins tested against *Streptococcus mutans*. Caries Res. **14**:258–264.
6. **Freedman, M., D. Birkhed, and K. Granath.** 1978. Analyses of glucans from cariogenic and mutant *Streptococcus mutans*. Infect. Immun. **21**:17–27.
7. **Gibbons, R. J.** 1979. On the mechanisms of bacterial attachment to teeth, p. 267–273. *In* Kleinberg, Ellison, and Mandel (ed.), Proceedings: Saliva and Dental Caries (a special supplement to Microbiology Abstracts). Information Retrieval Inc., Washington, D.C.
8. **Gibbons, R. J., and J. V. Qureshi.** 1979. Inhibition of adsorption of *Streptococcus mutans* strains to saliva-treated hydroxyapatite by galactose and certain amines. Infect. Immun. **26**:1214–1217.
9. **Gibbons, R. J., and J. van Houte.** 1973. On the formation of dental plaques. J. Periodontol. **44**:347–360.
10. **Gibbons, R. J., and J. van Houte.** 1975. Bacterial adherence in oral microbioal ecology. Annu. Rev. Microbiol. **29**:19–44.
11. **Gibbons, R. J., and J. van Houte.** 1980. Bacterial adherence and the formation of dental plaques, p. 63–104. *In* E. H. Beachy (ed.), Receptors and recognition, series B, vol. 6. Bacterial adherence. Chapman and Hall, London.
12. **Holt, S. C., A. C. R. Tanner, and S. S. Socransky.** 1980. Morphology and ultrastructure of oral strains of *Actinobacillus actinomycetemcomitans* and *Haemophilus aphrophilus*. Infect. Immun. **30**:588–600.
13. **Kelstrup, J., J. Theilade, and O. Fejerskov.** 1979. Surface ultrastructure of some oral bacteria. Scand. J. Dent. Res. **84**:415–423.
14. **Kilian, M., K. Roland, and J. Mestecky.** 1981. Interference of secretory immunoglobulin A with sorption of oral bacteria to hydroxyapatite. Infect. Immun. **31**:942-951.
15. **Kuramitsu, H. K., and A. Paul.** 1980. Role of bacterial interactions in the colonization of oral surfaces by *Actinomyces viscosus*. Infect. Immun. **29**:83–90.
16. **Lai, C. H., and M. A. Listgarten.** 1980. Comparative ultrastructure of certain *Actinomyces* species, *Arachnia, Bacterionema* and *Rothia*. J. Periodontol. **51**:136–154.
17. **Lie, T.** 1978. Ultrastructural study of early dental plaque formation. J. Periodontal Res. **13**:391–409.
18. **Liljemark, W. F., C. G. Bloomquist, and G. R. Germaine.** 1981. Effect of bacterial aggregation on the adherence of oral streptococci to hydroxyapatite. Infect. Immun. **31**:935–941.
19. **Liljemark, W. F., C. G. Bloomquist, and J. C. Ofstehage.** 1979. Aggregation and adherence of *Streptococcus sanguis*: role of human salivary immunoglobulin A. Infect. Immun. **26**:1104–1110.
20. **Listgarten, M. A.** 1976. Structure of the microbiol flora associated with periodontal health and disease in man. J. Periodontol. **47**:1–18.
21. **Listgarten, M. A., H. E. Mayo, and R. Tremblay.** 1975. Development of dental plaque on epoxy resin crowns in man. A light and electron microscopic study. J. Periodontol. **46**:10–26.
22. **Magnusson, I., and T. Ericson.** 1977. Variability in saliva concentration of the agglutinin specific for serotype c strains of *Streptococcus mutans*. Caries Res. **11**:109–113.
23. **Mandel, I. D.** 1976. Salivary products in plaque and saliva in relation to caries, p. 859–866. *In* H. M. Stiles, W. J. Loesche, and T. C. O'Brien (ed.), Proceedings: Microbial Aspects of Dental Caries (a special supplement to Microbiology Abstracts), vol. III. Information Retrieval Inc., Washington, D.C.
24. **Mandel, I. D.** 1979. In defense of the oral cavity, p. 473–491. *In* Kleinberg, Ellison, and Mandel (ed.), Proceedings: Saliva and Dental Caries (a special supplement to Microbiology Abstracts). Information Retrieval Inc., Washington, D.C.
25. **McBride, B. C., and M. T. Gisslow.** 1977. Role of sialic acid in saliva-induced aggregation of *Streptococcus sanguis*. Infect. Immun. **18**:35–40.
26. **Miller, C. H., and P. J. B. Somers.** 1978. Degradation of levan by *Actinomyces viscosus*. Infect. Immun. **22**:266–274.
27. **Mirth, D. B., C. J. Miller, A. Kingman, and W. H. Bowen.** 1981. Binding of salivary aggregating factors for *Streptococcus mutans* by concanavalin A and fucose-binding proteins. Caries Res. **15**:1–8.
28. **Mouton, C., H. S. Reynolds, and R. J. Genco.** 1980. Characterization of tufted streptococci isolated from the "corncob" configuration of human dental plaque. Infect. Immun. **27**:235–245.
29. **Osterberg, S. K. A., S. Z. Sudo, and L. E. A. Folke.** 1976. Microbial succession in subgingival plaque of man. J. Periodontal. Res. **11**:243–255.
30. **Pruitt, K. M., M. Adamson, and R. Arnold.** 1979. Lactoperoxidase binding to streptococci. Infect. Immun. **25**:304–309.

31. **Qureshi, J. V., and R. J. Gibbons.** 1981. Differences in the adsorptive behavior of human strains of *Actinomyces viscosus* and *Actinomyces naeslundii* to saliva-treated hydroxyapatite surfaces. Infect. Immun. **31:**261–266.

32. **Rogers, A. J., J. S. van der Hoeven, and F. H. M. Mikx.** 1978. Inhibition of *Actinomyces viscosus* by bacteriocin-producing strains of *Streptococcus mutans* in the dental plaque of gnotobiotic rats. Arch. Oral Biol. **23:**477–483.

33. **Rogers, A. H., J. S. van der Hoeven, and F. H. M. Mikx.** 1979. Effect of bacteriocin production by *Streptococcus mutans* on the plaque of gnotobiotic rats. Infect. Immun. **23:**571–576.

34. **Socransky, S. S., and A. D. Manganiello.** 1971. The oral microbiota of man from birth to senility. J. Periodontol. **42:**485–494.

35. **Svanberg, M.** 1980. *Streptococcus mutans* in plaque after mouthrinsing with buffers at varying pH value. Scand. J. Dent. Res. **80:**76–78.

36. **Weerkamp, A. H., and B. C. McBride.** 1980. Adherence of *Streptococcus salivarius* HB and HB-7 to oral surfaces and saliva-coated hydroxyapatite. Infect. Immun. **30:**150–158.

37. **Weerkamp, A., G. D. Vogels, and M. Skotnicki.** 1977. Antagonistic substances produced by streptococci from human dental plaque and their significance in plaque ecology. Caries Res. **11:**248–256.

38. **van Houte, J.** 1976. Oral bacterial colonization: mechanisms and implications, p. 3–32. *In* H. M. Stiles, W. J. Loesche, and T. C. O'Brien (ed.), Proceedings: Microbial Aspects of Dental Caries (a special supplement to Microbiology Abstracts), vol. I. Information Retrieval Inc., Washington, D.C.

39. **van Houte, J.** 1979. Bacterial adhesion in the mouth, p. 69–100. *In* S. A. Leach (ed.), Dental plaque and surface interactions in the oral cavity.

40. **van Houte, J.** 1980. Bacterial specificity in the etiology of dental caries. Int. Dent. J. **30:**305–326.

41. **van Houte, J., L. Yanover, and S. Brecher.** 1981. Relationship of levels of the bacterium *Streptococcus mutans* in saliva of children and their parents. Arch. Oral Biol. **26:**381–386.

Oral Colonization by Gram-Positive Bacteria Significant to Periodontal Disease

RICHARD P. ELLEN

Faculty of Dentistry, University of Toronto, Toronto, Ontario, Canada M5G 1G6

On what basis can the significance of various oral microorganisms to periodontal disease be compared? If solely by numerical associations derived from cross-sectional studies in humans, gram-positive species would be considered significant to both the maintenance of periodontal health and the etiology of inflammatory diseases such as gingivitis and moderate periodontitis (40, 47). Longitudinal experimental gingivitis studies also support a pathogenic role for members of the genus *Actinomyces*, not only because of their numerical predominance in disease-associated plaques but also because of the host's immune response during the course of the trial (31, 35). If animal experimentation were considered important, *A. viscosus* and *A. naeslundii* would have to be suspected most highly, for they have been the most consistent inducers of destructive periodontal lesions in laboratory animals (1, 26, 39). Also incriminating are a host of demonstrations of the ability of whole cells or extracts to (i) cause release of hydrolytic enzymes from leukocytes and macrophages, (ii) elaborate chemotactic factors, (iii) alter fibroblast function, (iv) directly stimulate immunoglobulin production by B lymphocytes, (v) act as mitogens for T and B cells, and (vi) stimulate osteoclastic bone resorption—all of which are mechanisms proposed to account for the complicated pathogenesis of periodontitis.

In contrast, cross-sectional studies of established disease in humans and longitudinal studies after its treatment tend to minimize the importance of gram-positive bacteria in advanced cases (40). On average, they comprise only a minor proportion of the subgingival microflora at sites of advanced lesions and tend to increase as the periodontal tissues return to health during therapy.

There can be no doubt that accumulation of gross plaques, even those dominated by gram-positive bacteria, can stimulate inflammation and probably some degree of destruction in supporting tissues. The objectives of this review are to summarize current knowledge of ecological pressures influencing the colonization of gram-positive periodontal pathogens and to focus attention on their significance in the overall pathogenesis of such a complex microbial disease. Unfortunately, much of the material will concern only one genus, *Actinomyces*, as a consequence of the paucity of published reports on colonization of other genera. However, examining first the well-studied intraoral establishment of gram-positive streptococci, though they are rarely considered periodontal pathogens, can be valuable in emphasizing ecological determinants of major consequence.

COLONIZATION BY GRAM-POSITIVE STREPTOCOCCI

Defined ecological habitats. It is well established that the major species of streptococci differ from one another in their colonization of distinct intraoral surfaces. Their selective ability to attach to various surfaces, and thus avoid

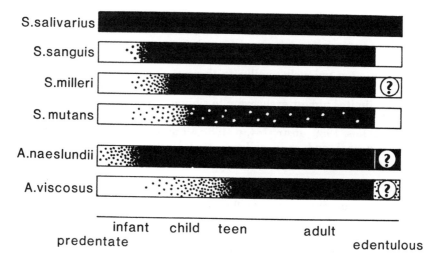

FIG. 1. *Frequency of isolation of* Streptococcus *and* Actinomyces *species during the human lifespan. Solid black bars represent virtually 100% carrier state in the population. Other symbols: white dots, the few individuals who remain S.* mutans *free; ?, no reports in the literature; area surrounding ? is predicted according to ecological range similarities with species for which information is available. (Based on references 2, 7, 8, 9, 17, 18, 25, 33.)*

removal through dilution by the bathing action of saliva, has been demonstrated repeatedly (23). This ecological determinant has one of its greatest impacts on the initial establishment of the oral flora in newborns (Fig. 1). It is no coincidence that one of the first permanent members of this flora is *Streptococcus salivarius* (7). *S. salivarius* is known to attach well to mucosal surfaces, but poorly to teeth. Its preferred habitat, the tongue, is one of the largest available oral surfaces in the newborn. In contrast, streptococci which usually attach better to dental surfaces, *S. sanguis* and *S. mutans*, are not consistently isolated from the mouth until after tooth eruption (2, 8, 9, 17). The establishment of *S. mutans*, which has a lower capacity than *S. sanguis* for attachment to smooth surfaces and usually occurs in very low numbers on nonretentive adult tooth surfaces, is often delayed beyond the first year of life. Therefore, the first requirement for successful colonization is also one of the most obvious: the availability of the favored habitat.

Size of inoculum. The ability to colonize a surface successfully also depends on the concentration of bacteria available in the fluids bathing that surface. Each streptococcal species seems to have its own required minimum infecting dose for becoming established on either a smooth or a retentive tooth surface. For example, the concentration for establishment of *S. mutans* in occlusal fissures is considerably lower than that for establishment on smooth surfaces (16; M. Svanberg, Thesis, University of Göteborg, Göteborg, Sweden, 1980).

Source of infection. It is likely that humans themselves serve as the largest infection pool, either directly or via food, eating utensils, or hygiene devices which they contaminate. Although little research has been reported for most members of the oral flora, several studies have attempted to trace the source of *S. salivarius* or *S. mutans* transmission to infants (for review, see 25). Taking advantage of nature's own labeling devices, investigators have demonstrated the natural acquisition by infants of specific serotypes, bacteriocin types, and odd colony types often uniquely similar to those of their mothers. A very recent study of family trees for a Japanese population demonstrated *S. mutans* similarities limited almost exclusively to siblings and their respective mothers (N. Masuda, T. Shimamoto, S. Sobue, and S. Hamada, Abstr. Annu. Meet. Int. Assoc. Dent. Res. 1980, abstr. 784, p. 463). Moreover, the reported correlations between maternal and child salivary concentrations of *S. mutans* further support the concept of intrafamilial transmission (30).

Microflora compatibility. After a resident flora becomes established, newly infecting bacteria must compete for space, nutrients, and other required environmental conditions to successfully sustain their colonization. Some pressures exerted by the established flora can be antagonistic, as in the case of bacteriocin or hydrogen peroxide production. Others can be supportive by supplying required nutrients or a compatible surface on which to attach. The latter has been proposed as a mechanism contributing to plaque cohesion and plaque formation by so-called "secondary" plaque bacteria which have limited ability to sorb directly to pellicle-coated teeth (23). Experimental animal systems have been particularly useful in demonstrating the impact of controlled *S. sanguis* and *A. viscosus* florae on the subsequent colonization of bacteriocin-positive and -negative *S. mutans* strains (43). Experiments with an artificial occlusal fissure system in humans have also demonstrated inhibitory effects of a resident flora (Svanberg, Thesis, University of Göteborg, 1980).

Host diet. The host's intake of foodstuff, particularly carbohydrates, can influence profoundly the colonization patterns of oral bacteria. In the case of aciduric bacteria, a major effect could be generated through maintenance of acidic microenvironments in plaques and carious lesions. Additionally, sucrose's enhancement of *S. mutans* accumulations via synthesis of adhesive glucans is well recognized (23, 25). Other oral streptococci also produce polysaccharides from sucrose, but there is no evidence that these polymers affect their intraoral colonization.

Saliva and salivary macromolecules. The influences of saliva on bacterial colonization are numerous (for review, see 23). In addition to its antibacterial and bathing actions, saliva contains many compounds which can aid in the clearance of bacteria, probably specifically, by coating them to limit adhesive interactions with either mucosal or tooth surfaces. Immunoglobulin (principally immunoglobulin A) and nonimmunoglobulin salivary agglutinins have been shown to prevent attachment of some oral streptococci to epithelial surfaces. Presumably, some of the nonimmune glycoprotein molecules can also enhance colonization if previously sorbed to the teeth in an accessible position in pellicle. The agglutinins are fairly specific for the various types of streptococci, and thus several types of molecular interactions are possible. Germane to the discussion below is the possible interaction of sugar groups on salivary glycoproteins with lectin-like surface molecules on the bacteria.

Host age. All of the colonization factors discussed above may vary with age and present an ever changing habitat. A whole host of physiological aging changes and pathological conditions may combine to determine whether a particular habitat is to be compatible with, or refractory toward, the establishment of a specific microbial type at any point in time. For example, van Houte et al. showed that it is easier to infect younger than older rats with some *S. mutans* strains (44). Problems with experimental attempts to implant *S. mutans* in adults may also mean that it has a fairly narrow optimal age range during which to implant in humans.

HUMAN ORAL COLONIZATION BY *ACTINOMYCES* SPECIES

Except for caries-motivated research on streptococci and lactobacilli, there has been little concerted effort to investigate the natural acquisition of other gram-positive bacteria with the exception of a study of *A. viscosus* and *A. naeslundii* performed in my laboratory (18). Whatever else is known about their intraoral distribution has been derived as by-products of broad-based cultural or serological studies performed for essentially other purposes. Concrete information on the establishment of *Actinomyces israelii*, an overt pathogen in humans, is also virtually nonexistent. This paucity of information and interest probably reflects the lack of sufficiently rapid methods to enumerate most of the nonstreptococcal gram-positive oral bacteria.

Acquisition and distribution of *A. viscosus* and *A. naeslundii.* The only reported attempt to systematically trace the natural oral colonization of facultatively anaerobic *Actinomyces* was a cross-sectional study of subjects ranging in age from predentate infants to young adults (18). The results were somewhat surprising in that the frequency of isolation of *A. naeslundii* and *A. viscosus* differed markedly and was related to the subjects' ages (Fig. 1). Reminiscent of streptococcal studies, *A. naeslundii* was detected in many samples from predentate infants and almost all samples from older subjects. In sharp contrast, and somewhat similar to previous observations with *S. sanguis* and *S. mutans*, *A. viscosus* was not detected in any predentate infants. However, in contrast to the streptococcal studies, *A. viscosus* remained undetected in the majority of subjects younger than 6 years of age.

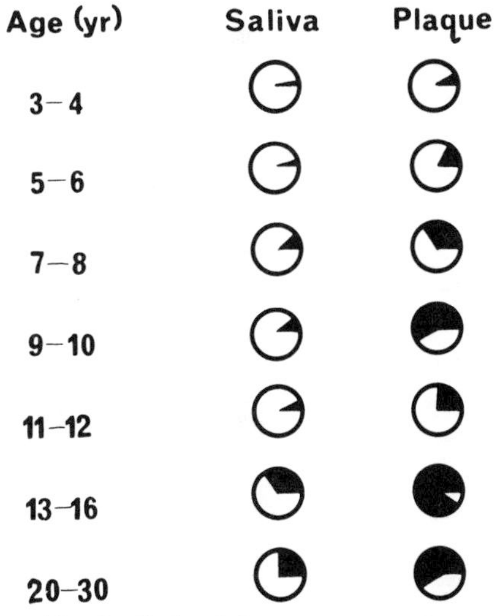

Although *A. naeslundii* was, on average, more numerous in both saliva and plaques collected from younger individuals, *A. viscosus*

FIG. 2. *Estimated mean percentage of facultatively anerobic* Actinomyces *isolates in saliva and dental plaques from subjects of different ages. Symbols:* ●, A. viscosus; ○, A. naeslundii. *(Based on reference 18.)*

TABLE 1. *Relative intraoral distribution of* Actinomyces viscosus *and* Actinomyces naeslundii[a]

Subject age (yr)	Mean ratio (A. viscosus/A. naeslundii)[b]	
	Saliva	Dental plaque
3–4	0.23	3.10
5–6	0.10	10.27
7–8	0.19	7.96
9–10	0.14	24.23
11–12	0.12	2.50
13–16	1.32	14.24
20–30[c]	0.73	13.34

[a]Data derived from Ellen (18).

[b]Includes only subjects from whom both A. *viscosus* and A. *naeslundii* were obtained.

[c]The tongue was also sampled for this last group, and the ratio was 0.67.

dominated over A. *naeslundii* in dental plaques collected from the teenage and adult patients (Fig. 2). A. *viscosus* averages were higher in plaques than in salivas at all ages. Calculations of the ratio of A. *viscosus* to A. *naeslundii* isolates for samples from which both were isolated showed a tendency for A. *viscosus* to be more tooth associated and A. *naeslundii* to be tongue and saliva associated (Table 1). A follow-up study of healthy adults selected according to the salivary A. *viscosus*/A. *naeslundii* ratio came to essentially the same conclusion (20). A. *viscosus* greatly outnumbered A. *naeslundii* in single-site plaque samples for subjects who had any detectable level of A. *viscosus* in unstimulated saliva (Fig. 3). The A. *viscosus*/A. *naeslundii* ratio for the plaque samples was always higher than that for the saliva sample collected at the same time from the same individual.

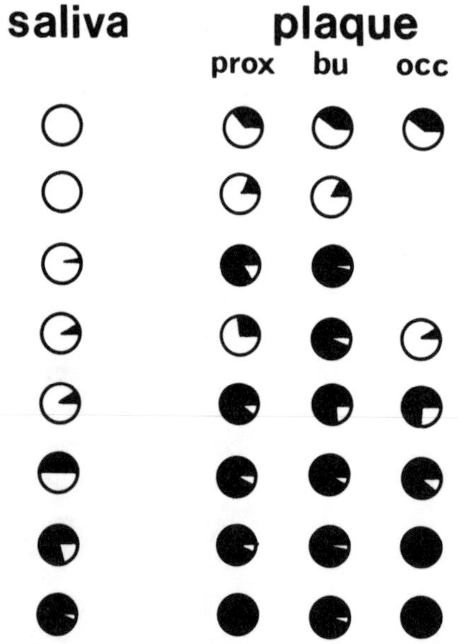

Caution should be exercised in labeling A. *viscosus* as solely a "tooth bug" and A. *naeslundii* a "tongue/saliva bug." The observed colonization differences, although obvious, were derived from averaged data with rather wide ranges. Certainly, A. *naeslundii* can be predominant in dental plaques, especially in retentive areas, and A. *viscosus* is abundant on the tongue dorsum in some individuals.

FIG. 3. *Estimated mean percentage of facultatively anaerobic* Actinomyces *composed of* A. viscosus (●) *and* A. naeslundii (○) *when comparing single-site plaque samples (proximal, buccal, occlusal) with unstimulated saliva collected simultaneously. (Based on reference 20.)*

Because *A. viscosus* and *A. naeslundii* are so closely related in terms of growth requirements and other cultural characteristics (39), it is plausible that differences in their colonization patterns reflect differing abilities to attach to available, preferred sites and their concentration differences in adult saliva, two of the principal determinants of streptococcal acquisition. Thus, *A. naeslundii,* which apparently favors the tongue and is often more numerous in adult saliva, should have a greater opportunity for early colonization. Unfortunately, no data are currently available concerning intrafamilial transfer or comparison of salivary concentrations among parent–child pairs.

Attachment related to distribution and host age. Do *A. viscosus* and *A. naeslundii* differ in attachment ability? The fact that *A. viscosus* usually recolonizes cleaned teeth almost immediately whereas repopulation by *A. naeslundii* is delayed supports this hypothesis (42; E. Theilade, J. Theilade, and L. Mikkelson, submitted for publication). A comparison for tongue surfaces in vivo or isolated tongue cells in vitro has not been made. Clark et al. (13) reported some comparisons of the abilities of a few strains to attach to saliva-coated and uncoated hydroxyapatite, and the *A. viscosus* strains apparently had greater attachment capability. Their adsorption to hydroxyapatite was enhanced by the saliva coating, whereas that of *A. naeslundii* strains was impaired. A significant finding bearing on the relationship between in vitro attachment and colonization age was reported recently by Qureshi and Gibbons (36). Comparing attachment to hydroxyapatite coated with saliva from young children and that of adolescents and adults, they too demonstrated better attachment of *A. viscosus* than *A. naeslundii* to apatite coated with adult saliva, but additionally they found increased adsorption with age of saliva donor for *A. viscosus* but not for *A. naeslundii*. These findings imply that the delay in *A. viscosus* colonization depends not only on the availability of its preferred habitat (essentially present at several months of age) and transmissible concentrations in saliva but also on physiological aging changes in the saliva itself. They may also help to explain why the emergence of *A. viscosus* in the oral flora is significantly delayed beyond that of *S. sanguis*, a species with a rather similar ecological range.

ACTINOMYCES COLONIZATION IN EXPERIMENTAL ANIMALS

Consideration of *A. viscosus* as a periodontal pathogen undoubtedly grew out of the classical experiments of Jordan and Keyes (26), who isolated an infectious agent able to transmit periodontal lesions among hamsters. *Odontomyces viscosus,* as it was called before acceptance into the genus *Actinomyces,* was also isolated from rats and able to induce periodontal lesions and root surface caries when mono-associated with germfree rats. Human isolates of both *A. viscosus* and *A. naeslundii* are pathogenic in both the rat and hamster systems, although colonization of the latter is not easily achieved. Several investigations have traced the histopathology of *Actinomyces*-induced periodontal disease and immune reactions in rats sensitized to *Actinomyces* antigens. More germane to this review are the few studies dealing with the host age at which *A. viscosus* best infects rodents and dietary conditions favoring implantation.

Host age. Using a minimum infection dose system similar to that used for studies of *S. mutans,* Brecher and van Houte (5) reported that host age affects the implantability of *A. viscosus* NY-1, a rat isolate, in conventional rats. Reminiscent of trends seen in humans, successful implantation of *A. viscosus* increased with age. Moreover, greater numbers of *A. viscosus* isolates could be recovered from the teeth than the tongues of infected animals.

Diet. Few studies have dealt with dietary conditions necessary for *A. viscosus* implantation. Apparently, there are no obvious carbohydrate requirements for establishment, accumulation of massive plaques, and induction of periodontal and root surface lesions (1, 27). However, implantation of human isolates in hamsters progresses more swiftly in animals fed glucose than in those fed sucrose-containing diets (1). These observations may not reflect direct effects on *Actinomyces,* but more likely resulted from sucrose stimulation of a competing microflora. The finding that antibiotic suppression of the resident flora negated differences between glucose- and sucrose-supported implantation favors this latter explanation. Impairment of *A. viscosus* colonization of gnotobiotic rats harboring bacteriocin-producing *S. mutans* has also been demonstrated (37). No particular diet favored colonization of *Actinomyces* in the one primate study reported (29).

T14V-T14AV system. Many investigators studying *A. viscosus* currently use a pair of strains designated T14V and T14AV. T14 was originally isolated by Socransky from human plaque and then maintained as a virulent ("V") culture by passage in germfree rats. T14AV (avirulent) was a T14 germfree rat reisolate which no longer induced periodontal lesions in these animals. Early comparisons demonstrated differences in the abilities of the two organisms to stimulate in vitro biological systems which measure possible host inflammatory responses; T14V was more potent than T14AV. Evidently, such stark differences between these strains can be traced to surface differences, for example, T14AV's more copious production of a cell-associated heteropolymer. Although it can establish in rodents, the "avirulence" of T14AV probably derives from its limited ability to attach and to colonize the gingival area (6, 46).

TAXONOMIC CONSIDERATIONS

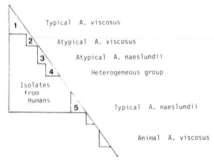

FIG. 4. *Proposed classification of human isolates of* A. viscosus *and* A. naeslundii *based on numerical taxonomy and serology (22) and on deoxyribonucleic acid homology (15).*

Most cultivation studies have considered *A. viscosus* and *A. naeslundii* to be separate species, essentially identifiable only by catalase activity. Immunofluorescence studies by Slack and Gerencser (39) demonstrated interspecies cross-reactions but also forecast separation into several groups based on antigenic specificity. Recent numerical taxonomy, serology, and deoxyribonucleic acid hybridization studies (15, 22) support a new classification which establishes

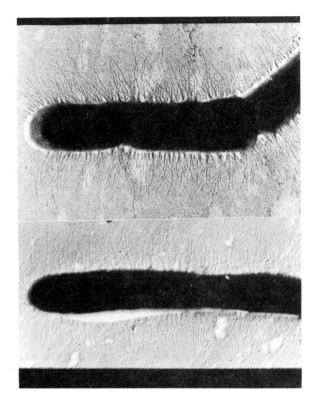

Fig. 5. *Electron photomicrograph of two shadow-cast* Actinomyces *strains illustrating different surface fibril morphologies.*

five subgroups among human isolates (Fig. 4). Most typical *A. viscosus* and *A. naeslundii* isolates from humans are members of Fillery's numerical taxonomy groups 1 and 5, respectively.

It is significant that *A. viscosus* strains of rodent oral origin are distinct from human strains by numerical taxonomy, serology, and deoxyribonucleic acid homology. In essence, they should be considered different species within the genus *Actinomyces*. However, no proposal has been made to change the current classification, in consideration of the fact that the rodent strains would probably have priority in maintaining the name *viscosus*. Regardless, care should be exercised in interpreting data derived from studies with rodent isolates and generalizing for strains isolated from humans.

ACTINOMYCES SURFACES AND ATTACHMENT

Surface fibrils. *A. viscosus* and *A. naeslundii* synthesize very long surface appendages which probably initiate and mediate contact with host tissues and other bacteria (21, 24). Although no morphological classification of fibril types similar to that for fimbriae of gram-negative bacteria has been proposed, *Actinomyces* fibrils vary greatly among strains in length, thickness, and degree of bundling and branching (Fig. 5). Fibrils of two adjacent cells are often tangled or connected, leaving the impression that they impart some of the cohesiveness characteristic of these species.

Fibrils of strain T14V and strains representing Fillery's taxonomic groups have been isolated and purified (12, 31a, 44; N. Masuda, R. P. Ellen, and D. A. Grove, Abstr. Annu. Meet. Int. Assoc. Dent. Res. 1981, abstr. 1121, p. 590). Chemical analyses yield mostly protein with small amounts of carbohydrate. Amino acid analysis demonstrates a majority of nonpolar and polar uncharged residues with little evidence of peptidoglycan contamination. Purified *A. viscosus* T14V and WVU627 fibril preparations contain one precipitable antigen (for T14V this is probably one of the so-called "virulence-related" antigens) and determinants demonstrable by agglutination reactions. Significantly, the fibril antigens of group 1 WVU627 can be detected in whole cell extracts of strains representing all taxonomic groups except typical *A. naeslundii* of group 5.

Several lines of evidence indicate that *Actinomyces* fibrils function in attachment (10, 12, 21, 45). Their physical removal from *A. naeslundii* cells impairs attachment to epithelial cells and reaggregation of bacterial suspensions. The fibrils of *A. viscosus* are sensitive to proteolytic enzyme treatment, which also impairs attachment to saliva-coated hydroxyapatite. Attachment of *A. viscosus* to hydroxyapatite can be completely abolished by its treatment with antifibril serum or impaired by competitive binding inhibition with fibril preparations. Direct fibril-mediated cell bridging can be seen in electron photomicrographs of *Actinomyces–Streptococcus* coaggregates.

Actinomyces surface lectin. McIntire et al. (34) first demonstrated a lectin-like mechanism in the coaggregation between *A. viscosus* T14V and a strain of *S. sanguis*. This β-galactoside–reversible mechanism was subsequently found by Cisar et al. (11) to govern many, but not all, of the coaggregation reactions of *A. viscosus* and *A. naeslundii* with oral streptococci, the heat-sensitive lectin-like component being traced to the *Actinomyces* cell. Subsequent investigations in my laboratory (19) and that of Costello et al. (14) demonstrated an interesting two-step mechanism active in *Actinomyces* interactions with erythrocytes. *A. viscosus* and *A. naeslundii* elaborate sialidases which are able to prime erythrocytes for hemagglutination by removing terminal sialic acid and exposing increased numbers of binding sites associated with penultimate β-galactoside. Probably using the same lectin responsible for streptococcal coaggregation, the *Actinomyces* cells are able to agglutinate readily the primed erythrocytes. Strains of *Actinomyces* and *A. naeslundii* differ in their ability to do the "two-step" (19). Again, strains belonging to group 5 *A. naeslundii* are odd in their feeble priming ability.

It is becoming evident that the β-galactoside-seeking ligand is located in the surface fibrils. Antiserum raised against purified group 1 WVU627 fibrils, shown by ferritin labeling to localize only on fibrils of whole cells, impairs hemagglutination only by strains having fibril antigens detectable with that serum (all groups except group 5 *A. naeslundii*) (31a). Furthermore, immune complexes between T14V fibrils and monoclonal antibodies raised against them agglutinate streptococci and neuraminidase-treated erythrocytes (10). These reactions are β-galactoside sensitive.

Although it is tempting to ascribe most *Actinomyces* attachment functions to β-galactoside ligands in the fibrils, real life host–*Actinomyces* interactions are probably far more complex. A recent study of attachment to saliva-coated hydroxyapatite demonstrated no consistent β-galactoside or other lectin-like activities, and neuraminidase enhancement of attachment was marginal at best (36). Preliminary studies of *Actinomyces* agglutination by saliva (R. P. Ellen and D. Bratthall, unpublished data) have demonstrated that β-galactoside can slow down agglutination for only a few minutes before being dominated by another agglutination system not reversible by β-galactoside. It is possible that *Actinomyces* cells have several surface ligands capable of interacting with both free and pellicle-associated salivary macromolecules. The one known lectin system, the β-galactoside ligand in the fibrils, may serve merely to probe and establish initial contact with salivary molecules, whereas in the erythrocyte system it appears to be indispensable. The attachment of *A. naeslundii* to epithelial cells in vitro also seems more complex than the hemagglutination situation, but β-galactoside–inhibitable reactions are demonstrable (38).

Interactions with polysaccharides. Some strains of *A. viscosus* are known to produce levans from sucrose and heteropolymers when grown on a variety of carbohydrates. Although these polymers could conceivably foster *A. viscosus* accumulation in plaque, there is no experimental evidence supporting this hypothesis. Dextran agglutination of some rodent *A. viscosus* strains and their agglutination with sucrose-grown *S. mutans* and *S. sanguis* strains have been reported (3). Recent experiments with dozens of fresh human isolates in my laboratory cannot confirm this finding (R. P. Ellen, E. D. Fillery, and R. Sivendra, unpublished data). *A. viscosus* and *A. naeslundii* agglutination with commercial dextrans, inulin, starch, and mannan and polysaccharides prepared from sucrose-grown *S. mutans, S. sanguis,* and *S. salivarius* was not common.

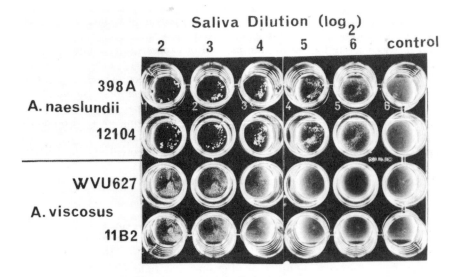

FIG. 6. *Salivary agglutination of two strains each of group 5* A. naeslundii *and group 1* A. viscosus. *Paraffin-stimulated saliva was collected from a 6-year-old child.*

Interactions with salivary macromolecules. There are few published reports about *Actinomyces*–saliva interactions, only some "honorable mentions" in papers dealing with streptococcal agglutination (23). Recent preliminary studies (R. P. Ellen and D. Bratthall, unpublished data) have compared salivary agglutination titers among human subjects and have begun to characterize the agglutination system. Agglutinating activity for both *A. viscosus* and *A. naeslundii* was detected in most stimulated whole saliva samples from a group of 6-year-old children and a group of adults. The few negative samples related to *A. viscosus* agglutination by children only. In all cases, agglutination titers for group 5 *A. naeslundii* strains were significantly higher than for group 1 *A. viscosus* (Fig. 6). The average titers for *A. viscosus* were slightly higher for the adults than for the children. For two adults tested, saliva collected sublingually had much greater agglutinating activity than saliva collected simultaneously from the parotid ducts. Sublingual agglutinating activity for both species was decreased after 2 h of adsorption with hydroxyapatite and was only weakly β-galactoside inhibitable.

It is not known whether these salivary *Actinomyces* agglutinins include specific antibody or can inhibit *Actinomyces* attachment to oral surfaces in a manner analogous to streptococcal agglutinins. Recent studies by Kilian et al. (28), using purified colostrum immunoglobulin A with *Actinomyces* agglutinating activity, demonstrated no impairment of attachment to saliva-coated hydroxyapatite in vitro. *A. viscosus* and *A. naeslundii* probably have multiple systems for strongly interacting with salivary macromolecules. *A. viscosus* must be incredibly versatile in its ability to attach to teeth. It seems difficult to prevent its attachment or to dislodge it by altering the environment to affect only one of its binding mechanisms.

ACTINOMYCES AND OTHER GRAM-POSITIVE BACTERIA IN HUMAN HEALTH AND DISEASE

Because *A. viscosus* and *A. naeslundii* are such prevalent members of the oral flora after adolescence, it seems inappropriate to determine their relationship to dental diseases solely by the routine method of expressing predominance as a percentage of the cultivable flora. Doing so has yielded wide ranges of findings for both healthy and diseased sites in various studies. Results such as these led Bowden and co-workers to propose the existence of a microbial community on the tooth surface, "basic plaque," which, although compatible with health in many situations, is able to cause some disease, depending on environmental conditions (4). *Actinomyces* species would be considered members of this "basic plaque." Presumably some of its periodontal pathogenic potential would depend on accumulations in amounts which overwhelm the defensive capabilities of the host. In this respect, some gram-positive periodontal pathogens would be significant in the etiology of those dental diseases which usually can be controlled by strict oral hygiene (i.e., most disease).

Predominant "basic plaque" species may also affect the course of periodontal disease by influencing colonization of older plaques by more virulent species or by providing nutrients required by other pathogens for growth or synthesis of virulence factors. Increasing numbers of gram-negative and anaerobic bacteria, some being overt pathogens, are known to colonize plaque as it is allowed to accumulate. Specific surface interactions between gram-positive bacteria and proposed gram-negative pathogens have been demonstrated, and in the case of *Bacteroides asaccharolyticus* (now *gingivalis*), the ability to bind to plaques formed by gram-positive bacteria has been proposed as the major means by which it colonizes periodontal pockets (23, 41). Furthermore, pathogenicity of *B. asaccharolyticus* in a guinea pig system has been linked to its access to succinate or succinate-producing bacteria (31). *Actinomyces* and some other hetero-fermentative gram-positive plaque species produce appreciable amounts of succinate during hexose metabolism. This metabolic link in virulence augmentation is but one example of how intraplaque food chains can affect the course of periodontal disease. Several other required nutrients which would be expected to support the propagation of gram-negative bacteria and spirochetes in the gingival environment can be traced either directly to products of gram-positive bacteria or to by-products of an inflammatory response to plaques rich in gram-positive bacteria. To minimize the importance of gram-positive bacteria in the pathogenesis of periodontal disease would be shortsighted indeed. Although perhaps more directly associated with the types of inflammatory processes attributable to plaque mass, the indirect effects of gram-positive bacteria can be devastating to periodontal tissues. By further understanding the events surrounding our acquisition of gram-positive bacteria and the mechanisms by which they accumulate at the dentogingival area, it may be possible to interfere with their direct impact on periodontal diseases as well as that of the gram-negative opportunistic pathogens receiving so much recent attention.

SUMMARY

Gram-positive species may be associated with conditions of either periodontal health or inflammatory disease. The most frequently studied genus, *Actinomyces,* induces lesions in experimental animals and can account for many host responses usually implicated in periodontitis. Among gram-positive bacteria considered periodontal pathogens, oral colonization studies have concentrated on only *A. viscosus* and *A. naeslundii.*

A. *viscosus* and *A. naeslundii* differ in the host age at which they colonize and in their relative intraoral distribution. *A. naeslundii* can establish in predentate infants and is more prominent in the tongue and salivary flora. *A. viscosus* colonization is delayed beyond the age of tooth eruption. It colonizes smooth tooth surfaces more readily than *A. naeslundii.* The colonization differences may be attributed to the relative abilities of the two organisms to attach to surfaces, their salivary numbers available for transmission, and qualitative changes of the host's saliva and resident flora during aging. The impact of diet may be minimal.

Many of the attachment functions may be mediated by long surface appendages termed fibrils. Fibrils of strains belonging to the major taxonomic groups of human isolates have been purified and compared chemically and serologically. Fibril antigens are particularly different between group 1 typical *A. viscosus* and group 5 typical *A. naeslundii.* Surface fibrils may contain the β-galactoside ligand which functions like a lectin during interbacterial coaggregation and hemagglutination. Other surface-related functions, especially with free and tooth-associated salivary macromolecules, seem more complex. *A. viscosus* apparently has multiple attachment systems. Prominent members of the "basic plaque" gram-positive flora may be considered pathogens for their direct induction of inflammatory responses and their indirect influence on subsequent colonization of opportunistic gram-negative pathogens. The role of gram-positive bacteria in periodontal diseases should not be underestimated.

ACKNOWLEDGMENTS

I gratefully acknowledge The Swedish Medical Research Council's fellowship (5823) support as a Visiting Scientist with D. Bratthall, Department of Cariology, University of Lund, during the period when this manuscript was written. The original investigations are being supported by grants MT-5619 from The Medical Research Council of Canada and 5999 from Medical Research Council Sweden. I thank G. Torkelsson for her secretarial assistance.

LITERATURE CITED

1. **Behbehani, M. J., and H. V. Jordon.** 1980. Comparative colonization of human *Actinomyces* species in hamsters under different dietary conditions. J. Periodontal Res. **15**:395–404.

2. **Berkowitz, R. J., H. V. Jordan, and G. White.** 1975. The early establishment of *Streptococcus mutans* in the mouths of infants. Arch. Oral Biol. **20**:171–174.

3. **Bourgeau, G., and B. McBride.** 1976. Dextran-mediated interbacterial aggregation between dextran-synthesizing streptococci and *Actinomyces viscosus*. Infect. Immun. **13**:1228–1234.

4. **Bowden, G. W., J. M. Hardie, E. D. Fillery, P. D. Marsh, and G. L. Slack.** 1978. Microbial analysis related to caries susceptibility, p. 83–97. *In* B. Bibby and R. J. Shern (ed.), Proceedings: Methods in Caries Prediction (a special supplement to Microbiology Abstracts). Information Retrieval Inc., Washington, D.C.

5. **Brecher, S. M., and J. van Houte.** 1979. Relationship between host age and susceptibility to oral colonization by *Actinomyces viscosus* in Sprague-Dawley rats. Infect. Immun. **26**:1137–1145.

6. **Brecher, S. M., J. van Houte, and B. F. Hammond.** 1978. Role of colonization in the virulence of *Actinomyces viscosus* strains T14-Vi and T14-AV. Infect. Immun. **22**:603–614.

7. **Carlsson, J., H. Grahnén, G. Jonsson, and S. Wikner.** 1970. Early establishment of *Streptococcus salivarius* in the mouths of infants. J. Dent. Res. **49**:415–418.

8. **Carlsson, J., H. Grahnén, G. Jonsson, and S. Wikner.** 1970. Establishment of *Streptococcus sanguis* in the mouths of infants. Arch. Oral Biol. **15**:1143–1148.

9. **Catalanotto, F. A., I. L. Shklair, and H. J. Keene.** 1975. Prevalence and localization of *Streptococcus mutans* in infants and children. J. Am. Dent. Assoc. **91**:606–609.

10. **Cisar, J. O., E. L. Barsumian, S. H. Curl, A. E. Vatter, A. L. Sandberg, and R. P. Siraganian.** 1980. The use of monoclonal antibodies in the study of lactose-sensitive adherence of *Actinomyces viscosus* T14. RES J. Reticuloendothel. Soc. **28**:73s–79s.

11. **Cisar, J. O., P. E. Kolenbrander, and F. C. McIntire.** 1979. The specificity of coaggregation reactions between human oral streptococci and strains of *Actinomyces viscosus* or *Actinomyces naeslundii*. Infect. Immun. **24**:742–752.

12. **Cisar, J. O. and A. E. Vatter.** 1979. Surface fibrils (fimbriae) of *Actinomyces viscosus* T14V. Infect. Immun. **24**:523–531.

13. **Clark, W. B., L. L. Bamman, and R. J. Gibbons.** 1978. Comparative estimates of bacterial affinities and adsorption sites on hydroxyapatite surfaces. Infect. Immun. **19**:846–853.

14. **Costello, A. H., J. O. Cisar, P. E. Kolenbrander, and O. Gabriel.** 1979. Neuraminidase-dependent hemagglutination of human erythrocytes by human strains of *Actinomyces viscosus* and *Actinomyces naeslundii*. Infect. Immun. **26**:563–572.

15. **Coykendall, A. L., and A. J. Munzenmaier.** 1979. Deoxyribonucleic acid hybridization among strains of *Actinomyces viscosus* and *Actinomyces naeslundii*. Int. J. Syst. Bacteriol. **29**:236–240.

16. **Duchin, S., and J. van Houte.** 1978. Colonization of teeth in humans by *Streptococcus mutans* as related to its concentration in saliva and host age. Infect. Immun. **20**:120–125.

17. **Edwardsson, S., and B. Mejàre.** 1978. *Streptococcus milleri* (Guthof) and *Streptococcus mutans* in the mouths of infants before and after tooth eruption. Arch. Oral Biol. **23**:811–814.

18. **Ellen, R. P.** 1976. Establishment and distribution of *Actinomyces viscosus* and *Actinomyces naeslundii* in the human oral cavity. Infect. Immun. **14**:1119–1124.

19. **Ellen, R. P., E. D. Fillery, K. H. Chan, and D. A. Grove.** 1980. Sialidase-enhanced lectin-like mechanism for *Actinomyces viscosus* and *Actinomyces naeslundii* hemagglutination. Infect. Immun. **27**:335–343.

20. **Ellen, R. P., D. N. Segal, and D. A. Grove.** 1978. Relative proportions of *Actinomyces viscosus* and *Actinomyces naeslundii* in dental plaques collected from single sites. J. Dent. Res. **57**:550.

21. **Ellen, R. P., D. L. Walker, and K. H. Chan.** 1978. Association of long surface appendages with adherence-related functions of the gram-positive species *Actinomyces naeslundii*. J. Bacteriol. **134**:1171–1175.

22. **Fillery, E. D., G. H. Bowden, and J. M. Hardie.** 1978. A comparison of strains of bacteria designated *Actinomyces viscosus* and *Actinomyces naeslundii*. Caries Res. **12**:299–312.

23. **Gibbons, R. J.** 1980. Adhesion of bacteria to the surfaces of the mouth, p. 351–388. *In* J. M. Lynch, J. Melling, P. R. Rutter, and B. Vincent (ed.), Microbial adhesion to surfaces. Society of Chemical Industry, London.

24. **Girard, A. E., and B. H. Jacius.** 1974. Ultrastructure of *Actinomyces viscosus* and *Actinomyces naeslundii*. Arch. Oral Biol. **19:**71–79.

25. **Hamada, S., and H. D. Slade.** 1980. Biology, immunology, and cariogenicity of *Streptococcus mutans*. Microbiol. Rev. **44:**331–384.

26. **Jordan, H. V., and P. H. Keyes.** 1964. Aerobic gram-positive filamentous bacteria as etiologic agents of experimental periodontal disease in hamsters. Arch. Oral Biol. **9:**401–414.

27. **Jordan, H. V., P. H. Keys, and S. Lim.** 1969. Plaque formation and implantation of *Odontomyces viscosus* in hamsters fed different carbohydrates. J. Dent. Res. **48:**824–831.

28. **Kilian, M., K. Roland, and J. Mestecky.** 1981. Interference of secretory immunoglobulin A with sorption of oral bacteria to hydroxyapatite. Infect. Immun. **31:**942–951.

29. **Kilian, M., and G. Rölla.** 1976. Initial colonization of teeth in monkeys as related to diet. Infect. Immun. **14:**1022–1027.

30. **Köhler, B., and D. Bratthall.** 1978. Intrafamilial levels of *Streptococcus mutans* and some aspects of the bacterial transmission. Scand. J. Dent. Res. **86:**35–42.

31. **Loesche, W. J., and S. A. Syed.** 1978. Bacteriology of human experimental gingivitis: effect of plaque and gingivitis score. Infect. Immun. **21:**830–839.

31a. **Masuda, N., R. P. Ellen, and D. A. Grove.** 1981. Purification and characterization of surface fibrils from taxonomically typical *Actinomyces viscosus* WVU627. J. Bacteriol. **147:**1095–1104.

32. **Mayrand, D., and B. C. McBride.** 1980. Ecological relationships of bacteria involved in a simple mixed anaerobic infection. Infect. Immun. **27:**44–50.

33. **McCarthy, C., M. L. Snyder, and R. B. Parker.** 1965. The indigenous oral flora of man. I. The newborn to the 1-year-old infant. Arch. Oral Biol. **10:**61–70.

34. **McIntire, F. C., A. E. Vatter, J. Baros, and J. Arnold.** 1978. Mechanism of coaggregation between *Actinomyces viscosus* T14V and *Streptococcus sanguis* 34. Infect. Immun. **21:**978–988.

35. **Patters, M. R., N. Sedransk, and R. J. Genco.** 1979. The lymphoproliferative response during human experimental gingivitis. J. Periodontal Res. **14:**269–278.

36. **Qureshi, J. V., and R. J. Gibbons.** 1981. Differences in the adsorptive behavior of human strains of *Actinomyces viscosus* and *Actinomyces naeslundii* to saliva-treated hydroxyapatite. Infect. Immun. **131:**261–266.

37. **Rogers, A. H., J. S. van der Hoeven, and F. H. M. Mikx.** 1978. Inhibition of *Actinomyces viscosus* by bacteriocin-producing strains of *Streptococcus mutans* in the dental plaque of gnotobiotic rats. Arch. Oral Biol. **23:**477–483.

38. **Saunders, J. M., and C. H. Miller.** 1980. Attachment of *Actinomyces naeslundii* to human buccal epithelial cells. Infect. Immun. **29:**981–989.

39. **Slack, J. M., and M. A. Gerencser.** 1975. Actinomyces filamentous bacteria. Biology and pathogenicity. Burgess Publishing Co., Minneapolis.

40. **Slots, J.** 1979. Subgingival microflora and periodontal disease. J. Clin. Periodontol. **6:**351–382.

41. **Slots, J., and R. J. Gibbons.** 1978. Attachment of *Bacteroides melaninogenicus* subsp. *asaccharolyticus* to oral surfaces and of periodontal pockets. Infect. Immun. **19:**254–264.

42. **Socransky, S. S., A. D. Manganiello, D. Propas, V. Oram, and J. van Houte.** 1977. Bacteriological studies of developing supragingival dental plaque. J. Periodontal Res. **12:**90–106.

43. **van der Hoeven, J. S., and A. H. Rogers.** 1979. Stability of the resident microflora and the bacteriogenicity of *Streptococcus mutans* as factors affecting its establishment in specific pathogen free rats. Infect. Immun. **23:**206–212.

44. **van Houte, J., V. N. Upeslacis, and S. Edelstein.** 1977. Decreased oral colonization of *Streptococcus mutans* during aging of Sprague-Dawley rats. Infect. Immun. **16:**203–212.

45. **Wheeler, T. T., and W. B. Clark.** 1980. Fibril-mediated adherence of *Actinomyces viscosus* to saliva-treated hydroxyapatite. Infect. Immun. **28:**577–584.

46. **Wheeler, T. T., W. B. Clark, and D. C. Birdsell.** 1979. Adherence of *Actinomyces viscosus* T14V and T14AV to hydroxyapatite surfaces in vitro and human teeth in vivo. Infect. Immun. **25:**1066–1074.

47. **Williams, B. L., R. M. Pantalone, and J. C. Sherris.** 1976. Subgingiva microflora and periodontitis. J. Periodontal Res. **11:**1–8.

Colonization of Subgingival Areas by Motile Rods and Spirochetes: Clinical Implications

MAX A. LISTGARTEN

University of Pennsylvania School of Dental Medicine
and Center for Oral Health Research, Philadelphia, Pennsylvania 19104

INTRODUCTION

The colonization of the subgingival area by gram-negative microorganisms can be viewed from a variety of perspectives. One of these is the establishment and ontogenetic evolution of the oral microbiota. A number of authors have discussed plaque development in subjects of different ages from birth through senility (2–5, 7, 20–22, 27). Most of these studies have dealt primarily with the supragingival or mucosa-associated rather than the subgingival microbial population. Certain organisms which are associated primarily with the subgingival microbiota, for example, pigmented *Bacteroides* and spirochetes, tend to appear in older children around the time of puberty (2, 7, 27). Socransky and Manganiello (27) suggest that the appearance of these organisms coincides with the availability of critical nutrients which are host derived or produced by other microbial species. Eh and pH of the subgingival area may also be important to the establishment of a subgingival microbiota (10, 11).

Recent reports have also addressed the problem of retention and spread of microorganisms in the subgingival area. Gibbons and van Houte (9) and Gibbons et al. (8) have discussed the importance of selective adherence of bacteria to certain surfaces as a principal ecological determinant. Of particular relevance to the subgingival microbiota, Celesk et al. (6) have shown in vitro that *Capnocytophaga*-like organisms tend to selectively colonize cementum surfaces. Details may be found in the presentations by J. van Houte and J. London elsewhere in this volume. E. R. Leadbetter and S. C. Holt (J. Dent. Res. Spec. Issue A **57**:316, abstr. 967, 1978), L. To, S. Sasaki, and S. S. Socransky (J. Dent. Res. Spec. Issue A **57**:316, abstr. 968, 1978), and S. S. Socransky, S. Sasaki, and L. To (J. Dent. Res. Spec. Issue A **57**:317, abstr. 969, 1978) have hypothesized that motile bacteria such as *Capnocytophaga* and spirochetes may play an important role as carriers of nonmotile forms, thereby favoring the subgingival spread of nonmotile species. Their in vitro experiments provided some support for this "piggyback" theory of microbial spread. A simpler although somewhat slower mechanism that might enable microbial spread along the root surface is the expansion of the microbial mass by cell division in an apical direction.

At least in the early stages of gingivitis, edematous changes in the marginal gingiva may contribute to increasing the subgingival area of the root surface available for microbial colonization. Dimensional changes of the gingiva in a coronal direction due to tissue swelling can result in a covering over by gingival tissue of portions of the root surface previously located supragingivally. In later stages of periodontal disease, the volumetric increase in the subgingival compartment available for microbial colonization is due primarily to a gradual apical displacement of the pocket bottom, with a concomitant apical relocation of the connective tissue attachment level (Fig. 1).

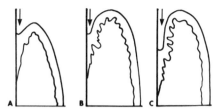

FIG. 1. *Diagrammatic illustration of changes in sulcus depth from the situation in periodontal health (A) characterized by a shallow sulcus to the situation in the presence of edematous gingivitis (B) in which sulcus depth is increased primarily as a result of tissue swelling, to the situation (C) in which deepening of the sulcus is also accompanied by an apical displacement of the anatomic sulcus bottom.*

In this report, I would like to confine most of my remarks to the results of selected clinical studies designed to clarify the relationship between certain subgingival microbial forms and various clinical aspects of chronic periodontitis. Because most treatment procedures tend to disturb the complex microbiota of the periodontal pocket, the observations regarding the subgingival microbiota during the posttreatment period provide some insight into microbial repopulation patterns of the subgingival area. Instead of dealing with the detailed mechanisms which may underlie the recolonization process, I would like to review some microbial repopulation patterns which are detectable microscopically after mechanical debridement of the resident microbiota.

PATTERNS OF COLONIZATION

Earlier studies in my laboratory (17) showed that introduction of a bacteria-free surface, in the form of an artificial crown, into the mouth of human volunteers resulted in the crown surface becoming colonized over a 2-month period by a complex microbial community which resembles the microbiota on natural tooth surfaces (13). In the first week, the adherent microbial layer is composed predominantly of microcolonies of coccoid cells in a supragingival location. Between the first and third weeks the coccoid population is displaced by a dense mass of filamentous microorganisms. A distinctive subgingival microbiota, composed largely of gram-negative and motile microorganisms, first appears around the third week. The appearance of the subgingival microbiota probably results from a number of environmental changes which culminate in the creation of a suitable environment for the new microbial population. The changes may be due in part to the preexisting microbial population, the metabolic activity of which may favor the establishment of the new arrivals. In addition, anatomical changes such as the appearance of a deepened sulcus as a result of inflammatory swelling of the gingiva, as described previously, also may favor the development of the subgingival microbiota.

Regardless of the underlying mechanisms, it is clear that the appearance of a typical subgingival microbiota is a time-dependent event which may require a number of weeks from the initial colonization by gram-positive coccoid cells to the final establishment of a predominantly gram-negative, anaerobic microbiota with numerous motile forms, including spirochetes (17, 18).

Separate morphological studies by myself and others (13, 25) have demonstrated that the microbiota which is associated with certain forms of periodontal disease closely resembles the subgingival microbiota which developed in the human experimental gingivitis model. It should be noted that, although the general pattern of microbial successions observed in the human gingivitis model is superficially uniform, substantial differences exist between individual subjects regarding the *rate* at which these microbial successions take place. It is also likely that the *final composition* of the established subgingival microbiota will vary among individual subjects, with some, for example, harboring greater proportions of certain microbial species than others.

To assess the subgingival microbial composition along individual tooth surfaces of human subjects, we found it necessary to develop a simple, rapid, albeit crude assay to facilitate multiple comparisons between individual sites, individual subjects, or groups of experimental subjects. By means of differential dark-field microscopic counts of microbial samples obtained from the subgingival area, we were able to demonstrate distinct patterns in the distribution of certain microbial forms at healthy and periodontally diseased sites in untreated subjects (14). Diseased sites were characterized by relatively elevated proportions of spirochetes and motile rods and relatively lower proportions of coccoid cells as compared with periodontally healthy sites. Furthermore, changes in these proportions could be induced with various treatment procedures so that the microbial composition of a diseased site could be shifted toward one typically observed at a clinically healthy site (16). Of particular interest was the observation that such a microbial shift lasted for several weeks after the treatment procedure. Could this prolonged change in composition of the microbial population have been due to the time required for a relatively bacterium-free site to become recolonized by its original microbiota?

To gain some additional information on the rate of recolonization of mechanically debrided areas, Mousques et al. (23) selected untreated patients with chronic periodontitis and multiple periodontal pockets. After a single therapeutic intervention of scaling and root planing (mechanical debridement), affected sites in each subject were randomly sampled at various intervals to determine overall changes in the distribution of selected subgingival microbial forms. The results indicated a marked decrease in the proportions of spirochetes and motile rods for the first few days after the treatment procedure with a

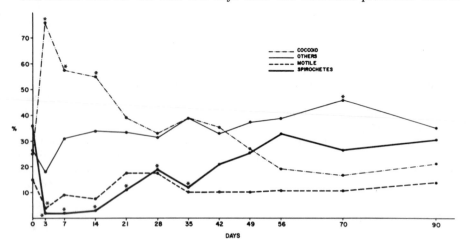

FIG. 2. *Temporal changes in the percentage of certain subgingival microbial forms as the result of a single intervention of mechanical debridement. Each point represents the mean of single sites in each of 14 subjects. An asterisk designates values which deviate significantly from the 0 or base-line value. From Mousques et al. (23).*

concomitant proportional increase in the percentage of coccoid cells. These microbial groups returned to treatment levels after postoperative time intervals that varied from a few days to several weeks, depending on the microbial form monitored. Spirochetes were the last to reach preoperative proportions, after an interval of 42 days following debridement (Fig. 2). Slots et al. (26) and Loesche et al. (19) reported similar findings after mechanical or chemical debridement, or both. In some of the cases reported in their studies, spirochetes and certain motile rods had not returned to base line even several months after the treatment procedure. The results of these investigations confirmed our suspicion that recolonization of a debrided subgingival site follows a pattern similar to that observed on artificial surfaces, with coccoid cells predominating in the early stages and motile cells and spirochetes predominating in the later stages. One could also infer that the microbial composition in the earlier stages of recolonization was compatible with periodontal health, whereas the flora in the later stages was more likely to be associated with periodontal disease.

It is generally recognized that conventional therapy for periodontitis is of limited value unless the patients are recalled periodically for mechanical cleansing of their dentition. The intervals between such visits are usually determined on an arbitrary basis. It has been shown that, with debridement at 2-week intervals, periodontal breakdown can be completely halted (1, 24). However, good results have been achieved with recall intervals of up to 3 months (12). It is tempting to speculate that the effectiveness of a recall program is dependent on keeping the proportions of spirochetes and motile rods suppressed between successive visits.

The intervals between sessions of mechanical debridement which appear to be effective in the prevention of periodontal tissue breakdown parallel those required for microbial proportions in the subgingival area to return to pretreatment levels after various treatment procedures (19, 26). By mechanically or chemically interfering with the normal process of microbial colonization of the subgingival area at strategic intervals, the establishment of certain groups of microorganisms such as spirochetes, certain motile rods, and other microbial forms may be successfully prevented.

Since the subgingival microbiota becomes established after the supragingival microbiota, it might be argued that preventing supragingival accumulations of bacteria should have a preventive effect on the establishment and maintenance of the subgingival microbial population. Although this may be applicable to the oral cavity with a normal periodontium, it may not be true when deepened sulci or pockets are present. A recent report by Tabita et al. (28) indicated that prevention of supragingival microbial deposits during a 14-day period following mechanical debridement did not affect the development of a subgingival microbiota. The subjects studied had pockets with a probing depth in the 4- to 6-mm range.

RECOLONIZATION OF TREATED HOSTS

The associations between certain microbial forms and the periodontal status of a test population do not necessarily imply a cause and effect relationship, nor is it always apparent whether the microbial changes observed precede or follow changes in the clinical status of the host. To clarify this point, we recruited a group of 21 adult subjects previously treated for periodontitis and maintained in good periodontal health. Nineteen subjects completed the study. The subjects were informed that periodic professional cleaning of their dentition would be suspended for a 1-year period. However, they were to receive a clinical and microbiological examination of the dentogingival area every 2 months. Should periodontal probing reveal a significant increase in probing depth (3 mm or more) from base line along any surface, the surface would be treated and the tooth would be eliminated from the study. We had expected to find in this population of treated patients relatively low proportions of spirochetes and motile rods and relatively shallow probing depth measurements. We expected over the 1-year period to find a relative increase in the proportions of motile cells and spirochetes, accompanied by a worsening of the clinical parameters, and we hoped to discover whether the microbial changes preceded or followed the clinical changes. For the purpose of this experiment, the microbial sample was obtained as a pooled sample of six surfaces considered to be at greatest risk, i.e., the surface with the greatest probing depth in each of the jaw sextants. The results provided several surprises (15).

TABLE 1. *Mean proportional distribution of certain subgingival microbial forms in 19 subjects previously treated for chronic periodontitis[a]*

Subject	Coccoid cells	Motile rods	Spirochetes	Others
1	41	6	0	53
2	45	3	1	51
3	37	3	1	59
4	36	8	2	54
5	49	4	2	45
6	27	9	4	60
7	33	9	4	54
8	32	7	6	55
9	35	7	7	51
10	22	12	10	56
11	16	7	10	67
12	28	14	10	48
13	28	9	12	51
14	29	19	13	39
15	30	11	14	45
16	26	11	14	49
17	34	7	21	38
18	26	11	24	39
19	14	15	31	40
Means	31	9	10	50

[a]The means were derived from seven examinations at 2-month intervals for each of the 19 subjects. The subjects are arranged in order of increasing proportions of spirochetes. None of the subjects had their teeth professionally cleaned during the 1-year experimental period. Note the range in the distribution of the microbial forms among the patients in this group. (From reference 15.)

Despite an overall similarity in their clinical status, the subjects exhibited widely differing proportions of subgingival microbial forms at the base-line examination and throughout the experimental period (Table 1). The proportions varied from values compatible with those at untreated healthy sites to values generally observed at untreated diseased sites. Unlike untreated patients, the clinical status of this group of subjects at a given examination could not be readily correlated with the observed proportions of certain bacterial forms. Furthermore, contrary to expectations, the bacterial proportions observed at base line tended to remain relatively stable for individual subjects throughout the experimental period (Table 2). However, if the number of teeth treated in the course of the study because of progressive disease was taken as an indication of susceptibility to disease, the most susceptible individuals tended to have elevated mean proportions of spirochetes and motile cells subgingivally as compared with the less susceptible subjects. In fact, a good correlation could be established between the percentage of spirochetes with or without motile rods recorded at base line and the number of teeth which required treatment over the 1-year experimental period (Table 3).

The results from the above study indicated that the subgingival microbial composition may vary significantly among subjects at risk for chronic periodontitis. Furthermore, increased proportions of spirochetes were not well correlated with mean pocket depth, an observation which suggests that spirochetes do not increase their proportion only as a result of the availability of suitable anatomic sites. On the contrary, the presence of a microbiota rich in spirochetes or motile rods, or both, tended to precede a clinically detectable deterioration of the periodontium as determined by subsequent increases in probing depth measurements.

Spirochetes and motile rods may not be the primary pathogens, but may act simply as indicator organisms of a pathogenic microbiota and to some extent as predictors of future clinical deterioration. By taking advantage of the time interval required for these organisms to repopulate a debrided site, maintenance visits could theoretically be tailored to individual patient needs.

TABLE 2. *Mean proportional distribution of certain microbial forms in a population of 19 subjects previously treated for chronic periodontitis*[a]

Exami- nation	Time (mo)	Coccoid cells	Motile rods	Spiro- chetes	Others
1	0	34	10	8	48
2	2	34	9	6	51
3	4	32	7	9	52
4	6	29	10	8	53
5	8	28	8	8	56
6	10	31	8	6	55
7	12	26	9	10	55
Mean (%)		31	9	8	53

[a]The means for the 19 subjects were calculated every 2 months for a 1-year period during which none of the subjects had their teeth professionally cleaned. Note the remarkable stability of the microbial proportions during the experimental period. (From reference 15.)

TABLE 3. *Correlation of the proportions of spirochetes and motile rods observed at base line in 19 subjects at risk for periodontitis and the number of teeth in each subject which had to be "exited"*[a]

Subjects	% Spirochetes plus motile rods	No. of exited teeth
1	1	0
2	5	0
3	7	1
4	8	0
5	12	0
6	14	0
7	14	1
8	14	1
9	15	1
10	16	2
11	19	1
12	20	2
13	25	1
14	25	3
15	31	0
16	36	3
17	36	3
18	45	4
19	43	3

[a]Teeth were "exited" from the experiment for treatment during the 1-year experimental period if an increase in probing depth of ≥ 3 mm from the base-line measurements occurred. Correlation coefficient $(r) = 0.77$; $P < 0.001$. (From reference 15.)

CONCLUSIONS

The results of the experiments referred to in this report provide the basis for the following conclusions:

1. Microbial colonization of the subgingival region is a relatively slow process, whether it occurs de novo or after debridement of a subgingival region. The rate of recolonization of a debrided area varies among subjects with chronic periodontitis. It is likely to require several weeks and in some subjects possibly several months.

2. The pattern of microbial colonization may also vary in individual sites and individual subjects. Different endpoints may be reached in the course of the numerous microbial successions which culminate in the establishment of a stable microbiota for a given site in a given subject.

3. In untreated subjects, the presence of elevated proportions of spirochetes or motile rods is positively correlated with certain signs of chronic periodontitis, namely, increased gingival inflammation and probing depth. In treated patients, elevated proportions of these microbial forms may not correlate with existing clinical signs, but may reflect a greater susceptibility to future periodontal deterioration.

4. Since spirochetes, and to a lesser extent motile rods, tend to be late arrivals in the colonization sequence, microbial debridement of diseased areas performed at judicious intervals should be effective in controlling the relative proportions of spirochetes and motile cells at these sites. Such intervals may have to be established on an individual basis with the aid of a suitable monitoring technique such as differential dark-field microscopy of appropriate subgingival samples.

5. Whether therapeutic strategies aimed at controlling spirochetes and motile rods are effective in arresting the progressive destruction of the periodontal tissues remains to be tested.

6. The association of spirochetes and motile rods with chronic periodontitis in adults, as outlined above, neither implies a direct etiological role for these microorganisms nor excludes the participation of other microorganisms as etiological agents. However, on the basis of the available evidence, the role of spirochetes and motile rods in the periodontal disease process deserves to be examined with renewed emphasis.

SUMMARY

Microbial colonization of the subgingival region begins at the time of tooth eruption. Throughout life, the composition of the resident microbiota changes as a result of environmental alterations caused in part by maturation of the host (tooth eruption and succession, immunological responses to host-associated microorganisms, etc.), and local alterations such as diet, oral hygiene habits, and interactions of the resident microorganisms with one another or adjacent surfaces ("piggyback" theory of microbial spread, bacteriocins, adhesive properties, etc.). The delicate ecological balance which controls the composition of the subgingival flora may be altered by mechanical debridement or antimicrobial agents used for therapeutic ends. Such therapeutic interventions may result in the elimination of the bulk of the resident microbiota and start a competitive recolonization process. This process has been studied by differential dark-field microscopy of subgingival scrapings as well as by cultural techniques. The results of these studies indicate that the rate of recolonization of a site to its pretreatment status varies a great deal according to the site and the subject. The rate of return to former proportions also varies between different microbial types. By judiciously timing antimicrobial therapeutic interventions (mechanical or chemical, or both), it may be possible to keep the resident microbiota from reaching the critical equilibrium required for the establishment of disease-associated microorganisms. Since elevated proportions of spirochetes, with or without motile rods, are associated with certain forms of periodontal disease, monitoring of these organisms by differential dark-field microscopy could facilitate the optimal scheduling of visits for the maintenance of periodontal health. Microbial cultures on appropriate selective media may serve a similar function for other clinically relevant microorganisms.

ACKNOWLEDGMENTS

This review is based in part on research activities supported by Public Health Service grant DE-02623 from the National Institute for Dental Research to the Center for Oral Health Research at the University of Pennsylvania.

LITERATURE CITED

1. **Axelsson, P., and J. Lindhe.** 1978. Effect of controlled oral hygiene procedures on caries and periodontal disease in adults. J. Clin. Periodontol. **5**:133–151.
2. **Bailit, H. L., D. C. Baldwin, and E. E. Hunt, Jr.** 1964. The increasing prevalence of gingival *Bacteroides melaninogenicus* with age in children. Arch. Oral Biol. **9**:435–438.
3. **Berkowitz, R. J., H. V. Jordan, and G. White.** 1975. The early establishment of *Streptococcus mutans* in the mouths of infants. Arch. Oral Biol. **20**:171–174.
4. **Carlsson, J., and L. Gothefors.** 1975. Transmission of *Lactobacillus jensenii* and *Lactobacillus acidophilus* from mother to child at time of delivery. J. Clin. Microbiol. **1**:124–128.
5. **Carlsson, J., H. Grahnen, and G. Jonsson.** 1975. Lactobacilli and streptococci in the mouth of chidren. Caries Res. **9**:333–339.
6. **Celesk, R. A., R. M. McCabe, and J. London.** 1979. Colonization of the cementum surface of teeth by oral gram-negative bacteria. Infect. Immun. **26**:15–18.
7. **De Araujo, W. C., and J. B. Macdonald.** 1964. The gingival crevice microbiota of preschool children. J. Periodontol. **35**:285–289.
8. **Gibbons, R. J., D. M. Spinell, and Z. Skobe.** 1976. Selective adherence as a determinant of the host tropisms of certain indigenous and pathogenic bacteria. Infect. Immun. **13**:238–246.
9. **Gibbons, R. J., and J. van Houte.** 1971. Selective bacterial adherence to oral epithelial surfaces and its role as an ecological determinant. Infect. Immun. **3**:567–573.
10. **Kenney, E. B., and M. M. Ash, Jr.** 1969. Oxidation reduction potential of developing plaque, periodontal pockets and gingival sulci. J. Periodontol. **40**:630–633.
11. **Kleinberg, I., and G. Hall.** 1968. pH and depth of gingival crevices in different areas of the mouths of fasting humans. J. Periodontal Res. **3**:109–117.
12. **Knowles, J., F. Burgett, E. Morrison, R. Nissle, and S. Ramfjord.** 1980. Comparison of results following three modalities of periodontal therapy related to tooth type and initial pocket depth. J. Clin. Periodontol. **7**:32–47.
13. **Listgarten, M. A.** 1976. Structure of the microbial flora associated with periodontal health and disease in man. A light and electron microscopic study. J. Periodontol. **47**:1–18.
14. **Listgarten, M. A., and L. Helldén.** 1978. Relative distribution of bacteria at clinically healthy and periodontally diseased sites in humans. J. Clin. Periodontol. **5**:115–132.
15. **Listgarten, M. A., and S. Levin.** 1981. Positive correlation between the proportions of subgingival spirochetes and motile bacteria and susceptibility of human subjects to periodontal deterioration. J. Clin. Periodontol. **8**:122–138.
16. **Listgarten, M. A., J. Lindhe, and L. Helldén.** 1978. Effect of tetracycline, and/or scaling on human periodontal disease. Clinical, microbiological and histological observations. J. Clin. Periodontol. **5**:246–271.
17. **Listgarten, M. A., H. E. Mayo, and R. Tremblay.** 1975. Development of dental plaque on epoxy resin crowns in man. A light and electron microscopic study. J. Periodontol. **46**:10–26.
18. **Loe, H., E. Theilade, and S. B. Jensen.** 1965. Experimental gingivitis in man. J. Periodontol. **36**:177–187.
19. **Loesche, W. J., S. A. Syed, E. C. Morrison, B. Laughon, and N. S. Grossman.** 1981. Treatment of periodontal infections due to anaerobic bacteria with short-term treatment with metronidazole. J. Clin. Periodontol. **8**:29–44.
20. **Long, S. S., and R. M. Swenson.** 1976. Determinants of the developing oral flora in normal newborns. Appl. Environ. Microbiol. **32**:494–497.
21. **Mackler, S. B., and J. J. Crawford.** 1973. Plaque development and gingivitis in the primary dentition. J. Periodontol. **44**:18–24.
22. **McCarthy, C., M. L. Snyder, and R. B. Parker.** 1965. The indigenous oral flora of man. I. The newborn to the 1-year old infant. Arch. Oral Biol. **10**:61–70.
23. **Mousques, T., M. A. Listgarten, and R. W. Phillips.** 1980. Effect of scaling and root planing on the composition of the human subgingival microbial flora. J. Periodontal Res. **15**:144–151.
24. **Nyman, S., B. Rosling, and J. Lindhe.** 1975. Effect of professional tooth cleaning on healing after periodontal surgery. J. Clin. Periodontol. **2**:80–86.
25. **Österberg, S. K.-Å, S. Z. Sudo, and L. E. A. Folke.** 1976. Microbial succession in subgingival plaque of man. J. Periodontal Res. **11**:243–255.
26. **Slots, J., P. Mashimo, M. J. Levine, and R. J. Genco.** 1979. Periodontal therapy in humans. I. Microbiological and clinical effects of a single course of periodontal scaling and root planing, and of adjunctive tetracycline therapy. J. Periodontol. **50**:495–509.
27. **Socransky, S. S., and S. D. Manganiello.** 1973. The oral microbiology of man from birth through senility. J. Periodontol. **42**:485–496.
28. **Tabita, P. V., N. F. Bissada, and J. E. Maybury.** 1981. Effectiveness of supragingival plaque control on the development of subgingival plaque and gingival inflammation in patients with moderate pocket depth. J. Periodontol. **52**:88–93.

Coaggregation Reactions Between Oral Bacteria: Studies of Specific Cell-to-Cell Adherence Mediated by Microbial Lectins

JOHN O. CISAR

Laboratory of Microbiology and Immunology, National Institute of Dental Research, Bethesda, Maryland 20205

INTRODUCTION

The microbial colonization of a tooth begins with the adherence of certain species to an acquired pellicle of salivary glycoproteins which are adsorbed to the enamel surface. Once the early plaque formers are established, the colonization by other microorganisms depends on their adherence to the developing plaque rather than to the pellicle. This simple but important concept was illustrated initially by Bladen and co-workers (1), who found that strains of *Veillonella*, which were unable to form plaque on nichrome wire, colonized the plaque formed by *Actinomyces viscosus*. Direct evidence for the adherence of one microorganism to another was provided by Gibbons and Nygard (13), who observed aggregations when specific pairs of plaque bacteria were mixed together. These interactions, or coaggregations, were postulated to contribute to the sequential colonization of a tooth surface by different microbial species.

Coaggregation results from the affinity of one cell surface for another and occurs rapidly when washed bacterial cells are mixed together. While certain coaggregation reactions are Ca^{2+} dependent, none is thought to involve direct cell-to-cell bridging by this ion. In addition, soluble polymers such as dextran or salivary glycoproteins, which cause the self-aggregation of certain oral microorganisms (14), are not involved in specific coaggregations between different organisms. Over the past few years, coaggregations involving various gram-positive and gram-negative bacteria have been reported (Table 1). Although the ability to coaggregate is clearly a property of several species, these interactions occur selectively. Thus, although many isolates of certain species coaggregate with one another, the isolates of other species fail to interact or do so with low frequency. Observations of this type suggest that coaggregation may play a role in organizing bacteria into efficient microbial communities. Indeed, the possibility that coaggregation promotes symbiotic relationships is illustrated by the interaction of *S. mutans,* which produces lactic acid as an end product, with *V. alcalescens,* which requires lactate (B. C. McBride and H. Merilees, J. Dent. Res. Spec. Issue A **60**:549, abstr. 957, 1981).

An important mechanism of coaggregation involves the interaction of carbohydrate-binding proteins, or lectins, on one cell, with complementary carbohydrate-containing receptors on another cell. This is perhaps not surprising as the same basic mechanism accounts for many specific cell-to-cell interactions which occur throughout nature, including the adherence of certain microorganisms to mammalian cells (24, 32, 34). The important discovery by McIntire et al. (26) that lactose completely inhibits the interaction of a protein on *A. viscosus* T14V with a carbohydrate on *S. sanguis* 34 provided the first

TABLE 1. *Coaggregations between oral bacteria*

Coaggregating pair		Reference
Gram Positive	**Gram Positive**	
Streptococcus sanguis	*Actinomyces viscosus*	2, 4, 8, 19, 21, 23, 26
or	*A. naeslundii*	4, 8, 13, 19
S. mitis	*A. odontolyticus*	4, 19
	Bacterionema matruchotii	22, 28–30
	Propionibacterium acnes	19
Gram Positive	**Gram Negative**	
Streptococcus sp.	*Bacteroides* sp.	37, 38
or	*Capnocytophaga* sp.[a]	37
Actinomyces sp.	*Fusobacterium nucleatum*[b]	18, 37, 38
	Eikenella corrodens	37
	Veillonella sp.[c]	38
Gram Negative	**Gram Negative**	
Bacteroides melaninogenicus	*F. nucleatum*[b]	

[a] P. Kolenbrander and S. Hurst-Calderone, J. Dent. Res. Spec. Issue A **60**:333, abstr. 90, 1981.

[b] B. C. McBride, J. King, T. Edwards, and M. Gisslow, J. Dent. Res. Spec. Issue A **56**:156, abstr. 452, 1977.

[c] B. C. McBride and H. Merilees, J. Dent. Res. Spec. Issue A **60**:549, abstr. 957, 1981.

clear evidence for lectin–carbohydrate binding as a mechanism of coaggregation. Subsequent studies have shown that most human strains of *A. viscosus* and *A. naeslundii* exhibit a similar lectin activity which accounts for both the coaggregation of these bacteria with certain streptococci (4, 19) and the bacterium-mediated hemagglutination reactions with neuraminidase-treated erythrocytes (6, 9). Moreover, a surprisingly large number of other oral bacteria exhibit galactose- or lactose-inhibitable adherence to various other bacterial and mammalian cells (Table 2). Taken together, these observations imply that microbial adherence to receptors formed by galactose residues or related structures may play an important role in the colonization of certain oral surfaces, including the teeth. The following discussion summarizes the evidence for this concept which has emerged from the study of coaggregation reactions between oral actinomycetes and streptococci.

SPECIFIC ADHERENCE OF ORAL ACTINOMYCETES TO STREPTOCOCCI

In vivo and in vitro bacterial interactions. Studies of the microbial composition of developing dental plaque have shown that *S. sanguis* makes up a high percentage of those organisms which initially colonize a cleaned tooth surface (17). As the early plaque matures, a shift in the microbial population occurs which is characterized by a decline in the percentage of streptococci and an increase in the percentage of actinomycetes. This population shift and the

TABLE 2. *Oral bacteria which exhibit galactose or lactose-sensitive adherence*

Bacterium	Adherence to:	Reference
Actinomyces viscosus or A. naeslundii	Streptococcus sanguis	3, 4, 19, 26
	Erythrocytes (neuraminidase-treated)	3, 6, 9
	Epithelial cells	36
	Glycoprotein-coated latex beads[a]	
Capnocytophaga ochracea	Actinomyces sp. and S. sanguis[b]	
Eikenella corrodens	Epithelial cells	40
Fusobacterium nucleatum	Erythrocytes	27
	Salivary glycoproteins	12
Leptotrichia buccalis	Erythrocytes and saliva-coated enamel powder	20
Streptococcus sanguis	A. naeslundii and Propionibacterium acnes S. sanguis[c]	19

[a] A. H. Costello and O. Gabriel, J. Dent. Res. Spec. Issue A **60**:548, abstr. 954, 1981.

[b] P. Kolenbrander and S. Hurst-Calderone, J. Dent. Res. Spec. Issue A **60**:333, abstr. 90, 1981.

[c] F. C. McIntire, personal communication.

consistent presence of both streptococci and actinomycetes in human dental plaque (17) raise the possibility that interactions might occur between these organisms in vivo.

Results from several studies of in vitro coaggregation show that most human strains of *A. viscosus* and *A. naeslundii* interact specifically with many isolates of *S. sanguis* and *S. mitis* (4, 8, 19). By using freshly isolated strains, all of 24 *A. viscosus* isolates and 37 of 43 *A. naeslundii* isolates were found to coaggregate with members of a representative panel of *S. sanguis* strains (19); however, other oral actinomycetes, including strains of *A. odontolyticus, A. israelii,* and rodent strains of *A. viscosus,* often failed to coaggregate (4). Similarly, 17 of 25 *S. sanguis* or *S. mitis* strains interacted with many human strains of *A. viscosus* and *A. naeslundii,* whereas isolates of *S. mutans* and *S. salivarius* did not (4, 8). These findings emphasize the selective nature of in vitro coaggregation and suggest specific in vivo adherence between different groups of plaque bacteria.

Mechanisms of cell-to-cell adhesion. The coaggregations of *A. viscosus* and *A. naeslundii* with *S. sanguis* and *S. mitis* identify three types of cell-to-cell interaction (4, 19). The first (Fig. 1A) is inhibited by galactose or lactose and involves a lectin on the actinomycete with its receptor on the streptococcus. These reactions are abolished by heat or protease treatment of the actinomycete but not by similar treatment of the streptococcus. The second type of coaggregation (Fig. 1B) is postulated to result from cell-associated lectins on strains of streptococci and their receptors on certain actinomycetes. In these interactions, the streptococcus is the heat- or protease-sensitive member of the coaggregating pair. Although some coaggregations of this type are lactose

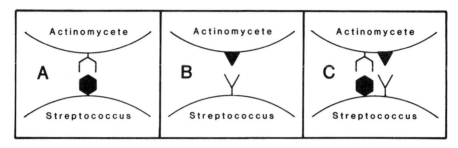

FIG. 1. *Types of coaggregation reactions observed between human strains of* A. viscosus *and* A. naeslundii *with isolates of* S. sanguis *and* S. mitis. *Coaggregation is postulated to depend on cell-associated lectins* (⌒ , Y) *that bind receptors which are galactose-like* (●) *or not yet identified* (▲). *Cells which are heat or protease treated lose their lectin activity but not their receptor activity.*

reversible (19), many are not, and these could involve individual lectins of a different specificity, multiple lectins on certain streptococci (P. Kolenbrander, personal communication), or perhaps mechanisms other than lectin–carbohydrate interactions. The term "unimodal" has been used to describe these coaggregations (Fig. 1A and B) because they are abolished by the heat or protease treatment of one cell type but are unaffected by similar treatment of the other cells.

The third type of coaggregation is "bimodal" (Fig. 1C) and can be prevented only when both cell types are inactivated. If bimodal interactions are rendered unimodal by the heat inactivation of one cell type, lactose then inhibits the coaggregation between the untreated actinomycete and the inactivated streptococcus. In most cases this sugar does not inhibit the reciprocal reaction between the untreated streptococcus and the heat-treated actinomycete. These properties suggest that bimodal coaggregations result from separate unimodal interactions involving lectins on each cell type.

Coaggregations between actinomycete and streptococcal strains may provide an important means for grouping these bacteria. This possibility is suggested by the identification of groups of actinomycetes or streptococci which display characteristic differences in the patterns of their coaggregation reactions (4, 19). These patterns have been interpreted as resulting from sets of cell-associated lectins and receptors (i.e., carbohydrates) which determine the coaggregation potential of a given cell type. Moreover, the ability to place a relatively large number of actinomycete and streptococcal strains into a limited number of distinct groups encourages the view that the system of cell-to-cell recognition between these bacteria has remained relatively simple at a molecular level.

Cell-associated lectin of A. viscosus T14V. Studies of the cell surface components involved in coaggregation have begun to provide a firm basis for understanding the specificity of these reactions. Human isolates of *A. viscosus* and *A. naeslundii* are covered by fimbriae (i.e., fibrils) which have been isolated and shown to be protein (5, 39). From their first description (16), a role for these structures in adherence was suspected. In support of this role, Ellen and co-workers (10) found that the removal of fimbriae from strains of *A. naeslundii* impaired bacterial attachment to buccal epithelial cells. Similarly, the importance of the fimbriae in lactose-inhibitable coaggregation of *A. viscosus*

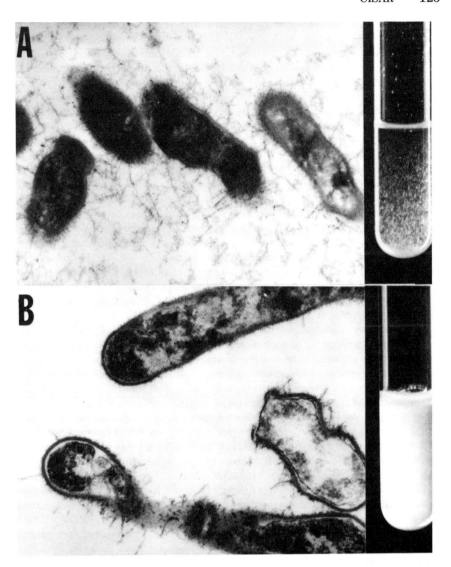

FIG. 2. *Electron micrographs of thin sections of* A. viscosus *T14V: (A) cells before the removal of fimbriae; (B) cells after the removal of fimbriae by mechanical shearing for 8 h in a high speed blender. Coaggregation with* S. sanguis *34 was used to detect the lactose-inhibitable lectin activity of the* A. viscosus *T14V: (A) cells tested before the removal of fimbriae; (B) cells tested after the removal of fimbriae which resulted in a loss of cell-associated lectin activity. (Electron micrographs provided by A. E. Vatter.)*

T14V with *S. sanguis* 34 has been demonstrated (Fig. 2). Although the loss of fimbriae resulted in an obvious loss of cell-associated lectin activity, it had no effect on coaggregations of the type illustrated in Fig. 1B (data not shown). These observations associate the *A. viscosus* lectin with the fimbriae and are consistent with the idea that distinct cell surface components mediate specific coaggregation reactions.

The fimbriae prepared from *A. viscosus* T14V contain two antigenic components (i.e., Ag 1 and Ag 2) which are distinguishable by crossed immunoelectrophoresis (3; J. O. Cisar et al., J. Immunol., in press) but difficult to separate completely by conventional biochemical methods. Initial assays for the agglutination of *S. sanguis* 34 or neuraminidase-treated erythrocytes with isolated fimbriae did not detect their lectin activity; however, multivalent complexes of the fimbriae, formed by cross-linking with antibodies against both antigens, caused lactose-inhibitable agglutination reactions. These observations indicated that the appearance of this activity after the specific cross-linking of Ag 1 or Ag 2 would provide a means of further localizing the lectin. This was accomplished after the production of several different monoclonal antibodies that were specific for either Ag 1 (unpublished data) or Ag 2 (3; J. O. Cisar et al., in press). The detection of agglutinating activity after the formation of immune complexes only with the Ag 2-specific antibodies favored an association of the lectin with Ag 2 and not Ag 1. Similar experiments performed with fimbriae isolated from other actinomycete strains also detected their lectin activity and associated this activity with structures which are antigenically related to Ag 2. The requirement of multivalent Ag 2 complexes for the appearance of agglutinating activity may be related to a low affinity of individual lectin sites (3, 6) or to the distribution of these sites on an individual structure. Monoclonal antibodies against Ag 1 and Ag 2 have been used to prepare affinity columns for the purification of each fimbrial antigen. Electron microscopic examination of each monoclonal antibody has shown that both Ag 1 and Ag 2 have a similar fibrillar morphology (unpublished data). These findings establish two antigenic types of fimbriae on *A. viscosus* T14V and associate a lectin activity with one of these components.

The results of two other investigations provide excellent support for, and also extend, the above findings. G. Revis and co-workers (submitted for publication), using Fab fragments prepared from monospecific rabbit antisera against Ag 1 and Ag 2, found that lactose-inhibitable coaggregation was blocked by the anti-Ag 2 but not by the anti-Ag 1 Fab preparation. In addition, P. E. Kolenbrander and S. Hurst-Calderone (Abstr. Annu. Meet. Am. Soc. Microbiol. 1981, I50, p. 95) have isolated mutants of *A. viscosus* T14V which are specifically defective in their ability to exhibit lactose-reversible coaggregation and have demonstrated the presence of Ag 1 and the absence of Ag 2 on these strains. Therefore, the combined results from three independent experimental approaches establish that the cell-associated lectin activity of *A. viscosus* T14V is a property of one type of fimbriae.

Receptors for the *A. viscosus* lectin. Lactose-reversible coaggregation presumably involves the binding of lectin sites on the Ag 2 fimbriae to terminal D-galactose residues or related structures on the streptococcal surface. All saccharides which inhibit binding of the lectin show an obvious structural similarity to D-galactose, and a number of other saccharides have been tested which do not inhibit binding (3, 9, 26). While the specificity of the *A. viscosus* lectin appears to be for β-linked rather than α-linked galactosides, this does not necessarily mean that only terminal β-linked structures function as receptors on the cell surface. Indeed, *A. viscosus* T14V exhibits lactose-inhibitable adherence to latex beads coated with purified mucins containing only α-N-acetyl-D-galactosamine as nonreducing end groups (A. H. Costello and O. Gabriel, J.

Dent. Res. Spec. Issue A **60**:548, abstr. 954, 1981). Additional information on the specificity of the lectin has shown that, on a molar basis, Galβ(1→3)GalNAc is a better inhibitor of coaggregation than Galβ(1→4)Glc (i.e., lactose), and that both of these structures are at least 10-fold more active than a β(1→6)-linked tetramer of galactose (F. C. McIntire, personal communication). These results indicate a relatively high degree of specificity for interactions of the *A. viscosus* lectin with various galactosides.

The identification of the lectin receptors on *S. sanguis* will require their extraction, purification, and structural characterization from representative strains. Such studies with *S. sanguis* 34 have resulted in the isolation from cell walls of a carbohydrate-containing fraction which is quite active as an inhibitor of coaggregation, and structural studies of this material are in progress (F. C. McIntire, personal communication). Indirect evidence that the receptors in question may be galactose-like structures has come from studies using a D-galactose–specific lectin (RCA-120) from the castor bean (31). A good, though not perfect, correlation exists between those strains of *S. sanguis* which react with the *A. viscosus* lectin in coaggregation and those which are agglutinated by the castor bean lectin (unpublished data). While this correlation suggests the recognition of similar receptors by both lectins, this remains to be firmly established.

Recent studies have examined the role of terminal galactose residues in the adherence of *A. viscosus* T14V to latex beads coated with individual, well-characterized glycoproteins (Costello and Gabriel, J. Dent. Res. Spec. Issue A **60**:548, abstr. 954, 1981). The receptors on these artificial surfaces represent well-defined structures which can be precisely modified by enzymatic or chemical treatments of the purified soluble glycoprotein prior to its adsorption on the bead. The use of this approach has shown that: surface-associated asialofetuin displays receptors for lactose-inhibitable microbial adherence; these receptors are sensitive to treatment with the enzyme galactose oxidase, which modifies the galactose termini to aldehyde derivatives; and the effect of this enzyme on the receptor is reversed by the subsequent addition of $NaBH_4$, which reduces the aldehyde derivatives back to galactose termini. Thus, the molecular mechanism of adherence to the coated bead involves binding of the *A. viscosus* lectin to the β-linked galactose termini of asialofetuin. Similar attempts to modify cell surface receptors with galactose oxidase, or to remove them with preparations of β-galactosidase, have been unsuccessful when applied to either streptococci (F. C. McIntire, personal communication) or neuraminidase-treated erythrocytes (O. Gabriel, personal communication). The findings with cells and those with glycoprotein-coated beads are not inconsistent, and differences are likely to result from a number of possibilities, all related to the structural complexity of various cell surfaces. In this regard, it is likely that β(1→4)-linked galactose termini of glycoprotein chains represent only one member in a family of structurally related receptors which function in lactose-inhibitable adherence of the actinomycetes to various bacterial and mammalian cells.

CONCLUDING REMARKS

The study of coaggregations between oral actinomycetes and streptococci has provided a glimpse of a fundamental mechanism involved in the specific adherence of many microorganisms to a wide variety of different cells and tissue surfaces. This insight has revealed basic similarities in the adherence of *A.*

viscosus to streptococci in dental plaque and of *Escherichia coli* to intestinal epithelium. Both adherence phenomena involve the action of cell-associated lectins. The lectin activity on *A. viscosus* is lactose (i.e., galactose) sensitive and results from the Ag 2 fimbriae, whereas the activity on *E. coli* is mannose sensitive and is a property of type 1 pili (35). The differing specificities of these lectins would be expected to contribute, in some important way, to differences in the adherence and colonization of these bacteria. This view is encouraged by the presence of galactose-sensitive lectins on most human isolates of *A. viscosus, A. naeslundii,* and certain other oral bacteria (Table 2), and by the occurrence of mannose-sensitive lectins on many *E. coli* strains and certain other enteric bacteria (32, 33). In addition to structures with known lectin activity, both *A. viscosus* and *E. coli* possess other types of fimbriae or pili which function differently. For example, the Ag 1 fimbriae of *A. viscosus,* also called VA 1, are not involved in lactose-sensitive adherence, but may play an important role in the adherence of bacteria to the glycoprotein pellicle of teeth (39). Likewise, the presence of mannose-resistant pili on strains of *E. coli* is widely recognized and certain types are associated with specific patterns of colonization and disease production (11). Thus, distinct structures on the cell surfaces of each microorganism seem to perform specific adherence functions.

In addition to providing support for the role of lectin-carbohydrate interactions in microbial adherence, the study of the *A. viscosus* lectin has suggested an important property of this, and perhaps certain other microbial lectins, which contributes to the understanding of their function. A number of observations indicate that the *A. viscosus* lectin has a relatively low affinity for what is thought to be its natural receptor on a streptococcus, and indeed, it was the inability of streptococcal cells to absorb the lectin activity from preparations of isolated fimbriae which initially raised this possibility. In accounting for the firm attachment of one cell to another, it seems likely that an effect of multivalence (7), achieved by the binding of many lectin combining sites on one actinomycete cell to many receptors on a streptococcus or neuraminidase-treated erythrocyte (6), plays an important role. The acceptance of this mechanism, however, raises the question as to why evolution would favor it over one involving fewer interactions of higher affinity and, consequently, a need for fewer fimbriae on the bacterial surface. A possible explanation is suggested by the fact that fimbriae must promote surface-to-surface adherence in an environment which is rich in soluble receptors formed by the galactose termini of salivary asialoglycoproteins. In such an environment, lectins with high-affinity combining sites would bind soluble glycoproteins and surface-to-surface adherence would be blocked. By contrast, the expression of many low-affinity lectin combining sites by a microorganism would favor adherence. A low affinity would allow many sites to remain unoccupied, and through multivalent binding, these could provide the strength for surface-to-surface adherence.

The adherence mechanism proposed clearly favors the idea that glycoproteins in secretions represent an important host defense (15). To compete with this defense mechanism, evolution would have to provide a microorganism with an adequate number of relatively low-affinity lectin combining sites on fimbriae or pili; however, a significant overproduction of these structures might not be favored for reasons of economy. Thus, microbial adherence to secretory surfaces may involve a rather delicate balance among the glycoprotein concentration of a secretion, the affinity of the microbial lectin combining site, and the number of such sites expressed by a microorganism in its natural environment. As a result of this balance, subtle changes in any of these variables could significantly influence microbial adherence.

Further studies of bacterial coaggregation phenomena, both in vitro and in vivo, should help to reveal the manner in which these interactions contribute to the development and organization of the oral microbial community. The in vitro specificities of various coaggregation reactions imply that they mediate a highly ordered type of adherence in vivo. This possibility has already been illustrated by Mouton and co-workers (28–30), who found that the characteristic and highly ordered "corncob" configurations of bacteria observed in human dental plaque could be formed in vitro by the coaggregation of *Bacterionema matruchotii* with only the specific strains of *S. sanguis* isolated from in vivo "corncobs." This proof for the in vivo role of a coaggregation phenomenon implies the existence of a self-assembly process in which specific microbial combinations, and thus communities, are formed according to instructions built into the architecture of each member's cell surface. Finally, the possibility should be mentioned that specific combinations of oral bacteria may have a greater potential for promoting periodontal disease than each individual member alone. This possibility, which has long been recognized (25), suggests that certain coaggregations may be regarded as early events in periodontal disease in much the same way that adherence represents the first step of infections caused by individual pathogens.

SUMMARY

The binding of one microorganism to another is a type of adherence exhibited by many oral bacteria, especially those which colonize the teeth. This type of adherence is detected by the phenomenon of coaggregation which occurs when different bacteria are mixed together. Although several plaque bacteria coaggregate, these interactions are specific and occur selectively between different organisms. The specificity of in vitro coaggregation implies an ordered type of in vivo adherence and raises the possibility that certain coaggregations function in the organization of different bacteria into efficient microbial communities. In addition, the association of specific microbial communities with periodontal disease suggests that coaggregation may represent an early event in this disease process in much the same way that adherence represents the first step of infections caused by individual pathogens. The mechanism of coaggregation between certain oral actinomycetes and streptococci has been examined. Like a number of other specific cell-to-cell interactions which occur in nature, these coaggregations appear to involve carbohydrate binding proteins, or lectins, on one cell type (i.e., the actinomycete or the streptococcus) and carbohydrate-containing receptors for these lectins on the other cell type. The lectin activity on human strains of *A. viscosus* and *A. naeslundii* is inhibited by β-linked galactosides (i.e., lactose) and results from a specific type of fimbriae on these bacteria. A number of other oral bacteria also exhibit galactose-sensitive adherence to certain cells and tissue surfaces. This specificity may characterize the adherence of many oral bacteria in the same way that mannose-sensitive adherence is exhibited by a number of different enteric bacteria. The findings with both groups of microorganisms emphasize the importance of lectin–carbohydrate interactions as a mechanism of specific microbial adherence.

ACKNOWLEDGMENTS

The electron micrographs provided by A. E. Vatter, the assistance of Shelley Curl, and the help of Carol Oesch in preparation of the manuscript are all gratefully acknowledged.

LITERATURE CITED

1. **Bladen, H., G. Hageage, F. Pollock, and R. Harr.** 1970. Plaque formation *in vitro* on wires by gram-negative oral microorganisms *(Veillonella).* Arch. Oral Biol. **15:**127–133.
2. **Bourgeau, G., and B. C. McBride.** 1976. Dextran-mediated interbacterial aggregation between dextran-synthesizing streptococci and *Actinomyces viscosus.* Infect. Immun. **13:**1228–1234.
3. **Cisar, J. O., E. L. Barsumian, S. H. Curl, A. E. Vatter, A. L. Sandberg, and R. P. Siraganian.** 1980. The use of monoclonal antibodies in the study of lactose-sensitive adherence of *Actinomyces viscosus* T14V. RES J. Reticuloendothel. Soc. **28:**73s–79s.
4. **Cisar, J. O., P. E. Kolenbrander, and F. C. McIntire.** 1979. Specificity of coaggregation reactions between human oral streptococci and strains of *Actinomyces viscosus* or *Actinomyces naeslundii.* Infect. Immun. **24:**742–752.
5. **Cisar, J. O., and A. E. Vatter.** 1979. Surface fibrils (fimbriae) of *Actinomyces viscosus* T14V. Infect. Immun. **24:**523–531.
6. **Costello, A. H., J. O. Cisar, P. E. Kolenbrander, and O. Gabriel.** 1979. Neuraminidase-dependent hemagglutination of human erythrocytes by human strains of *Actinomyces viscosus* and *Actinomyces naeslundii.* Infect. Immun. **26:**563–572.
7. **Crothers, D. M., and H. Metzger.** 1972. The influence of polyvalency on the binding properties of antibodies. Immunochemistry **9:**341–357.
8. **Ellen, R. P., and I. B. Balcerzak-Raczkowski.** 1977. Interbacterial aggregation of *Actinomyces naeslundii* and dental plaque streptococci. J. Periodontal Res. **12:**11–20.
9. **Ellen, R. P., E. D. Fillery, K. H. Chan, and D. A. Grove.** 1980. Sialidase-enhanced lectin-like mechanism for *Actinomyces viscosus* and *Actinomyces naeslundii* hemagglutination. Infect. Immun. **27:**335–343.
10. **Ellen, R. P., D. L. Walker, and K. H. Chan.** 1978. Association of long surface appendages with adherence-related functions of the gram-positive species *Actinomyces naeslundii.* J. Bacteriol. **134:**1171–1175.
11. **Evans, D. G., D. J. Evans, Jr., S. Clegg, and J. A. Pauley.** 1979. Purification and characterization of the CFA/I antigen of enterotoxigenic *Escherichia coli.* Infect. Immun. **25:**738–748.
12. **Falkler, W. A., Jr., J. R. Mongiello, and B. W. Burger.** 1979. Haemagglutination inhibition and aggregation of *Fusobacterium nucleatum* by human salivary mucinous glycoproteins. Arch. Oral Biol. **24:**483–489.
13. **Gibbons, R. J., and M. Nygard.** 1970. Interbacterial aggregation of plaque bacteria. Arch. Oral Biol. **15:**1397–1400.
14. **Gibbons, R. J., and J. van Houte.** 1973. On the formation of dental plaques. J. Periodontol. **44:**347–360.
15. **Gibbons, R. J., and J. van Houte.** 1975. Bacterial adherence in oral microbiol ecology. Annu. Rev. Microbiol. **29:**19–44.
16. **Girard, A. E., and B. H. Jacius.** 1974. Ultrastructure of *Actinomyces viscosus* and *Actinomyces naeslundii.* Arch. Oral Biol. **19:**71–79.
17. **Hardie, J. M., and G. H. Bowden.** 1976. The microbial flora of dental plaque: bacterial succession and isolation considerations, p. 63–87. *In* M. Stiles, W. Loesche, and T. O'Brien, (ed.), Microbial aspects of dental caries, vol. 1. Information Retrieval, Inc., Washington, D.C.
18. **Kelstrup, J., and T. D. Funder-Nielson.** 1974. Aggregation of oral streptococci with *Fusobacterium* and *Actinomyces.* J. Biol. Buccale **2:**347–362.
19. **Kolenbrander, P. E., and B. L. Williams.** 1981. Lactose-reversible coaggregation between oral actinomycetes and *Streptococcus sanguis.* Infect. Immun. **33:**95–102.
20. **Kondo, W., N. Sato, and H. Ozawa.** 1976. Haemagglutinating activity of *Leptotrichia buccalis* cells and their adherence to saliva-coated enamel powder. Arch. Oral Biol. **21:**363–369.
21. **Kuramitsu, H. K., and A. Paul.** 1980. Role of bacterial interactions in the colonization of oral surfaces by *Actinomyces viscosus.* Infect. Immun. **29:**83–90.
22. **Lancy, P., Jr., B. Appelbaum, S. C. Holt, and B. Rosan.** 1980. Quantitative in vitro assay for "corncob" formation. Infect. Immun. **29:**663–670.
23. **Liljemark. W. F., C. G. Bloomquist, and G. R. Germaine.** 1981. Effect of bacterial aggregation on the adherence of oral streptococci to hydroxyapatite. Infect. Immun. **31:**935–941.
24. **Lis, H., and N. Sharon.** 1977. Lectins: their chemistry and application to immunology, p. 429–529. *In* M. Sela (ed.), The antigens, vol. 4. Academic Press, Inc., New York.
25. **MacDonald, J. B., R. J. Gibbons, and S. S. Socransky.** 1960. Bacterial mechanisms in periodontal disease. Ann. N.Y. Acad. Sci. **85:**467–478.
26. **McIntire, F. C., A. E. Vatter, J. Baros, and J. Arnold.** 1978. Mechanism of coaggregation between *Actinomyces viscosus* T14V and *Streptococcus sanguis* 34. Infect. Immun. **21:**978–988.
27. **Mongiello, J. R., and W. A. Falkler, Jr.** 1979. Sugar inhibition of oral *Fusobacterium nucleatum* haemagglutination and cell binding. Arch. Oral Biol. **24:**539–545.

28. **Mouton, C., H. S. Reynolds, E. A. Gasiecki, and R. J. Genco.** 1979. *In vitro* adhesion of tufted oral streptococci to *Bacterionema matruchotii.* Curr. Microbiol. **3:**181–186.
29. **Mouton, C., H. Reynolds, and R. J. Genco.** 1978. Combined micro-manipulation, culture and immunofluorescent techniques for isolation of the coccal organisms comprising the "corncob" configuration of human dental plaque. J. Biol. Buccale **5:**321–332.
30. **Mouton, C., H. S. Reynolds, and R. J. Genco.** 1980. Characterization of tufted streptococci isolated from the "corncob" configuration of human dental plaque. Infect. Immun. **27:**235–245.
31. **Nicolson, G. L., and J. Blaustein.** 1972. The interaction of *Ricinus communis* agglutinin with normal and tumor cell surfaces. Biochim. Biophys. Acta **266:**543–547.
32. **Ofek, I., E. H. Beachey, and N. Sharon.** 1978. Surface sugars of animal cells as determinants of recognition in bacterial adherence. Trends Biochem. Sci. **3:**159–160.
33. **Ottow, J. C. G.** 1975. Ecology, physiology, and genetics of fimbriae and pili. Annu. Rev. Microbiol. **29:**79–108.
34. **Pereira, M. E. A., and E. A. Kabat.** 1979. Immunochemical studies on lectins and their application to the fractionation of blood group substances and cells. Crit. Rev. Immunol. **1:**33–78.
35. **Salit, I. E., and E. C. Gotschlich.** 1977. Hemagglutination by purified type I *Escherichia coli* pili. J. Exp. Med. **146:**1169–1181.
36. **Saunders, J. M., and C. H. Miller.** 1980. Attachment of *Actinomyces naeslundii* to human buccal epithelial cells. Infect. Immun. **29:**981–989.
37. **Slots, J., and R. J. Gibbons.** 1978. Attachment of *Bacteroides melaninogenicus* subsp. *asaccharolyticus* to oral surfaces and its possible role in colonization of the mouth and of periodontal pockets. Infect. Immun. **19:**254–264.
38. **Weerkamp, A. H., and B. C. McBride.** 1980. Characterization of the adherence properties of *Streptococcus salivarius.* Infect. Immun. **29:**459–468.
39. **Wheeler, T. T., and W. B. Clark.** 1980. Fibril-mediated adherence of *Actinomyces viscosus* to saliva-treated hydroxyapatite. Infect. Immun. **28:**577–584.
40. **Yamazaki, Y., S. Ebisu, and H. Okada.** 1981. *Eikenella corrodens* adherence to human buccal epithelial cells. Infect. Immun. **31:**21–27.

Age, Supragingival Plaque, and Steroid Hormones as Ecological Determinants of the Subgingival Flora

KENNETH S. KORNMAN

University of Connecticut School of Dental Medicine
Farmington, Connecticut 06032

In recent years, the life span of patients with defects in their host defense systems has been extended. As a result there has been an increased awareness of infections which commonly affect compromised hosts. This type of bacterial disease has been called an "opportunistic" disease because the altered host provides an opportunity for specific bacteria to cause pathology. Although the term "opportunistic disease" is usually applied to infection in a host who is immunologically defective, it may also refer to diseases involving an overgrowth of organisms such that normal host defense mechanisms are incapable of controlling the bacterial insult. This basically represents a threshold phenomenon in which potentially pathogenic bacteria produce no overt disease as long as their levels are below the host's detoxifying capacity. Those same organisms which in low numbers were compatible with health can produce pathology if the levels exceed an individual's threshold. Thus, opportunistic disease may result from a shift in the indigenous microflora such that potential pathogens are allowed to increase above the disease threshold. This would be comparable to antibiotic-induced candidiasis or ulcerative colitis, in which *Candida albicans* and *Clostridium difficile,* respectively, are present in low numbers in health but increase after antibiotic therapy to a level which damages the host.

The microbial flora of the gingival sulcus is a complex mixture of organisms which is generally similar from individual to individual. Many of the anaerobic bacteria isolated from the gingival sulcus are not routine isolates from other sites in the oral cavity. Since bacteriological studies of different periodontal conditions (18, 25, 26, 29, 31, 32) suggest that the organisms which are in high proportions in disease are also detectable in health but in lower numbers, ecological conditions which foster the growth and selection of periodontopathic bacteria are of primary importance in the determination of disease etiology.

Recent longitudinal studies of induced periodontitis in monkeys (11, 28) confirm the impression from cross-sectional studies that the development of periodontitis is associated with a shift in specific components of the normal microflora in an opportunistic manner. If bacterial changes can be shown to precede disease, then the essential question becomes what factors initiate or allow shifts in the indigenous bacterial population.

Levels of bacteria in the normal flora are determined by host defense mechanisms and local environmental factors. An indigenous organism with pathogenic potential is kept below the disease threshold by these factors, and therefore one may postulate that the threshold may be overcome by a break in host defenses or an alteration in the environment.

132

Although it is well established that plaque bacteria, and most probably subgingival bacteria interacting with host defense mechanisms, initiate periodontitis, other factors—specifically, age, supragingival plaque control, and hormonal disturbances—have been repeatedly identified as modifying factors in the disease process. These factors may influence the disease by altering the tissue reaction to a previously innocuous microflora or by altering the microflora in an adverse way. Since immune mechanisms are discussed extensively elsewhere in this volume, this report will focus on the effects of age, supragingival plaque control, and hormonal fluctuations on the subgingival ecosystem.

AGE

Chronic periodontitis is a disease of adults, and epidemiologically its severity is correlated with age. When preschool children were compared with young adults for 21 days in an experimental gingivitis model, adults had a significant increase in gingival exudate and the number of bleeding units, but no change in these parameters of gingivitis was observed in the children. In sites with the same development of plaque, the increase in gingivitis was greater in adults than in children (20). Changes with age may greatly influence the microflora inhabiting the skin and mucosa. For example, ringworm of the scalp, a superficial mycotic infection, occurs commonly in childhood, heals spontaneously at puberty, and is rare in adults. This change is thought to be due to the increase in long-chain fatty acids in the adult. Some of these same fatty acids which are fungistatic appear to promote the growth of *Propionibacterium acnes,* an etiological agent in acne. Thus, subtle metabolic changes with aging may be manifested by different microbial floras and by different disease patterns.

Very little is known about the normal mucosal flora associated with different age groups. It is generally accepted that oral anaerobes do not have an appropriate physical environment available to them until the gingival sulcus forms during tooth eruption.

In a recent study (4) of the microflora of neonates, α-hemolytic streptococci and *Streptococcus salivarius* dominated the oral flora for the first 6 days after birth, a finding which is in agreement with earlier reports (21, 34). Although anaerobes were not isolated on the first day, on the second day 7 of 23 subjects were colonized by anaerobic cocci and 2, by bifidobacteria (4). This is in spite of clear exposure to anaerobic bacteria as evidenced by the presence at 3 days of age of *Bacteroides* species, *Bifidobacterium* species, eubacteria, lactobacilli, and anaerobic cocci in the feces at levels approaching those found in adults. By 1 year of age the oral cavity contains both gram-positive and gram-negative filamentous bacteria, including *Fusobacterium, Lactobacillus,* and *Actinomyces* species (21).

Newman et al. (22) studied the subgingival flora associated with periodontal health in seven subjects over 55 years of age. The microflora was quite variable, but the distribution of bacterial species was within the range reported for middle-aged subjects (26) with a comparable periodontal status.

Ellen (5) has described the relationship of age to isolation of facultatively anaerobic *Actinomyces* species. *A. naeslundii* was found in the oral cavity of most infants even prior to tooth eruption, with *A. viscosus* becoming dominant in plaque only in subjects over 13 years of age.

We have recently observed what appear to be age-associated microflora differences in monkeys. It is difficult to determine the age of an animal with a fully erupted dentition. For studies of ligature-induced periodontitis, we selected female monkeys with third molars in position with fully formed roots, on the assumption that these were adults. In this model the subgingival flora of adult monkeys exhibits proportional increases in surface translocating bacteria and *Bacteroides gingivalis* associated with clinical and radiographic evidence of periodontitis (11). Two animals, which on the basis of dental development were estimated to be comparable in age to 16- to 20-year-old humans, exhibited a very different bacterial pattern after ligature placement (unpublished data). These animals were menstruating but had unerupted third molars or incomplete root formation. Prior to ligature placement, the subgingival bacterial flora of the young animals was similar to that of the adults, with the trend toward fewer anaerobic cocci and more gram-negative rods in the young animals. Six weeks after the ligature was placed, the basic pattern of morphological types was surprisingly similar between the young and adult monkeys. The subgingival flora of the young animals, however, had no detectable surface translocating bacteria at this stage, compared with 14.3% in the adults. In addition, 36.2% of the flora were saccharolytic black-pigmented *Bacteroides,* including both *intermedius* and *melaninogenicus* subspecies of *B. melaninogenicus. B. gingivalis* was never isolated from these animals. Adult animals after 6 weeks had 34.2% *B. gingivalis* and less than 1% saccharolytic black-pigmented *Bacteroides.* The young animals showed an increase in gingivitis but no detectable loss of attachment or radiographic bone loss during the 15 weeks of the experiment. During this same period the adults had a mean increase in pocket depth of 2.0 mm and radiographic evidence of bone loss. The frequency of isolation of *B. melaninogenicus* (subspecies not identified) from the gingival sulcus of erupted teeth has been previously reported to vary with age. Bailit et al. (1) noted that of subgingival samples taken from 320 children only 40% of the 6- to 8-year-old children were positive for black-pigmented *Bacteroides,* whereas over 90% of those aged 13 to 15 years were positive. The authors speculated that this pattern was compatible with a cumulative infection. Using a different sampling technique, Kelstrup (8) reported isolation of *B. melaninogenicus* from 20% of 94 gingival samples from children 5 to 12 years old and from 58% of 65 samples from those aged 14 to 16 years.

With improvements in techniques and refined methods of identifying species of many organisms, it would be of interst to reevaluate the isolation frequency of specific organisms at different ages. This information might allow us to focus our prevention efforts better as well as to introduce potential avenues for modifying the indigenous flora.

SUPRAGINGIVAL PLAQUE

In the normal host, bacteria colonize in a predictable succession, with one group of organisms altering the environment to allow new organisms to become established or to allow certain existing bacteria to achieve dominance. It is therefore logical to expect the accumulation of supragingival plaque to affect the establishment of the subgingival flora. Supragingival plaque has been shown to go from an oxidation–reduction potential (Eh) of greater than $+200$ mV the first day of plaque development to below -100 mV after 4 days (9). A low Eh is known to facilitate the initiation of the growth of anaerobic bacteria.

Population shifts in developing plaque have been attributed to a lowering of the oxidation–reduction potential of the environment, the initially dominant organisms being facultative and anaerobes becoming prominent after 7 days of plaque development (16, 23, 24).

In addition, specific members of the supragingival ecosystem produce compounds which are essential growth factors for members of the subgingival flora. Many of these nutritional interrelationships have been reviewed by Loesche (16). *B. melaninogenicus* and *B. asaccharolyticus* require vitamin K for optimal energy transduction. This compound is produced by other plaque organisms, including *B. oralis, Veillonella alcalescens,* and anaerobic gram-positive rods (7). Some oral spirochetes require spermine, spermidine, or putrescine as well as isobutyrate, which can be provided by gram-positive rods and fusobacteria, respectively (30). A few subgingival bacteria such as *Vibrio succinogenes* and *Bacteroides ureolyticus* require the addition of hydrogen or formate as electron donors and fumarate as a terminal electron acceptor. Formate is a metabolic end product of several plaque organisms including *Fusobacterium* and *Bacteroides* species (17). Therefore, many of the organisms which inhabit the subgingival area appear to be dependent on specific coexistent bacteria for essential metabolic processes.

In a monkey model of periodontitis, we have observed in vivo correlates of some of these pure culture studies. *B. gingivalis* increased after infection only at sites with elevated proportional levels of *Capnocytophaga* species. The increase in *B. gingivalis* was accompanied by a significant decrease in plaque proportions of *Capnocytophaga* species (R. A. Kiel, K. S. Kornman, and P. B. Robertson, J. Dent. Res. Spec. Issue A, **60**:415, abstr. 418, 1981).

Supragingival bacteria may also influence the subgingival flora by providing sites for the attachment of subgingival organisms. Slots and Gibbons (27) showed that *B. asaccharolyticus* as well as other anaerobic and capnophilic gram-negative rods readily attach to cells of several gram-positive bacteria commonly found in both supragingival and subgingival plaque. Oral rinses of labeled *B. asaccharolyticus* were found primarily attached to preformed plaque, suggesting an important role for supragingival plaque in the initial colonization by organisms which have been associated with periodontal disease.

On a theoretical basis the development of the subgingival microflora appears to be dependent on supragingival plaque. Short-term studies indicate that a mature complex gingival microflora dominated by diverse morphological types does not develop when supragingival plaque is controlled by mechanical or chemical means (15). The real influence of the supragingival flora on the subgingival flora in periodontitis, however, can be assessed only after a stable subgingival ecosystem has developed. Listgarten et al. (14) reported that for pockets greater than 5 mm supragingival plaque control alone reduced the gingival index but had no effect on the subgingival microflora as evaluated microscopically. Determination of the effects of supragingival plaque control on a preformed subgingival flora are not yet available but may provide important information relative to the treatment of gingivitis and periodontitis.

STEROID HORMONES

The gingival sulcus is continually flushed with a serum exudate which includes a variety of serum proteins as well as glucose, steroids, urea, inflammatory cells, and desquamated epithelial cells (2). Alterations in steroid hormone levels have been repeatedly implicated as a modifying factor in periodontal disease. An exaggerated gingivitis has been reported in association with puberty, pregnancy, menstruation, stress, and the use of oral contraceptives. In addition, women taking oral contraceptives for more than 18 months exhibited a significantly greater loss of periodontal attachment than age- and plaque-matched controls (10). A recent survey of plasma hormone levels (33) in 23 subjects with various degrees of periodontal disease found significantly elevated progesterone levels in all male and in five of eight females with periodontal inflammation. Plasma progesterone was in the normal range in patients with clinically healthy gingiva.

Elevated plasma steroids are known to alter vascular permeability (13) as well as a variety of immunological functions (3, 19) and cellular levels of proteins and carbohydrates. Changes in endogenous steroid levels have been associated with alterations in the vaginal tract microflora, the urinary tract flora, and the gastrointestinal tract flora. An increase in steroid hormones may represent a strong environmental factor on mucous membranes. Recently, the subgingival microflora has been shown to undergo changes during pregnancy, with a statistically significant increase in proportions of B. melaninogenicus subsp. intermedius evident during the second trimester (12). Also in the second trimester, subgingival plaque samples were found to take up greater quantities of estradiol and progesterone per microgram of plaque protein than at other time periods. This observation led to an evaluation of the direct interaction between B. melaninogenicus and steroid hormones.

Resting-cell suspensions of B. melaninogenicus subsp. intermedius and subsp. melaninogenicus were found to take up 2.6×10^{-4} μmol of ^{14}C-estradiol or ^{14}C-progesterone per μg of cell protein; minimal steroid uptake was observed with B. gingivalis and five other oral organisms (K. S. Kornman and W. J. Loesche, J. Dent. Res. Spec. Issue A, **58**:107, abstr. 58, 1979).

Uptake of steroids by B. melaninogenicus subsp. intermedius was temperature dependent and resulted in a labeled product as detected on thin-layer chromatography. Growth curves indicated that intermedius and melaninogenicus subspecies but not B. gingivalis could substitute progesterone or estradiol for vitamin K, an essential growth factor for these organisms. Since vitamin K compounds are involved in electron transport in the saccharolytic B. melaninogenicus, fumarate, the terminal electron acceptor, was evaluated for interaction with steroid uptake. Addition of fumarate to resting cells of B. melaninogenicus subspecies and B. gingivalis increased steroid uptake and resulted in the detection of succinate by gas-liquid chromatography. Resting cells given fumarate alone or steroids alone produced no succinate. Endogenous steroids appear to interact directly with the fumarate reductase system of B. melaninogenicus such that changes in the availability of hormones may influences the microbial ecology.

Steroid hormones are known to be present in the crevicular fluid (2) although they have not been quantitated. That the gingiva may even be a target tissue for steroids is suggested by reports that tritiated estradiol which was injected subcutaneously in rats became concentrated in the gingiva and uterus (6).

Both vitamin K compounds and steroids seem to be readily available to bacteria in the subgingival area. Given that steroids supported growth of Bacteroides species only within a narrow concentration range, the relative ecological influence of vitamin K and steroids may involve complex interactions among local synthesis of vitamin K, the rate of flow of gingival crevice fluid, and the hormonal status of the individual. Since *B. melaninogenicus* subsp. *intermedius* and *B. gingivalis* both required menadione but differed in their ability to use steroids for growth, the relative availability of vitamin K and steroids may influence the ecological balance of these two organisms. Thus, the present bacteriological findings, in conjunction with various clinical observations, implicate steroids as a factor in the ecological balance of the subgingival microflora.

Shifts in the subgingival flora during pregnancy demonstrate opportunistic changes. Direct interactions between steroid hormones and *Bacteroides* species represent one potential mechanism for inducing changes in the flora.

SUMMARY

In recent years, although the incidence of diseases due to classical bacterial pathogens has declined, this has been more than offset by opportunistic bacterial disease. Opportunistic diseases are definable in terms of a threshold phenomenon, in which levels of potentially pathogenic bacteria increase beyond the detoxifying capacity of the host. Since periodontitis appears to be an indigenous opportunistic disease which involves an alteration of the normal microflora, it is essential to determine the relationship between factors repeatedly associated wilth disease and the subgingival ecology. Age, supragingival plaque, and steroid hormones appear to be capable of influencing the levels of specific bacteria in the subgingival flora. Bacterial changes with age have been observed in the oral cavity and may be of importance to the development of periodontitis in adulthood. Supragingival plaque may influence the subgingival flora by providing nutrients, making the gingival area more anaerobic, and allowing attachment of specific subgingival organisms. The effect of supragingival plaque on the flora in a periodontal pocket has not been determined. In addition, the composition of the crevicular fluid may influence the flora by the availability of growth factors. For example, changes in steroid hormones have been associated with a change in the subgingival flora. These steroids are capable of interacting with specific organisms as growth factors, which represents one mechanism by which host factors may alter the flora.

LITERATURE CITED

1. **Bailit, H. L., D. C. Baldwin, and E. E. Hunt.** 1964. The increasing prevalence of gingival *Bacteroides melaninogenicus* with age in children. Arch. Oral Biol. **9**:435–438.
2. **Cimasoni, G.** 1974. The crevicular fluid. Monogr. Oral Sci. **3**:15–24.
3. **Dodson, M. G., R. H. Kerman, C. F. Lange, S. S. Stefani, and J. A. O'Learly.** 1976. T and B cells in pregnancy. Obstet. Gynecol. **49**:299–302.
4. **Duerden, B. I., and V. O. Rotimi.** 1981. The development of the bacterial flora in normal neonates. J. Med. Microbiol. **14**:51–62.
5. **Ellen, R. P.** 1976. Establishment and distribution of *Actinomyces viscosus* and *Actinomyces naeslundii* in the human oral cavity. Infect. Immun. **14**:1119–1124.
6. **Formicola, A. J., T. Weatherford, and H. Grupe.** 1970. The uptake of H^3-estradiol by the oral tissues of rats. J. Periodontal Res. **5**:269–275.
7. **Gibbons, R. J., and L. P. Engel.** 1964. Vitamin K compounds in bacteria that are obligate anaerobes. Science **146**:1307–1309.
8. **Kelstrup, J.** 1966. The incidence of *Bacteroides melaninogenicus* in human gingival sulci, and its prevalence in the oral cavity at different ages. Periodontics **4**:14–18.
9. **Kenney, E. B., and M. M. Ash.** 1969. Oxidation reduction potential of developing plaque, periodontal pockets and gingival sulci. J. Periodontol. **40**:630–633.
10. **Knight, G. M., and A. B. Wade.** 1974. The effects of hormonal contraceptives on the human periodontium. J. Periodontal Res. **9**:18–22.

11. **Kornman, K. S., S. C. Holt, and P. B. Robertson.** 1981. The microbiology of ligature induced periodontitis in the cynomolgus monkey. J. Periodontal Res. **16:**116–126.
12. **Kornman, K. S., and W. J. Loesche.** 1980. The subgingival microbial flora during pregnancy. J. Periodontal Res. **15:**111–122.
13. **Lindhe, J., R. Attstrom, and A.-L. Bjorn.** 1968. Influence of sex hormones on gingival exudation in dogs with chronic gingivitis. J. Periodontal Res. **3:**279–283.
14. **Listgarten, M. A., J. Lindhe, and L. Hellden.** 1978. The effect of tetracycline and/or scaling on human periodontal disease—clinical, microbiological and histological observations. J. Clin. Periodontol. **5:**246–271.
15. **Löe, H., and C. R. Schiott.** 1970. The effect of mouth rinses and topical application of chlorhexidine on the development of dental plaque and gingivitis in man. J. Periodontal Res. **5:**79–83.
16. **Loesche, W. J.** 1968. Importance of nutrition in gingival crevice microbial ecology. Periodontics **6:**245–251.
17. **Loesche, W. J., and R. J. Gibbons.** 1965. A practical scheme for identification of the most numerous oral Gram-negative anaerobic rods. Arch. Oral Biol. **10:**723–725.
18. **Loesche, W. J., and S. A. Syed.** 1978. Bacteriology of human experimental gingivitis: effect of plaque and gingivitis score. Infect. Immun. **21:**830–839.
19. **Lopatin, D. E., K. S. Kornman, and W. J. Loesche.** 1980. Modulation of immunoreactivity to periodontal disease-associated microorganisms during pregnancy. Infect. Immun. **28:**713–718.
20. **Matsson, L.** 1978. Development of gingivitis in pre-school children and young adults. J. Clin. Periodontol. **5:**24–34.
21. **McCarthy, C., M. L. Snyder, and P. B. Parker.** 1965. The indigenous oral flora of man. The newborn to the 1 year old infant. Arch. Oral Biol. **10:**61–73.
22. **Newman, M. G., V. Grinenco, M. Weiner, I. Angel, H. Karge, and R. Nisengard.** 1978. Predominant microbiota associated with periodontal health in the aged. J. Periodontol. **49:**553–559.
23. **Ritz, H. L.** 1967. Microbial population shifts in developing human dental plaque. Arch. Oral Biol. **12:**1561–1578.
24. **Slack, G. L., and G. H. Bowden.** 1965. Preliminary studies of experimental dental plaque *in vivo.* Adv. Fluorine Res. Dent. Caries Prev. **3:**193–198.
25. **Slots, J.** 1977. The predominant cultivable microflora of advanced periodontitis. Scand. J. Dent. Res. **85:**114–121.
26. **Slots, J.** 1977. Microflora in the healthy gingival sulcus in man. Scand. J. Dent. Res. **85:**247–254.
27. **Slots, J., and R. J. Gibbons.** 1978. Attachment of *Bacteroides melaninogenicus* subsp. *asaccharolyticus* to oral surfaces and its possible role in colonization of the mouth and of periodontal pockets. Infect. Immun. **19:**254–264.
28. **Slots, J., and E. Hausmann.** 1979. Longitudinal study of experimentally induced periodontal disease in *Macaca arctoides:* relationship between microflora and alveolar bone loss. Infect. Immun. **23:**260–269.
29. **Slots, J., D. Moenbo, and J. Langebaek.** 1978. Microbiota of gingivitis in man. Scand. J. Dent. Res. **86:**174–181.
30. **Socransky, S. S., W. J. Loesche, C. Hubersak, and J. B. MacDonald.** 1964. Dependency of *Treponema microdentium* on other oral organisms for isobutyrate, polyamines, and a controlled oxidation-reduction potential. J. Bacteriol. **88:**200–209.
31. **Tanner, A. C. R., C. Haffer, G. T. Bratthall, R. A. Viconti, and S. S. Socransky.** 1979. A study of the bacteria associated with advancing periodontitis in man. J. Clin. Periodontol. **6:**278–307.
32. **VanPalenstein-Helderman, W. H.** 1976. Total viable count and differential count of *Vibrio (Campylobacter) sputorum, Fusobacterium nucleatum, Selenomonas sputigena, Bacteroides ochraceous* and *Veillonella* in the inflamed and non-inflamed human gingival crevice. J. Periodontal Res. **10:**294–305.
33. **Vittek, J., S. C. Rappaport, G. G. Gordon, P. R. Munnangi, and A. L. Southren.** 1979. Concentration of circulating hormones and metabolism of andorgens by human gingiva. J. Periodontol. **50:**254–264.
34. **Zinner, D. D., and J. M. Jablon.** 1968. Human streptococcal strains in experimental caries, p. 128–136. *In* R. H. Harris (ed.), Art and science of dental caries research. Academic Press, Inc., New York.

PATHOGENIC AND VIRULENCE FACTORS IN PERIODONTAL DISEASES

Bacterial Surface Structures and Their Role in Periodontal Disease

STANLEY C. HOLT

Department of Microbiology, University of Massachusetts, Amherst, Massachusetts 01003

INTRODUCTION

The past several years have seen the development of a large body of experimental evidence which implicates microorganisms in the pathogenesis of several forms of gingivitis and periodontitis (9, 19, 24, 103, 104, 113, 119). These inflammatory diseases appear to be a result of the accumulation of bacteria (i.e., plaque) both supra- and subgingivally. This causal relationship between the development of destructive periodontal disease and a microbial flora is based on at least three significant observations: (i) a positive correlation between plaque index and gingival inflammation, (ii) the use of antibiotics, which not only controls the deposition of bacterial plaque but also the clinical manifestations of disease, and (iii) animal model experiments which are of major significance in ascribing a bacterial etiology to periodontal disease (17, 50–53, 73). Recent studies (87–89, 100, 101) suggest that the major forms of periodontal destruction are associated with a specific subgingival microbial flora. The vast array of microorganisms recovered from both healthy and diseased tissue include several which stand out as potentially significant periodontopathogens. Included in this group of microorganisms possessing disease-producing potential are members of the genera *Actinobacillus, Actinomyces, Bacteroides, Capnocytophaga,* and *Eikenella* (86, 113). Several studies (86, 101, 113, 119) have shown that this "predictable group" of microorganisms is consistently recovered from periodontal pockets. Inoculation of these microorganisms into gnotobiotic animals leads to the formation of periodontal pockets (see Irving and his associates [50–53]).

Although several gram-positive bacteria have been shown to cause alveolar bone loss in gnotobiotic animals (i.e., *Streptococcus mutans, S. salivarius,* and *Bacillus cereus*), these organisms do not appear to be major contributors to the ecology of the developing periodontal pocket. It is more than likely that, for microorganisms to function as contributors to disease, they must in some way adhere or colonize a specific surface or locale (102). These microorganisms, although they cause alveolar bone loss in animal model systems, do not constitute a significant proportion of the periodontal pocket microflora and thus are most probably not major contributors to periodontal tissue destruction. In addition to growing and maintaining themselves in restricted environments, potentially pathogenic microorganisms must be capable of evading both the host defense and immune mechanisms, as well as initiating the destruction of the host tissue.

Bacteria have developed a variety of mechanisms to evade destruction or neutralization by host cells and tissues, as well as to cause disease (see 102 for pertinent references). For example, they may elaborate surface capsules and slimes which not only interfere with host defenses (i.e., phagocytosis) but are also capable of functioning in, for example, abscess formation. In addition to these capsules and slimes, bacteria also elaborate a variety of surface components (i.e., lipopolysaccharides [LPS], toxins, lipoteichoic acids, glycoproteins) which are also detrimental to cell and tissue integrity and viability. Not to be overlooked are bacterial surface appendages such as pili and flagella which in diseases such as gonorrhea (110, 121), pyelonephritis, diphtheria, and cholera (30, 32, 59), for example, are active mediators of bacterial virulence. The discussion presented here focuses upon several of the principal bacterial outer membrane-associated components which may be involved in bacterial pathogenesis, especially as their manifestations may be related to periodontal disease.

BACTERIAL SURFACE COMPONENTS AND VIRULENCE

Electron microscopic and histological examination of periodontal tissue during the course of infection reveals the absence of intact microorganisms from intracellular locations *within* tissue (34). Acute necrotizing ulcerative gingivitis appears to be an exception in that bacterial infiltration of the host tissue occurs (72). Even though Frank (29) has reported on the presence of bacteria in the apical wall of periodontal pockets in advanced cases of periodontitis, the majority of observations reveal the absence of intact bacteria in periodontal lesions. This has generated the hypothesis that the involved tissues are penetrated by bacterial products or components, that is, cell fractions, and it is the action of these materials on the host tissue which results in eventual manifestations of response. Whether these manifestations result from a direct action of bacterial components on the host tissue or indirectly by the stimulation of the host immune or inflammatory responses, or from a combination of these effects, is not clear.

Several investigations (4, 32, 64, 70, 83, 84, 103) have shown that human bacterial plaque components could be involved in the destruction of the periodontium. For example, the classical endotoxin (LPS) has been shown to have cytotoxic effects on a broad range of mammalian tissue, including periodontal tissue (15, 82, 93, 98). It is especially significant that LPS is capable of penetrating gingival crevicular epithelial tissue (98), as well as being highly effective in the in vitro stimulation of bone resorption (37–39; E. Hausmann, M. J. Levine, and P. Chen, J. Dent. Res. Spec. Issue A **56**:A69, abstr. 106, 1977; E. Hausmann, O. Lüderitz, K. Knox, and N. Weinferd, J. Dent. Res. Spec. Issue B **54**:B94–B99, 1975). In addition, both gram-positive and gram-negative plaque bacteria are capable of eliciting a broad spectrum of toxic end products which have the capability of destroying tissue constituents, their integrity, and ultimately their viability. These end products include fatty and organic acids (74, 75, 106, 107, 120) as well as amines (104) and glycans (99). Cell wall–cell envelope constituents such as peptidoglycans (12, 18, 23, 42, 95), capsules, and slimes are also all strong mediators of tissue destruction, the latter two being especially significant in abscess formation (60–63, 91).

CAPSULE

In several infectious diseases, virulence has been shown to be associated with the bacterial cell surface. Rowley (96), for example, has suggested that the thickness of the bacterial capsule is a major factor in virulence. In *Streptococcus pneumoniae,* cell virulence varied with the amount of polysaccharide synthesized by different strains of the same type of cell (78). In a very interesting series of studies, Kasper and his associates (60–63) examined the outer membrane from strains of *Bacteroides fragilis* subsp. *fragilis* by electron microscopy, fluorescence microscopy, and immunochemistry. They observed the surface of the outer membrane to be covered with a thick ruthenium red-positive layer. These investigators (62, 91) then employed a rat model to examine the potential virulence capability of encapsulated (ruthenium red-positive?) and nonencapsulated *B. fragilis.* They found that encapsulated *B. fragilis,* when implanted into a rat's pelvic region, produced an abscess, whereas nonencapsulated *B. fragilis* did not. Interestingly, the nonencapsulated *B. fragilis,* when implanted with other bacteria, did produce abscesses, possibly the result of residual capsule or the presence of a microcapsule which imparted virulence and protection to the nonencapsulated *B. fragilis* strains. Heat-killed *B. fragilis* also was capable of producing abdominal abscesses in the rat, indicating to these investigators that the abscess-potentiating ability of *B. fragilis* may be related in part to a surface component, such as a capsular polysaccharide.

Purification and fractionation of the *B. fragilis* outer membrane produced several fractions: a capsular polysaccharide–protein complex, an LPS, and a purified capsular polysaccharide. Chemical analysis of these fractions revealed all of them to contain carbohydrates that were similar to those found in the purified capsular polysaccharide.

When nonencapsulated *B. fragilis* plus any of the outer membrane fractions were implanted in the rat pelvic region, abscess formation was evident. The response, that is, abscess production, appeared to be dose related, with the only common denominator being the capsular polysaccharide. Implantation of *B. fragilis* purified capsular polysaccharide without viable bacteria into the rat abdominal region produced abscesses in all the animals tested. Thus, the abscess-potentiating ability of *B. fragilis* appears to be related to the capsular polysaccharide, which may be functioning as a "virulence factor," similar, for example, to that reported for a slime component produced by *Pseudomonas aeruginosa* (99).

Woo et al. (123) and Woo and Holt (unpublished data) have separated the ruthenium red exopolymer and an outer membrane-associated microcapsule layer from an oral strain of *B. asaccharolyticus* (i.e., *B. gingivalis*). Although the ruthenium red exopolymer possessed little bone-resorptive potential as measured by the release of ^{45}Ca from cultured fetal bones, the microcapsule as well as the microcapsule with associated outer membrane possessed significant bone-resorptive potential.

B. asaccharolyticus (i.e., *B. melaninogenicus* subsp.) has also been studied for its role in mixed infection (48, 77, 105), as well as for its abscess-forming ability. Takazoe et al. (112) showed several years ago that one strain of *B. melaninogenicus* was capable of inducing abscesses in animal models. Similar *Bacteroides* subspecies have been isolated as a predominant member of the anaerobic flora from pleuropulmonary infections (5) and from anaerobic infections of soft tissues, the pelvis, etc. (27, 28, 35).

It is thus possible that the capsular polysaccharide associated with the *B. asaccharolyticus* surface may be responsible, in part, for virulence in certain infections, i.e., periodontitis, as has been observed for the *B. fragilis* capsular polysaccharide.

PEPTIDOGLYCAN

Not only does peptidoglycan act to maintain cell shape (90), but also it has an array of biological activities (42), including immunopotentiating properties (44, 58, 67), an ability to stimulate the reticuloendothelial system (21), and complement activation (7, 36, 92), and possesses immunosuppressive effects (22). Two strains of *Staphylococcus aureus* (3528 and 845) have a peptidoglycan that has significant in vitro mitogenic activity toward lymphocytes (23), specifically toward mouse splenocytes and human peripheral blood lymphocytes. In the latter case, the specific responding cells are B lymphocytes. Thus, peptidoglycan has interactions with host tissues which could have significant biological consequences (40, 94). There are several well-documented reports in the literature showing that peptidoglycan possesses adjuvanticity (1, 2), is capable of inhibiting macrophage migration (8), and possesses mitogenic activity (18, 108). In addition, several forms of peptidoglycan have arthridogenic potential (66). Synthetic muramyl dipeptides have recently been shown to be potent stimulators of bone resorption in fetal bone culture. In addition, the muramyl dipeptide peptidoglycan subunits are also capable of stimulating macrophage secretion of prostaglandins and collagenases, both potential mediators of tissue destruction (F. E. Dewhirst and D. A. Gamache, Abstr. Annu. Meet. Int. Assoc. Dent. Res. 1981, abstr. 759, p. 499; S. P. Whitehead et al., Abstr. Annu. Meet. Int. Assoc. Dent. Res. 1981, abstr. 760, p. 499).

When purified peptidoglycan was "solubilized" by ultrasound, or treated with lysozyme, it lost its mitogenic potential. Lysostaphin treatment did not affect blastogenic activity (12), possibly indicating a requirement for intact glycan units.

Thus, the potential of peptidoglycan to play an active role in cell and tissue destruction in periodontitis is clear. Bacterial death, with its accompanying cell lysis, will not only yield membrane fragments but also peptidoglycan fragments, which could easily interact with or cross host epithelial tissue, resulting in the numerous manifestations of disease.

LPS

The LPS of gram-negative bacteria has a high potential for causing significant modification or alteration of a wide variety of mammalian tissues and cells (see 65 for some pertinent references). However, the role of, or mechanism of action of, LPS in periodontal tissue destruction remains unclear, primarily as a result of observations that not all LPS preparations are chemically similar (43). *Bacteroides* species, for example, differ from other gram-negative bacteria in possessing a modified LPS; heptose, ketodeoxyoctonate, and lipid A components in these organisms are either absent or modified. The LPS in fact is low in endotoxic activity; however, it does, in some instances, possess high activity in the activation of several host cell responses (bone resorption, macrophage and polymorphonuclear leukocyte activation). Similar observations were obtained by Kiley and Holt (65) for LPS of *Actinobacillus actinomycetemcomitans* strains Y4 and N27. Both LPS preparations were low in classical endotoxic activity but possessed significant bone-resorptive activity. In an in vitro organ culture, a variety of LPS preparations (isolated by the Westphal phenol-water procedure [122]) from several gram-negative genera were capable of stimulating osteoclastic bone resorption. It appears that an intact lipid A is required for this activity, since removal of the lipid A moiety resulted in the loss of activity. In addition, lipid A alone was stimulatory for bone resorption. What other components (hydrolytic enzymes, structural proteins, or lipids) are attached to the lipid A moiety of LPS which could render it active in organ culture has not been determined; this subject represents one exciting aspect for future investigation. It is clear that LPS does have outer membrane components associated with it (11; T. P. Poirier and S. C. Holt, Abstr. Annu. Meet. Am. Soc. Microbiol. 1981, J6, p. 84), and these must be dissected from the LPS molecule and examined for endotoxic and other biological activities. LPS is also capable of initiating numerous metabolic and cellular changes both in vivo and in vitro (43, 57, 59, 68, 69, 79). It can, for example, act as a T-independent antigen; it possesses high adjuvant activity, as well as being capable of inhibiting the induction of tolerance to normally intolerant cellular antigens.

Unfortunately, direct comparisons between LPS preparations will be impossible until standard methods of isolation and purification are established. Westphal's hot phenol-water procedure (122) must be combined with other approaches (i.e., protein precipitation, electrodialysis, etc.) to remove all non-LPS-associated molecules.

HYDROLYTIC ENZYMES

Several investigators (103, 114) have shown the subgingival plaque microbiota to be capable of elaborating a variety of hydrolytic enzymes, such as phosphatases, collagenases, hyaluronidases, and elastases.

The localized environment has a profound effect on the activity and substrate specificity of several of these hydrolytic enzymes, notably, alkaline phosphatase (71, 80). This enzyme has clearly been shown to be localized within the periplasmic region (10, 85). There is provocative evidence (11, 14, 49) which localizes alkaline phosphatase both within the periplasm and bound to the outer membrane by structural components, i.e., structural proteins (11, 76). Poirier and Holt (Abstr. Annu. Meet. Am. Soc. Microbiol. 1981, J6, p. 84) have succeeded in recovering alkaline phosphatase complexed to LPS from the surrounding environment, as well as after extraction of intact cells. Day and Ingram (20) showed that alkaline phosphatase from *Pseudomonas aeruginosa* was modified with respect to substrate specificity by complexing it with LPS and phosphatidylethanolamine, indicating quite clearly that the substrate specificity of this enzyme is controlled in part by its microenvironment. In a very interesting but difficult to interpret series of experiments, Tsang et al. (117) found that endotoxin extracted with trichloroacetic acid and aqueous ether from *Serratia marcescens* had high amounts of an alkaline phosphatase activity. It is unclear from their report why trichloroacetic acid did not destroy the enzyme activity.

In *Capnocytophaga sputigena,* approximately 30 to 40% of the alkaline phosphatase is localized within the periplasmic space, the remainder being associated with the outer membrane. Preliminary observations (T. P. Poirier and S. C. Holt, Abstr. Annu. Meet. Am. Soc. Microbiol. 1980, J20, p. 83) reveal that the alkaline phosphatase found in the outer membrane is associated with LPS. Both periplasmic and outer membrane-released alkaline phosphatases are active in the release of phosphate from phosphoserine residues of the phosphopeptide phosvitin. In fact, almost 40% of the bound orthophosphate is released by the action of alkaline phosphatase. Interestingly, almost 11% of noncollagenous dentin is composed of phosphoserine residues.

In *B. gingivalis*, we have observed that a major percentage of the cell collagenase is associated with the outer membrane, the remainder being found in cell protoplasts (Holt et al., unpublished data). The enzyme appears to be tightly bound in the cell, as it was not released into the growth medium at any stage of growth.

The associations between bacterial hydrolytic enzymes, surface and outer membrane or cell envelope components such as structural proteins, and the localized microenvironment in which the bacteria are found is unclear; however, ascertaining the function of these surface-associated or excreted components in periodontal disease, especially as they are related to host tissue destruction, is crucial to an understanding of the interactions of bacteria and their host. We know, for example, that various components in bacterial cell homogenates (purified LPS, bacterial end products) are active and potentially central to the destruction of host tissue, especially cells of the periodontium (see 37–39; Hausmann et al., J. Dent. Res. Spec. Issue A **56**:A69, 1977; J. Dent. Res. Spec. Issue B **54**:B94, 1975). How this destruction occurs, or for that matter what common denominator may exist (chemical, physical, etc.) for this pathogenesis, is unknown.

BACTERIAL CULTURE–HOST INTERACTIONS

There are an increasing number of reports dealing with the role of bacteria and their components (including end products) in host tissue damage in periodontal disease (15, 16, 81, 98, 115, 118). In most instances, these studies have been concerned with the effects of LPS or bacterial homogenates on polymorphonuclear leukocytes (especially from *A. viscosus*) in eliciting cell-mediated host response. *A. viscosus* homogenates and culture supernatants are capable of eliciting cell-mediated immunity and are chemotactic for human polymorphonuclear leukocytes (26), as well as being mitogenic for mouse splenocytes (25). The homogenates are also active in bone resorption (37–39; Hausmann et al., J. Dent. Res. Spec. Issue A **56**:A69, 1977; J. Dent. Res. Spec. Issue B **54**:B94, 1975; C. L. Trummel, M. J. Pabst, and J. O. Cisar, J. Dent. Res. Spec. Issue B **56**:B156, 1977).

Engel et al. (26) have examined the morphology and function of human fibroblasts when exposed to *A. viscosus* homogenates. Since the fibroblast is the principal connective tissue-producing cell, its role in any connective tissue disorder (i.e., inflammation) may be a significant one in long-term diseases such as periodontal disease. Fibroblasts engulfed significant amounts of *A. viscosus* homogenate, but this material was not toxic to the fibroblast. There was some decrease in proline incorporation, indicative of a slight decline in protein–collagen synthesis. Interestingly, that this *A. viscosus* substance bound to the surface of the fibroblast membranes possibly is indicative of a specificity between bacterial components (i.e., polysaccharide or protein components) and these cultured cells.

The function of these bacterial components in the coating of, or adherence to, mammalian cell surfaces may provide the events required for the initiation of cell destruction. For example, lymphocytes which have been previously sensitized to bacterial substances may "recognize" the coated fibroblasts as "foreign" and destroy them, whereas antibody to these substances could bind specific microbial antigenic components, making them susceptible to further attack and destruction by inflammatory cells. Macrophages and polymorphonuclear leukocytes could clearly function in this way (6, 41).

In two interesting reports (3, 116), *A. actinomycetemcomitans* (strain Y4) was shown to be cytotoxic for human polymorphonuclear leukocytes in vitro. Various physical treatments, including drastic sonication, autolysis, and exposure to fresh human serum released a presumptive cell-associated component (protease?) which was cytotoxic for human polymorphonuclear leukocytes and human peripheral blood monocytes. The chemical nature of this Y4 "leukotoxin" is unknown.

It is clear that complex carbohydrates, glycoproteins, and glycolipids play an important antigenic and structural role in many pro- and eucaryotic cells (13, 31, 33). Several of these complex carbohydrates are known to be essential constituents of the surface of the mammalian plasma membrane (109), possibly involved in cell–cell recognition or serving as antigenic determinants, or both. Clearly, bacteria contain a wide range of surface-associated components or antigens, including pili, fimbriae, and flagella, as well as M proteins, LPS, lipoteichoic acids, and exopolymers. All of these structures and membrane-associated molecules are easily lost from a bacterium during the normal events of bacterial growth, being extruded into the environment. Thus, it is possible for any or all of these potentially mitogenic and resorptive antigens to gain access to periodontal epithelial tissue (82, 98) where they could stimulate host-mediated events (6, 37–39, 54–56; Hausmann et al., J. Dent. Res. Spec. Issue A **56**:A69, 1977; J. Dent. Res. Spec. Issue B **54**:B94, 1975), resulting ultimately in destruction of host cell tissue. Horton et al. (45–47) have clearly implicated bacterial products and their effect on the host immune response as potentially responsible for bone resorption.

The interaction between bacterial cells and their component parts, as well as several of their end products of metabolism, and host cells and tissues is only now starting to emerge as a concentrated area of investigation. How the host cell recognizes, incorporates, and ultimately processes these components is unknown and clearly represents one of the most exciting areas of investigation into the interactions between bacteria and host tissues.

SUMMARY

For a bacterium to initiate a disease process, it appears that it must interact in some way (i.e., adhere) with the host cell surface. What determinants on, or embedded in, the bacterial surface or on the host surface result in cell–bacterium "recognition" is only now starting to emerge. The role of bacterial exopolymers, glycoproteins, glycolipids, complex carbohydrates, and surface appendages (fibrils, pili, flagella, filaments) in bacterium–host interactions will continue to be examined in an effort to gain a more complete understanding of these potentially complex relationships. The interaction of a microorganism with its host leads to the production of an inflammatory response, a response which, in most instances, is essential for the protection of the host. However, there are several instances in which these bacterium–host interactions are not protective, but in fact lead to tissue destruction and fibrosis. These interactions include gingivitis, the various forms of periodontal disease, rheumatoid arthritis, and tuberculosis. These destructive inflammatory events which lead to host cell activation and the release of tissue-destructive enzymes are undoubtedly stimulated by a variety of external factors or agents, many of them clearly linked to specific microorganisms.

The major questions to be addressed in the future are what are the bacterial components and end products of growth and metabolism involved in host tissue destruction in periodontal disease and when during the bacterial growth cycle are they produced. By controlled bacterial growth and careful attention to fractionation and purification of bacterial components and end products, we can then attempt to clarify the mechanism of activation of host cellular responses leading to destruction of tooth-supporting connective tissues.

The results of these studies will have significance in an understanding of other inflammatory diseases. The tools and the biological material are in hand to advance another ". . . interesting chapter [in the study] of these disorders" (111).

ACKNOWLEDGMENT

This work was supported in part by Public Health Service grant DE-05123 from the National Institute of Dental Research.

LITERATURE CITED

1. **Adam, A. R., R. Ciorbaru, F. Ellouz, J. F. Petit, and E. Lederer.** 1974. Adjuvant activity of monomeric bacterial cell wall peptidoglycans. Biochem. Biophys. Res. Commun. **56:**561–567.
2. **Audibert, F., L. Chedid, P. Lefrancier, J. Choay, and E. Lederer.** 1977. Relationship between chemical structure and adjuvant activity of some synthetic analogs of N-acetyl-muramyl-L-alanyl-D-isoglutamine (MDP). Ann. Immunol. (Paris) **128C:**653–666.
3. **Baehni, P., C.-C. Tsai, W. P. McArthur, B. F. Hammond, and N. S. Taichman.** 1979. Interaction of inflammatory cells and oral microorganisms. VIII. Detection of leukotoxic activity of a plaque-derived gram-negative microorganism. Infect. Immun. **24:**233–243.
4. **Bahn, A. N.** 1970. Microbial potential in the etiology of periodontal disease. J. Periodontol. **41:**603–610.
5. **Bartlett, J. C., and S. M. Finegold.** 1972. Anaerobic pleuropulmonary infections. Medicine (Baltimore) **51:**413–450.
6. **Berken, A., and B. Benacerraf.** 1966. Properties of antibodies cytophilic for macrophages. J. Exp. Med. **123:**119–144.
7. **Bokisch, V. A.** 1975. Interaction of peptidoglycans with anti-lgGs and with complement. Z. Immunitaetsforsch. Exp. Klin. Immunol. **149:**320–330.
8. **Bultmann, B., B. Heymer, K. H. Schleifer, H. P. Seidl, and O. Haferkamp.** 1975. Migration inhibition of peritoneal macrophages by peptidoglycan. Z. Immunitaetsforsch. Exp. Klin. Immunol. **149:**289–294.
9. **Carranza, F. A.** 1979. The role of microorganisms in the etiology of gingival and periodontal disease, p. 374–405. *In* Glickman's clinical periodontology: prevention, diagnosis, and treatment of periodontal disease in the practice of general dentistry, 5th ed. The W. B. Saunders Co., Philadelphia.
10. **Cheng, K.-J., and J. W. Costerton.** 1973. Localization of alkaline phosphatase in three gram-negative rumen bacteria. J. Bacteriol. **116:**424–440.
11. **Cheng, K.-J., J. M. Ingram, and J. W. Costerton.** 1971. Interactions of alkaline phosphatase and the cell wall of *Pseudomonas aeruginosa*. J. Bacteriol. **107:**325–336.
12. **Ciorbaru, R., J.-F. Petit, E. Lederer, E. Zissman, C. Bona, and L. Chedid.** 1976. Presence and subcellular localization of two distinct mitogenic fractions in the cells of *Nocardia rubra* and *Nocardia opaca:* preparation of soluble mitogenic peptidoglycan fractions. Infect. Immun. **13:**1084–1090.
13. **Cook, G. M. W., and R. W. Stoddart.** 1973. Surface carbohydrates of the eukaryotic cell. Academic Press, Inc., New York.
14. **Costerton, J. W., J. M. Ingram, and K. J. Cheng.** 1974. Structure and function of the cell envelope of gram-negative bacteria. Bacteriol. Rev. **38:**87–110.
15. **Courant, P. R., and H. Bader.** 1966. *Bacteroides melaninogenicus* and its products in the gingiva of man. Periodontics **1:**131–136.
16. **Courant, P. R., I. Paunio, and R. J. Gibbons.** 1965. Infectivity and hyaluronidase activity of debris from healthy and diseased gingiva. Arch. Oral Biol. **10:**119–125.

17. **Crawford, A., S. Socransky, E. Smith, and R. Philips.** 1977. Pathogenicity testing of oral isolates in gnotobiotic rats. J. Dent. Res. **56:**275–294.
18. **Damais, C., C. Bona, L. Chedid, J. Fleck, C. Nauciel, and J. P. Martin.** 1975. Mitogenic effect of bacterial peptidoglycans possessing adjuvant activity. J. Immunol. **115:**268–271.
19. **Darwish, S., T. Hyppa, and S. S. Socransky.** 1978. Studies of the predominant cultivable microbiota and early periodontitis. J. Periodontal. Res. **13:**1–16.
20. **Day, D. F., and J. M. Ingram.** 1975. In vitro studies of an alkaline phosphatase cell wall complex from Pseudomonas aeruginosa. Can. J. Microbiol. **21:**9–16.
21. **Dziarski, R.** 1977. Stimulation of reticuloendothelial system and toxicity to macrophage of Staphylococcus aureus cell wall, peptidoglycan and teichoic acid. Zentralbl. Bakteriol. Parasitenkd. Infektionskr. Hyg. Abt. 1 Orig. Reihe A **238:**320–329.
22. **Dziarski, R.** 1978. Immunosuppressive effect of Staphylococcus aureus peptidoglycan on antibody response in mice. Int. Arch. Allergy Appl. Immunol. **57:**304–311.
23. **Dziarski, R., and A. Dziarski.** 1979. Mitogenic activity of staphylococcal peptidoglycan. Infect. Immun. **23:**706–710.
24. **Ellison, S. A.** 1970. Oral bacteria and periodontal disease. J. Dent. Res. **49:**198–202.
25. **Engel, D., J. Clagett, R. C. Page, and B. Williams.** 1977. Mitogenic activity of Actinomyces viscosus. I. Effects on murine B and T lymphocytes and partial characterization. J. Immunol. **118:**1466–1471.
26. **Engel, D., D. van Epps, and J. Clagett.** 1976. In vivo and in vitro studies on possible pathogenic mechanisms of Actinomyces viscosus. Infect. Immun. **14:**548–554.
27. **Finegold, S. M.** 1972. Anaerobic bacteria in human disease. Academic Press, Inc., New York.
28. **Finegold, S. M.** 1979. Taxonomy, enzymes, and clinical relevance of anaerobic bacteria. Rev. Infect. Dis. **1:**248–263.
29. **Frank, R. M.** 1980. Bacterial penetration in the apical pocket wall of advanced periodontitis. J. Periodontol. Res. **15:**563–573.
30. **Freter, R., and G. W. Jones.** 1976. Adhesive properties of Vibrio cholerae: nature of the interaction with intact mucosal surfaces. Infect. Immun. **14:**246–256.
31. **Gibbons, R. J.** 1977. Adherence of bacteria to host tissue. Position paper, p. 395–406. In D. Schlessinger (ed.), Microbiology—1977. American Society for Microbiology, Washington, D.C.
32. **Gibbons, R. J., and J. B. MacDonald.** 1961. Degradation of collagenous substrates by Bacteroides melaninogenicus. J. Bacteriol. **81:**614–621.
33. **Gibbons, R. J., and J. Van Houte.** 1975. Bacterial adherence in oral microbiology. Annu. Rev. Microbiol. **29:**19–44.
34. **Gibson, W. A., and I. L. Shannon.** 1964. Microorganisms in human gingival tissues. Periodontics **2:**119–121.
35. **Gorbach, S. L., and J. G. Bartlett.** 1974. Anaerobic infections. N. Engl. J. Med. **290:**1177, 1237–1245.
36. **Greenblatt, J., R. J. Boackle, and J. H. Schwab.** 1978. Activation of the alternate complement pathway by peptidoglycan from streptococcal cell wall. Infect. Immun. **19:**296–303.
37. **Hausmann, E., B. C. Nair, M. Reed, and M. Levine.** 1978. Partial characterization of a bone resorptive factor from Actinomyces viscosus, p. 115–122. In J. E. Horton, T. M. Tarpley, and W. F. Davis (ed.), Proceedings, Mechanisms of Localized Bone Loss (a special supplement to Calcif. Tissue Abstr.).
38. **Hausmann, E., L. G. Raisz, and W. A. Miller.** 1970. Endotoxin: stimulation of bone resorption in tissue culture. Science **168:**862–864.
39. **Hausmann, E., N. Weinfeld, and W. A. Miller.** 1972. Effects of lipopolysaccharides on bone resorption in tissue culture. Calcif. Tissue Res. **9:**272–282.
40. **Hebeler, B. H., W. Wong, S. A. Morse, and F. E. Young.** 1979. Cell envelope of Neisseria gonorrhoeae CS7: peptidoglycan-protein complex. Infect. Immun. **23:**353–359.
41. **Henson, P. M.** 1969. The adherence of leukocytes and platelets induced by fixed IgG antibody or complement. Immunology **16:**107–112.
42. **Heymer, B.** 1975. Biological properties of the peptidoglycan. Z. Immunitaetsforsch. Exp. Klin. Immunol. **149:**245–257.
43. **Hofstad, T.** 1974. Endotoxins of anaerobic gram-negative microorganism, p. 295–305. In A. Balows, R. M. DeHaan, V. R. Dowell, Jr., and L. B. Guze (ed.), Anaerobic bacteria: role in disease. Charles C Thomas, Publisher, Springfield, Ill.
44. **Holton, J. B., and J. H. Schwab.** 1966. Adjuvant properties of bacterial cell wall mucopeptides. J. Immunol. **96:**134–138.
45. **Horton, J. E., S. Leikin, and J. J. Oppenheim.** 1972. Human lymphoproliferative reaction to saliva and dental plaque deposits: an in vitro correlation with periodontal disease. J. Periodontol. **43:**522–527.
46. **Horton, J. E., J. J. Oppenheim, and S. E. Mergenhagen.** 1973. Elaboration of lymphotoxin by cultured human peripheral blood leukocytes stimulated with dental plaque deposits. Clin. Exp. Immunol. **13:**383–393.
47. **Horton, J. E., L. G. Raisz, H. A. Simmons, J. J. Oppenheim, and S. E. Mergenhagen.** 1972. Bone resorbing activity in supernatant fluid from cultured human-peripheral blood leukocytes. Science **177:**793–795.

48. **Ingham, H. R., P. R. Sisson, D. Tharagonnet, J. B. Selkon, and A. A. Codd.** 1977. Inhibition of phagocytosis *in vitro* by obligate anaerobes. Lancet ii:1252–1254.
49. **Ingram, J. M., K.-J. Cheng, and J. W. Costerton.** 1973. Alkaline phosphatase of *Pseudomonas aeruginosa.* II. The mechanism of secretion and release of the enzyme from whole cells. Can. J. Microbiol. 19:1407–1415.
50. **Irving, J. T., J. D. Heeley, and S. S. Socransky.** 1975. Cellular response to subgingival injection of bacterial products in the rat. J. Periodontal Res. 10:324–331.
51. **Irving, J. T., M. G. Newman, S. S. Socransky, and J. D. Heeley.** 1975. Histological changes in experimental periodontal disease in rats mono-infected with a gram-negative organism. Arch. Oral Biol. 20:219–220.
52. **Irving, J. T., S. S. Socransky, and J. D. Heeley.** 1974. Histologic changes in experimental periodontal disease in gnotobiotic rats and conventional hamsters. J. Periodontal Res. 9:73–84.
53. **Irving, J. T., S. S. Socransky, M. G. Newman, and E. Savitt.** 1976. Periodontal destruction induced by *Capnocytophaga* in gnotobiotic rats. J. Dent. Res. B55:257.
54. **Ivanyi, C., and T. Lehner.** 1970. Stimulation of lymphocyte transformation by bacterial antigens in patients with periodontal disease. Arch. Oral Biol. 15:1089–1096.
55. **Ivanyi, L., and T. Lehner.** 1971. Lymphocyte transformation by sonicates of dental plaque in human periodontal disease. Arch. Oral Biol. 16:1117–1121.
56. **Ivanyi, C., J. M. A. Wilton, and T. Lehner.** 1972. Cell-mediated immunity in periodontal disease; cytotoxicity, migration inhibition and lymphocyte transformation studies. Immunology 22:141–145.
57. **Johnson, D. A., U. H. Behling, C.-H. Lai, M. Listgarten, S. S. Socransky, and A. Nowotny.** 1978. Role of bacterial products in periodontitis: immune response in gnotobiotic rats monoinfected with *Eikenella corrodens.* Infect. Immun. 19:246–253.
58. **Jolles, P., D. Migliore-Samour, L. Maral, F. F. Foch, and G. H. Werner.** 1975. Low molecular weight water-soluble peptidoglycans and immunostimulants. Z. Immunitaetsforsch. Exp. Klin. Immunol. 149:331–340.
59. **Jones, G. W., and R. Freter.** 1976. Adhesive properties of *Vibrio cholerae:* nature of the interaction with isolated rabbit brush border membranes and human erythrocytes. Infect. Immun. 14:240–245.
60. **Kasper, D. L.** 1976. The polysaccharide capsule of *Bacteroides fragilis* subspecies *fragilis:* immunochemical and morphologic definition. J. Infect. Dis. 133:79–87.
61. **Kasper, D. C., M. E. Hayes, B. G. Reinap, F. O. Craft, A. B. Onderdonk, and B. F. Polk.** 1977. Isolation and identification of encapsulated strains of *Bacteroides fragilis.* J. Infect. Dis. 136:75–81.
62. **Kasper, D. C., A. B. Onderdonk, and J. G. Bartlett.** 1977. Quantitative determination of the antibody response to the capsular polysaccharide of *Bacteroides fragilis* in an animal model of intraabdominal abscess formation. J. Infect. Dis. 136:789–795.
63. **Kasper, D. L., and M. W. Seiler.** 1975. Immunochemical characterization of the outer membrane complex of *Bacteroides fragilis* subspecies *fragilis.* J. Infect. Dis. 132:440–450.
64. **Kelstrup, J., and E. Theilade.** 1974. Microbes and periodontal disease. J. Clin. Periodontol. 1:15–35.
65. **Kiley, P., and S. C. Holt.** 1980. Characterization of the lipopolysaccharide from *Actinobacillus actinomycetemcomitans* Y4 and N27. Infect. Immun. 30:862–873.
66. **Kohashi, O., C. M. Pearson, Y. Watanabe, and S. Kotani.** 1977. Preparation of arthritogenic hydrosoluble peptidoglycans from both arthritogenic and non-arthritogenic bacterial cell walls. Infect. Immun. 16:861–866.
67. **Kotani, S., Y. Watanabe, T. Shimono, T. Narita, K. Kato, D. E. S. Steart-Tull, F. Konoshita, K. Yokogawa, S. Kawata, T. Shiba, S. Kasumoto, and Y. Tarumi.** 1975. Immunoadjuvant activities of cell walls, their water-soluble fractions and peptidoglycan subunits, prepared from various Gram-positive bacteria, and synthetic N-acetylmuramyl peptides. Z. Immunitaetsforsch. Exp. Klin. Immunol. 149:302–319.
68. **Kreutzer, D. L., L. A. Dreyfus, and D. C. Robertson.** 1979. Interaction of polymorphonuclear leukocytes with smooth and rough strains of *Brucella abortus.* Infect. Immun. 23:737–742.
69. **Kreutzer, D. L., and D. C. Robertson.** 1979. Surface macromolecules and virulence in intracellular parasitism: comparison of cell envelope components of smooth and rough strains of *Brucella abortus.* Infect. Immun. 23:819–828.
70. **Levine, M., and G. L. Cowley.** 1974. Human dental plaque extracts: their crude chemical composition and toxicity to cultured HeLa cells. Arch. Oral Biol. 19:583–588.
71. **Lindsay, Shelagh, S. B. Wheeler, K. E. Sanderson, and J. W. Costerton.** 1973. The release of alkaline phosphatase and of lipopolysaccharide during the growth of rough and smooth strains of *Salmonella typhimurium.* Can. J. Microbiol. 19:335–343.
72. **Listgarten, M. A.** 1965. Electron microscopic observation on the bacterial flora of acute necrotizing ulcerative gingivitis. J. Periodontol. 36:328–339.
73. **Listgarten, M. A., D. Johnson, A. Nowotny, A. C. R. Tanner, and S. S. Socransky.** 1978. Histopathology of periodontal disease in gnotobiotic rats monoinfected with *Eikenella corrodens.* J. Periodontal Res. 13:134–148.
74. **Loesche, W. J., and R. J. Gibbons.** 1968. Amino acid fermentation by *Fusobacterium nucleatum.* Arch. Oral Biol. 13:191–202.

75. **Loesche, W. J., S. S. Socransky, and R. J. Gibbons.** 1964. *Bacteroides oralis,* proposed new species isolated from the oral cavity of man. J. Bacteriol. **88:**1329–1337.

76. **MacAlister, T. J., J. W. Costerton, L. Thompson, J. Thompson, and J. M. Ingram.** 1972. Distribution of alkaline phosphatase within the periplasmic space of gram-negative bacteria. J. Bacteriol. **111:**827–832.

77. **MacDonald, J. B., S. S. Socransky, and R. J. Gibbons.** 1963. Aspects of the pathogenesis of mixed anaerobic infections of mucous membranes. J. Dent. Res. **42:**529–544.

78. **MacLeod, C. M., and M. R. Krauss.** 1950. Relation of virulence of pneumococcal strains for mice to the quantity of capsular polysaccharide formed *in vitro.* J. Exp. Med. **92:**1–9.

79. **Mansheim, B. J., and D. L. Kasper.** 1977. Purification and immunochemical characterization of the outer membrane complex of *Bacteroides melaninogenicus* subspecies *asaccharolyticus.* J. Infect. Dis. **135:**787–799.

80. **Marceau-Day, M. C., D. F. Day, and J. M. Ingram.** 1978. An alkaline phosphatase mutant of *Pseudomonas aeruginosa.* I. Effects of regulatory, structural, and environmental shifts on enzyme function. Can. J. Microbiol. **24:**427–432.

81. **Maryon, L. W., and R. J. Loiselle.** 1973. Bacterial antigens and antibodies in human periodontal tissue. J. Periodontol. **44:**164–182.

82. **McDougal, W. A.** 1971. Penetration pathways of a topically applied foreign protein into rat gingiva. J. Periodontal Res. **6:**89–95.

83. **Mlinek, A., A. Buchner, S. Hennig, and A. Begleiter.** 1974. Cytotoxic effects of soluble plaque extract on cells *in vitro.* J. Periodontal Res. **9:**342–354.

84. **Murphy, P. J., and R. E. Stallar.** 1968. An altered gingival attachment epithelium; a result of the enzyme hyaluronidase. Periodontics **6:**105–108.

85. **Neu, H. C., and L. A. Heppel.** 1965. The release of enzymes from *Escherichia coli* by osmotic shock and during formation of spheroplasts. J. Biol. Chem. **240:**3685–3692.

86. **Newman, M. G.** 1979. The role of *Bacteroides melaninogenicus* and other anaerobes in periodontal infections. Rev. Infect. Dis. **1:**313–323.

87. **Newman, M. G., and S. S. Socransky.** 1977. Predominant cultivable microbiota in periodontosis. J. Periodontal Res. **12:**129–128.

88. **Newman, M. G., S. S. Socransky, E. D. Savitt, D. A. Propas, and A. Crawford.** 1976. Studies of the microbiology of periodontosis. J. Periodontol. **47:**373–379.

89. **Newman, M. G., R. C. Williams, A. Crawford, A. D. Manganiello, and S. S. Socransky.** 1973. Predominant cultivable microbiota of periodontitis and peridontosis. III. Periodontosis. J. Dent. Res. **52:**290.

90. **Nowotny, P., J. A. Short, and P. D. Walker.** 1975. An electron microscope study of naturally occurring and cultured cells of *Neisseria gonorrhoeae.* J. Med. Microbiol. **8:**413–427.

91. **Onderdonk, A. B., D. L. Kasper, R. L. Cisneros, and J. G. Bartlett.** 1977. The capsular polysaccharide of *Bacteroides fragilis* as a virulence factor: comparison of the pathogenic potential of encapsulated and unencapsulated strains. J. Infect. Dis. **136:**82–89.

92. **Pryjma, J., K. Pryjma, A. Grov, and P. B. Heczko.** 1975. Immunological activity of staphylococcal cell wall antigens. Zentralbl. Bakteriol. Parasitenkd. Infektionskr. Hyg. Abt. 1 Suppl. **5:**873–881.

93. **Ranney, R.** 1978. Immunofluorescent localization of soluble dental plaque components in human gingiva affected by periodontitis. J. Periodontal Res. **13:**99–108.

94. **Rosenthal, R. S.** 1979. Release of soluble peptidoglycan from growing gonococci: hexaminidase and amidase activities. Infect. Immun. **24:**869–878.

95. **Rotta, J.** 1975. Endotoxin-like properties of the peptidoglycan. Z. Immunitaetsforsch. Exp. Klin. Immunol. **149:**230–244.

96. **Rowley, D.** 1971. Endotoxins and bacterial virulence. J. Infect. Dis. **123:**317–323.

97. **Schuster, G. S., J. A. Hayashi, and A. N. Bahn.** 1967. Toxic properties of the cell wall of gram-positive bacteria. J. Bacteriol. **93:**47–52.

98. **Schwartz, J., F. C. Stinson, and R. B. Parker.** 1972. The passage of tritiated bacterial endotoxin across intact gingival crevicular epithelium. J. Periodontol. **43:**270–276.

99. **Sensakovic, J. W., and P. F. Bartell.** 1974. The slime of *Pseudomonas aeruginosa:* biological characterization and possible role in experimental infection. J. Infect. Dis. **129:**101–109.

100. **Slots, J.** 1976. The predominant cultivable organisms in juvenile periodontitis. Scand. J. Dent. Res. **84:**1–10.

101. **Slots, J.** 1977. The predominant cultivable microflora of advanced periodontitis. Scand. J. Dent. Res. **85:**114–121.

102. **Smith, H.** 1977. Microbial surfaces in relation to pathogenicity. Bacteriol. Rev. **41:**475–500.

103. **Socransky, S. S.** 1970. Relationship of bacteria to etiology of periodontal disease. J. Dent. Res. **49**(Suppl. 2):203–222.

104. **Socransky, S. S.** 1977. Microbiology of periodontal disease—present status and future considerations. J. Periodontol. **48:**497–504.

105. **Socransky, S. S., and R. J. Gibbons.** 1965. Required role of *Bacteroides melaninogenicus* in mixed anaerobic infections. J. Infect. Dis. **115:**247–253.

106. **Socransky, S. S., M. A. Listgarten, C. Hubersak, J. Cotmore, and A. Clark.** 1969. Morphological and biochemical differentiation of three types of small oral spirochetes. J. Bacteriol. **98:**878–882.

107. **Socransky, S. S., W. J. Loesche, C. Hubersak, and J. B. MacDonald.** 1964. Dependency of *Treponema microdentium* on other oral organisms for isobutyrate, polyamines, and a controlled oxidation-reduction potential. J. Bacteriol. **88:**200–209.
108. **Specter, S., H. Friedman, and L. Chedid.** 1977. Dissociation between the adjuvant vs. mitogenic activity of a synthetic muramyl dipeptide for murine splenocytes. Proc. Soc. Exp. Biol. Med. **155:**349–352.
109. **Suttajit, M., and R. J. Winzler.** 1971. Effect of N-acetylneuraminic acid on the binding of glycoproteins to influenza virus and on susceptibility to cleavage by neuraminidase. J. Biol. Chem. **246:**3398–3404.
110. **Swanson, J.** 1973. Studies on gonococcus infection. IV. Pili: their role in attachment of gonococci to tissue culture cells. J. Exp. Med. **137:**571–589.
111. **Taichman, N. S., B. F. Hammond, C.-C. Tsai, P. C. Baehni, and W. P. McArthur.** 1978. Interaction of inflammatory cells and oral microorganisms. VII. In vitro polymorphonuclear responses to viable bacteria and to subcellular components of avirulent and virulent strains of *Actinomyces viscosus.* Infect. Immun. **21:**594–604.
112. **Takazoe, I., M. Tanaka, and T. Homma.** 1971. A pathogenic strain of *Bacteroides melaninogenicus.* Arch. Oral Biol. **16:**817–822.
113. **Tanner, A. C. R., C. Haffer, G. T. Bratthall, R. A. Visconti, and S. S. Socransky.** 1979. A study of the bacteria associated with advancing periodontitis in man. J. Clin. Periodontol. **6:**278–307.
114. **Theilade, E., and J. Theilade.** 1976. Role of plaque in the etiology of periodontal disease and caries. Oral Sci. Rev. **9:**23–63.
115. **Tolo, K., and J. Jonsen.** 1975. In vitro penetration of tritiated dextrans through rabbit oral mucosa. Arch. Oral Biol. **20:**419–422.
116. **Tsai, C.-C., W. P. McArthur, P. C. Baehni, B. F. Hammond, and N. S. Taichman.** 1979. Extraction and partial characterization of a leukotoxin from a plaque-derived gram-negative microorganism. Infect. Immun. **25:**427–439.
117. **Tsang, J. C., J. C. Landes, and D. A. Brown.** 1978. Alkaline phosphatase activity associated with endotoxin preparations from *Serratia marcescens.* Microbios Lett. **7:**7–14.
118. **Tsuitsui, M., N. Utsumi, and K. Tsubakimoto.** 1968. Cellular components of staphylococci and streptococci in inflamed human gingiva. J. Dent. Res. **47:**663–674.
119. **Van Palenstein Helderman, W. H.** 1975. Total viable counts and differential count of *Vibrio (Campylobacter) Sputorum, Bacteroides ochraceus,* and *Veillonella* in the inflamed and non-inflamed human gingival crevice. J. Periodontal Res. **10:**294–305.
120. **Wahren, A., and R. J. Gibbons.** 1970. Amino acid fermentation by *Bacteroides melaninogenicus.* Antonie van Leuwenhoek J. Microbiol. Serol. **36:**149–159.
121. **Ward, M. E., and P. J. Watt.** 1972. Adherence of *Neisseria gonorrhea* to urethral muscosal cells: an electron microscopic study of human gonorrhea. J. Infect. Dis. **126:**601–605.
122. **Westphal, Ö., O. Lüderitz, and F. Bister.** 1952. Uber die Extraktion von Bakterien mit Phenol/Wasser. Z. Naturforsch. **76:**148–155.
123. **Woo, D. D. L., S. C. Holt, and E. R. Leadbetter.** 1979. Ultrastructure of *Bacteroides* species: *Bacteroides asaccharolyticus, Bacteroides fragilis, Bacteroides melaninogenicus* subspecies *melaninogenicus,* and *B. melaninogenocus* subspecies *intermedius.* J. Infect. Dis. **139:**534–546.

Bacterial Components Which Result in Bone Loss

ERNEST HAUSMANN, BALA CHANDRAN NAIR, AND ROSEMARY DZIAK

Department of Oral Biology and Periodontal Disease Clinical Research Center,
State University of New York at Buffalo, Buffalo, New York 14226

INTRODUCTION

A feature which characterizes bones in adult nongrowing humans is turnover (22). That is, there is constant deposition and resorption without any net change in bone mass. The fact that there is no change in bone mass under these circumstances indicates that there must be some means of control which links deposition to resorption. This linkage in bone biology has been termed coupling (13). Manson and Lucas (23) demonstrated that alveolar bone in adults has turnover. They examined microradiographs of undecalcified sections of alveolar bone from human autopsy material. Surfaces exhibiting Howship's lacunae were related to resorption, and surfaces adjacent to hypomineralized regions were related to deposition. In patients after periodontal surgery, ^{125}I absorptiometry measurements reveal a transient decrease in alveolar bone mass, reaching a minimum after 4 weeks, followed by a return of presurgery bone mass after 24 weeks (3). This transient effect on alveolar bone has been taken as evidence of coupling. Frost (11) has formulated a hypothesis for coupling which he calls remodeling by basic multicellular units or packets of bone cells. It is theorized that the order of events is resorption by osteoclasts followed by osteoblasts at the same site redepositing the bone previously lost. Baylink's group (20) recently obtained evidence in an in vitro chick bone system that bone resorption results in the release of a coupling factor into the culture system which in turn stimulates deposition. One possibility for alveolar bone loss in periodontal disease may be a result of the appearance of a factor in the gingival tissues which uncouples deposition from resorption.

Limited histopathological examination has been done on alveolar bone from sites of periodontitis in humans. Osteoclasts as evidence of resorption as well as arrest and reversal lines as evidence of deposition have been observed (29).

Bone loss in periodontal disease, therefore, may be the consequence of an enhancement of resorption, a decrease in deposition, or a combination of the two. Furthermore, there may be a degree of uncoupling when the rate of deposition does not keep pace with an enhanced resorptive rate. Studies of experimental periodontal disease in gnotobiotic rats and conventional hamsters suggest that inhibition of deposition contributes to the alveolar bone loss observed (2, 21).

BACTERIAL PRODUCTS ON BONE IN ORGAN CULTURE

A relationship in humans between periodontal tissue destruction, including alveolar bone resorption, and dental microbial plaque is well documented (17). Electron microscopic observation of gingival biopsy samples of patients with periodontal disease usually does not demonstrate any bacteria (10). Recent studies by Frank and Voegel (8, 9) did show bacteria in the periodontal connective tissue and in lacunae on the alveolar bone surface in some patients

151

adjacent to very severe pockets, 8 to 12 mm in depth. For the most part, however, the link between subgingival organisms and alveolar bone loss must be indirect, mediated by a soluble factor(s) released from the organisms residing in the pockets.

Model systems of fetal bones in organ culture have been used to assay the effect(s) of bacterial products on bone. An assay system, developed by Raisz (26), that is particularly responsive to resorptive agents has been used. Resorption stimulated in this system is associated with osteoclasia indistinguishable from that observed in vivo.

The essential steps of the assay procedure follow:

1. Rats are injected with $^{45}CaCl_2$ on the 18th day of gestation.
2. The rats are sacrificed on the 19th day, and radii and ulnae of the embryos with their cartilagenous ends removed are placed for culturing in chemically defined medium.
3. The release of ^{45}Ca into culture media from bones incubated in the presence of an experimental agent is compared with the release from bones incubated in control media, and the results are expressed as a ratio. A ratio significantly greater than 1 signifies stimulation of cell-mediated bone resorption. The assay procedure usually includes a 24-h preculture period in control media with a 2-day culture period in experimental media. The use of a preculture period permits a more precise timing and the removal of most of the exchangeable ^{45}Ca due to active resorption is proportionally larger. Raisz (4) has also developed a fetal rat calvaria system particularly responsive to agents which influence bone-collagen deposition.

The essential steps of the assay procedure follow:

1. Calvaria are obtained from 21-day-old fetal rats.
2. The calvaria containing the frontal and parietal bones are divided along the sagittal suture, and half calvaria are cultured in chemically defined media.
3. Two hours prior to the end of the culture period, [^{3}H]proline is added.
4. The incorporation of [^{3}H]proline into collagen and noncollagen protein is measured.

Since the two in vitro model systems are specifically designed to be very sensitive to agents affecting either resorption or deposition, they would be inappropriate for the testing of potential coupling or uncoupling agents. In the later instances, one requires a model system in which resorption as well as deposition takes place with comparable facility. Such an in vitro system has been developed in which tibias from 8-day-old embryonic chicks are used (19). Deposition is assessed by the incorporation of [^{3}H]proline into bone, and resorption is assessed by the release into the culture media of previously incorporated [^{3}H]proline. This model system was used by Baylink and co-workers (20) to demonstrate that, when chick bones are stimulated to resorb by parathyroid hormone, a nondialyzable factor is released into the culture medium which stimulates bone deposition when added to another set of chick bones.

A number of crude and purified bacterial products singly or in combination have been tested for their ability to stimulate resorption of fetal long bones in organ culture (Table 1). Lipopolysaccharides (LPS) derived from nonoral gram-negative bacteria such as *Salmonella typhimurium,* as well as LPS from plaque-derived organisms such as *Bacteroides gingivalis,* stimulate resorption in submicrogram concentrations (15; B. C. Nair and E. Hausmann, J. Dent. Res. Spec. Issue A, vol. 60, abstr. 132F, 1981) (Fig. 1). Lipoteichoic acid (15) from *Lactobacillus fermenti* and the amphipathic macromolecule (AcA) from *Actinomyces viscosus* (16) stimulate resorption with a threshold concentration on the order of 1 to 3 μg/ml in the culture medium. Muramyl dipeptide (MDP), the repeating unit of the peptidoglycan backbone in the cell wall of gram-negative organisms, stimulates the release of ^{45}Ca from prelabeled cultured bones at a concentration as low as 10^{-6} M (1). The combination of LPS and MDP, LPS and prostaglandin E_2, or LPS and osteoclast-activating factor (28) results in a greater release of ^{45}Ca from prelabeled bone than does the arithmetic sum of LPS and MDP, LPS and prostaglandin E_2, or LPS and osteoclast-activating factor acting on the fetal bones by themselves (Table 1). Since the peptidoglycan layer is closely associated with LPS in the bacterial cell wall, it seems reasonable to suspect that LPS preparations may be contaminated with MDP. Therefore, we examined purified LPS from *B. gingivalis* and *S. typhimurium* for muramic acid. No such contamination could be detected. At the sensitivity of our method, a contamination of MDP of 0.5% by weight could have been detected.

Supragingival plaque from humans was extracted with tissue culture medium, and the extract was sterilized by passage through a membrane filter (Millipore Corp.). The filtrate from every plaque sample tested from a series of patients stimulated resorption (18), suggesting that soluble factors are present in situ in dental plaques which can stimulate bone resorption.

Only one report in abstract form exists on the effect of a bacterial product on bone deposition in an in vitro model system. C. L. Trummel and P. Cosgrove (J. Dent. Res. Spec. Issue A, vol. 58, abstr. 106, 1979) reported that AcA from *A. viscosus* inhibits collagen synthesis of fetal rat calvaria in organ culture.

No experiments have been done to determine whether a bacterial factor(s) may also function to uncouple resorption from deposition. For example, let us assume that LPS not only stimulates resorption but also acts to uncouple deposition from resorption. In that instance, a net loss of alveolar bone could occur. If, on the other hand, LPS stimulates resorption only, this might not lead to bone loss because increased resorption could result in the formation of increased coupling factor which in turn could stimulate enhanced deposition.

Bacterial factors may also initiate resorption by stimulating the host to form and release into the periodontal tissues factors such as prostaglandin E_2, the

TABLE 1. *Bacterial products which stimulate release of ^{45}Ca from prelabeled fetal rat long bones in organ culture*

Product	Reference
LPS[a]	15
Lipoteichoic acid	15
AcA	16
MDP	1
Soluble extract from human supragingival plaque	18

[a]LPS in combination with MDP, prostaglandin E_2, or osteoclast-activating factor acts synergistically to stimulate ^{45}Ca release (28).

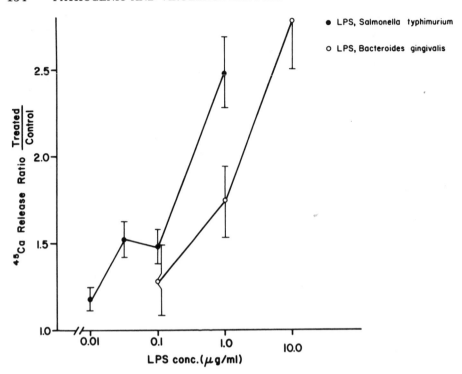

FIG. 1. *Dose-response relationship for treatment of cultured bones with LPS from S. typhimurium (●) and B. gingivalis (○) as measured by ratio of ^{45}Ca released by paired control bones during 48 h of incubation after 24 h of preincubation. Each point represents mean ± standard error of six pairs of cultures.*

lymphokine, osteoclast-activating factor, and an activated component of complement (27, 30).

MOLECULAR BIOLOGY OF BACTERIAL PRODUCTS ON ISOLATED BONE CELLS

Based on presently available evidence, the molecular biology for stimulating formation of active osteoclasts by mediators of bone resorption is schematically represented in Fig. 2. Stimulators of resorption are believed to interact with specific receptors on the surface of osteoclast precursor cells or inactive osteoclasts in a reversible manner. This interaction is postulated to result in the formation of a second messenger(s) which has the ability to influence various intracellular events, such as specific enzyme activities and function of specific ribonucleic acid molecules. Such biochemical events in all likelihood are necessary for formation and activity of osteoclasts.

Both in vivo (33) and in vitro (7) experiments performed with parathyroid hormone in the late 1960s and early 1970s suggested that cyclic adenosine monophosphate (cAMP) is the second messenger associated with active osteoclast formation and, therefore, bone resorption. The role of cAMP as the obligatory second messenger involved in resorption has recently been cast in doubt for several reasons. (i) Parathyroid hormone has been demonstrated not

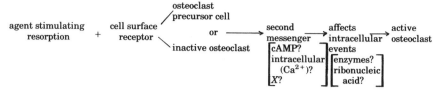

FIG. 2. *Schema of the molecular biology for the activation of osteoclast precursor cells or inactive osteoclasts by bacterial products.*

only to stimulate resorption but also to inhibit deposition by osteoblasts (4). Some data suggest that the elevation of bone cAMP by parathyroid hormone is the result of the effect of this hormone on osteoblasts (J. N. M. Heersche, L. G. Rao, and D. Dunn, J. Dent. Res. Spec. Issue A, vol. 60, abstr. 1306, 1981). (ii) The work of Dziak and Stern (7) has demonstrated that parathyroid hormone also results in an influx of calcium into bone cells, an effect which is independent of changes in cAMP. An increase of intracellular Ca^{2+} also may act as the second messenger in resorption.

Our laboratory has examined systematically the effects of bacterial factors on cAMP and calcium influx into isolated bone cells from collagenase-treated fetal or newborn calvaria (6, 16). A schematic representation of the results is given in Table 2. These results lead to several interesting possibilities. (i) Since purified LPS from an oral as well as a nonoral source (7) appears to decrease calcium uptake by an active intracellular pool but increase calcium binding to a passive, rapidly exchangeable pool, it can be hypothesized that changes in the dynamics of cellular calcium are involved in the agents' mechanism of action. (ii) Since changes in neither bone cell cAMP nor Ca^{2+} influx are observed with lipoteichoic acid or AcA, the possibilities should be considered that these two agents get into bone cells, making a second messenger unnecessary, or that there may be other second messengers associated with the formation of active osteoclasts not yet identified.

Our results with MDP are very intriguing in that a 2-h preincubation of the isolated bone cells with the agent is required to demonstrate an increased influx of Ca^{2+}. These results suggest a more complex interaction of MDP than a reversible interaction with a surface receptor on an osteoclast precursor cell.

Besides the demonstration that prostaglandins, exogenously added or endogenously produced, can stimulate bone resorption in vitro (27), it has been suggested that prostaglandins may act as mediators for the stimulatory effects of LPS on bone. The inhibition of this effect of LPS by indomethacin, an inhibitor of prostaglandin synthesis, has been taken as evidence for the role of prostaglandin in mediating the effect of LPS on bone. The results from several laboratories (15; L. G. Raisz and C. L. Trummel, personal communication) indicate no effect of indomethacin, and the results from some other laboratories (25; J. M. Goodson, S. Offenbacher, and R. B. Bloomfield, J. Dent. Res. Spec. Issue A, vol. 58, abstr. 110, 1979) indicate an inhibition. The reasons for this difference in results are not absolutely clear; however, some possibilities are suggested: (i) the LPS used in some of the experiments is contaminated with another bone-resorbing agent and indomethacin is inhibiting the effects of the contaminant; (ii) indomethacin is highly insoluble in water and the vehicle used to dissolve it may have a toxic inhibitory effect on the bone cultures. Furthermore, results obtained when indomethacin is used as a "specific"

TABLE 2. *Effect of bacterial products on calcium uptake and on cAMP by isolated bone cells*[a]

Expt	Treatment, bacterial product, and concn	Preincubation time (min)	cAMP[b]	Ca^{2+} influx[b]
I	LPS, 1 μg/ml, *S. minnesota*	15	—	↓[c]
	LPS, 1 μg/ml, *B. gingivalis*	15	—	↓[c]
II	Lipoteichoic acid, 10 μg/ml, *L. fermenti*	15	—	—
III	AcA, 10 μg/ml, *A. viscosus*	15	—	—
IVa	MDP, 10^{-6} M, muramyl, L-alanine, D-isoglutamine; synthetic	15	0	—
IVb	MDP, 10^{-6} M	120	—	↑

[a] Calvaria were incubated for 1 h with collagenase and the released cells were isolated (heterogeneous population used in experiments I–III) or the calvaria were treated for four sequential periods of 15 min. MDP demonstrated an effect on calcium influx in the population of cells obtained in the first two collagenase digestions. These represent enriched populations of osteoclast-like cells.

[b] Ca^{2+} influx represents uptake into active intracellular pool (6). Symbols: —, cells treated with experimental agent behaved the same as cells in control media; ↑, effect in experimental cells greater than in control cells; ↓, effect in experimental cells less than in control cells; 0, experiment not done.

[c] The decreases were accompanied by an increase into a passive cellular pool.

inhibitor of prostaglandin synthetase are difficult to interpret because indomethacin also has been shown to inhibit cAMP-dependent protein kinase and phosphodiesterase. Thus, it is not sufficient to add a prostaglandin inhibitor to a system and then ascribe any effects noted to inhibition of prostaglandin synthesis. As a minimum it seems reasonable to use two structurally unrelated prostaglandin synthetase inhibitors. Further evidence is provided if the readdition of prostaglandins into the system overcomes the effect of the prostaglandin synthetase inhibitors (12).

WHICH BACTERIAL PRODUCT(S) CAUSES ALVEOLAR BONE LOSS IN VIVO?: AN EXPERIMENTAL APPROACH

It is difficult to extrapolate results obtained with various bacterial factors in organ culture to alveolar bone resorption in humans. This requires study in human periodontal disease or a closely approximating model such as ligature-induced periodontitis in *Macaca arctoides* monkeys (32) or beagle dogs (K. S. Kornman, K. Nuki, and A. Soskolne, J. Dent. Res. Spec. Issue A, vol. 59, abstr. 478, 1980). Associated with alveolar bone loss in these models is a significant increase of *B. gingivalis* in the adjacent subgingival microflora. This is the predominant gram-negative anaerobic organism found in pockets of humans with periodontitis (24).

Let us suppose that a highly specific inhibitor of LPS from *B. gingivalis* were available. One could then determine whether administration of this inhibitor to beagles or *M. arctoides* monkeys would prevent the alveolar bone loss subsequent to the placement of a ligature around a tooth at the level of the gingival margin. A monospecific antibody to LPS from *B. gingivalis* could serve as such an inhibitor. Such an antibody could be produced if a homogeneous preparation of the LPS were available which could serve as an immunogen. We have prepared such an LPS from *B. gingivalis* (Nair and Hausmann, J. Dent. Res., vol. 60, abstr. 132F, 1981) in the following manner: (i) ethylene-diaminetetraacetate extraction of the cell walls of the organisms; (ii) phenol-water extraction; (iii) repeated ultracentrifugation of the water phase; (iv) chromatography in the presence of deoxycholate on Sephadex G-100; (v) electrodialysis to remove tightly bound small charged contaminants. Homogenicity is based on the following criteria: a single symmetrical peak on ultracentrifugation, a single symmetrical peak with one small shoulder in the included volume on chromatography with Sephadex G-100, a symmetrical profile on re-chromatography of the eluate in the center of the original peak, and one precipitin arc on immunoelectrophoresis against antiserum to sonic extract of *B. gingivalis*. Furthermore, the purified LPS on immunodiffusion gives lines of identity against antisera to different strains of the same organism but does not give precipitin bands with antiserum against different oral species of *Bacteroides*. The marked cross-reactivity of LPS with antisera of different strains of *B. gingivalis* makes LPS ideally suited as an immunogen and distinguishes it from the LPS of oral *Veillonella* (24). Inhibition of ligature-induced bone loss in an animal immunized against this homogeneous preparation of LPS suggests that the bone loss in an unimmunized animal is a result of a direct effect of LPS on the activation of osteoclasts in the alveolar bone. However, lack of inhibition does not exclude an indirect effect of LPS in stimulating resorption. For example, LPS could bind to the surface of osteoclast precursor cells, and a component of complement activated by an LPS–antibody complex could stimulate resorption (14, 30).

With the present state of the art, we are at the threshold of determining the specific agents responsible for periodontal bone loss through use of specific inhibitors.

SUMMARY

Since alveolar bone is characterized in health by a balance of resorption and deposition, alveolar bone loss in disease may be the result of increased resorption, decreased deposition, or an uncoupling of these processes. Several factors such as LPS, lipoteichoic acid, AcA, and MDP, constituents of plaque bacteria, have been shown to have the potential to stimulate bone resorption. The molecular biology underlying resorption stimulated by these factors appears to be different. Whereas LPS decreases the uptake of Ca^{2+} into bone cells by an active intracellular pool, MDP stimulates an increased uptake. Lipoteichoic acid and AcA have no effect on the uptake of Ca^{2+} by bone cells. A model for determining the role of LPS in ligature-induced alveolar bone loss in animals is described.

ACKNOWLEDGMENTS

We thank Michael J. Levine for muramic acid analysis on our LPS preparations.

This work was supported by Public Health Service grants DEO 19320, DE 04898, DE 04637, and DE 07034 from the National Institute of Dental Research. B.C.N. is a recipient of National Research Service award DE 05143 and R.D. is a recipient of Research Career Development Award 1KO 4AM0072601 from the National Institutes of Health.

LITERATURE CITED

1. **Alander, B., K. Nuki, and L. G. Raisz.** 1980. Effects of two bacterial products, muramyl dipeptide and endotoxin on bone resorption in organ culture. Calcif. Tissue Int. **31**(Suppl.):1A.
2. **Baron, R., and J. L. Saffar.** 1978. A quantitative study of bone remodeling during experimental periodontal disease in the golden hamster. J. Periodontal Res. **13**:309–315.
3. **Bergstrom, J., and C. O. Henrikson.** 1974. Quantitative long-term determination of the alveolar bone mineral mass in man by ^{125}I. II. Following periodontal surgery. Acta Radiol. Ther. **13**:489.
4. **Chen, T. L., and L. G. Raisz.** 1975. The effects of ascorbic acid deficiency on calcium and collagen metabolism in cultured fetal rat bones. Calcif. Tissue Res. **17**:113–127.
5. **Dietrich, J. W., E. M. Canalis, D. M. Maina, and L. G. Raisz.** 1976. Hormonal control of bone collagen synthesis *in vitro:* effects of parathyroid hormone and calcitonin. Endocrinology **98**:943–949.
6. **Dziak, R., E. Hausmann, and Y. W. Chang.** 1979. Effects of lipopolysaccharides and prostaglandins on rat bone cell calcium and cyclic AMP. Arch. Oral Biol. **24**:347–353.
7. **Dziak, R., and P. H. Stern.** 1975. Calcium transport in isolated bone cells. II. Effects of parathyroid hormone and cyclic 3′, 5′ AMP. Endocrinology **97**:1281–1287.
8. **Frank, R. M.** 1980. Bacterial penetration in the apical pocket wall of advanced human periodontitis. J. Periodontal Res. **15**:563–573.
9. **Frank, R. M., and J. C. Voegel.** 1978. Bacterial bone resorption in advanced cases of human periodontitis. J. Periodontal Res. **13**:251–261.
10. **Freedman, H. L., M. A. Listgarten, and N. S. Taichman.** 1968. Electron microscopic features of chronically inflamed human gingiva. J. Periodontal Res. **3**:313–327.
11. **Frost, H. M.** 1979. Treatment of osteoporosis by manipulating coherent bone cell populations. Clin. Orthop. Relat. Res. **143**:227–244.
12. **Goodwin, J. S., and D. R. Webb.** 1980. Regulation of the immune response by prostaglandins. Clin. Immunol. Immunopathol. **15**:106–122.
13. **Harris, W. H., and R. P. Heaney.** 1969. Skeletal renewal and metabolic bone disease. N. Engl. J. Med. **280**:193–202, 253–259, 303–311.
14. **Hausmann, E., R. Genco, N. Weinfeld, and R. Sacco.** 1973. Effects of sera on bone resorption in tissue culture. Calcif. Tissue Res. **13**:311–317.
15. **Hausmann, E., O. Luderitz, N. Weinfeld, and A. Wicken.** 1975. Structural requirements for bone resorption by endotoxin and lipoteichoic acid. J. Dent. Res. **54**(Spec. Issue B):B94–B99.
16. **Hausmann, E., B. C. Nair, K. W. Knox, K. W. Broady, A. J. Wicken, M. Brown, and R. Dziak.** 1981. Partial purification and characterization of the bone resorption factor from *Actinomyces viscosus.* Calcif. Tissue Int., in press.
17. **Hausmann, E., and L. Ortman.** 1979. Present status of bone resorption in human periodontal disease. J. Periodontol. Spec. Issue **50**:7–10.
18. **Hausman, E., and N. Weinfeld.** 1973. Human dental plaque: stimulation of bone resorption in tissue culture. Arch. Oral Biol. **18**:1509–1515.
19. **Howard, G. A., B. L. Bottemiller, and D. J. Baylink.** 1980. Evidence for the coupling of bone formation to bone resorption *in vitro.* Metab. Bone Dis. Relat. Res. **2**:131–135.
20. **Howard, G. A., B. L. Bottemiller, R. T. Turner, J. I. Rader, and D. J. Baylink.** 1981. Parathyroid hormone stimulates formation and resorption in organ culture: evidence for a coupling mechanism. Proc. Natl. Acad. Sci. U.S.A. **78**:3204–3208.
21. **Irving, J. T., S. S. Socransky, and J. D. Heeley.** 1974. Histological changes in experimental periodontal disease in gnotobiotic rats and conventional hamsters. J. Peridontal Res. **9**:73–80.
22. **Lacroix, P.** 1971. The internal remodeling of bones, p. 119–142. *In* G. H. Bourne (ed.), The biochemistry and physiology of bone, vol. 3. Academic Press, Inc., New York.
23. **Manson, J. D.** 1962. A microradiographic study of age changes in the human mandible. Arch. Oral Biol. **7**:761–769.
24. **Mergenhagen, S. E., and E. Varah.** 1963. Serologically specific lipopolysaccharides from oral *Veillonella.* Arch. Oral Biol. **8**:31–36.
25. **Meryon, S. D., and A. D. Perris.** 1981. Lipopolysaccharide-induced bone resorption is mediated by prostaglandins. Life Sci. **28**:1061–1065.
26. **Raisz, L. G.** 1965. Bone resorption in tissue culture. Factors influencing the response to parathyroid hormone. J. Clin. Invest. **44**:103–116.
27. **Raisz, L. G.** 1979. Physiological and pharmacologic regulation of bone resorption—a 1978 update. J. Periodontol. Spec. Issue **50**:3–6.
28. **Raisz, L. G., K. Nuki, C. B. Alander, and R. G. Craig.** 1981. Interaction between bacterial endotoxin and other stimulators of bone resorption in organ culture. J. Periodontal Res. **16**:1–7.
29. **Rowe, D. J., and L. S. Bradley.** 1981. Quantitative analysis of osteoclasts, bone loss and inflammation in human periodontal disease. J. Periodontal Res. **16**:13–19.
30. **Sandberg, A. L., L. G. Raisz, J. M. Goodson, H. A. Simmons, and S. E. Mergenhagen.** 1977. Initiation of bone resorption by the classical and alternate C pathways and its mediation by prostaglandins. J. Immunol. **119**:1378–1381.
31. **Slots, J.** 1979. Subgingival microflora and periodontal disease. J. Clin. Periodontol. **6**:351–382.

32. **Slots, J., and E. Hausmann.** 1979. Longitudinal study of experimentally induced periodontal disease in *Macaca arctoides:* relationship between microflora and alveolar bone loss. Infect. Immun. **23:**260–269.
33. **Wells, H., and W. Lloyd.** 1967. Effects of theophylline on the serum calcium of rats after parathyroidectomy and administration of parathyroid hormone. Endocrinology **81:**139–144.

Cellular Basis of Endotoxin Susceptibility

STEFANIE N. VOGEL[1] AND STEPHAN E. MERGENHAGEN

Laboratory of Microbiology and Immunology, National Institute of Dental Research, Bethesda, Maryland 20205

INTRODUCTION

The presence of gram-negative bacteria in the oral cavity, their abundance in dental plaque, and their association with the tissue destruction observed in chronic periodontitis have focused attention on the endotoxic cell wall component of these bacteria as an important pathogenetic factor in this disease. Specifically, biologically active endotoxin, the lipopolysaccharide (LPS) cell wall component of gram-negative bacteria, has been isolated from a number of *Fusobacterium, Bacteroides, Selenomonas, Borrelia,* and *Veillonella* species (reviewed in 6). Unlike bacterial exotoxins, LPS is an integral component of the outer cell membrane of gram-negative bacteria and appears to exert its toxic effects through the stimulation of inflammatory cells with concomitant production of soluble mediators, rather than by a direct action on host tissue. This report will focus on the cellular basis for susceptibility to the inflammatory effects of LPS.

ENDOTOXIN SENSITIVITY IS GENETICALLY CONTROLLED

The injection of adequate amounts of LPS into a susceptible host results in the induction of a number of complex physiological alterations, including hypoglycemia, severe diarrhea, tumor necrosis, the activation of the complement, clotting, and kinin-generating pathways, and the production of a number of circulating "early" and "late" acute-phase reactants and mediators (i.e., interferon, interleukin 1, colony-stimulating factor, tumor necrosis factor, and serum amyloid A), as well as antibodies directed primarily against the polysaccharide moiety of the LPS (reviewed in 2 and 13). The complex interaction of these physiological responses may culminate in endotoxic shock or even death. The diversity of the toxic effects elicited by LPS has been appreciated for many years and is mainly attributable to the lipid A portion of the molecule (reviewed in 2 and 13). However, an understanding of the cell types required for the observed biological alterations has only recently been delineated.

The ability to examine the effects of LPS at the cellular level was greatly facilitated by the discovery of an animal model expressing an innate resistance or "hyporesponsiveness" to all of the in vivo effects of endotoxin. The LPS-hyporesponsive C3H/HeJ mouse strain arose spontaneously at Jackson Laboratories some time between 1960 and 1965 (7, 27) as the result of a single autosomal mutation which has been mapped on the fourth chromosome (26; Fig. 1). The gene controlling sensitivity to LPS (*Lps*) is codominantly inherited (F_1 progeny of responder and nonresponder parents respond to LPS in an intermediate fashion; 8, 16). A defect or deletion of the gene at this locus results

[1]Present address: Department of Microbiology, Uniformed Services University of the Health Sciences, Bethesda, MD 20814.

in a decreased ability of both B lymphocytes and macrophages to respond to endotoxin in vitro (16) and specifically to the lipid A moiety of the LPS. In fact, every cell type derived from C3H/HeJ mice examined in vitro (including B and T lymphocytes, macrophages, and fibroblasts) reflects the in vivo hyporesponsiveness to LPS (reviewed in 13). It has been proposed that the genetic defect is the result of the defective expression of a receptor for the LPS molecule in hyporesponsive cells (4); however, this theory is still very controversial and is currently the subject of active investigation in a number of laboratories.

SENSITIVITY TO LPS IS MEDIATED BY LYMPHORETICULAR CELLS

The LPS-"unresponsive" mouse strain has been employed in a number of studies of the mechanisms underlying the biological manifestations of LPS. Certain LPS-mediated responses remain intact in C3H/HeJ mice. LPS-induced activation of the alternative complement pathway is normal in these mice (5, 11); thus, this humoral element appears not to be a principal factor in the induction of endotoxicity. In a recent series of experiments by Michalek et al. (10), the cellular basis for the multiple effects of endotoxin was firmly established. Chimeric animals were prepared from syngeneic LPS responder (C3H/HeN) and nonresponder (C3H/HeJ) mouse strains by infusing bone marrow cells into lethally irradiated recipients. When responder bone marrow cells were administered to an irradiated nonresponder recipient, the surviving chimeras were found to be responsive to endotoxin challenge. Conversely, when C3H/HeJ bone marrow cells were used to repopulate lethally irradiated C3H/HeN recipients, the resulting chimeras were LPS resistant. This study clearly demonstrated that the toxic effects of LPS are mediated by a radiosensitive, bone marrow-derived cell type. Since athymic nude mice derived from LPS-sensitive mouse strains (e.g., BALB/c [nu/nu]) are fully sensitive to the lethal effects of LPS (8), and since the in vitro responses of nu/nu B cells and macrophages to LPS are completely normal (22), this would suggest that T lymphocytes are not primarily involved in mediating the toxic effects of LPS. The CBA/N mouse strain possesses an X-linked defect which results in a lack of endotoxin-responsive B lymphocytes (20). However, these mice are fully LPS responsive in vivo (28), suggesting that LPS-sensitive B lymphocytes are also not involved as a primary mediator of endotoxic phenomena. Several lines of evidence do, however, support the role of the macrophage as the central effector cell in endotoxic reactions. First, LPS-stimulated macrophages produce in vitro many of the same mediators produced in vivo in response to LPS. For instance,

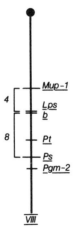

LOCATION OF Lps ON CHROMOSOME 4

FIG. 1. *Chromosome map showing location of the* Lps *gene on murine chromosome 4. The* Lps *gene was demonstrated by Watson et al. (26) to map between the markers for major urinary protein (MUP-1) and polysyndactyly (Ps). (Figure kindly provided by J. Watson.)*

TABLE 1. *LPS-induced lethality in C3H/HeN and C3H/HeJ mice*[a]

Mouse strain	Pretreatment, day 0	LD_{50} (μg of LPS)[b], day 11
C3H/HeJ	Saline	>8,000
	BCG	282
C3H/HeN	Saline	76
	BCG	9

[a]Data taken from reference 22.
[b]Lethal dose of phenol-extracted *Escherichia coli* K235 LPS required to kill 50% of the experimental animals.

LPS-stimulated macrophages produce endogenous pyrogen, the monokine responsible for the fever that results from the administration of endotoxin. Similarly, LPS-stimulated macrophages produce other products associated with endotoxicity in vivo such as prostaglandin E_2 (associated in vivo with both fever and the abortifacient effects of LPS), colony-stimulating factor (associated with LPS-induced resistance to X-irradiation), interferon, and tumor necrosis factor. Second, agents previously demonstrated to exert direct or indirect effects on macrophages (i.e., carrageenan, zymosan, glucan, or *Mycobacterium bovis* BCG infection) alter endotoxin sensitivity in vivo. Agents which result in increased macrophage activation render mice much more sensitive to the effects of endotoxin. This was demonstrated more than a decade ago in studies in which mice were challenged with LPS after BCG infection or exposure to zymosan yeast cell extracts (1, 21). Mice pretreated in this fashion were rendered up to 1,000 times more sensitive to the lethal effects of LPS.

RELATIONSHIP OF MACROPHAGE ACTIVATION AND SENSITIVITY TO LPS

Preinfection of C3H/HeJ mice with BCG renders them much more sensitive to the lethal effects of endotoxin (23). As can be seen in Table 1, the amount of endotoxin required to kill BCG-infected C3H/HeJ mice is approximately one-thirtieth of the amount required to kill saline-pretreated control animals. This finding illustrates two important points. First, the genetic defect of C3H/HeJ mice is not irreversible; however, the "corrected" response approaches, but does not equal, the normal level of LPS sensitivity observed in control animals (saline-pretreated C3H/HeN mice). As Suter et al. had previously reported (21), BCG infection of endotoxin-sensitive mice renders them "hyperreactive" to the toxic effects of LPS. These observations based on lethality were confirmed by examining a number of other endotoxin-mediated effects, including weight loss,

TABLE 2. *BCG enhancement of endotoxin responsiveness of C3H/HeJ mice*[a]

Pretreatment	LPS-induced response			
	LD_{50} (μg)	Blood glucose level (mg/dl)	Serum interferon titer (U/ml)	Serum amyloid A (μg/ml)
Saline	>8,000	113.6	21	111
BCG	282	85.2	94	485

[a]All data were taken from reference 22.

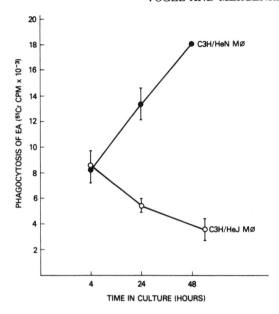

FIG. 2. *Kinetics of the ingestion of* ^{51}Cr-*labeled, opsonized sheep erythrocytes (EA) by macrophages. (Data taken from reference 23.)*

hypoglycemia, and the production of serum interferon and the late-acute-phase protein, serum amyloid A, in response to endotoxin challenge (Table 2). It is noteworthy that the ability to produce anti-LPS antibodies was not corrected in the BCG-infected C3H/HeJ mice, suggesting that this B lymphocyte-dependent humoral function was not essential for the enhanced endotoxicity observed in these mice.

RELATIONSHIP BETWEEN MACROPHAGE DIFFERENTIATION AND LPS SENSITIVITY IN VITRO

C3H/HeJ macrophages exhibit a differentiation defect in vitro. Since there apparently is a relationship between the state of macrophage differentiation and LPS sensitivity, as suggested by the in vivo data, a comparison was made of the differentiation state of C3H/HeN and C3H/HeJ macrophages in vitro by monitoring Fc receptor function. An increased state of macrophage differentiation is accompanied by enhanced expression of receptors for the Fc portion of immunoglobulin (3). These receptors are essential in certain macrophage Fc receptor-dependent functions, such as the ingestion of antibody-coated bacteria or antibody-dependent cell cytotoxicity. As can be seen in Fig. 2, LPS-responsive C3H/HeN macrophages exhibit increased Fc receptor capacity when cultured over a 48-h period, as assessed by increased ingestion of ^{51}Cr-labeled, opsonized sheep erythrocytes. In contrast, C3H/HeJ mice not only fail to develop the normal increase in Fc-mediated phagocytosis, but also exhibit in vitro a loss of phagocytic capacity over a 48-h culture period (24). Thus, C3H/HeJ macrophages exhibit a marked differentiation defect in vitro. The loss of Fc receptor-mediated phagocytosis was not due to a loss in cell viability, cell numbers, or a generalized decrease in phagocytosis, since ingestion of latex particles by C3H/HeJ macrophages was normal. The decrease in Fc-mediated phagocytosis appeared to be secondary to a loss of Fc receptor binding capacity. When binding, rather than phagocytosis, capacities of ^{51}Cr-labeled opsonized erythrocytes by C3H/HeN and C3H/HeJ macrophages were compared, it was clear that the C3H/HeJ macrophage differentiation defect was related to deficient Fc receptor binding (Fig. 3).

Correction of C3H/HeJ differentiation and LPS defects in vitro by T lymphocytes or their products. Macrophage activation in vivo by exposure to BCG is believed to involve the production of soluble macrophage-activating factors (lymphokines) derived from T lymphocytes (18). To mimic this effect in vitro, we prepared lymphokine-rich culture supernatants by activating splenic T lymphocytes in vitro with the T-cell mitogen concanavalin A. Such supernatants have been utilized in previous studies to activate macrophages in vitro to a microbicidal or tumoricidal state (15, 19) and are clearly heterogeneous with respect to the quality and quantity of immunoregulatory factors present. Treatment of C3H/HeJ macrophages with the lymphokine-rich supernatant completely corrected the Fc receptor defect by increasing the ability of C3H/HeJ macrophages to bind, and therefore phagocytose, through the Fc receptor (24; Fig. 4). Control supernatants were not stimulatory. Furthermore, treatment of C3H/HeJ macrophages with the lymphokine-rich supernatant rendered the macrophages sensitive to activation in vitro with 10 µg of LPS as assessed by the ability of the macrophages to produce lymphocyte activating factor (LAF). LAF (recently renamed interleukin 1) has been shown to be closely related to or identical to endogenous pyrogen (14). Since fever is a prominent manifestation of LPS toxicity, the production of the mediator believed to induce fever was measured as an in vitro correlate of in vivo LPS sensitivity.

As shown in Fig. 5, treatment of C3H/HeJ macrophages with the lymphokine-rich supernatant alone or with LPS alone did not result in the production of

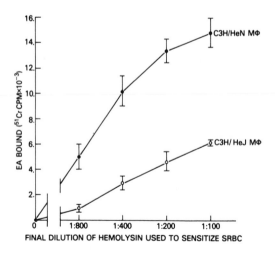

FIG. 3. *Binding of ^{51}Cr-labeled, opsonized sheep erythrocytes (EA) by macrophages. (Data taken from reference 23.)*

LAF (left panel). However, when the cells were exposed to both the lymphokine-containing supernatant and LPS, a dose-dependent enhancement of LAF production was observed (right panel). Hence, in vitro macrophage differentiation by lymphokines (as monitored by enhanced Fc-mediated phagocytosis and binding) was accompanied by increased macrophage sensitivity to LPS (as evidenced by the production of LAF). Thus, the in vivo effect of BCG preinfection on the PS sensitivity of the C3H/HeJ mouse was mirrored in vitro by lymphokine activation of the macrophages. We have recently

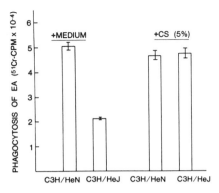

FIG. 4. *Correction of C3H/HeJ phagocytic defect by incubation with a concanavalin A-stimulated spleen cell supernatant (CS). (Data taken from reference 23.)*

characterized the Fc receptor enhancing factor as the T-cell lymphokine, γ (immune or type II)-interferon (S. N. Vogel et al., Fed. Proc. **40**:770, 1981; S. N. Vogel et al., submitted for publication), and are currently in the process of

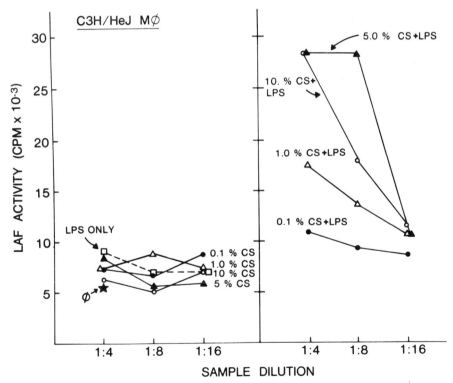

FIG. 5. *Effect of concanavalin A-stimulated spleen cell supernatant (CS) on LAF production by C3H/HeJ macrophages. The symbol Ø represents supernatants generated in the presence of tissue culture medium alone. The final concentration of LPS used in the cultures was 10 μg/ml. (Data taken from reference 24.)*

examining the effects of our highly purified γ-interferon on the enhancement of LPS sensitivity in C3H/HeJ macrophage cultures; however, we are not, at this time, able to say whether the two effects are mediated by the same lymphokine.

To further support the hypothesis that the state of macrophage activation greatly influences the LPS responsiveness of this cell type, we performed the following series of in vitro experiments. Highly purified peritoneal T lymphocytes were prepared from C3H/HeN or C3H/HeJ mice previously injected with saline or BCG. These T-lymphocyte preparations (depleted of macrophages) were cocultured with C3H/HeJ peritoneal macrophages. When challenged with LPS (10 μg/ml), the normally LPS-unresponsive macrophages in the cocultures produced LAF, the quantity of which reflected the in vivo LPS sensitivity of the mouse from which the T lymphocytes were prepared (Fig. 6). Briefly, T cells from endotoxin-"hyporesponsive" mice (C3H/HeJ mice pretreated with saline) were unable to render unresponsive C3H/HeJ macrophages capable of producing LAF in response to LPS. However, T cells derived from fully endotoxin-responsive mice (saline-pretreated C3H/HeN mice) or nearly fully responsive mice (BCG-infected C3H/HeJ mice) were able to impart comparable levels of LPS sensitivity on the C3H/HeJ macrophages as evidenced by the equivalent amounts of LAF produced by the previously unresponsive macrophages upon LPS stimulation. Finally, T lymphocytes derived from LPS-"hyperreactive" mice (BCG-infected C3H/HeN mice) were clearly the most potent in their ability to sensitize LPS-unresponsive macrophages to produce large amounts of LAF after exposure to LPS. Therefore, the T lymphocyte can serve as an immunoregulator of macrophage LPS sensitivity in vitro and probably acts on the macrophage through the production of soluble factors analogous or identical to those present in the concanavalin A-stimulated T-cell supernatants which serve to enhance macrophage differentiation and LPS sensitivity concomitantly.

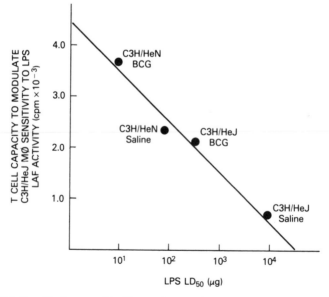

FIG. 6. *Relationship between T-cell capacity to enhance macrophage LPS sensitivity and the in vivo LPS sensitivity of the T-cell donors. (Vogel et al., submitted for publication.)*

Clearly, these findings suggest that soluble products of T lymphocytes can modulate macrophage LPS sensitivity by altering the activation state of the macrophage. However, these findings do not preclude the potential immunoregulatory effects of other differentiating "signals" derived from non-T-lymphocyte populations. In this regard, fibroblast-derived colony-stimulating factor has been shown to lower the threshold for LPS sensitivity of C3H/HeN macrophages (12), and another recent report has implicated a nonphagocytic, adherent "B-lymphocyte" as contributing to the enhancement of macrophage activation and, thus, LPS sensitivity of C3H/HeJ macrophages (13). Therefore, any cell type with the potential for producing factors which increase the differentiation state of the macrophage may participate as the immuno-regulatory potentiators of macrophage sensitivity to LPS. However, the products and activities of the endotoxin-stimulated macrophage point to this cell type as the central executor of LPS-mediated toxic phenomena.

SUMMARY

In this report we have examined some of the experimental evidence obtained with the endotoxin-hyporesponsive C3H/HeJ mouse strain which has formed a framework for an understanding of endotoxic effects at a cellular level. The cell responsible for eliciting many of the in vivo LPS-induced manifestations is radiosensitive and bone marrow derived. The susceptibility of a host to the toxic effects of LPS appears to be an accurate reflection of the state of activation exhibited by the host's macrophages. As the state of macrophage activation is increased, the LPS sensitivity of the host increases in parallel. However, the state of macrophage activation, and therefore LPS sensitivity, is modulated by soluble immunoregulatory factors produced by lymphoid and nonlymphoid cells. The role of macrophages in carrying out tissue destruction at an inflamed site in response to local populations of gram-negative bacteria may serve as a focus of attention in future attempts to alter tissue reactivity in localized chronic inflammatory lesions.

LITERATURE CITED

1. **Benacerraf, B., G. J. Throbecke, and D. Jacoby.** 1959. Effect of zymosan on endotoxin toxicity in mice. Proc. Soc. Exp. Biol. Med. **100:**796–799.
2. **Berry, L. J.** 1977. Bacterial toxins. Crit. Rev. Toxicol. **5:**239–318.
3. **Bianco, C., F. M. Griffin, and S. C. Silverstein.** 1975. Studies of the complement receptor. Alteration of receptor function upon macrophage activation. J. Exp. Med. **141:**1278–1290.
4. **Coutinho, A., L. Forri, F. Melchers, and T. Watanabe.** 1977. Genetic defect in responsiveness to the B cell mitogen lipopolysaccharide. Eur. J. Immunol. **7:**325–328.
5. **Curry, B. J., and D. C. Morrison.** 1979. Role of complement in endotoxin initiated lethality in mice. Immunopharmacology **1:**125–135.
6. **Daly, C. G., G. J. Seymour, and J. P. Kieser.** 1980. Bacterial endotoxin: a role in chronic inflammatory periodontal disease? J. Oral Pathol. **9:**1–15.
7. **Glode, L. M., and D. L. Rosenstreich.** 1976. Genetic control of B cell activation by bacterial lipopolysaccharide is mediated by multiple distinct genes or alleles. J. Immunol. **117:**2061–2066.
8. **McGhee, J. R., S. M. Michalek, H. Kiyono, M. P. Clark, and J. L. Babb.** 1980. Effect of endotoxin on lymphoreticular cells and toxicity in normal and immunocompromised mice, p. 283–309. In M. K. Agarwal (ed.), Bacterial endotoxins and host response. Elsevier-North Holland Biomedical Press, Amsterdam.
9. **McGhee, J. R., S. M. Michalek, R. N. Moore, S. E. Mergenhagen, and D. L. Rosenstreich.** 1979. Genetic control of in vivo sensitivity to lipopolysaccharide: evidence for codominant inheritance. J. Immunol. **122:**2052–2058.
10. **Michalek, S. M., R. N. Moore, J. R. McGhee, D. L. Rosenstreich, and S. E. Mergenhagen.** 1980. The primary role of lymphoreticular cells in the mediation of host responses to bacterial endotoxins. J. Infect. Dis. **141:**55–63.

11. **Möeller, G. R., L. Terry, and R. Snyderman.** 1978. The inflammatory response and resistance to endotoxin in mice. J. Immunol. **120:**116–123.
12. **Moore, R. N., S. N. Vogel, L. M. Wahl, and S. E. Mergenhagen.** 1980. Factors influencing lipopolysaccharide-induced interferon production, p. 131–134. *In* D. Schlessinger (ed.), Microbiology—1980. American Society for Microbiology, Washington, D.C.
13. **Morrison, D. C., and J. L. Ryan.** 1979. Bacterial endotoxins and host immune responses. Adv. Immunol. **28:**293–450.
14. **Murphy, P. A., P. L. Simon, and W. F. Willoughby.** 1980. Endogenous pyrogens made by rabbit peritoneal exudate cells are identical with lymphocyte activating factors made by rabbit alveolar macrophages. J. Immunol. **124:**2498–2501.
15. **Nogueira, N., and Z. A. Cohn.** 1978. *Trypanosoma cruzi: in vitro* induction of macrophage microbicidal activity. J. Exp. Med. **148:**288–300.
16. **Rosenstreich, D. L., S. N. Vogel, A. R. Jacques, L. M. Wahl, and J. J. Oppenheim.** 1978. Macrophage sensitivity to endotoxin: genetic control by a single codominant gene. J. Immunol. **121:**1664–1670.
17. **Rosenstreich, D. L., S. N. Vogel, A. Jacques, L. M. Wahl, I. Scher, and S. E. Mergenhagen.** 1978. Differential endotoxin sensitivity of lymphocytes and macrophages from mice with an X-linked defect in B cell maturation. J. Immunol. **121:**685–690.
18. **Ruco, L. P., and M. S. Meltzer.** 1977. Macrophage activation for tumor cytotoxicity: induction of tumoricidal macrophages by supernatants of PPD-stimulated Bacillus Calmette-Guérin immune spleen cell cultures. J. Immunol. **119:**889–896.
19. **Ruco, L. P., and M. S. Meltzer.** 1978. Macrophage activation for tumor cytotoxicity: tumoricidal activity by macrophages from C3H/HeJ mice requires at least two activation stimuli. Cell. Immunol. **41:**35–51.
20. **Scher, I., S. O. Sharrow, and W. E. Paul.** 1976. X-linked B-lymphocyte defect in CBA/N mice. III. Abnormal development of B-lymphocyte populations defined by their density of surface immunoglobulin. J. Exp. Med. **144:**507–518.
21. **Suter, E., G. E. Ullman, and R. G. Hoffman.** 1958. Sensitivity of mice to endotoxin after vaccination with BCG (Bacillus Calmette Guérin). Proc. Soc. Exp. Biol. Med. **99:**167–169.
22. **Vogel, S. N., C. T. Hansen, and D. L. Rosenstreich.** 1979. Characterization of a congenitally LPS-resistant, athymic mouse strain. J. Immunol. **122:**619–622.
23. **Vogel, S. N., R. N. Moore, J. D. Sipe, and D. L. Rosenstreich.** 1980. BCG-induced enhancement of endotoxin sensitivity in C3H/HeJ mice. I. *In vivo* studies. J. Immunol. **124:**2004–2009.
24. **Vogel, S. N., and D. L. Rosenstreich.** 1979. Defective Fc receptor mediated phagocytosis in C3H/HeJ macrophages. I. Correction by lymphokine-induced stimulation. J. Immunol. **123:**2842–2850.
25. **Vogel, S. N., and D. L. Rosenstreich.** 1981. LPS-unresponsive mice as a model for analyzing lymphokine-induced macrophage differentiation *in vitro.* Lymphokines **3:**149–180.
26. **Watson, J., K. Kelly, M. Largen, and B. A. Taylor.** 1978. The genetic mapping of a defective LPS response gene in C3H/HeJ mice. J. Immunol. **120:**422–424.
27. **Watson, J., and R. Riblet.** 1974. Genetic control of responses to bacterial lipopolysaccharide in mice. I. Evidence for a single gene that influences mitogenic and immunogenic responses to lipopolysaccharide. J. Exp. Med. **140:**1147–1161.
28. **Zaldivar, N. M., and I. Scher.** 1979. Endotoxin lethality and tolerance in mice: analysis with the B-lymphocyte-defective CBA/N strain. Infect. Immun. **24:**127–131.

Pathogenicity of *Actinomyces* Species

HAROLD V. JORDAN

Forsyth Dental Center, Boston, Massachusetts 02115

INTRODUCTION

The pathogenic potential of members of the genus *Actinomyces* has long been recognized because of their role in classical actinomycotic infections occurring in humans and in certain domestic animals. The disease usually takes the form of a slowly progressive, granulomatous infection with sinus formation and suppuration. Lesions are located most commonly in the head and neck region although they can occur elsewhere and can affect both soft tissues and bone. There is no evidence of transmission of actinomycotic infections in the usual sense of contagion from an active lesion. It is now accepted that actinomycosis is endogenously acquired and that the mouth is the source of infection. Organisms identical to the pathogenic agents in lesions are routinely isolated from tonsils, carious teeth, periodontal pockets, and dental plaque (16, 33, 53, 54). Comprehensive reviews of actinomycosis have been presented by Rosebury (52) and by Guidry (25).

Over the past two decades evidence has accumulated that implicates certain *Actinomyces* species in a different and more prevalent type of actinomycotic infection. In this case the infection becomes established around the gingival areas of the dentition. The pathological process can involve the gingival tissues, the exposed cemental surfaces, or the supporting structures of the teeth. Interest in these periodontal infections has now focused attention on the more aerobic to facultative *Actinomyces* species in the mouth. It has been difficult to define the extent of participation of these organisms in periodontal infections because the potential exists for a wide range of oral organisms to become involved at different stages of the disease.

The purpose of the present discussion is to examine current knowledge about the pathogenicity of the *Actinomyces* as a group. This will include their role in extraoral actinomycoses as well as in the more recently described intraoral periodontal infections. It is outside the scope of this paper to attempt a complete review of the extensive literature bearing on this subject. Instead, pertinent references will be cited insofar as they help to clarify the topics being examined and as a guide to the literature in this area.

EXTRAORAL INFECTIONS

Despite the universal occurrence of oral *Actinomyces* and the constant opportunities for dissemination from the mouth, the prevalence of extraoral infections is relatively rare, which suggests that their primary infectivity for the host is low. However, once the lesions are established, serious chronic infections can result. *A. israelii* is generally considered to be the major etiological agent in human infections (55), although other *Actinomyces* species can be isolated from actinomycotic lesions (11, 20, 49). A related organism, *Arachnia propionica* previously classified in the genus *Actinomyces* (7), appears to possess a similar pathogenicity. Actinomycoses are usually classified clinically as cervicofacial, thoracic, or abdominal, with the highest prevalence of lesions seen in the cervicofacial region (62). Although factors governing the pathogenicity of the *Actinomyces* are not well understood, it is generally agreed that most infections of the cervicofacial tissues are preceded by dental infections, dental surgery, or accidental tissue trauma. *Actinomyces* may reach the lungs from the oral cavity via the tracheobronchial tree by aspiration, via the blood stream, or along the fascial planes of the neck and mediastinal structures. There is strong evidence that abdominal actinomycosis is usually preceded by some disease process or trauma (25). However, attempts to induce experimental actinomycotic infections in animals by using various forms of trauma have not been successful (52). In general, early attempts to establish laboratory models of actinomycosis in a variety of animals gave highly variable results (52). It has been observed that weanling mice (48) and hamsters (27) are susceptible to infection by *Actinomyces,* and the former have proved to be very useful for the study of experimental actinomycosis.

Meyer and Verges (48) reported that gastric mucin enhanced the invasiveness of *A. bovis* in young male mice when injected intraperitoneally. These authors observed that older animals were often completely resistant to infection and stressed the importance of using young mice weighing no more than 10 to 15 g. The mouse model of actinomycosis was described as a two-stage infectious process by Geister and Meyer (19). They reported that lesions appeared on the viscera by the 5th day and active invasion continued until about the 20th or 25th day, when a status quo was reached. After that the disease was chronic in most animals with slow expansion of the lesions.

The development and histopathology of actinomycotic lesions in mice have been described by Brown and von Lichtenberg (6). These workers pointed out that the age of the mice and the size of the bacterial aggregates are the two most important factors leading to infection. Weanling mice weighing 10 g or less were the most susceptible. Rough strains of *A. israelii* produced infections, whereas smooth strains or homogenized inocula generally did not. The evolution of the infection in mice was described as following the course of other chronic infections. An initial acute phase of growth and expansion was followed by a static period when some animals aborted the infection and others did not. This was followed by a prolonged chronic phase characterized by host–parasite balance with slow growth of the lesions. Histologically, the actinomycotic granules showed a fine eosinophilic fringe composed of delicate barlike projections enclosing or alternating with bacterial cells. In the chronic state of disease, an equilibrium appeared to exist between growth of the organism and its removal and destruction. The process probably consisted of a constant and fairly high turnover of bacteria and neutrophils, with macrophages removing the debris. The authors consider this eosinophilic fringe to be the critical site of host–parasite equilibirium.

Crawford (12) examined the nature of acidophilic hyaline clubs located at the periphery of *Actinomyces* colonies in infected lung tissue. Arginine-rich polypeptides were demonstrated in the acidophilic areas and in the cytoplasm of granulocytic leukocytes surrounding the colonies. It was concluded that the acidophilic hyaline clubs represent a combination of a capsular component of the actinomycete and a cationic antibacterial polypeptide derived from the host leukocytes.

Beaman et al. (3) compared resistance to actinomycotic infections in athymic nude mice and heterozygous littermates. Lung clearance data and 50% lethal doses were comparable, indicating that T lymphocytes were probably not necessary for pulmonary clearance or prevention of systemic actinomycosis. However, it was suggested that T cells may be involved in resistance to the localized cervicofacial form of the disease since 30% of the nude mice infected intranasally developed cervicofacial lesions or abscesses of the tracheobronchial region.

The susceptible mouse model has been used to compare the pathogenicity of various species of *Actinomyces* (10, 21). *A. israelii* and *Arachnia propionica* produced lesions in most of the animals inoculated. *A. naeslundii* produced lesions in a high percentage of animals and was considered to have significant potential as an agent of human actinomycosis, particularly in view of the fact that this species is frequently isolated from suppurative lesions. *A. viscosus* showed a more limited ability to produce lesions, and these were less severe than lesions produced by *A. israelii*. *A. odontolyticus* showed little pathogenicity in mice.

We have examined the comparative pathogenicity of different species of *Actinomyces* in mice in our laboratory (M. J. Behbehani and H. V. Jordan, Proc. Int. Assoc. Dent. Res., abstr. 993, 1979) and have observed significant differences between species, particularly during the chronic stage of infection. Numerous abscesses were produced on abdominal organs after intraperitoneal injection of *A. viscosus, A. naeslundii,* or *A. israelii*. After 1 to 2 months, fewer lesions were noted in the animals injected with *A. viscosus* or *A. naeslundii*. The lesions did not contain viable organisms and appeared to be resolving. Lesions in *A. israelii*-infected animals increased in size and spread to extra-abdominal sites in some cases. Viable cultures of *A. israelii* could be recovered from the lesions for periods up to 1 year.

Apparently, human actinomycosis can involve an acute and a chronic stage (1). According to Bently and de Vries (4), the acute form may be indistinguishable in the early stages from any other acute pyogenic abscess. Specific diagnosis at this stage depends on isolation and identification of the causative actinomycete. The authors point out that chronic cervicofacial actinomycosis is considered to be rare today, and the classical textbook picture is seldom seen, probably because of the widespread availability and the effectiveness of antibiotics.

INTRAORAL INFECTIONS

A clear and comprehensive picture of the pathogenicity of *Actinomyces* species in the oral cavity is lacking. However, a partial understanding of some of the mechanisms by which these organisms may participate in oral disease has begun to emerge in recent years. Direct evidence for the association of *Actinomyces* with this type of infection was obtained from studies on the etiology of a naturally occurring transmissible periodontal infection in Syrian hamsters (43). The specific infectious component in the hamster infection was found to be a unique catalase-positive *Actinomyces*-like organism (41). A more extensive characterization of the organism illustrated its close relationship to *Actinomyces* (30–32). Similar organisms were eventually isolated from humans, and the animal and human organisms are now considered to be different serotypes of the same species, *A. viscosus* (22). The pathogenic potential of the human and animal strains appears similar (42).

Numerous studies with hamsters and gnotobiotic rats (36, 39, 41, 58) have clearly illustrated the plaque-forming ability of *A. viscosus* and *A. naeslundii* as well as the associated pathological changes in the periodontal tissues of infected animals. These studies have also served to demonstrate the specific ability of these organisms to colonize exposed cemental surfaces and to invade this tissue and the underlying dentin to form carious lesions analogous to root surface caries in humans (40). There have been reports of enamel caries in gnotobiotic rats monoinfected with strains of *A. viscosus* and *A. naeslundii* (45) (H. V. Jordan, S. Bellack, P. H. Keyes, and M. A. Gerencser, Proc. Int. Assoc. Dent. Res., abstr. 73, 1978) as well as reports of an association between *Actinomyces* and coronal caries in humans (34). However, significant primary involvement of *Actinomyces* in the initiation of lesions on enamel surfaces in humans seems unlikely because of the relatively lower acidogenic potential of these organisms compared with the lactic acid bacteria (15).

Insight into the mechanisms of intraoral pathogenicity and virulence of *Actinomyces* has been gained through comparative studies on a strain of *A. viscosus* (T14V), normally pathogenic in experimental animals, and its avirulent mutant strain (T14Av). Hammond and co-workers (26) identified a specific cell wall antigen containing 6-deoxytalose in strain T14V that was associated with the presence of a plasmid. The antigen was found to be present in *A. naeslundii* as well. An extracellular heteropolysaccharide known to be elaborated by *A. viscosus* (51) was produced in larger amounts by the avirulent strain than by the virulent strain.

The existence of a different virulence-associated antigen in *A. viscosus* T14V was reported by Cisar et al. (9). This antigen is located in the fine fibrils coating the cell surface. A greater amount of fibrils and V-antigen was associated with the T14V cell wall compared with the T14Av cell wall, suggesting a quantitative rather than a qualitative difference between the two strains. Girard and Jacius (23) had previously noted fibril-like structures on the outer surface of *A. viscosus* and *A. naeslundii* and had speculated on their potential role in adhesion and colonization.

Brecher, van Houte, and Hammond (5) studied the comparative colonization of *A. viscosus* T14V and T14Av in conventional and gnotobiotic rats. They found the virulent strain, T14V, to be more efficient in colonizing the tooth surfaces, particularly near the gingivae. The virulent strain had a higher tendency to attach to hydroxyapatite beads coated with rat saliva than the avirulent strain. The lower tendency of the avirulent strain in this respect appeared to be due to the greater amount of cell surface-associated polysaccharide synthesized by this strain. These workers hypothesized that cell surface receptors involved in initial attachment could be masked by the excess polysaccharide. It was concluded that the essential difference in pathogenicity between the two strains was related to their different abilities to colonize the teeth.

Qureshi and Gibbons (50) reported that the in vitro abilities of *A. viscosus* and *A. naeslundii* to attach to saliva-coated hydroxyapatite reflect the in vivo colonization patterns of these two species known to occur in humans (14).

In addition to the properties of *Actinomyces* that relate to establishment and colonization, there is evidence that these organisms possess pathogenic determinants that may be more directly related to possible mechanisms for tissue destruction in periodontal disease. Temple et al. (61) demonstrated the production of a chemotactic factor for polymorphonuclear leukocytes (PMNs) by *A. viscosus* and discussed the evidence for alternative roles for PMNs in protecting against gingival infection as well as promoting tissue destruction through the release of intracellular products.

Production of a PMN chemotactic factor by *A. viscosus* was confirmed by Engle, van Epps, and Clagett (18), who also reported that *A. viscosus* generates chemotactic activity when incubated with fresh human serum. Injection of homogenates of *A. viscosus* into footpads of nonimmunized mice induced an acute inflammatory response with a predominance of PMNs. Injection of the same homogenate into footpads of immunized mice induced an acute inflammatory response followed by a mononuclear cell infiltrate. Thus, it was speculated that the pathogenicity of *A. viscosus* may result in part from a direct chemotactic effect on PMNs, a cytotaxigenic effect on serum, and a stimulation of host immune cells to produce and release mediators of inflammation.

It has been speculated that tissue breakdown in periodontal disease may be partially the result of lysosomal activity released from PMNs which accumulate at the site of gingival inflammation (59). Taichman and co-workers (60) have reported that *A. viscosus* T14V stimulated the discharge of PMN lysosomes in serum-free cultures, whereas the avirulent mutant strain, T14Av, did not. Lysosome release was correlated with phagocytic activity since PMNs ingested T14V but not T14Av. Thus, the authors suggested a relationship between the in vivo periodontal pathogenicity of the virulent and avirulent strains and their comparative abilities to stimulate PMN lysosomal release in vitro.

Ivanyi and Lehner (38) showed that antigen from *A. viscosus* stimulated lymphocytes obtained from subjects with different levels of periodontal disease but failed to stimulate lymphocytes from nondiseased control subjects. Presumably, the latter have not been sensitized by those bacterial antigens which stimulate lymphocytes in periodontal patients. These observations were extended by Baker et al. (2) to include *A. naeslundii* and *A. israelii* in addition to *A. viscosus*. Lymphocyte proliferation was induced by using an extracellular heteroglycan and sonicated cell supernatant from *A. viscosus* by Burckhardt, Guggenheim, and Hefti (8). These fractions were tested against spleen and thoracic duct cells from germfree rats as well as spleen cells from nude mice. It was concluded that these fractions of *A. viscosus* were mitogenic for B cells.

Engle et al. (17) reported that *A. viscosus* homogenate contains substances which cause spleen cells from conventional and germfree mice to undergo increased deoxyribonucleic acid synthesis. This mitogenic effect is primarily on the B cells. The authors suggest that B-cell mitogens from *Actinomyces* may play a role in the elicitation of the plasma cell component seen in the long-term inflammatory response of actinomycotic lesions.

In vitro immunoglobulin production by lymphocytes from non-periodontally diseased subjects was induced by a soluble extract of *A. viscosus* (47). Antibodies were not specific for *A. viscosus*, indicating that a polyclonal B-lymphocyte response was activated.

Thus, it is clear that *A. viscosus* and *A. naeslundii* possess efficient mechanisms for becoming established at the site of gingival inflammation, and furthermore, they are able to participate in the activation of host reactions assumed to be involved in tissue destruction.

Most studies on the intraoral pathogenicity of *Actinomyces* have been concerned with the role of *A. viscosus* and *A. naeslundii*. Little is known about the pathogenic potential of other *Actinomyces* species in this regard. We have studied the intraoral colonization and pathogenicity of *A. israelii* strains in laboratory animals (H. V. Jordan and M. J. Behbehani, Proc. Am. Assoc. Dent. Res., abstr. 96, 1980). Certain rough strains of this species did not colonize germfree rats as readily as *A. viscosus,* and multiple inoculations were required to implant these strains. Once established, populations of *A. israelii* were higher on teeth by a factor of 10^2 to 10^3 compared with tongue, cheek, or palate. Histological sections of maxillary molar teeth showed evidence of extensive pocketing, alveolar bone resorption, and cemental invasion.

A. odontolyticus 17982 was tested in a single experiment in gnotobiotic rats fed diet 2000 (unpublished data). After 146 days, there was little evidence of gingival plaque formation, and alveolar bone loss was minimal compared with that seen in gnotobiotic rats infected with *A. viscosus.*

ASSOCIATED PATHOGENS

There has been considerable controversy about whether members of the genus *Actinomyces* should be considered sole etiological agents in actinomycosis. Although the main character of the disease is undoubtedly due to the presence of *Actinomyces,* other organisms are commonly isolated from the lesions as well. Holm (28) reviewed the early literature on this subject and presented evidence that actinomycotic infections depend on a synergistic relationship between *Actinomyces* and certain other microbes, mainly gram-negative anaerobes. These associated organisms were usually identified as *Actinobacillus actinomycetemcomitans* or the "corroding bacillus" later described by Eiken (13) and now classified as *Eikenella corrodens.* Other organisms commonly isolated from the lesions included streptococci, gram-negative coccobacilli, bacilli, and fusiforms. Holm (28) hypothesized that neither the actinomycete nor the associated pathogen was capable of inducing the lesion by itself and that the combination of organisms was required for development of the lesion. However, once established, the gram-negative organism could maintain the infection after chemotherapeutic elimination of the actinomycete (29). The concept of a mixed microbial etiology for actinomycosis was supported by Glahn (24), who suggested that variations in the severity of clinical disease may be dependent on the combination of organisms involved.

In contrast, Georg and Coleman (21) did not concur with the hypothesis of a multiple etiology and believed that establishment of typical actinomycotic lesions in experimental animals by pure cultures of *A. israelii* was evidence of its pathogenicity in the absence of other bacteria. Roseburry (52) also expressed the opinion that other organisms were not necessary for development of the disease.

For purposes of the present discussion, the significant point may not be whether *A. israelii* or another *Actinomyces* species has the potential to be pathogenic by itself. It is important that other organisms are commonly associated with *Actinomyces* in the lesions and that the nature of the disease may be influenced by their presence. Whether the same situation applies to intraoral actinomycotic infections is not known. However, there is increasing evidence that bacteria similar to the anaerobic, gram-negative organisms routinely isolated by Holm (28) from actinomycotic abscesses are prominent in periodontal infections (56). Organisms such as *A. actinomycetemcomitans* and *E.*

corrodens have been shown to induce destructive periodontal tissue changes in gnotobiotic rats (35, 37).

The buildup of gram-negative bacteria and filamentous forms in plaque which accompanies periodontitis is well known (44, 46). Thus, if a cooperative association exists between certain organisms in actinomycosis as suggested by Holm (28), it could exist in some form between the same organisms in the mouth since this is the source of these organisms. Such a synergy could occur as enhanced colonization of gram-negative bacteria associated with *Actinomyces,* as suggested by Slots and Gibbons (57), or an enhanced tissue pathogenicity of *Actinomyces* where gram-negative bacteria are present, or both.

CONCLUSIONS

It is clear from this limited review that *Actinomyces* species exhibit a wide range of pathogenicity involving most of the tissues in the body. In addition to the classical and well-studied extraoral actinomycoses, it has been established that some species of *Actinomyces* are involved in intraoral infections affecting the gingival and periodontal tissues as well as the teeth. Thus, it may be desirable to broaden the existing clinical classification scheme of actinomycotic infections (i.e., cervicofacial, thoracic, abdominal) to include a periodontal category. Alternatively, the present classification could be modified to indicate a primary separation into intraoral and extraoral infections. The latter suggestion is incorporated into the diagram shown in Fig. 1, which attempts to present a composite view of actinomycotic infections based on current knowledge. Included in the diagram is the observed tendency for certain species to be associated primarily with one type of infection or the other. It does not appear that this association is absolute, and there is undoubtedly some degree of overlapping, as indicated on the diagram. However, considerably more information is needed about the limits of pathogenicity of individual species. The pathogenic potential of other species such as *A. odontolyticus* remains obscure. Figure 1 also illustrates the likely involvement of associated gram-negative organisms

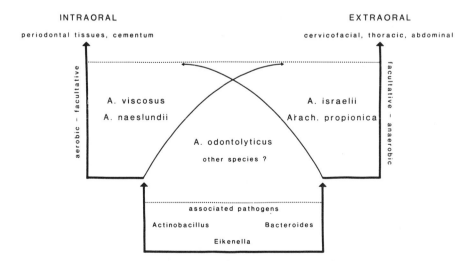

FIG. 1. *Spectrum of pathogenicity in actinomycosis.*

including *Actinobacillus, Eikenella,* or certain *Bacteroides* in both intra- and extraoral infections. The extent of this association and the mechanisms involved remain to be clarified.

It is reasonable to assume that some level of unity exists in the pathological activities of *Actinomyces* and that certain fundamental mechanisms of disease production should apply in varying degrees to both intraoral and extraoral infections. As we learn more about these pathogens, it may be possible to describe a more comprehensive spectrum of pathogenicity for the genus and to relate this specifically to the contributions of individual species.

SUMMARY

A variety of *Actinomyces* species and types inhabit the oral cavity. Certain of these organisms, notably the aerobic to facultative species *A. viscosus* and *A. naeslundii,* appear adapted to colonize the cervical areas of the teeth and participate in periodontal infections. The pathogenic mechanisms involved in these intraoral actinomycotic infections are not well understood, but may include leukocyte chemotaxis, stimulation of the immune system, and mitogenic activity.

Transport of oral *Actinomyces* species to other sites in the body may occur as a result of disease processes, surgical procedures, or trauma. Extraoral actinomycotic lesions can become established and may develop into slowly progressive, suppurative, chronic infections. The anaerobic species *A. israelii* is commonly involved in these extraoral infections and may be accompanied by certain anaerobic, gram-negative oral organisms. The potential role of these associated pathogens in either intraoral or extraoral actinomycotic infections has not been elucidated.

LITERATURE CITED

1. **Arnott, A. J., and C. H. Ritchie.** 1949. Cervicofacial actinomycosis. Oral Surg. Oral Med. Oral Pathol. **2:**252–257.
2. **Baker, J. J., S. P. Chan, S. S. Socransky, J. J. Oppenheim, and S. E. Mergenhagen.** 1976. Importance of *Actinomyces* and certain gram-negative anaerobic organisms in the transformation of lymphocytes from patients with periodontal disease. Infect. Immun. **13:**1363–1368.
3. **Beaman, B. L., M. E. Gershwin, and S. Maslan.** 1979. Infectious agents in immunodeficient murine models: pathogenicity of *Actinomyces israelii* serotype I in congenitally athymic (nude) mice. Infect. Immun. **24:**583–585.
4. **Bentley, K. C., and J. de Vries.** 1973. Diagnosis and treatment of cervicofacial actinomycosis. J. Can. Dent. Assoc. **39:**715–718.
5. **Brecher, S. M., J. van Houte, and B. J. Hammond.** 1978. Role of colonization in the virulence of *Actinomyces viscosus* strains T14-Vi and T14-Av. Infect. Immun. **22:**603–614.
6. **Brown, J. R., and F. von Lichtenberg.** 1970. Experimental actinomycosis in mice. Arch. Pathol. **91:**391–402.
7. **Buchanan, B. B., and L. Pine.** 1962. Characterization of a propionic acid producing actinomycete *Actinomyces propionicus* sp. *nov.* J. Gen. Microbiol. **28:**305–323.
8. **Burckhardt, J. J., B. Guggenheim, and A. Hefti.** 1977. Are *Actinomyces viscosus* antigens B cell mitogens? J. Immunol. **118:**1460–1465.
9. **Cisar, J. O., A. E. Vatter, and F. C. McIntire.** 1978. Identification of the virulence-associated antigen on the surface fibrils of *Actinomyces viscosus* T14. Infect. Immun. **19:**312–319.
10. **Coleman, R. M., and L. K. Georg.** 1969. Comparative pathogenicity of *Actinomyces naeslundii* and *Actinomyces israelii.* Appl. Microbiol. **18:**427–432.
11. **Coleman, R. M., L. K. Georg, and A. R. Rozzell.** 1969. *Actinomyces naeslundii* as an agent of human actinomycosis. Appl. Microbiol. **18:**420–426.
12. **Crawford, J. J.** 1971. Interaction of *Actinomyces* organisms with cationic polypeptides. I. Histochemical studies of infected human and animal tissues. Infect. Immun. **4:**632–641.
13. **Eiken, M.** 1958. Studies on an anaerobic rod-shaped Gram-negative microorganism: *Bacteroides corrodens N.* sp. Acta Pathol. Microbiol. Scand. **43:**404–416.
14. **Ellen, R. P.** 1976. Establishment and distribution of *Actinomyces viscosus* and *Actinomyces naeslundii* in the human oral cavity. Infect. Immun. **14:**1119–1124.

15. **Ellen, R. P., and H. Onose.** 1978. pH measurements of *Actinomyces viscosus* colonies growing on media containing dietary carbohydrates. Arch. Oral Biol. **23:**105–109.
16. **Emmons, C. W.** 1935. *Actinomyces* and actinomycosis. Puerto Rico J. Public Health Trop. Med. **11:**63–76.
17. **Engel, D., J. Clagett, R. Page, and B. Williams.** 1977. Mitogenic activity of *Actinomyces viscosus.* I. Effects on murine B and T lymphocytes, and partial characterization. J. Immunol. **118:**1466–1471.
18. **Engel, D., D. van Epps, and J. Clagett.** 1976. In vivo and in vitro studies on possible pathogenic mechanisms of *Actinomyces viscosus.* Infect. Immun. **14:**548–554.
19. **Geister, R. S., and E. Meyer.** 1951. The effect of aureomycin and penicillin on experimental actinomycosis infections in mice. J. Lab. Clin. Med. **38:**101–111.
20. **Georg, L. K., J. M. Brown, H. J. Baker, and G. H. Cassell.** 1972. *Actinomcyes viscosus* as an agent of actinomycosis in the dog. Am. J. Vet. Res. **33:**1457–1470.
21. **Georg, L. K., and R. M. Coleman.** 1970. Comparative pathogenicity of various *Actinomyces* species, p. 35–45. *In* H. Prauser (ed.), The Actinomycetales. The Jena International Symposium on Taxonomy, September 1968. VEB Gustav Fischer Verlag, Jena.
22. **Gerencser, M. A., and J. M. Slack.** 1969. Identification of human strains of *Actinomyces viscosus.* Appl. Microbiol. **18:**80–87.
23. **Girard, A. E., and B. H. Jacius.** 1974. Ultrastructure of *Actinomyces viscosus* and *Actinomyces naeslundii.* Arch. Oral Biol. **19:**71–79.
24. **Glahn, M.** 1954. Cervicofacial actinomycosis—etiology and diagnosis. Acta Chir. Scand. **108:**183–192.
25. **Guidry, D. J.** 1971. Actinomycosis, p. 1019–1058. *In* R. D. Baker (ed.), The pathologic anatomy of mycoses: human infection with fungi, actinomyces and algae. Springer-Verlag, New York.
26. **Hammond, B. F., C. F. Steel, and K. S. Peindl.** 1976. Antigens and surface components associated with virulence of *Actinomyces viscosus.* J. Dent. Res. **55**(Spec. Issue A):A19–A25.
27. **Hazen, E. L., G. N. Little, and H. Resnick.** 1952. The hamster as a vehicle for the demonstration of pathogenicty of *Actinomyces bovis.* J. Lab. Clin. Med. **40:**914–918.
28. **Holm, P.** 1950. Studies on the etiology of human actinomycosis. I. The "other microbes" of actinomycosis and their importance. Acta Pathol. Microbiol. Scand. **27:**736–751.
29. **Holm, P.** 1951. Studies in the etiology of human actinomycosis. II. Do the "other microbes" of actinomycosis possess virulence? Acta Pathol. Microbiol. Scand. **28:**391–406.
30. **Howell, A., Jr.** 1963. A filamentous organism isolated from periodontal plaque in hamsters. Isolation, morphology, and general cultural characteristics. Sabouraudia **3:**81–92.
31. **Howell, A., Jr., and H. V. Jordan.** 1963. A filamentous microorganism isolated from periodontal plaque in hamsters. II. Physiological and biochemical characteristics. Sabouraudia **3:**93–105.
32. **Howell, A., Jr., H. V. Jordan, L. K. Georg, and L. Pine.** 1965. *Odontomyces viscosus,* gen. nov., spec. nov., a filamentous microorganism isolated from periodontal plaque in hamsters. Sabouraudia **4:**65–68.
33. **Howell, A., Jr., W. C. Murphy III, F. Paul, and R. M. Stephan.** 1959. Oral strains of *Actinomyces.* J. Bacteriol. **78:**82–95.
34. **Howell, A., Jr., R. M. Stephan, and F. Paul.** 1962. Prevalence of *Actinomyces israelii, A. naeslundii, Bacterionema matruchotti* and *Candida albicans* in selected areas of the oral cavity and saliva. J. Dent. Res. **41:**1050–1059.
35. **Irving, J. T., M. G. Newman, S. S. Socransky, and J. D. Heeley.** 1975. Histological changes in experimental periodontal disease in rats mono-infected with a Gram-negative organism. Arch. Oral Biol. **20:**219–220.
36. **Irving, J. T., S. S. Socransky, and J. D. Heeley.** 1974. Histological changes in experimental periodontal disease in gnotobiotic rats and conventional hamsters. J. Periodontal Res. **9:**73–80.
37. **Irving, J. T., S. S. Socransky, and A. C. R. Tanner.** 1978. Histological changes in experimental periodotonal disease in rats monoinfected with Gram-negative organisms. J. Periodontal Res. **13:**326–332.
38. **Ivanyi, L., and T. Lehner.** 1971. Lymphocyte transformation by sonicates of dental plaque in human periodontal disease. Arch. Oral Biol. **16:**1117–1121.
39. **Jordan, H. V., R. J. Fitzgerald, and H. R. Stanley.** 1965. Plaque formation and periodontal pathology in gnotobiotic rats infected with an oral actinomycete. Am. J. Pathol. **47:**1157–1167.
40. **Jordan, H. V., and B. F. Hammond.** 1972. Filamentous bacteria isolated from human root surface caries. Arch. Oral Biol. **17:**1333–1342.
41. **Jordan, H. V., and P. H. Keyes.** 1964. Aerobic, Gram-positive filamentous bacteria as etiologic agents of experimental periodontal disease in hamsters. Arch. Oral Biol. **9:**401–414.
42. **Jordan, H. V., P. H. Keyes, and S. Bellack.** 1972. Periodontal lesions in hamsters and gnotobiotic rats infected with *Actinomyces* of human origin. J. Periodontal Res. **7:**21–28.
43. **Keyes, P. H., and H. V. Jordan.** 1964. Periodontal lesions in the Syrian hamster. III. Findings related to an infectious and transmissible component. Arch. Oral Biol. **9:**377–400.
44. **Listgarten, M. A.** 1976. Structure of the microbial flora associated with periodontal health and disease in man. A light and electron microscopic study. J. Periodontol. **47:**1–18.
45. **Llory, H., B. Guillo, and R. M. Frank.** 1971. A cariogenic *Actinomyces viscosus*—a bacteriological and gnotobiotic study. Helv. Odontol. Acta **15:**134–138.

46. **Loesche, W. J., and S. A. Syed.** 1978. Bacteriology of human experimental gingivitis: effect of plaque and gingivitis score. Infect. Immun. **21:**830–839.
47. **Mangan, D. F., and D. E. Lopatin.** 1981. In vitro stimulation of immunoglobulin production from human peripheral blood lymphocytes by a soluble preparation of *Actinomyces viscosus*. Infect. Immun. **31:**236–244.
48. **Meyer, E., and P. Verges.** 1950. Mouse pathogenicity as a diagnostic aid in the identification of *Actinomyces bovis*. J. Lab. Clin. Med. **36:**667–674.
49. **Mitchell, P. D., C. S. Hintz, and R. C. Haselby.** 1977. Molar mass due to *Actinomyces odontolyticus*. J. Clin. Microbiol. **5:**658–660.
50. **Qureshi, J. V., and R. J. Gibbons.** 1981. Differences in the adsorptive behavior of human strains of *Actinomyces viscosus* and *Actinomyces naeslundii* to saliva-treated hydroxyapatite surfaces. Infect. Immun. **31:**261–266.
51. **Rosan, B., and B. F. Hammond.** 1974. Extracellular polysaccharides of *Actinomyces viscosus*. Infect. Immun. **10:**304–308.
52. **Rosebury, T.** 1944. The parasitic actinomycetes and other filamentous microorganisms of the mouth. A review of their characteristics and relationships, of the bacteriology of actinomycosis, and of salivary calculus in man. Bacteriol. Rev. **8:**189–223.
53. **Rosebury, T., L. J. Epps, and A. R. Clark.** 1944. A study of the isolation, cultivation and pathogenicity of *Actinomyces israelii* recovered from the human mouth and from actinomycosis in man. J. Infect. Dis. **74:**131–143.
54. **Slack, J.** 1942. The source of infection in actinomycosis. J. Bacteriol. **43:**193–209.
55. **Slack, J. M., and M. A. Gerencser.** 1975. *Actinomyces*, filamentous bacteria and pathology. Burgess Publishing Co, Minneapolis.
56. **Slots, J.** 1977. The predominant cultivable microflora of advanced periodontitis. Scand. J. Dent. Res. **85:**114–121.
57. **Slots, J., and R. J. Gibbons.** 1978. Attachment of *Bacteroides melaninogenicus* subsp. *asaccharolyticus* to oral surfaces and its possible role in colonization of the mouth and of periodontal pockets. Infect. Immun. **19:**254–264.
58. **Socransky, S. S., C. Hubersak, and D. Propas.** 1970. Induction of periodontal destruction in gnotobiotic rats by a human oral strain of *Actinomyces naeslundii*. Arch. Oral Biol. **15:**933–995.
59. **Taichman, N. S., H. L. Freedman, and T. Uriuhara.** 1966. Inflammation and tissue injury—the response to intradermal injections of human dentogingival plaque in normal and leucopenic rabbits. Arch. Oral Biol. **11:**1385–1392.
60. **Taichman, N. S., B. F. Hammond, C. Tsai, P. C. Baehni, and W. P. McArthur.** 1978. Interaction of inflammatory cells and oral microorganisms. VII. In vitro polymorphonuclear responses to viable bacteria and to subcellular components of avirulent and virulent strains of *Actinomyces viscosus*. Infect. Immun. **21:**594–604.
61. **Temple, T. R., R. Snyderman, H. V. Jordan, and S. E. Mergenhagen.** 1970. Factors from saliva and oral bacteria, chemotatic for polymorphonuclar leucocytes; their possible role in gingival inflammation. J. Periodontol. **41:**71–80.
62. **Wilson, G. S., and A. A. Miles (ed.).** 1964. Topley and Wilson's principles of bacteriology and immunology, 5th ed., p. 1677–1679. The William & Wilkins Co., Baltimore.

Noncytolytic Effects of *Actinobacillus actinomycetemcomitans* on Leukocyte Functions

WILLIAM P. McARTHUR, CHI-CHENG TSAI, PIERRE BAEHNI, B. J. SHENKER, AND NORTON S. TAICHMAN

Department of Pathology and Center for Oral Health Research, School of Dental Medicine, University of Pennsylvania, Philadelphia, Pennsylvania 19104

INTRODUCTION

Although the exact etiology is unknown, it is now generally accepted that gingival inflammation (8) as well as periodontal diseases (9) is the result of bacterial plaque accumulations at the dental–gingival borders and the inflammatory response to the plaque microorganisms or their products (10). One peculiar feature of the host–parasite confrontation in periodontal diseases is the general lack of invasion by the plaque microorganisms. Although classic histological features of inflammation are observed in gingival tissues during development of periodontal diseases, the primary inflammatory cell to actually contact plaque microorganisms is the polymorphonuclear leukocyte (PMN). During all stages of periodontal diseases as well as during "clinically" normal, non-inflammatory periods, PMNs are constantly migrating from capillaries, through the gingival tissue, into the gingival crevice, eventually ending up in the oral cavity (11). Systemically PMNs are the initial cellular defense against bacterial infection, and it is likely that they play a similar role in the gingival crevice area (1). In contrast to their defensive role, PMNs play a major pathogenic role by mediation of host tissue destruction in many hyperimmune diseases. A primary mechanism by which PMNs cause localized tissue destruction is through their active extracellular release of lysosomes in response to stimuli such as opsonized bacteria, immune complexes, and activated complement components (i.e., C5). PMN lysosomes contain a variety of proteases and other components with bactericidal and inflammatory modulating activities. Collagenase and elastase are examples with the potential ability to break down connective tissue components. Bactericidal agents from lysosomes are lysozyme, cationic proteins, myeloperoxidase, and lactoferrin. Elastase (3) and lactoferrin (4; W. McArthur and R. L. Duncan. J. Dent. Res. Spec. Issue A, vol. 60, abstr. 267, 1981) have been reported to modulate mononuclear cell functions.

As a consequence of the obvious roles that PMNs could play in periodontal diseases, we have been interested in the interactions of human PMNs with plaque and plaque components (15). We specifically have been studying the response of PMNs to selected plaque-derived bacterial isolates in an attempt to define the pathogenic potential of those organisms. Whole plaque (16) as well as periodontally pathogenic gram-positive bacteria (15) have been found in vitro to be potent stimulators of PMN lysosomal release. Similar results were seen with many gram-negative plaque isolates associated with periodontal diseases (17). Interestingly and unexpectedly, whole bacterial plaques as well as most bacterial isolates were not directly toxic to the PMNs under the conditions used for experimentation (15–17). From the study of the response(s) of PMNs to potentially periodontally pathogenic plaque microorganisms, leukotoxic activity of *Actinobacillus actinomycetemcomitans* microorganisms was discovered (2, 18). The toxicity of *A. actinomycetemcomitans* and its potential ramifications in disease are described in detail in a separate paper (N. S. Taichman et al., this volume). Identification of the leukotoxicity of this organism for human PMNs and monocytes, as well as the identification of antileukotoxic antibodies in juvenile periodontitis (JP) patients (9), has subsequently helped to stimulate extensive investigation into the potential etiological role of this organism in JP.

The focus of this paper will not be on the leukotoxicity of *A. actinomycetemcomitans* but rather on the potential noncytotoxic influences it has on human leukocytes as identified by in vitro experimentation.

Evidence has been accumulating which suggests that *A. actinomycetemcomitans* may certainly play a role in the etiology of JP. It was isolated in relatively high numbers from disease sites in patients with JP as opposed to normal crevicular sites (12). In addition, it was not isolated in relevant numbers from sites in adult periodontitis. High levels of antibodies against the *A. actinomycetemcomitans* leukotoxin (5, 9; C.-C. Tsai, W. P. McArthur, P. C. Baehni, C. Evian, R. J. Genco, and N. S. Taichman, J. Clin. Periodontol., in press) and antigens (5; J. L. Ebersole, D. E. Frey, M. A. Taubman, D. J. Smith, R. J. Genco, and B. F. Hammond, J. Dent. Res. Spec. Issue A, vol. 59, 255, 1980) have been detected in >90% of sera from JP patients. Strain Y4 has been shown to cause extensive alveolar bone destruction in germfree monoinfected rats (6). Many isolates were cytotoxic for human PMNs and monocytes (2, 14, 18). Taken together, the evidence certainly suggests that more investigation into the relationship of *A. actinomycetemcomitans* and JP is warranted.

Nonleukotoxic effects of *A. actinomycetemcomitans* are also of potential interest in defining the host–parasite relationships that may be occurring in the diseased gingival sulcus in JP.

NONTOXIC *A. ACTINOMYCETEMCOMITANS* STRAINS

Recent results indicated that individual *A. actinomycetemcomitans* isolates vary in their leukotoxic potential (Table 1). When tested for their ability to kill human peripheral blood PMNs in vitro by methods described elsewhere (2), 4 of 14 strains were found to be essentially nonleukotoxic, both as viable microorganisms (Table 1) and as sonic extracts (P. C. Baehni, C.-C. Tsai, W. P. McArthur, B. F. Hammond, B. J. Shenker, and N. S. Taichman, Arch. Oral Biol., in press). The addition of normal human serum enhanced the toxicity of all the leukotoxic strains but did not affect the nonleukotoxic strains. To ensure that the apparent lack of toxicity was real and not bacterium-mediated inhibition of lactate dehydrogenase (LDH), we conducted a morphological examination of the PMNs. Studies using electron microscopy revealed that, in the absence of extracellular LDH in the PMN culture, the PMNs appeared morphologically normal (2). In contrast, PMNs exposed to known leukotoxic organisms and from cultures with high levels of extracellular LDH were obviously not normal (2). Immunological analysis revealed that all *A. actinomycetemcomitans* strains shared common species-specific antigens but

TABLE 1. *Leukotoxic effects of* A. actinomycetemcomitans *in serum-free cultures*[a]

Strain	Bacterial cells/PMN		
	25	50	100
Plaque isolates			
Y4	55 ± 5	56 ± 4	62 ± 8
N27	44 ± 5	56 ± 5	78 ± 7
511	33 ± 4	56 ± 4	67 ± 5
650	27 ± 2	35 ± 4	39 ± 3
651	17 ± 2	37 ± 3	51 ± 4
2043	56 ± 3	66 ± 5	78 ± 6
2097	76 ± 5	83 ± 7	89 ± 7
2112	28 ± 5	33 ± 4	67 ± 5
627	<1	<1	<1
652	<1	<1	<1
653	<1	<1	<1
ATCC strains			
2952	70 ± 5	76 ± 6	82 ± 6
29523	2 ± 1	3 ± 2	2 ± 2
29524	76 ± 6	85 ± 8	84 ± 5

[a] Human peripheral blood PMNs were exposed to freshly harvested bacteria at the ratios indicated. Results are expressed as the mean percent LDH released ± the standard error of three or more experiments.

that a unique antigen was identified in sonic extracts of leukotoxic organisms which was not detected in extracts of nonleukotoxic organisms (Baehni et al., Arch. Oral Biol., in press). Rabbit antisera against the sonic extract of strain Y4 and antiserum against a component(s) of the Y4 extract that bound to disrupted PMN membranes (N. S. Taichman, R. Stevens, B. Hammond, C. Tsai, P. Baehni, and W. P. McArthur, J. Dent. Res. Spec. Issue A, vol. 60, abstr. 855, 1981), as well as many JP patients' sera (C.-C. Tsai, W. P. McArthur, P. Baehni, and N. S. Taichman, J. Dent. Res. Spec. Issue A, vol. 60, abstr. 856, 1981), were able to serotypically differentiate leukotoxic from nonleukotoxic organisms. An exception was in the case of the leukotoxic strain 511, which had a specific antigen not found in any other A. *actinomycetemcomitans* strain or other plaque bacterium tested (Table 1).

A. *actinomycetemcomitans* strain ATCC 29523 has been catalogued as being nonleukotoxic; however, studies have indicated that leukotoxicity is variable. The reason for the observed variability in leukotoxicity is not understood.

Although both leukotoxic and nonleukotoxic strains of A. *actinomycetemcomitans* isolated initially from JP disease sites suggested that both types populate the gingival crevice, the roles of the leukotoxic and nonleukotoxic strains must be clarified. The recently described immune targeting of A. *actinomycetemcomitans* colonies on initial isolation agar plates (N. S. Taichman, R. S. Stevens, B. Hammond, C. Tsai, P. Baehni, and W. P. McArthur, J. Dent. Res. Spec. Issue A, vol. 60, abstr. 855, 1981) may help define the ratio of isolatable leukotoxic and nonleukotoxic organisms from diseased and nondiseased sites. However, at the present time immunodiffusion and enzyme-linked immunosorbent assay studies used to test the reaction of a number of JP patient sera with sonic extracts of various strains indicated that the isolates can

TABLE 2. *Immunological analysis of different*
strains of A. actinomycetemcomitans

Antigenic group	Toxicity	Strains	No. of positive reactions	
			Immunodiffusion[a]	ELISA[b]
1	Leukotoxic	Y4, ATCC 29522, ATCC 29524, 2043, 2097, 650, 651, N27	17/28 (61%)	15/28 (54%)
2	Leukotoxic	511	2/28 (7%)	5/28 (18%)
3	Nonleukotoxic	ATCC 29523, 627	3/28 (11%)	7/28 (25%)
4	Nonleukotoxic	652, 653	3/28 (11%)	3/28 (11%)

[a] Results indicate the development of an immunoprecipitin line not seen when serum was run against sonic extracts of bacteria in other groups.

[b] ELISA (enzyme-linked immunosorbent assay) results indicate the predominant immune binding by each serum.

be serotyped into four groups (Table 2). Groups 1 and 2 are leukotoxic organisms, but groups 3 and 4 consist of antigenically distinct nonleukotoxic strains. Serotype group 3 consists of ATCC 29523 and 627, and group 4 contains 652 and 653. Of the total number of JP sera tested, a small but significant number of sera reacted with antigens detected only on the nonleukotoxic organisms. Enzyme-linked immunosorbent assay data also indicated that a comparable number of individuals had significant levels of antibody against the nonleukotoxic indicator antigen(s). Consequently, it appeared that at least these JP patients had been exposed to nonleukotoxic strains and had made antibodies against them. This evidence plus the isolation of the nonleukotoxic strains from diseased sites suggested that nontoxic strains were in plaque but their role in the pathogenesis of the JP remained to be defined.

In addition to the identification of nonleukotoxic strains of *A. actinomycetemcomitans,* strain Y4 leukotoxin has been found to be inactivated by specific antibody from JP sera (9). As mentioned previously antileukotoxin antibodies have been identified in the sera from a majority (>90%) of individuals with active JP, and a number of studies have identified high levels of anti-*A. actinomycetemcomitans* antibodies in JP patient sera (5; R. J. Genco, N. S. Taichman, and C. A. Sadowski, J. Dent. Res. Spec. Issue A, vol. 59, abstr. 246, 1980; J. L. Ebersole, D. E. Frey, M. A. Taubman, D. J. Smith, and R. J. Genco, J. Dent. Res. Spec. Issue A, vol. 59, abstr. 249, 1980). Relatively high levels of anti-*A. actinomycetemcomitans* antigen antibodies have also been identified in gingival sulcus fluid from diseased sites in JP patients (P. A. Murry and R. J. Genco, J. Dent. Res. Spec. Issue A, vol. 59, abstr. 245, 1980). Although antileukotoxin antibodies have not specifically been identified in sulcus fluid, there is reason to believe that they are there. Antileukotoxin levels in serum parallel levels of antibodies against other *A. actinomycetemcomitans* antigens (C.-C. Tsai, personal communication). Since anti-*A. actinomycetemcomitans* antigen activity was found in the gingival sulcus fluid, antileukotoxin activity, being predominantly immunoglobulin G (9), should also be present. In the sulcus antileukotoxin would have been expected to neutralize the toxin, at least in the individuals with high antileukotoxin titers. Data at this time suggest that the higher antileukotoxin titers were detected in individuals with active disease (C.-C. Tsai, unpublished data). Consequently, much of the leukotoxic activity in an established diseased sulcus would be expected to have been neutralized. In addition to neutralization by antibody, the leukotoxin could have been inactivated by other means. Proteinases and lysosomal enzymes have been reported to inactivate Y4-derived leukotoxin activity in vitro (18). The diseased gingival sulcus has been reported to contain high levels of soluble lysosomal proteinases and other components.

INTERACTIONS OF PMNs AND *A. ACTINOMYCETEMCOMITANS*

Keeping in mind the environment in which *A. actinomycetemcomitans* resides in the gingival crevice, we asked the question of how these bacteria could mediate the inflammatory response and tissue destruction seen in JP lesions.

The direct interactions of the organisms and PMNs was examined under a variety of conditions. Nonleukotoxic as well as leukotoxic organisms under conditions which neutralize the leukotoxin may come into direct contact with PMNs in the gingival sulcus. Unlike all gram-positive periodontal pathogens (15) and most gram-negative ones (17) so far tested, nonleukotoxic *A. actinomycetemcomitans* organisms (ATCC 29523) were not phagocytosed by human peripheral blood PMNs (Fig. 1). However, in the presence of antibody-

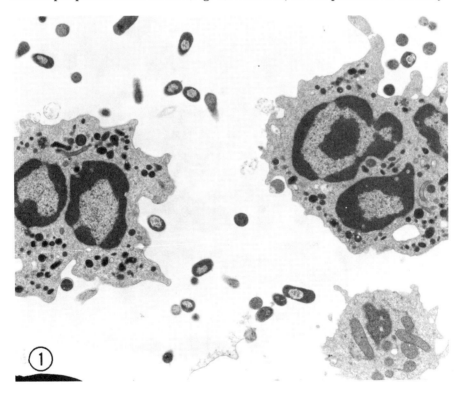

FIG. 1. *PMNs were exposed to viable nonleukotoxic* A. actinomycetemcomitans *(ATCC 29523, 100 bacteria/PMN) for 60 min at 37°C in the absence of serum.* ×9,200.

containing JP serum (not illustrated) or fresh normal serum (Fig. 2) phagocytosis of organisms did occur. Parallel to the phagocytosis of the organisms (ATCC 29523) lysosomal release also occurred (Fig. 3). Viable ATCC 29523 organisms at various bacteria per PMN ratios were tested for their ability to stimulate PMN lysosome release (Fig. 3) by methods published in detail elsewhere (16). As illustrated, ATCC 29523 in serum-free cultures did not trigger PMN lysozyme release. If normal human serum (5%) was added to the mixture of bacteria and PMNs, lysozyme release was detected after a 1-h incubation period. Fresh serum was more effective than heated serum, but JP serum with anti-*A. actinomycetemcomitans* antibody was the most effective in enhancing *A. actinomycetemcomitans*-triggered PMN lysozyme release. PMN release of other lysosomal marker components, myeloperoxidase and lactoferrin, paralleled the lysozyme release (not illustrated). As expected, other non-leukotoxic strains (627, 652, and 653) as well as heated (56°C for 15 min) leukotoxic strain Y4 (Table 3) reacted in a manner similar to that observed with ATCC 29523.

Leukotoxic bacteria (e.g., strain Y4) were also potent triggers of PMN lysosomal release as a result of their toxic effects. Lysosomal contents were released extracellularly during the cytotoxic events in parallel with LDH (Table 3). As expected in the presence of an excess of rabbit anti-*A. actinomycetemcomitans* (Y4) sonic extract or JP serum, LDH release did not

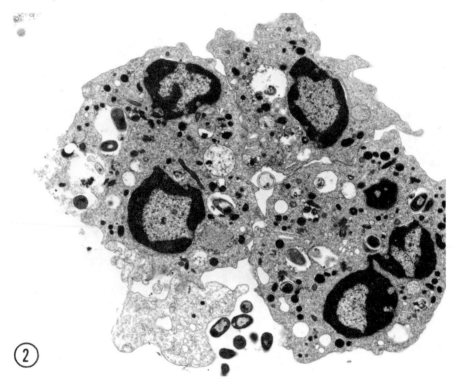

(2)

FIG. 2. *PMNs were exposed to viable nonleukotoxic* A. actinomycetemcomitans *(ATCC 29523, 100 bacteria/PMN) for 20 min at 37°C in the presence of 5% (vol/vol) fresh normal human serum.* ×9,200.

occur, as a result of the neutralization of the leukotoxin, but lysozyme release was detected. Heated (56°C for 30 min), which inactivates the leukotoxin) Y4 bacteria were not toxic (Table 3), but in the presence of fresh human serum with no detectable antibody activity or in the presence of JP serum, they were a potent stimulator of lysozyme release. The release due to bacteria in the presence of fresh serum, but not heated serum, also suggested that strain Y4 may have activated the alternate complement pathway.

Since it is conceivable that *A. actinomycetemcomitans* in the gingival sulcus is exposed to serum-derived components, one must consider what effect exposure to serum components has on the interactions of these organisms and PMNs. The effect of antibodies is obviously the first consideration, and the results of lysosomal release were illustrated. However, serum has also been shown

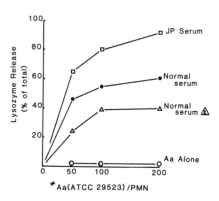

FIG. 3. *PMN lysosome release response to A. actinomycetemcomitans (ATCC 29523). PMNs were incubated with various ratios of viable bacteria per PMN in the presence and absence of various sera. Incubations were for 60 min at 37°C. Normal human serum (●), heat-inactivated (58°C, 30 min) normal human serum (Δ), and serum from a JP patient (□) were all used at 5% (vol/vol). The levels of lysozyme released into the culture supernatants during the culture period are illustrated as the percentage of total lysozyme activity in the cultures. No LDH was detected in the culture supernatants.*

to extract leukotoxic activity from viable strain Y4 organisms (18). The leukotoxic activity in the serum extract supernatant appeared to be bound to materials with a molecular weight of $>2 \times 10^6$, probably cell membrane

TABLE 3. *Effect of serum on the PMN response to* A. actinomycetemcomitans *Y4[a]*

Bacterial cells (100/PMN)	Serum (5%)	Enzyme release (% of total)	
		Lysozyme	LDH
Viable	None	9	30
	Normal,[b] fresh	47	75
	Normal, heated[c]	24	55
	JP	85	0
	Rabbit anti-Y4	80	2
Heated[c]	None	0	0
	Normal, fresh	24	0
	Normal, heated	0	0
	JP	65	0
	Rabbit anti-Y4	50	0

[a] PMNs (2×10^7) were exposed to bacteria for 1 h at 37°C. Extracellular lysozyme and LDH were assayed in the culture supernatants.

[b] Contained no detectable anti-*A. actinomycetemcomitans* antibody.

[c] 56°C for 30 min.

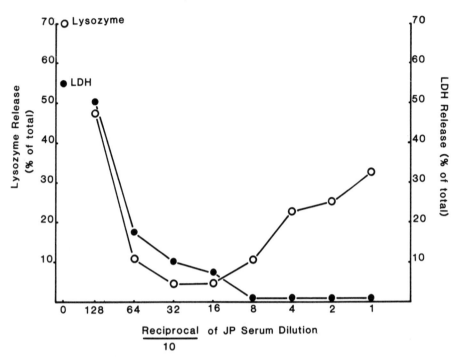

FIG. 4. *Lysozyme and LDH (●) release responses of PMNs to a sonic extract (0.5 mg [dry weight]/ml) of A. actinomycetemcomitans Y4 in the presence of various dilutions of a serum from a JP patient. PMNs were incubated for 60 min at 37°C, and the enzyme activities in the culture supernatants were measured. Enzyme activities are illustrated as the percentage of total activities in the cultures.*

fragments or blebs (unpublished data). Strain Y4 in culture has been reported to liberate "blebs" into the culture medium (A. Nowotny, U. H. Behling, B. Hammond, C. H. Lai, M. Listgarten, P. H. Pham, and F. Sanavi, J. Dent. Res. Spec. Issue A, vol. 60, abstr. 851, 1981). Blebs were found to contain leukotoxic activity (B. F. Hammond, M. Darkes, C. Lai, and C.-C. Tsai, J. Dent. Res. Spec. Issue A, vol. 60, abstr. 89, 1981). It is possible that serum may enhance *A. actinomycetemcomitans* bacterial bleb release or cell breakdown. Experimentally, sonic extraction of the organisms results in similar bleb, cell fragment preparations (unpublished data). Therefore, the PMN response to crude sonic extracts of strain Y4 in the presence of various serum components was studied.

As published previously (9), JP serum inhibited the leukotoxicity of *A. actinomycetemcomitans* in a dose-dependent manner. When exposed to a standard dose of strain Y4 sonic extract in the presence of various dilutions of JP serum, PMNs released lysozyme in biphasic patterns (Fig. 4). Sonic extract alone triggered lysozyme as well as LDH release. Similarly, the extract in the presence of low levels of JP serum was toxic to the PMN as indicated by LDH release and resulted in lysozyme release. As the concentration of serum increased, the levels of both LDH and lysozyme release sharply decreased, indicating antibody neutralization of the toxin. However, in the presence of high levels of serum, lysozyme but not LDH release was observed. These data suggested that at low serum levels the toxin was not neutralized and lysozyme was being released from dying PMNs. As the serum levels increased, the PMNs were protected as a result of neutralization of the toxin. At high serum concentration the PMNs were still viable but lysozyme release was induced. Substitution of normal serum for JP serum resulted in LDH and lysozyme release at all serum concentrations. Testing of an immunoglobulin G fraction from a JP patient's serum gave results essentially identical to those seen with JP serum (Fig. 5). Consequently, the data suggest that in an environment where the toxin is neutralized by antibody PMNs can still be activated. The activating agent(s) in this case was probably immune complexes (e.g., cell membrane fragments or soluble antigens bound to antibody). The low levels of lysozyme released at intermediate concentrations of serum or antibody suggested a dose response to the immune complexes formed in the PMN culture. Electron microscopy confirmed that the lysozyme release was due to stimulation by immune complexes, since aggregated sonic extract material was phagocytosed by the PMNs (Fig. 6). A similar phenomenon was seen when viable bacteria were exposed to PMNs in the presence of various concentrations of JP serum (results not illustrated).

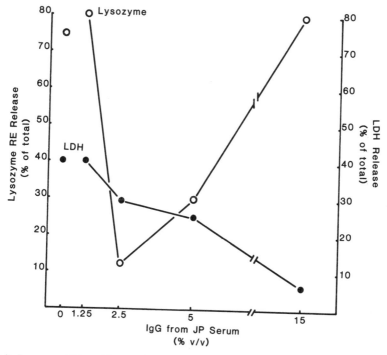

FIG. 5. Lysozyme (○) and LDH release responses of PMNs to a sonic extract (0.5 mg [dry weight]/ml) of A. actinomycetemcomitans Y4 in the presence of various concentrations of an immunoglobulin G-rich fraction from a JP serum. Immunoglobulin G was purified by diethylaminoethyl chromatography and resuspended in the original serum volume. PMNs were incubated for 60 min at 37°C, and the enzyme activities in the culture supernatants were measured. Enzyme activities are illustrated as the percentage of total activities in the cultures.

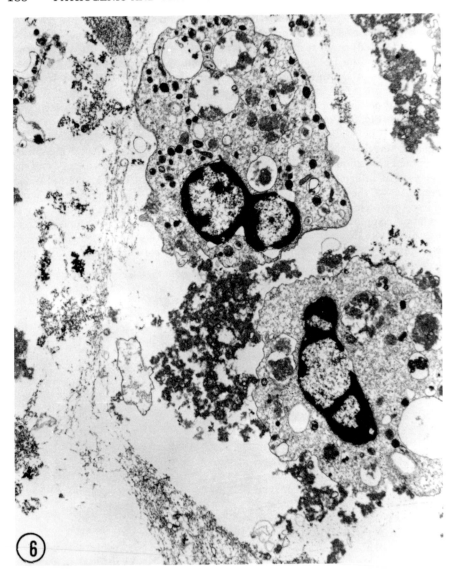

FIG. 6. *PMNs were exposed to* A. actinomycetemcomitans *Y4 sonic extract (1 mg [dry weight]/ml) for 30 min at 37°C in the presence of serum (5%, vol/vol) from a patient with JP. ×6,400.*

INTERACTIONS OF *A. ACTINOMYCETEMCOMITANS* AND MONONUCLEAR CELLS

In addition to directly stimulating PMNs, immune complexes also activate complement, which can stimulate a number of inflammatory processes, all of which would tend to perpetuate the inflammatory process initiated against the *A. actinomycetemcomitans* organisms. Strain Y4 organisms can activate complement by the alternate pathway (C.-C. Tsai, unpublished data). Endotoxin

TABLE 4. *Suppression by* A. actinomycetemcomitans *of human peripheral blood mononuclear cell proliferation*[a]

Sonic extract	Lymphocyte proliferation (cpm ± SD)[b]		
	Control	Phytohemagglutinin[c]	Pokeweed mitogen[d]
None	1,297	45,511 ± 2,691	29,058 ± 1,843
Strain 29522			
50 µg/ml	173 ± 62	6,099 ± 184	3,098 ± 381
25 µg/ml	375 ± 43	5,888 ± 1,242	4,239 ± 853
Strain 29523			
50 µg/ml	710 ± 160	4,708 ± 402	5,274 ± 282
25 µg/ml	942 ± 41	7,636 ± 1,869	5,130 ± 562
Strain Y4			
50 µg/ml	100 ± 24	1,423 ± 590	345 ± 177
25 µg/ml	537 ± 152	2,156 ± 1,468	3,787 ± 642

[a] Human peripheral blood mononuclear cells purified from blood by Ficoll-Hypaque separation were exposed to various concentrations (dry weight) of *A. actinomycetemcomitans* sonic extracts for 1 h at 37°C followed by stimulation with mitogen. The mononuclear cell cultures containing both the mitogen and the sonic extract material were incubated for 3 days. During the last 16 h of culture, [^{3}H]thymidine was present in cultures. At the end of the culture period, cells were harvested and the incorporation of [^{3}H]thymidine was monitored by liquid scintillation counting.

[b] Mean counts per minute of three or more replicate cultures ± standard deviation.

[c] Dose = 1:1,000 dilution of stock.

[d] Dose = 2.5 µg/ml.

from *A. actinomycetemcomitans* has also been reported to be a potent stimulator of bone resorption in vitro (7), suggesting yet another potential inflammatory stimulator in this organism.

The majority of the work on *A. actinomycetemcomitans* and its potential association with JP has focused on the interactions of these organisms with PMNs or the humoral immune response to *A. actinomycetemcomitans* antigens. Data presented recently suggested that this organism could modulate the proliferative response to human peripheral blood mononuclear cells to concanavalin A (B. Shenker, W. McArthur, C.-C. Tsai, P. Baehni, and N. Taichman, J. Dent. Res. Spec. Issue A, vol. 60, abstr. 858, 1981). Similar data are illustrated in Table 4. A soluble factor(s) in the sonic extract of both leukotoxic and nonleukotoxic strains suppressed the proliferative response of human mononuclear cells to phytohemagglutinin and pokeweed mitogens. No significant cell cytotoxicity was noted in the cultures exposed to the sonic extracts compared with that in controls. As reported previously by Shenker et al. (J. Dent. Res. Spec. Issue A, vol. 60, abstr. 858, 1981), both leukotoxic and nonleukotoxic strains have a soluble factor which is not cytotoxic but inhibits human peripheral blood lymphocyte proliferation in vitro. The suppressive activity was blocked by JP serum, seemed to affect both adherent and nonadherent mononuclear cell functions, and showed maximum suppressive activity when the cells were exposed to the factor 1 h before addition of concanavalin A. The authors proposed that *A. actinomycetemcomitans*-mediated mononuclear cell inhibitory activity may result in local immune suppression and play a role in the pathogenesis of JP.

DISCUSSION

At the present time, one can merely hypothesize about the in vivo pathogenic events that occur during the initiation and perpetuation of JP. Evidence exists to suggest that *A. actinomycetemcomitans* microorganisms may be involved in the etiology of the disease. The leukotoxin in these organisms is one of the first "virulence" factors to be identified in plaque bacteria. The recognition of the leukotoxin has provided a pathogenic activity which may depress the locally protective host-leukocyte response (discussed by N. S. Taichman et al., this volume), especially early in the development of the disease. The immune response to the leukotoxin provides a definitive tool for recognition of JP. However, evidence also exists that these organisms exist in the diseased crevice, probably in the presence of antileukotoxin antibody. Some of these organisms are undoubtedly nonleukotoxic, as suggested by isolation and serotyping data.

In the presence of normal human serum and PMNs, both leukotoxic and nonleukotoxic strains trigger PMN lysozyme release. In the presence of anti-*A. actinomycetemcomitans* (including antileukotoxin antibody), PMNs are protected from the leukotoxin, but can be stimulated by immune complexes (e.g., leukotoxin–leukotoxin), insoluble immune complexes (e.g., blebs–antibody, bacterial membrane fragments–antibody, whole bacteria–antibody), and activated complement components (e.g., C3 on the bacterial surface or soluble C5a). The biological implications of lysosomal release in response to these stimuli have been discussed elsewhere. Suffice it to mention that factors in lysosomal granules have been shown to kill bacteria, break down connective tissue, and modulate the activities of other inflammatory cells as well as connective tissues.

Activation of complement either directly by *A. actinomycetemcomitans* or in cooperation with antibodies has biological effects other than induction of PMN lysosomal release. They include chemotactic activity for leukocytes, cytotoxicity, and vascular permeability changes, all of which could have significant effects on the inflammatory process in JP disease.

Lastly, the apparent suppressive effect(s) of a soluble agent(s) from *A. actinomycetemcomitans* on human mononuclear cell proliferation provides another way in which this organism could modify the host locally if not systemically to allow itself as well as other organisms to gain a foothold in the gingival crevice. Once established in the crevice, a systemic immune response combined with a sluggish leukocyte response (19) may not be adequate to prevent the disease. The inflammatory response to the established plaque population and specifically to *A. actinomycetemcomitans* may actually be responsible for many of the connective tissue changes noted in JP disease areas. Further investigation into basic questions concerned with the inflammatory and immune response to isolated plaque bacteria from normal and diseased sites will help delineate the role of both the host response and the plaque microorganisms in the initiation and perpetuation of periodontal diseases.

SUMMARY

Microbiological and immunological data strongly suggest that *A. actinomycetemcomitans* is associated with JP. The leukotoxic activity of this organism may be one potential pathogenic mechanism by which it alters the local PMN defense response. However, the presence of nonleukotoxic *A.*

actinomycetemcomitans strains in JP diseased sites, as well as high levels of leukotoxin-neutralizing activity in the sera of essentially all JP patients, strongly suggests that during clinical disease the pathogenic role of *A. actinomycetemcomitans* may be noncytolytic. Stimulation of active PMN lysosome release by plaque bacteria has been proposed as one mechanism to account for the breakdown of gingival tissues during periodontal diseases. Nonleukotoxic (ATCC 29523) and leukotoxic (Y4) strains were both potent triggers of PMN lysosome release in the presence of JP patient sera or immune rabbit serum in the absence of cytotoxic effects on the PMNs. Similarly, a JP serum or immunoglobulin G from a JP serum neutralized, in a dose-dependent manner, the cytolytic effects of a soluble sonic extract of strain Y4. Dilutions of <1:16 of JP serum in combination with the sonic extract induced active PMN lysosome release due to formation of immune complexes. The nonleukotoxic strain (ATCC 29523) also stimulated active PMN lysosome release when mixed with normal human serum but had no effect on the PMNs in serum-free cultures. In addition to inducing high levels of humoral immunity in vivo, *A. actinomycetemcomitans* may also be able to modulate mononuclear cell activities. Consequently, this organism in the JP diseased crevice has the potential to potentiate the inflammatory response in a noncytolytic manner by its stimulation of PMN lysosome release. As in many other chronic immune diseases, PMN responses could be one of many mechanisms responsible for the tissue changes noted in JP.

ACKNOWLEDGMENTS

This work was supported by Public Health Service grants DE 0263 and DE 03995 from the National Institutes of Dental Research. W.M. is a recipient of Research Career Development Award DE00070 from the National Institute of Dental Research.

LITERATURE CITED

1. **Attstrom, R.** 1975. The roles of gingival epithelium and phagocytosing leukocytes in gingival defense. J. Clin. Periodontol. 2:25–32.
2. **Baehni, P., C.-C. Tsai, W. P. McArthur, B. F. Hammond, and N. S. Taichman.** 1979. Interaction of inflammatory cells and oral microorganisms. VIII. Detection of leukotoxic activity of a plaque-derived gram-negative microorganism. Infect. Immun. 24:233–243.
3. **Bretz, U., B. Dewald, M. Baggiolini, and T. L. Vischer.** 1976. *In vitro* stimulation of lymphocytes by neutral proteinases from human polymorphonuclear leukocyte granules. Schweiz. Med. Wochenschr. 106:1371.
4. **Broxmeyer, H. E., A. Smithyman, R. R. Eger, P. A. Meyers, and M. deSousa.** 1978. Identification of lactoferrin as the granulocyte-derived inhibitor of colony-stimulating activity production. J. Exp. Med. 148:1052–1067.
5. **Ebersole, J. L., D. E. Frey, M. A. Taubman, and D. J. Smith.** 1980. An ELISA for measuring serum antibodies to *Actinobacillus actinomycetemcomitans*. J. Periodontal Res. 15:621–632.
6. **Irving, J. T., M. G. Newman, S. S. Socransky, and J. D. Heeley.** 1975. Histologic changes in experimental periodontal disease in rats monoinfected with a gram-negative organism. Arch. Oral Biol. 20:219–220.
7. **Kiley, P., and S. C. Holt.** 1980. Characterization of the lipopolysaccharide from *Actinobacillus actinomycetemcomitans* Y4 and N27. Infect. Immun. 30:862–873.
8. **Loe, H., E. Theilade, and S. B. Jensen.** 1965. Experimental gingivitis in man. J. Periodontol. 36:177–187.
9. **McArthur, W. P., C.-C. Tsai, P. C. Baehni, R. J. Genco, and N. S. Taichman.** 1981. Leukotoxic effects of *Actinobacillus actinomycetemcomitans*. Modulation by serum components. J. Periodontal Res. 16:159–170.
10. **Page, R. C., and H. E. Schroeder.** 1976. Pathogenesis of inflammatory periodontal disease. A summary of current work. Lab. Invest. 33:235–249.
11. **Schiott, C. R., and H. Loe.** 1970. The origin and variation in number of leukocytes in the human saliva. J. Periodontal Res. 5:36–41.

12. **Slots, J., H. S. Reynolds, and R. J. Genco.** 1980. *Actinobacillus actinomycetemcomitans* in human periodontal disease: a cross-sectional microbiological investigation. Infect. Immun. **29:**1013–1020.

13. **Socransky, S. S.** 1977. Microbiology of periodontal disease—present status and future considerations. J. Periodontol. **48:**497–504.

14. **Taichman, N. S., R. T. Dean, and C. J. Sanderson.** 1980. Biochemical and morphological characterization of the killing of human monocytes by a leukotoxin derived from *Actinobacillus actinomycetemcomitans.* Infect. Immun. **28:**258–268.

15. **Taichman, N. S., and W. P. McArthur.** 1976. Interaction of inflammatory cells and oral bacteria: release of lysosomal hydrolases from rabbit polymorphonuclear leukocytes exposed to Gram-positive plaque bacteria. Arch. Oral Biol. **21:**257–263.

16. **Taichman, N. S., C.-C. Tsai, P. C. Baehni, N. Stoller, and W. P. McArthur.** 1977. Interaction of inflammatory cells and oral microorganisms. IV. In vitro release of lysosomal constituents from polymorphonuclear leukocytes exposed to supragingival and subgingival bacterial plaque. Infect. Immun. **16:**1013–1023.

17. **Tsai, C.-C., B. F. Hammond, P. Baehni, W. P. McArthur, and N. S. Taichman.** 1978. Interaction of inflammatory cells and oral microorganisms. VI. Exocytosis of PMN lysosomes in response to Gram-negative plaque bacteria. J. Periodontal Res. **13:**504–512.

18. **Tsai, C.-C., W. P. McArthur, P. C. Baehni, B. F. Hammond, and N. S. Taichman.** 1979. Extraction and partial characterization of a leukotoxin from a plaque-derived gram-negative microorganism. Infect. Immun. **25:**427–439.

19. **van Dyke, T. E., H. U. Horoszewicz, L. J. Cianciola, and R. J. Genco.** 1980. Neutrophil chemotaxis dysfunction in human periodontitis. Infect. Immun. **27:**124–132.

Bacterial Immunoglobulin A Proteases and Mucosal Diseases: Use of Synthetic Peptide Analogs to Modify the Activity of These Proteases

ANDREW G. PLAUT, JOANNE V. GILBERT, AND JAMES BURTON

Gastroenterology Unit, Department of Medicine, New England Medical Center Hospital and Tufts University School of Medicine, Boston, Massachusetts 02111; Department of Medicine, Cardiac Unit, Massachusetts General Hospital, Boston, Massachusetts 02114; and Department of Medicine, Harvard Medical School, Boston, Massachusetts 02115

During the course of studies on the metabolism of immunoglobulin A (IgA) by the gastrointestinal microflora, Mehta et al. (17) reported the existence of a unique proteolytic enzymatic specificity in gut contents. This enzyme specifically cleaved human IgA so that the products of hydrolysis included an intact, recoverable Fcα fragment; earlier attempts to obtain Fc region from IgA digests with other proteolytic enzymes such as papain, trypsin, and pepsin led to extensive degradation of the Fc. Once the IgA protease had been clearly shown to be of bacterial origin, attempts to isolate the species from which it arose were undertaken; however, the complexities of the intestinal bacterial flora led to the suggestion (by Robert Genco) that a similar enzyme be sought in the oral cavity, where bacterial taxonomy is somewhat less complicated and better defined. Fulfilling the prediction, IgA-lytic activity was found in mixed saliva and plaque of most normal individuals, and a detailed test of many oral bacteria showed that *Streptococcus sanguis* produced IgA protease activity in abundance (8, 23). Since then, *S. sanguis,* in particular strain 10556 of the American Type Culture Collection, has been the prototype bacterium providing IgA protease for our work. Several other bacteria causing infections in humans also yield IgA protease enzymes, and comparison of the enzymes of these other species with that of *S. sanguis* has provided insight into the specificity, at the biochemical level, of bacterium–host interaction (S. J. Kornfeld and A. G. Plaut, J. Infect. Dis., in press). Despite the acquisition of much data on the IgA proteases in the past few years, it is still not known how these enzymes participate in the infectious process.

In humans and rabbits, the two species studied in greatest detail, approximately 80% of antibody-synthesizing cells at mucosal sites secrete immunoglobulins of the IgA class. In luminal fluids the IgA is of the secretory type, being a dimer bearing both J chain and secretory component, a protein synthesized by the epithelial cell and added to the IgA during its passage through this cell toward the lumen of the organ (4). The molecular weight of secretory IgA is approximately 385,000, and its dimeric form gives it four potential antigen-combining sites. Circulating serum IgA is in large part monomeric in form, has a molecular weight of about 160,000, and bears no secretory component. The most interesting aspect of the substrate specificity of IgA proteases relates to the structural differences between the two isotypes (formerly called subclasses) of human IgA (7, 22). Human IgA1 and IgA2 proteins are isotypic, because both forms occur in all normal individuals. In addition, there are true allotypes of human IgA that segregate by Mendelian rules, but these are found only within the IgA2 isotype and have been designated A2m(1) and A2m(2) (29). The isotypic and allotypic assignment of human IgA proteins is done serologically, most recently by the use of monoclonal antibodies (6). The most pronounced structural difference among the IgA1 and IgA2 isotypes is in the hinge region of the alpha chain, where IgA2 proteins lack a continuous stretch of 13 amino acids (composed entirely of threonyl, prolyl, and seryl residues) that is present in the IgA1 heavy chain. This deletion shortens the IgA2 heavy chain and changes its carbohydrate composition because the seryl residues to which oligosaccharides are linked in IgA1 proteins (2) are among those deleted in IgA2. The deleted segment is of central importance in understanding IgA protease specificity, because all the peptide bonds cleaved lie in the IgA1 segment that is lacking in IgA2 proteins, thereby rendering IgA2 insusceptible to hydrolysis. These relationships are shown in Fig. 1. Normal circulating IgA is approximately 90% IgA1, whereas in polyclonal human colostral secretory IgA preparations and among the cells synthesizing IgA in the mucosal tissue the isotypes are more evenly distributed, 30 to 50% being IgA2 and the remainder being IgA1 (1, 9). The significance of this differential distribution of the isotypes is not presently known, but the availability of highly specific anti-isotypic sera is of value in determining which ones participate in immunological reactions.

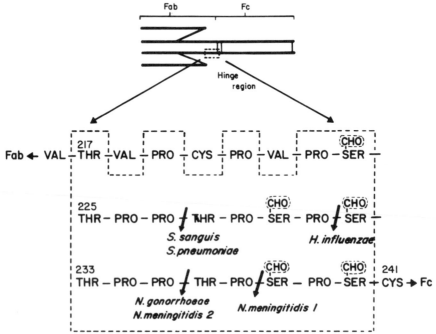

FIG. 1. *Primary structure of the human IgA1 heavy chain showing the peptide bonds in the hinge segment cleaved by the various microbial IgA proteases. Residues 228–240 are all lacking in IgA2 proteins, rendering this isotype protease resistant. The sequence is displayed to emphasize the unique replication found in this section of the IgA1 heavy chain. (Reprinted from reference 21 with permission of the Rockefeller University Press.)*

IgA proteases are neutral endopeptidases that cleave both human serum and secretory IgA1 in a limited way to yield intact Fabα and Fcα fragments (22). There are no other known substrates, including human immunoglobulins of the use of native human IgA as substrate. During such assays, cleavage products are quantitated after separation by electrophoretic techniques on cellulose acetate and polyacrylamide, or they are examined by more qualitative methods such as immunoelectrophoresis (19, 25, 27). The bacteria now known to secrete these proteases are *S. sanguis, S. mitior* (11), *S. pneumoniae* (13, 16, 19), *Haemophilus influenzae* (13, 16, 19), and the pathogenic *Neisseria* species *N. gonorrhoeae* and *N. meningitidis* (24). It has recently been shown (21) that *N. meningitidis* strains release two types of IgA proteases that have slightly different specificity for the IgA1 hinge region substrate, as will be discussed below. Within the genera *Neisseria* and *Haemophilus*, bacteria that are nonpathogenic for humans such as *N. cinerea, N. subflava, H. parainfluenzae*, and *H. haemolyticus* have no IgA protease activity (20); whether or not these species synthesize a corresponding protein that is enzymatically inactive is now known.

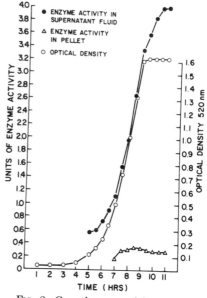

FIG. 2. *Growth curve of* S. sanguis *in Todd-Hewitt broth at 37°C. IgA protease activity appears in the supernatant fluid as cells enter the proliferative phase, and output continues to correspond closely to increase in bacterial numbers. About 5% of total activity remains with the bacterial pellet.*

As shown in Fig. 2, when *S. sanguis* is grown in liquid culture in Todd–Hewitt broth the IgA protease output into the cell-free supernatant phase parallels the rise in optical density caused by bacterial proliferation. In such studies approximately 5% of enzyme activity is sedimentable, associated firmly with the organism. This form of IgA protease may be particularly abundant in dental plaque.

The IgA proteases, through their capacity to divide the antibody molecule into antigen-binding (Fab) and effector (Fc) regions, have the potential for markedly interfering with the full expression of the biological function of IgA (26). The extent to which the IgA1 component of polyclonal secretory IgA antibodies is susceptible to IgA protease activity in vivo is not known because such studies are complicated both by the presence of antibody to the proteases in the secretory IgA antibody population itself (12; J. V. Gilbert, A. G. Plaut, M. E. Lamm, H. E. Longmaid, and N. Murkofsky, Fed. Proc. **38**:1224, 1979) and because of the technical difficulties of precisely assigning antibody specificity to the IgA1 or IgA2 isotypes.

The cleavage site of each protease at the IgA1 hinge region segment is now known, having been determined through the use of limited amino-terminal sequence analysis of Fcα fragments purified from digestion mixtures (12, 21). Each protease cleaves at one of several peptide bonds in the replicated IgA1 hinge region, and in each case proline contributes the carboxyl group to the susceptible bond. These cleavage sites are depicted in Fig. 1. Workers in our laboratory have recently reported (21) the existence of two types of IgA protease among *N. meningitidis* isolates that cleave specifically at hinge region peptide bonds that are only two residues apart (Fig. 1). The two enzymes are mutually exclusive in the sense that every meningococcal isolate so far examined expresses only one of these enzyme specificities. Of considerable interest is that the type of enzyme produced can be correlated to the serogroup in which the given isolate falls, indicating potential value of IgA proteases not only as an epidemiological marker but also in studies of the genetics of *N. meningitidis*. Preliminary work indicates that *H. influenzae* species also yield at least two different types of IgA protease specificities (unpublished data).

The IgA proteases isolated from culture filtrates of enzyme-positive bacterial species differ in many respects, including susceptibility to metal chelator inactivation, isoelectric point (3), and inhibition by human serum antienzyme antibody; the basis of these differences must await more detailed characterization of the enzyme proteins themselves. If these widely varying bacterial forms all produce an enzyme with pronounced similarity in substrate specificity but differences in protein structure, the likelihood that this activity is important in colonization or infectious disease will be strengthened because then IgA protease specificity can be considered a biochemical activity linking a rather diverse group of human pathogenic microorganisms.

DESIGN OF SYNTHETIC SUBSTRATES AND INHIBITORS OF IgA PROTEASE

Recent experiments in our laboratory by Fattaneh Shadanloo have shown that IgA protease is abundant in dental plaque, activity being found in nearly all specimens of supragingival and subgingival specimens removed from normal volunteers. Because approximately 25% of cultivatable streptococci in plaque produce IgA protease, and *S. mutans* and other oral bacteria are enzyme negative, it is likely that plaque IgA protease arises largely from alpha-hemolytic streptococci such as *S. sanguis* and *S. mitior*, as recently reported by Kilian and Holmgren (11). We have reasoned that *S. sanguis* enzyme may be involved in the establishment or maintenance of plaque, or both, by allowing bacteria to proliferate unencumbered by immune attack. Because the free tooth surface is essentially inaccessible to cellular components of the secretory immune system, it is uniquely dependent on soluble salivary antibody (principally IgA) for its immune defense; efforts at caries control by immunizing salivary glands with bacterial antigens are based on this supposition. Our present approach to exploring the role of IgA protease in the colonization process involves the synthesis of low-molecular-weight peptide substrates and enzyme-inhibiting analogs that may eventually be used to interrupt protease activity in vivo.

Highly specific enzymes offer a unique opportunity to construct inhibitors capable of specifically inactivating single biological events and thus the stages in the development of disease which are dependent on those enzymes' activities (5, 28, 30). Moreover, low-molecular-weight substrates are useful in identifying the enzymes of interest from among a number of other activities and therefore may be of considerable value in the course of enzyme isolation and characterization. Many drugs inhibit enzymatic activity but few have been applied in the control of proteolytic enzymes. Proteases of the intestinal tract such as trypsin and chymotrypsin evolved to degrade a variety of proteins and therefore have broad specificity; however, research has recently focused on proteolytic enzymes that are regulatory in type, involved in the control of numerous biological processes. Such enzymes typically show exquisite specificity and cleave only a single peptide bond in relevant substrates; examples of this would be the enzyme renin which cleaves angiotensinogens (5) or the enzymes involved in activation of the complement cascade. Because the bacterial IgA proteases represent similar examples of highly specific proteolytic activities, substrates and inhibitors offer the possibility of monitoring ongoing bacterial colonization steps and possibly preventing their occurrence. The rational design of peptides uses the recent rapid advances in understanding of how proteases bind to their substrate and the requisite conformation of peptides that will interact with the active site (10). Moreover, the recently simplified techniques for the synthesis of peptides of interest by the solid-phase technique (18) allows for the preparation of a large number of inhibitors in a reasonable period of time. Such substrates or inhibitors must be constructed so that in solution they assume a conformation which will fit into the active site. Once in the site, functional groups on the inhibitor must interact with constituents of the site so as to be in apposition to the appropriate binding areas of the enzyme. Thus, designing a peptide requires some knowledge of the likely conformation of a peptide in solution, the size and shape of the enzyme active site, and the interactive potential of various functional groups.

Because IgA proteases are highly specific and presumably relevant to disease processes, they are ideal enzymes for which to design inhibitors. We have recently synthesized (18) and examined the capacity of three peptides of 8, 16, and 24 amino acids in length to inhibit IgA protease; the structure of these peptides is shown in Fig. 3. In our preliminary work the enzyme used was that of *N. gonorrhoeae* because it is currently available in more purified form than is that of *S. sanguis*. The peptides were dissolved in tris(hydroxymethyl)aminomethane-hydrochloride buffer, pH 7.5, 0.05 M, and appropriate amounts were mixed with ^{125}I-labeled IgA and unlabeled IgA substrate at a final concentration of 1.6 μM in our protease assay procedure (25). Digestion was started by addition of 0.34 U of gonococcal IgA protease (25) and was continued for 20 min at 37°C, during which hydrolysis of the substrate was linear, as had been shown in preliminary experiments. The hydrolytic products of IgA were separated by polyacrylamide gel electrophoresis (15) and were then excised by cutting the dried gel; enzyme activity was determined by isotopic counting of ^{125}I on the fragments, as described earlier (25).

Table 1 shows the capacity of the 8-, 16-, and 24-residue peptides to inhibit the hydrolysis of native human serum IgA1 substrate. Although the octapeptide was not inhibitory, the 16-residue hexadecapeptide and 24-residue sequence had I_{50}'s (concentration at which substrate hydrolysis was inhibited by 50%) of 20 mM and 8 mM, respectively. We have not yet conclusively shown that the synthetic peptides are cleaved in the course of these experiments. It is evident from these experiments that length alone is not adequate for good binding to the bacterial protease, since synthetic peptides bound much less strongly than did native IgA; however, the data do indicate that IgA protease inhibition through use of such

	225	235
Native IgA₁ Hinge:	Cys-Pro-Val-Pro-Ser-Thr-Pro-Pro-Thr-Pro-Ser-Pro-Ser-Thr-Pro-Pro-Thr-Pro-Ser-Pro-Ser-Cys-Cys-His-Pro-Arg	
24-Residue Peptide:	Pro-Val-Pro-Ser-Thr-Pro-Pro-Thr-Pro-Ser-Pro-Ser-Thr-Pro-Pro-Thr-Pro-Ser-Pro-Ser-Cys-Aab-His-Pro	
16-Residue Peptide:	Thr-Pro-Pro-Thr-Pro-Ser-Pro-Ser-Thr-Pro-Pro-Thr-Pro-Ser-Pro-Ser	
8-Residue Peptide:	Thr-Pro-Pro-Thr-Pro-Ser-Pro-Ser	

FIG. 3. Structure of synthetic peptides modeled on the hinge region of IgA1. The sequence of the 8-, 16-, and 24-residue analogs of the native IgA1 hinge segment synthesized by the solid-phase technique is shown. In the 24-residue peptide one cysteine was replaced by α-amino butyric acid (Aab) to allow dimerization in future studies. S. sanguis IgA protease cleaves prolyl-threonyl bond 227-228, as shown in Fig. 1.

peptides is feasible. Because proteolytic enzymes typically have relatively small active sites that can only accommodate several amino acids, the weak binding of peptides as long as 16 or 24 residues strongly suggests that the native IgA hinge region is folded into a conformation that more favorably occupies the active site of the enzyme. The missing conformational element could be the hinge region carbohydrate; Labib et al. (14) have suggested that streptococcal IgA proteases copurify with a carbohydrase enzyme specificity. Kilian et al. (12) have, however, shown that not all IgA proteases possess a carbohydrase activity, so this issue is clearly unresolved. It has been proposed (13a) that the hinge region of IgG forms a trans-polyproline type of helix, the result being that this rodlike segment separates the antigen-binding and effector functions of the molecule. Other factors in the better binding of native IgA to enzyme could be that it is a dimeric heavy chain, unlike the monomeric form of the synthetic analogs; however, isolated alpha chains are readily cleaved by the IgA proteases. Clearly, other approaches will be required to yield efficient substrates and inhibitors by the techniques of peptide synthesis.

As is evident from the preliminary studies described above, our approach to the question of whether IgA proteases serve any role in the pathobiology of S. sanguis and other plaque bacteria is to design inhibitors to the enzyme that may interrupt the colonization sequence leading to mature plaque acquisition. Because the IgA protease enzymes are notably human specific and no clearly defined animal pathogen secretory immunoglobulin analogs are available, progress in under-

TABLE 1. *Inhibition of gonococcal IgA protease activity by hinge region peptide analogs*

Peptide concn in assay	% Inhibition of IgA protease activity	I_{50} (mM)
24 residue		
1.2 mM	17	
2.5 mM	23	
5.0 mM	35	8
16 residue		
1.2 mM	5	
2.5 mM	8	
5.0 mM	14	20
8 residue		
1.2 mM	0	—

standing the role of IgA protease as a virulence factor requires studies of humans. Although the isolation of protease-negative mutants is feasible, the testing of such bacteria as pathogens in humans will in most instances be inappropriate, and possibly hazardous. We are, therefore, proceeding under the assumption that the pharmacological inhibition of this protease, naturally present in the oral cavity, is a feasible alternative approach. During the course of our efforts to design substrates and inhibitors, we anticipate that a more complete understanding of this unique family of enzymes will be achieved.

SUMMARY

IgA proteases are a biochemically diverse group of extracellular bacterial enzymes that share the property of requiring human IgA proteins of the IgA1 isotype as substrate. IgA2 proteins are resistant to hydrolysis. The enzyme-positive species *S. pneumoniae*, *S. sanguis*, *S. mitior*, *N. meningitidis*, *N. gonorrhoeae*, and *H. influenzae* include major human pathogens responsible for meningitis, respiratory illness, and dental caries; the closely related but nonpathogenic species within several of these genera are enzyme negative. The IgA proteases each attack single peptide bonds involving proline in the unusual replicated human IgA1 heavy-chain hinge region segment. Our recent studies show that long (8- to 24-residue) IgA1 hinge peptide analogs synthesized by the solid-phase technique are only weakly competitive with the native IgA protein for the enzyme active site. This indicates that heavy chain dimerization, hinge region carbohydrate, or rigid conformational folding of the heavy chain play an important role in the specificity of these enzymes. The design of peptide substrates and inhibitors for use in examining the biological role of IgA proteases in streptococcal colonization in dental plaque is the objective of our present research.

LITERATURE CITED

1. **Andre, C., F. Andre, and C. Fargier.** 1978. Distribution of IgA$_1$ and IgA$_2$ plasma cells in various normal human tissues and in the jenunum of plasma IgA-deficient patients. Clin. Exp. Immunol. **33**:327–331.

2. **Baenziger, J., and S. Kornfeld.** 1974. Structure of the carbohydrate units of IgA₁ immunoglobulin. II. Structure of the O-glycosidically linked oligosaccharide units. J. Biol. Chem. **249:**7270–7281.

3. **Blake, M. S., and J. Swanson.** 1978. Studies on gonococcus infection. XVI. Purification of *Neisseria gonorrhoeae* immunoglobulin A₁ protease. Infect. Immun. **22:**350–358.

4. **Brown, W. R.** 1978. Relationships between immunoglobulins and the intestinal epithelium. Gastroenterology **75:**129–136.

5. **Burton, J., R. J. Cody, J. A. Herd, and E. Haber.** 1980. Specific inhibition of renin by an angiotensinogen analog. Proc. Natl. Acad. Sci. U.S.A. **77:**5476–5479.

6. **Conley, M. E., J. F. Kearney, A. R. Lawton, and M. D. Cooper.** 1980. Differentiation of human B cells expressing the IgA subclasses as demonstrated by monoclonal hybridoma antibodies. J. Immunol. **125:**2311–2316.

7. **Frangione, B., and C. Wolfenstein-Todel.** 1972. Partial duplication in the hinge region of the IgA1 myeloma proteins. Proc. Natl. Acad. Sci. U.S.A. **69:**3673–3676.

8. **Genco, R. J., A. G. Plaut, and R. C. Moellering, Jr.** 1975. Evaluation of human oral organisms and pathogenic streptococci for production of IgA protease. J. Infect. Dis. **131:**S17–S21.

9. **Grey, H. M., C. A. Abel, W. J. Yount, and H. G. Kunkel.** 1968. A subclass of human αA-globulins (IgA2) which lacks the disulfide bonds linking heavy and light chains. J. Exp. Med. **128:**1223–1236.

10. **Gross, E., and J. Meienhofer (ed.).** 1979. Peptides: structure and biological function. Pierce Chemical Co., Rockford, Ill.

11. **Kilian, M., and K. Holmgren.** 1981. Ecology and nature of immunoglobulin A1 protease-producing streptococci in the human oral cavity and pharynx. Infect. Immun. **31:**868–873.

12. **Kilian, M., J. Mestecky, R. Kulhavy, M. Tomana, and W. T. Butler.** 1980. IgA1 proteases from *Haemophilus influenzae, Streptococcus pneumoniae, Neisseriae meningitidis* and *Streptococcus sanguis:* comparative immunochemical studies. J. Immunol. **124:**2596–2600.

13. **Kilian, M., J. Mestecky, and R. E. Schrohenloher.** 1979. Pathogenic species of the genus *Haemophilus* and *Streptococcus pneumoniae* produce immunoglobulin A protease. Infect. Immun. **26:**143–149.

13a. **Klein, M., N. Haeffner-Cavaillon, D. E. Isenman, C. Rivat, M. A. Navia, D. R. Davies, and K. J. Dorrington.** 1981. Expression of biological effector functions by immunoglobulin G molecules lacking the hinge region. Proc. Natl. Acad. Sci. U.S.A. **78:**524–528.

14. **Labib, R. S., N. J. Calvanico, and T. B. Tomasi, Jr.** 1978. Studies on extracellular proteases of *Streptococcus sanguis:* purification and characterization of a human IgA1-specific protease. Biochim. Biophys. Acta **526:**547–559.

15. **Laemmli, U. K.** 1970. Cleavage of structural proteins during the assembly of the head of bacteriophage T4. Nature (London) **227:**680–685.

16. **Male, C. J.** 1979. Immunoglobulin A1 protease production by *Haemophilus influenzae* and *Streptococcus pneumoniae.* Infect. Immun. **26:**254–261.

17. **Mehta, S. K., A. G. Plaut, N. J. Calvanico, and T. B. Tomasi, Jr.** 1973. Human immunoglobulin A: production of an Fc fragment by an enteric microbial proteolytic enzyme. J. Immunol. **111:**1274–1276.

18. **Merrifield, R. B.** 1963. Solid phase peptide synthesis I. Synthesis of a tetrapeptide. J. Am. Chem. Soc. **85:**2149–2154.

19. **Mulks, M. H., S. Kornfeld, and A. G. Plaut.** 1980. *Streptococcus pneumoniae* and *Haemophilus influenzae* specifically proteolyze human IgA. J. Infect. Dis. **299:**973–976.

20. **Mulks, M. H., and A. G. Plaut.** 1978. IgA protease production as a characteristic distinguishing pathogenic from harmless Neisseriaceae. N. Engl. J. Med. **299:**973–976.

21. **Mulks, M. G., A. G. Plaut, H. A. Feldman, and B. Frangione.** 1980. IgA protease of two distinct specificities are released by *Neisseriae meningitidis.* J. Exp. Med. **152:**1442–1447.

22. **Plaut, A. G.** 1978. Microbial IgA proteases. N. Engl. J. Med. **298:**1459–1463.

23. **Plaut, A. G., R. J. Genco, and T. B. Tomasi, Jr.** 1974. Isolation of an enzyme from *Streptococcus sanguis* which specifically cleaves IgA. J. Immunol. **113:**289–291.

24. **Plaut, A. G., J. V. Gilbert, M. S. Artenstein, and J. D. Capra.** 1975. *Neisseria gonorrhoeae* and *N. meningitidis:* production of an extracellular enzyme which cleaves human IgA. Science **190:**1103–1105.

25. **Plaut, A. G., J. V. Gilbert, and I. Heller.** 1978. Assay and properties of IgA protease of *Streptococcus sanguis,* p. 489–495. *In* J. R. McGhee (ed.), Secretory immunity and infection. Plenum Press, New York.

26. **Plaut, A. G., J. V. Gilbert, and R. Wistar, Jr.** 1977. Loss of antibody activity in human immunoglobulin A exposed to extracellular immunoglobulin A proteases of *Neisseria gonorrhoeae* and *Streptococcus sanguis.* Infect. Immun. **17:**130–135.

27. **Plaut, A. G., R. Wistar, Jr., and J. D. Capra.** 1974. Differential susceptibility of human IgA immunoglobulins to streptococcal IgA protease. J. Clin. Invest. **54:**1295–1300.

28. **Smith, C. W., and R. Walter.** 1978. Vasopressin analog with extraordinarily high antidiuretic potency. A study of conformation and activity. Science **199:**297–299.

29. **Tomasi, T. B., Jr., and H. M. Grey.** 1972. Structure and function of immunoglobulin A. Prog. Allergy **16:**81.

30. **Veber, D. F., F. W. Holly, W. J. Paleveda, R. F. Mutt, S. J. Bergstrand, M. Torchiana, M. S. Glitzer, R. Saperstein, and R. Herschmann.** 1978. Conformationally restricted bicyclic analogs of somatostatin. Proc. Natl. Acad. Sci. U.S.A. **75:**2636–2640.

CELLULAR ASPECTS OF HOST RESPONSES

Cellular Immunity in Periodontal Disease: an Overview

THOMAS LEHNER

Guy's Hospital Medical and Dental School, London SE1 9RT, England

Host immune responses may be involved in the initiation and development of periodontal disease. The immune responses may be induced either non-specifically by baterial plaque or by a specific microorganism or, indeed, by any combination of microbial antigens. It is evident that an immunocompetent host can respond to antigenic stimulation either by an enhanced or by a suppressed immune reaction, irrespective of whether one specific or a number of nonspecific antigens are involved. Furthermore, if a specific microorganism were to be responsible for periodontal disease, immune responses to plaque would still need to be fully appreciated, as these might modulate the host responses to the specific organism.

As immunological investigations have progressed over the past decade, it is becoming clear that the responses to bacterial plaque are extremely complex and that any one or a combination of type I, II, III, and IV reactions might be involved. The prime significance of any one reaction has not been established and needs to be investigated, both from the local periodontal point of view and in terms of the influence it may have on the overall systemic immune load. This review will deal only with cellular immunity, though it should be emphasized that it is becoming rather difficult to differentiate the variety of immune responses in the pathogenesis of the disease.

FUNCTIONAL COMPONENTS OF DENTAL PLAQUE

Dental plaque may be considered to have two functional components which influence the development of periodontal disease (44): microorganisms which have the ability to induce periodontal disease and immunomodulating agents which have the capacity of enhancing or suppressing the immune response. The microbiological aspects of periodontal disease are extensively dealt with elsewhere, but the potential significance of the immunomodulating agents in dental plaque has not received adequate attention. Dental plaque contains about 8.5% soluble dextran with predominantly α-1→6 linkages (86) and about 1.4% insoluble dextrans with predominantly α-1→3 linkages (25). It also contains 1% (dry weight) levan (55). Lipopolysaccharides (LPS) from gram-negative bacteria are the most potent biological materials found in both supragingival (72) and subgingival (15) plaque. Lipoteichoic acid from gram-positive plaque bacteria may have biological properties similar to those found with LPS, though this still needs to be directly demonstrated with dental plaque (81).

CELLULAR RESPONSES TO DENTAL PLAQUE

The effects of plaque accumulation in vivo on the immune response were tested in young healthy subjects. They were asked to abstain from oral hygiene

202

for 28 days, and the plaque accumulation, gingival inflammation, and cellular and humoral immune responses were tested sequentially (48). Accumulation of dental bacterial plaque and the associated gingival inflammation were correlated with an increase in lymphocyte transformation and release of macrophage migration inhibition factor. Lymphocytes were activated by sonic extracts of autologous bacterial plaque, streptococci, *Veillonella* cells, and *Actinomyces* cells and by some unrelated antigens. Both cellular responses were of limited duration and returned to base-line values 28 days after plaque was removed. However, the response was often biphasic, the immune response reaching base-line values before plaque was removed (at day 21), so that a suppressor cellular mechanism might be involved. As plaque control is inadequate under clinical conditions, it seems that a suppressor mechanism might be essential in preventing an almost continuous immunostimulation.

The variations in cellular immune responses have been noted in experimental gingivitis (48), and the potential of this in evaluating the progress of periodontal disease and the response to treatment has been emphasized (64), though apparently not pursued.

The results of this experimental design also suggest that accumulation of bacterial plaque under entirely physiological conditions can stimulate not only a local gingival inflammation but also a systemic cell-mediated response. This must be associated with some plaque antigen penetrating the junctional epithelium. It would be of some importance to determine whether antigenic penetration of the junctional epithelium occurs before or after gingival inflammation has developed.

The hypothesis that dental bacterial plaque in vivo may both potentiate and recall previous sensitization to microorganisms was tested by repeating the plaque accumulation experiment in five subjects 210 days after plaque was removed and good oral hygiene was reinstituted (47). Significant lymphocyte transformation was found earlier, was greater in magnitude, and lasted longer in the second as compared with the first plaque accumulation experiment. These immunological features are usually ascribed to secondary antibody responses or to enhancement of an existing immune state. The results suggest that bacterial plaque in vivo recalls immunological memory for plaque antigens at the cellular level. It is not clear at present whether this is a measure of T- or B-lymphocyte memory, but both might be involved since pooled dental plaque and *Veillonella* can specifically stimulate T and B lymphocytes to undergo transformation into blast cells (35, 52).

IMMUNOPOTENTIATION BY DENTAL PLAQUE

Plaque contains substantial quantities of LPS, dextrans, and levans which can modulate the immune response to other antigens. An adjuvant effect of in vivo plaque accumulation on both the lymphoproliferative response and lymphokine formation was observed with unrelated stimulants (48; Fig. 1). Although purified cell preparations were not examined, both T- and B-lymphocyte functions were enhanced in the subjects who had accumulated plaque for 28 days, as tested by the mixed leukocyte culture reaction for T lymphocytes (39) and LPS activation for B lymphocytes (16, 46). There was no detectable increase in antibody titers to the plaque bacteria, but an increase in serum immunoglobulins was found (Fig. 2). This is consistent with the view that LPS, dextran, and levan act as polyclonal B-cell activators (13) (Fig. 2), and this

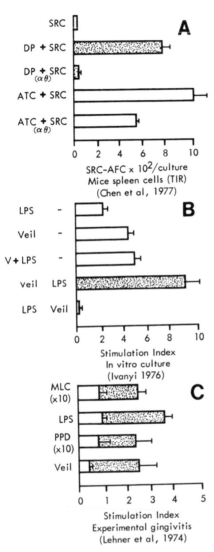

FIG. 1. *Immunopotentiation by dental bacterial plaque tested (A) in thymectomized irradiated reconstituted (TIR) mouse spleen cells (46), (B) in vitro with human lymphocytes (29), and (C) in vivo in experimental gingivitis in man (11). Abbreviations: Veil (V), Veillonella alcalescens; LPS, lipopolysaccharide; MLC, mixed leukocyte culture; ATC, Activated T cells; SRC, sheep erythrocytes; DP, dental plaque; $\alpha\theta$, anti-theta serum; AFC, antibody-forming cells; PPD, purified protein derivative.*

applies also to antigens from *A. viscosus* (5, 10). Polyclonal B-cell activation might also account for the increase in serum immunoglobulins in juvenile periodontitis (49; Fig. 2) and for the increased proliferative response by polyclonal B-cell activators in severe periodontitis in young adults (75). In view of these findings, it has been suggested that dental plaque may act as an endogenous adjuvant acting on both T and B lymphocytes. Among a multitude of antigens in dental plaque, LPS (38) from gram-negative bacteria and dextran (6) synthesized by *Streptococcus mutans* and *S. sanguis* have adjuvant properties. Dextran given to mice enhances the responses of lymphoid cells to both T-dependent (concanavalin A) and T-independent mitogens (1, 2). This is comparable to the enhanced responses of lymphocytes in humans in the T-dependent (mixed lymphocyte culture) and T-independent (LPS) reactions induced by bacterial plaque accumulation in vivo (48). The proliferative response of human lymphocytes to *Veillonella* has also been potentiated in vitro by levan and LPS (29). The enhanced responses are mediated through soluble factors elaborated by T lymphocytes. Some of them affect T cells and others, B cells; corresponding receptors are found on thymus cells and bone marrow cells, respectively (1). A similar but nonspecific factor derived from T cells has been described in relation to LPS (79).

The T-cell adjuvant properties of plaque were confirmed in both humans and monkeys (66). These experiments showed that plaque and phytohemagglutinin were synergistic for lymphocyte transformation. The T- and B-cell adjuvant properties of plaque were then studied (5). Using the antibody-forming cell assay to

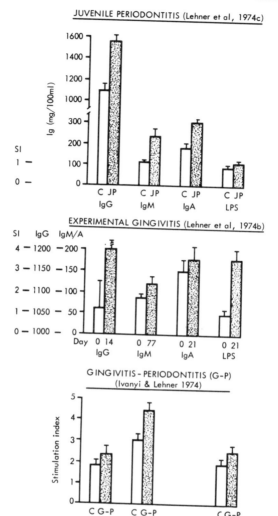

FIG. 2. *Polyclonal B-cell activation in juvenile periodontitis (49), experimental gingivitis (46), and gingivitis–periodontitis (35) in humans. Abbreviations: SI, stimulation index; C, control; JP, juvenile periodontitis; G–P, gingivitis–periodontitis.*

sheep erythrocytes (Fig. 1), Chen et al. (11) found a small direct effect of plaque on B cells in the mouse but a much larger T-cell stimulation. The adjuvant effect in vitro of LPS from oral bacteria and levan on antigen stimulation by *V. alcalescens* was also shown (29), but it was necessary to add the antigen 24 h before the mitogens (Fig. 1). If the mitogens were added first, the response was suppressed. Factors from plaque which either enhance or suppress T-cell transformation by phytohemagglutinin and plaque have been reported (51).

The mechanism of action of adjuvants is complex, but four points need to be emphasized in relation to dental plaque. (i) The persistence of dental plaque along the gingival margin enables LPS, dextran, and levan to be released continuously over an extensive epithelial surface. (ii) Dental plaque and LPS are potent agents causing release of lysosomal hydrolases from macrophages, and these may be involved in the action of adjuvants (62, 76). (iii) In order for dextran to potentiate immune responses (14) and to activate the alternative pathway of complement (20), it must be negatively charged. Indeed, sulfated macromolecules are found in dental plaque, some of which are sulfated glycoproteins (7, 67). Negatively charged polysaccharides can be formed by *S. mutans* and *S. sanguis*, which incorporate labeled phosphate into soluble and insoluble high-molecular-weight polysaccharides (57). In addition to the negative charge of dextrans, which may be necessary for adjuvanticity, the α-1→3, α-1→6, and α-1→4 linkages may influence their adjuvanticity, especially as the α-1→3-linked dextran is resistant to degradation and is slowly metabolized. (iv) Recruitment and proliferation of immunocompetent cells both in the gingival mononuclear cell infiltration and in the draining lymph nodes may follow exposure to high local concentrations of antigens.

IMMUNOSUPRESSION INDUCED BY DENTAL PLAQUE COMPONENTS

Although dental plaque has not been formally shown to have immunosuppressive properties, this has been demonstrated with LPS, dextran, and levan. LPS given to mice before sheep erythrocytes causes a depression in footpad swelling, but when given after the antigen it enhances the footpad reaction (41). The in vitro findings with human lymphocytes are comparable to the in vivo effects of LPS on the T cell-mediated hypersensitivity in mice: exposure of human lymphocytes to LPS or levan 24 h before exposure to *Veillonella* results in suppression of *Veillonella*-induced T-cell proliferation, and, conversely, if the sequence of antigen and mitogen is reversed, T-cell proliferation is enhanced (29; Fig. 1).

High-zone B-cell tolerance can be induced in mice by polysaccharides; 1 to 10 mg of a branched native levan, with a molecular weight of 20×10^6, rapidly induces direct B-cell tolerance, and if the levan is depolymerized to a molecular weight of 10,000, it still retains its tolerogenicity but not its immunogenicity (58). Low-zone tolerance is induced by immunization with 10 to 100 µg of levan (26). High- and low-zone tolerance can also be induced with a predominantly α-1→6-linked near-linear dextran, and depolymerization reduces immunogenicity and tolerogenicity, both of which are lost with a molecular weight of 200,000 (28). However, a more branched α-1→3-linked dextran is a poor tolerogen, and 10 mg of this dextran induced only minimal tolerance, although 1 mg was a potent immunogen (27). *S. mutans* is capable of synthesizing a continuous series of dextrans with a variable proportion of α-1→6 and α-1→3 linkages (4, 18, 50), and these may have a complex effect on tolerance, though this has not yet been demonstrated against unrelated antigens. The net result between factors favoring enhancement and tolerance may then depend on the proportion of α-1→3- and α-1→6-linked dextrans, the negative charge these may carry, epitope density, and the sequence of adding mitogen and antigen.

IMMUNOGENETIC MODEL OF T-CELL HELPER AND SUPPRESSOR FUNCTION IN HUMANS

The immune responses are controlled by a network of cellular interactions with helper and suppressor activities (17). These functions have now been investigated with reference to oral *S. mutans* in mice and monkeys (42, 43). It was found that specific T-cell helper activity can be elicited in vitro with 10 ng of a protein streptococcal antigen, whereas for suppressor activity 100 μg is required. This system was then converted to one in which putative helper cells were elicited in vivo and the corresponding helper factor was released in vitro by differential amounts of the streptococcal antigen (47a). It became evident that high-avidity T-cell helper function was elicited by 1 ng of streptococcal antigen and was associated with the DRw-6,1,2,3 cross-reacting antigens, whereas low-avidity helper function was released by 1,000 ng of streptococcal antigen and was associated with the HLA-DR4−related gene product. These findings suggest that one of the basic immunoregulatory responses to an oral bacterial antigen has an immunogenetic basis. Although the antigen isolated from *S. mutans* is unlikely to be involved in periodontal disease, it suggests the possibility that an immunogenetic basis of responses to bacterial antigens implicated in periodontal disease might exist. Elective avidities of T-cell helper function to one or more of these antigens might be one of the determinants in the T cell−B cell interaction affecting the development of periodontal disease. There is further evidence to suggest that high-avidity T helper lymphocytes are associated with low-avidity T suppressor lymphocytes, and, conversely, low-avidity T helper lymphocytes are associated with high-avidity T suppressor cells. The T suppressor cells effectively cause high-zone or low-zone tolerance. If cellular immune responses are damaging, a low-zone tolerance may well be the desired immunological state, for only small doses of antigen are likely to have a chance of stimulating the immune system, at least during the early phases of development of periodontal disease. Indeed, low-zone tolerance might prove to be the desired immunoprophylactic aim in periodontal disease.

LYMPHOPROLIFERATIVE RESPONSE

The potential role of lymphocytes in periodontal disease has been established by the demonstration that lymphoproliferative responses can be stimulated by *V. alcalescens*, *A. viscosus*, *Fusobacterium nucleatum*, and *Bacteroides melaninogenicus* (32). Although little activity was found in healthy subjects, the degree of stimulation in patients could not be correlated with the increasing severity of the disease, and patients with the most severe form of disease did not react to the stimulants. Plaque from both normal subjects and those with gingival disease induced a lymphoproliferative response, but only when the lymphocytes were collected from patients with periodontal disease (21, 33). This clearly shows that both normal and disease plaques contain antigens, but only patients with periodontal disease possess reactive lymphocytes. The inhibited responses of patients with severe periodontitis were serum dependent, since serum from these patients inhibited the lymphocyte response of patients with gingivitis and mild periodontitis, and culturing responder lymphocytes in severe periodontitis serum inhibited the lymphocyte proliferation (34). Both the enhancing and the depressing effects of serum in lymphocyte transformation by *V. alcalescens* could be specifically adsorbed from serum, and the blocking effect in patients with severe periodontitis was probably due to a cell-bound antibody (31). The plaque-induced lymphocyte transformation in patients with periodontal disease was confirmed by Horton et al. (21), who reported a correlation between lymphocyte stimulation and severity of periodontal disease.

The latter was confirmed by some investigators (5) but not by others (32, 74). However, the patient's age may also be important, since lymphocyte responses to plaque are decreased in older subjects, who tend to have the most severe disease (12). In contrast, in another investigation the highest responses were noted in advanced periodontitis (74). There is a consensus that lymphocytes from normal subjects are not responsive to plaque or to plaque bacteria with the exception of one study (40), but the antigens used in that study were sodium hydroxide extracts which might have functioned as mitogens, inducing lymphocyte stimulation as large as that caused by phytohemagglutinin. The differences in the results between these investigations can be ascribed to lack of standardization or either the culture technique or the antigen preparation.

The cells responding to plaque antigens are both T and B lymphocytes (52), and this may be accounted for by the finding that protein antigens of *Veillonella* stimulate T lymphocytes, whereas the LPS from *Veillonella* elicits a response only in B lymphocytes (35).

SOLUBLE MEDIATORS

Sensitized lymphocytes release soluble mediators (lymphokines), and these may be associated with or dissociated from the lymphoproliferative response. Lymphocytes from patients with gingivitis and periodontitis produced macrophage migration inhibition factor when stimulated with *V. alcalescens*, even in those patients with severe periodontitis who yielded weak or no lymphocyte transformation (37). The lymphocytes from these patients also showed cytotoxicity against chicken erythrocyte targets, indicating a dissociation between the different types of lymphocyte responses. A similar dissociation was noted in patients with juvenile periodontitis, in whom lymphocyte transformation to all oral bacteria tested was impaired, except that to *A. viscosus* and disease-unrelated antigens such as purified protein derivative

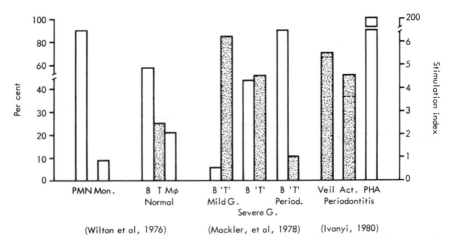

(Wilton et al, 1976)   (Mackler, et al, 1978)   (Ivanyi, 1980)

FIG. 3. *Proportion of T and B lymphocytes in crevicular fluid and gingiva and the lymphoproliferative response to gingival lymphocytes. Data from references 30, 54, and 84. Abbreviations: PMN, polymorphonuclear leukocytes; Mon, mononuclear cells; Mφ, macrophages; G, gingivitis; Period., periodontitis. Note: the discontinuous lines in the V. alcalescens (Veil) and A. viscosus (Act) bars show the lymphoproliferative response of blood lymphocytes.*

or herpes simplex virus. Almost all of the patients, however, produced migration inhibition factor to all the oral bacterial antigens tested (49).

Lymphocytes from patients with periodontal disease stimulated with plaque-derived antigens produced lymphotoxin which was cytotoxic for human gingival fibroblasts, and the amount of lymphotoxin produced by the cells was correlated with the severity of periodontal disease (23). An osteoclast-activating factor, distinct from Para-thor-mone and prostaglandins, is produced by lymphocytes from patients with periodontal disease when they are stimulated with plaque antigens (24). Furthermore, both T cells and B cells from patients with periodontal disease produced a monocyte chemotactic factor (52). LPS stimulates guinea pig B lymphocytes to release macrophage-activating factor (85). Leukocyte migration inhibitory factor was produced by lymphocytes from patients with gingivitis when stimulated with V. parvula antigens.

Lymphokines might be the agents predominantly responsible for local damage. Macrophage or leukocyte migration inhibitory factor might localize macrophages or neutrophils, and chemotactic factor might increase the number of monocytes attracted to the site of lymphocyte activation. The release of a number of enzymes would produce local damage. Specific damage, however, can be inflicted by lymphotoxin, which is cytotoxic to fibroblasts, and osteoclast-activating factor, which increases osteoclastic bone resorption.

LYMPHOCYTES IN THE GINGIVA AND CREVICULAR FLUID

Lymphocytes have been identified in crevicular fluid, but plasma cells have not been found (73). The number of mononuclear cells reported varies with the method of collection. It was up to 3% when the plastic strip method was used (3), but 8.5% when the gingival washing technique was applied (73; Fig 3). Of the mononuclear cells, 58% were B cells, as identified by EAC rosettes, 24% were identified as T cells by E rosetting, and 18% were identified as monocytes/macrophages by their ability to phagocytose latex particles (84).

Lymphocytes are found in gingival and periodontal disease on light and electron microscopic examination (63). Attempts have been made recently to identify the subsets of B and T cells in gingival and periodontal tissue. The proportion of B cells was assayed by membrane immunoglobulin fluorescence staining and Fc receptor-bearing cells; plasma cells were identified by cytoplasmic immunofluorescence (53, 54). The proportion of B cells and plasma cells increased from 6% B cells and a few plasma cells in mild gingivitis to 47% B cells and 33% plasma cells in severe gingivitis and 91% B cells and 57% plasma cells in periodontitis (Fig. 3).

Direct T-cell markers were not used, but surface immunoglobulin- and Fc-negative lymphocytes were considered to consist predominantly of T lymphocytes (53, 54). This suggests a progressive decrease in putative T lymphocytes from 85% in mild gingivitis to about 50% in severe gingivitis and 10% in periodontitis. C3- and Fc receptor-bearing B lymphocytes were also found in gingivae from the early lesions of experimental gingivitis and established gingivitis by a rosetting technique (80). Although T lymphoblasts were demonstrable by electron microscopy, T lymphocytes were not detected in sections by E rosetting, probably because viable T cells might be required. The predominantly B-cell nature of lymphocytic infiltration in chronic inflammatory periodontal disease has been confirmed by using enzyme markers and antisera

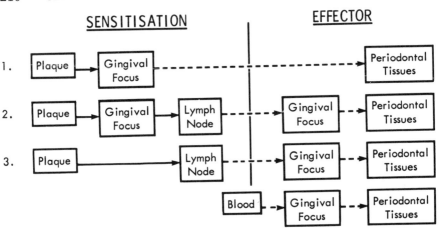

FIG. 4. *Possible routes of sensitization of plaque antigens and the functional relationship between the gingival focus, lymph nodes, and the target periodontal tissue.*

to Ia-like antigens in tissue sections (70, 71). However, the T-cell enzyme markers and a human T-lymphocyte antiserum identified a small proportion of T lymphocytes; it was estimated that 5 to 10% of the cells are T cells and 85 to 90% are B cells (71).

There is therefore broad agreement that lymphocytes are present in gingivitis and periodontitis but that about 90% of these cells are B cells and probably about 10% are T cells. However, as T lymphocytes are the dominant cells in immunoregulation, providing help or suppression of B-cell responses, the proportion of T cells to B cells is probably functionally just about right. It should also be noted that the approximate ratio of T to B cells of 4:1 in peripheral blood is reversed to 1:9 in the gingiva but is only 1:3 in crevicular fluid.

The use of membrane markers in the identification of subsets of lymphocytes in tissue section is fraught with many difficulties. The occurrence of cytophilic antibodies, nonspecific sticking of the surrounding immunoglobulins, and the acquisition of Ia antigens and Fc receptors by activated T cells are among these, and such difficulties suggest that this approach to characterization of the mononuclear cells involved in periodontal disease has its limitations. A functional approach has been adopted very recently by Ivanyi (30; Fig. 3), who isolated lymphocytes from gingival tissue from patients with moderate periodontitis and clearly demonstrated a lymphoproliferative response to the T-cell mitogen phytohemagglutinin, as well as *V. alcalescens* and *A. viscosus*. Furthermore, the response of gingival lymphocytes was correlated quantitatively with that of peripheral blood lymphocytes. The lymphoproliferative response of peripheral blood T and B lymhocytes has now been demonstrated and correlated with lymphocytes isolated from the site of periodontal disease.

The relationship between the gingival focus of lymphoid cells and organized lymphoid tissue in lymph nodes needs to be investigated. There are at least four possibilities to be considered (Fig. 4), and each of these must differentiate the afferent or sensitization arm and the efferent or effector arm of the immune response to plaque antigens. Plaque antigens may diffuse directly or be carried by antigen-binding cells to the gingival focus, where the relevant T–B cell interactions might take place and effector cells and soluble products would then affect the periodontal tissue. Alternatively, antigen-binding cells may pass on to the regional lymph nodes directly or via the gingival focus, and after the T–B cell interaction in the lymph nodes, which are best suited for such a function, the effector cells and soluble products are then passed back to the gingival focus to carry out their functions. Although the regional lymph nodes are likely to play an essential role in the immune response, the gingival focus may, in addition to the effector cells, have a subsidiary afferent function. Nonspecific homing of lymphoblasts to gingival foci of inflammation, however, is also likely to take place (56).

MONOCYTES AND MACROPHAGES

Monocytes and macrophages have been identified in the gingival fluid from normal gingivae by enzyme staining and functional assays. They comprise about 2% of the total cells recovered, although they account for 18% of the mononuclear cell population (84). Macrophages have also been detected by rosetting methods in the inflammatory cells of both early experimental gingivitis and established periodontal disease (80) and by ultrastructural analysis in both humans and experimental animals (69). These cells play an essential part as antigen-presenting cells in lymphocyte interactions, and, through the release of enzymes, they may be involved in periodontal damage and bone resorption. However, limitations of space prevent their being reviewed here, though some of their immunological functions have been described elsewhere.

ROLE OF CELL-MEDIATED IMMUNITY IN PERIODONTAL DISEASE

It is perhaps not entirely surprising that conflicting results have been reported concerning cellular immunity, as it may lead to both protection and destruction of periodontal tissue. Immunosuppression by antithymocyte serum caused a reduction of the cellular infiltrate in the gingivae of dogs developing plaque-induced gingivitis but did not affect the severity of disease as measured by the amount of gingival fluid and its cellular contents (60). In dogs with established gingivitis, no reduction in the tissue infiltrate or of clinical disease could be found (61). These results were interpreted as evidence that cell-mediated immunity played no part in gingival disease, but it was later realized that fluid flow, the cellular content of the fluid, and the tissue infiltrate reflect the chemotactic ability of plaque. In an interesting experiment in rats monoassociated with A. viscosus, the T cells were suppressed with cyclosporin A, but this had no significant effect on bone loss or on the chronic inflammatory cell reaction (19). Although some T-cell suppression was demonstrated by concanavalin A stimulation of spleen cells, this seems to have been inadequate to prevent an accumulation of chronic inflammatory cells in the periodontal tissues, and therefore the cellular responses at the site of disease might not have been affected.

Dinitrochlorobenzene can induce gingival disease in the absense of plaque, when applied topically to the gingiva of sensitized dogs, and this can be suppressed both clinically and histologically by antithymocyte serum (59). The early gingival lesion in particular resembles a delayed hypersensitivity reaction, and in both rhesus monkeys and rats these lesions developed in the gingiva 48 to 72 h after challenge with dinitrocholorbenzene in sensitized animals (82). The lesions could be passively transferred in rats with sensitized spleen cells but not with serum, and they were similar to those found in the tissues of subjects with early experimental gingivitis (65), except that a chemotactic effect of plaque on polymorphonuclear leukocytes was not observed and no polymorphonuclear leukocytes infiltrated the tissues. These results were confirmed in dogs, in tests in which a challenge of dinitrochlorobenzene was used and extensive gingival inflammation dominated by monoculear infiltration resulted in the sensitized animals (68). These investigations suggest that cell-mediated immunity is damaging to the periodontium. The effects of immunosuppression and immunoenhancement on periodontal tissue have been studied in humans (for a review, see 83).

CUMULATIVE IMMUNOLOGICAL–MICROBIOLOGICAL HYPOTHESIS FOR PERIODONTAL DISEASE

Within the limits of our present knowledge of the immunological and microbiological developments during the maternal–fetal and postnatal pre- and posteruptive periods, a cumulative hypothesis has been developed to account for periodontal disease (45). This takes into account the cumulative concept of periodontal disease (78) and has been extended and modified to account for the immunological–microbiological changes from gestation to mature adulthood (Fig. 5). In utero the mother's immune system and her dental plaque affect the fetus both by passive transfer of immunoglobulin G antibodies and by sensitization of lymphocytes (22, 36). These may selectively influence colonization of the sterile mouth of the neonate by microorganisms, as well as the active immune response of the infant. With eruption of the deciduous teeth, the developing dental plaque will be influenced by the oral microbiota and the infant's immunity, and these in turn will affect each other. It is becoming increasingly clear that ecological control of pathogens in dental plaque is exerted through a variety of commensal and antagonistic interactions (77). The

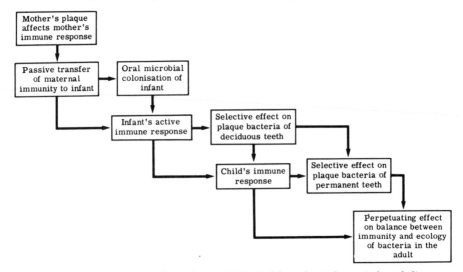

FIG. 5. *Cumulative immunological–microbiological hypothesis for periodontal disease.*

self-perpetuating effect of bacterial plaque on the immune response and of the latter on the bacteria can be enhanced by adjuvants in plaque (45) and maintained by long-lived memory and helper cells (43). The immune response can be suppressed again by agents in the plaque or by suppressor cells (42).

The complex interactions between bacteria and immunity, as well as the balance between helper and suppressor activities, influence the development of bacterial plaque on permanent teeth. The composition of dental plaque in the adult remains fairly constant (8), so that the greatest influence on the development of plaque might be the earliest one, with progressively diminishing effects from infancy to old age. The hypothesis thus suggests that the composition of dental plaque is most influenced during the perinatal period, with cumulative effects during infancy, childhood, and adulthood which become progressively less significant as the oral and dental microbiota and the immune responses become stabilized. If a specific pathogenic organism were to colonize the teeth, say, at the age of 20 years, then the outcome of such an infection would depend on the existing microbiota and the prevailing immune response. This concept of the pathogenesis of periodontitis shifts the onus of antimicrobial prevention of the disease from the middle age to youth.

SUMMARY

The cellular responses to dental bacterial plaque have been demonstrated both at the site of development of periodontal disease and in peripheral blood lymphocytes. Sensitization of lymphocytes occurs under the influence of plaque accumulation, but in addition to specific lymphoproliferative responses and release of soluble mediators, nonspecific T- and B-cell responses occur.

LPS, dextrans, and levans are important components in bacterial plaque, and these may act as immunopotentiating as well as immunosuppressive agents. Polyclonal B-cell mitogenicity may play some part in experimental gingivitis and juvenile periodontitis and may be an important nonspecific determinant in the development of periodontal disease. As gingivitis changes to periodontitis, there appears to be a progressive increase in B cells and a decrease in T cells at the gingival site. However, the relationship between the lymphoid tissues in the gingival focus and those in organized lymph nodes is not known, and it is possible that the gingival focus is the end result of the immune response controlled by the lymph nodes. The demonstration of high-zone and low-zone tolerance to an oral streptococcal antigen which seem to be under immunogenetic control suggests that periodontopathic bacteria might also show a similar high-zone and low-zone tolerance. If the cell-mediated immune responses are damaging, as the evidence would indicate, then low-zone tolerance may prove to be a desired aim in the prevention of periodontal disease.

LITERATURE CITED

1. **Alevy, T. G., and J. R. Battisto**. 1976. Dextran-triggered T cells heighten T- and B-cell reactions to mitogens. Immunology **30**:379–390.
2. **Alevy, T. G., and J. R. Battisto**. 1976. Characterization of dextran-activated T-cell factors. Immunology **30**:391–399.
3. **Attstrom, R.** 1970. Presence of leukocytes in crevices of healthy and chronically inflamed gingivae. J. Periodontal Res. **5**:42–47.
4. **Baird, J. K., V. M. C. Longyear, and D. C. Ellwood**. 1973. Water insoluble and soluble glucans produced by extracellular glycosyltransferases from Streptococcus mutans. Microbios **8**:143–150.
5. **Baker, J. J., S. P. Chan, S. S. Socransky, J. J. Oppenheim, and S. E. Mergenhagen**. 1976. Importance of *Actinomyces* and certain gram-negative anaerobic organisms in the transformation of lymphocytes from patients with periodontal disease. Infect. Immun. **13**:1363–1368.

6. **Battisto, J. R., and F. Pappas**. 1973. Regulation of immunoglobulin synthesis by dextran. J. Exp. Med. **138**:176–193.

7. **Baumhammers, S., and R. E. Stallard**. 1966. Salivary mucoprotein contribution to dental plaque and calculus. Periodontics **4**:229–232.

8. **Bowden, G. H., J. M. Hardie, and G. L. Slack**. 1975. Microbial variations in approximal dental plaque. Caries Res. **9**:253–277.

9. **Budtz-Jorgensen, E., J. Kelstrup, and A. Budtz-Jorgensen**. 1976. Leukocyte migration inhibition by dental plaque antigens as indicated by the capillary tube and agarose technique. J. Periodontal Res. **11**:86–95.

10. **Burckhardt, J. J., B. Guggenheim, and A. Hefti**. 1977. Are Actinomyces viscosus antigens B cell mitogens? J. Immunol. **118**:1460–1465.

11. **Chen, P., J. J. Farrar, J. J. Oppenheim, and S. E. Mergenhagen**. 1977. Mechanism of adjuvant activity of dental plaque: in vitro activation of residual helper T-cell precursors in T-cell deficient murine spleen cell cultures. Infect. Immun. **17**:567–571.

12. **Church, H., and A. E. Dolby**. 1978. The effect of age on the cellular immune response to dentogingival plaque extract. J. Periodontal Res. **13**:120–126.

13. **Coutinho, A., and G. Moller**. 1973. B cell mitogenic properties of thymus independent antigens. Nature (London) New Biol. **245**:12–14.

14. **Diamantstein, T., and E. Blitstein-Willinger**. 1975. Relationship between biological activities of polymers. I. Immunogenicity, C3 activation, mitogenicity for B cells and adjuvant properties. Immunology **29**:1087–1092.

15. **Fine, D. H., L. Tabak, H. Oshram, A. Salkind, and K. Siegel**. 1978. Studies in plaque pathogenicity. I. Plaque collection and limulus lysate screening of adherent and loosely adherent plaque. J. Periodontal Res. **13**:1460–1465.

16. **Gaumer, H. R., P. Holm-Pedersen, and L. E. A. Folke**. 1976. Indirect blastogenesis of peripheral blood leukocytes in experimental gingivitis. Infect. Immun. **13**:1347–1353.

17. **Gershon, R. K**. 1974. T cell control of antibody production. Contemp. Top. Immunobiol. **3**:1–40.

18. **Guggenheim, B**. 1970. Enzymatic hydrolysis and structure of water-insoluble glucan produced by glucosyltransferases from a strain of Streptococcus mutans. Helv. Odontol. Acta **14**(Suppl. 5):89–108.

19. **Guggenheim, B., R. Gaegauf-Zollinger, A. Hefti, and J. J. Burkhardt**. 1981. The effect of cyclosporin A on periodontal disease in rats monoassociated with Actinomyces viscosus Ny 1. J. Periodontal Res. **16**:26–38.

20. **Hadding, U., M. Dierich, W. Konig, M. Limbert, H. U. Schlorlemmer, and D. Bittersuermann**. 1973. Ability of the T cell-replacing polyanion dextran sulfate to trigger the alternate pathway of complement activation. Eur. J. Immunol. **3**:527–529.

21. **Horton, J. E., S. Leikin, and J. J. Oppenheim**. 1972. Human lymphoproliferative reaction to saliva and dental plaque deposits: an in vitro correlation with periodontal disease. J. Periodontol. **43**:522–527.

22. **Horton, J. E., J. J. Oppenheim, S. J. Chan, and J. J. Baker**. 1976. Relationship of transformation of newborn human lymphocytes by dental plaque antigens to the degree of maternal periodontal disease. Cell. Immunol. **21**:153–160.

23. **Horton, J. E., J. J. Oppenheim, and S. E. Mergenhagen**. 1973. Elaboration of lymphotoxin by cultured human peripheral blood leukocytes stimulated with dental plaque deposits. Clin. Exp. Immunol. **13**:383–393.

24. **Horton, J. E., L. G. Raisz, H. A. Simmons, J. J. Oppenheim, and S. E. Mergenhagen**. 1972. Bone resorbing activity in supernatant fluid from cultured peripheral blood leukocytes. Science **177**:793–795.

25. **Hotz, P., B. Guggenheim, and R. Schmid**. 1972. Carbohydrates in pooled dental plaque. Caries Res. **6**:103–121.

26. **Howard, J. G., and B. M. Courtenay**. 1974. Induction of tolerance to polysaccharides in B lymphocytes by exhaustive immunization and during immunosuppression with cyclophosphamide. Eur. J. Immunol. **4**:603–608.

27. **Howard, J. G., and B. M. Courtenay**. 1975. Influence of molecular structure on the tolerogenicity of bacterial dextrans. II. The α1–3 linked epitope of dextran B1355. Immunology **29**:599–610.

28. **Howard, J. G., B. M. Courtenay, and G. Vicari**. 1975. Influence of molecular structure on the tolerogenicity of bacterial dextrans. III. Dissociation between tolerance and immunity to the α1–6 and α1–3 linked epitopes of dextran B1355. Immunology **29**:611–619.

29. **Ivanyi, L**. 1976. Modulation of antigen-induced stimulation of human lymphocytes by LPS. Clin. Exp. Immunol. **23**:385–388.

30. **Ivanyi, L**. 1980. Stimulation of gingival lymphocytes by antigens from oral bacteria, p. 125–134. In T. Lehner and G. Cimasoni (ed.), The borderland between caries and periodontal disease, vol. 2. Academic Press, Inc., New York.

31. **Ivanyi, L., S. J. Challacombe, and T. Lehner**. 1973. The specificity of serum factors in lymphocyte transformation in periodontal disease. Clin. Exp. Immunol. **14**:491–500.

32. **Ivanyi, L., and T. Lehner**. 1970. Stimulation of lymphocyte transformation by bacterial antigens in patients with periodontal disease. Arch. Oral Biol. **14**:1089–1096.

33. **Ivanyi, L., and T. Lehner**. 1971. Lymphocyte transformation by sonicates of dental plaque in human periodontal disease. Arch. Oral Biol. **16**:1117–1121.
34. **Ivanyi, L., and T. Lehner**. 1971. The significance of serum factors in stimulation of lymphocytes from patients with periodontal disease by Veillonella alcalescens. Int. Arch. Allergy Appl. Immunol. **41**:620–627.
35. **Ivanyi, L., and T. Lehner**. 1974. Stimulation of human lymphocytes by B-cell mitogens. Clin. Exp. Immunol. **18**:347–356.
36. **Ivanyi, L., and T. Lehner**. 1977. Interdependence of in vitro responsiveness of cord and maternal blood lymphocytes to antigens from oral bacteria. Clin. Exp. Immunol. **30**:252–258.
37. **Ivanyi, L., J. M. A. Wilton, and T. Lehner**. 1972. Cell-mediated immunity in periodontal disease: cytotoxicity, migration inhibition and lymphocyte transformation studies. Immunology **22**:141–145.
38. **Johnson, A. G., S. Gaines, and M. Landy**. 1956. Studies on the O antigen of Salmonella typhosa. V. Enhancement of antibody response to protein antigens by the purified lipopolysaccharide. J. Exp. Med. **103**:225–246.
39. **Johnston, J. M., and D. B. Wilson**. 1970. Origin of immuno-reactive lymphocytes in rats. Cell. Immunol. **1**:430–444.
40. **Kiger, R. D., W. H. Wright, and H. R. Creamer**. 1974. The significance of lymphocyte transformation responses to various microbial strains. J. Periodontol. **45**:780–785.
41. **Lagrange, P. H., and G. B. Mackaness**. 1975. Effects of bacterial lipopolysaccharide on the induction and expression of cell-mediated immunity. II. Stimulation of the efferent arc. J. Immunol. **144**:447–451.
42. **Lamb, J. R., S. Kontiainen, and T. Lehner**. 1979. Generation of specific T-cell suppressor function induced by *Streptococcus mutans* in monkeys and mice. Infect. Immun. **26**:903–909.
43. **Lamb, J. R., S. Kontiainen, and T. Lehner**. 1980. A comparative investigation of the generation of specific T cell-helper function induced by Streptococcus mutans in monkeys and mice. J. Immunol. **124**:2384–2389.
44. **Lehner, T.** 1977. Immunological responses to bacterial plaque in the mouth. Ciba Found. Symp. **46**(New Series):135–159.
45. **Lehner, T.** 1980. Future possibilities for the prevention of caries and periodontal disease. Br. Dent. J. **149**:318–325.
46. **Lehner, T., S. J. Challacombe, J. M. A. Wilton, and L. Ivanyi**. 1974. The relationship between serum and salivary antibodies and cell-mediated immunity in oral disease in man. Adv. Exp. Med. Biol. **45**:485–495.
47. **Lehner, T., S. J. Challacombe, J. M. A. Wilton, and L. Ivanyi**. 1976. Immunopotentiation by intrinsic microbial plaque and its relationship to oral disease in man. Arch. Oral Biol. **21**:749–753.
47a. **Lehner, T., J. R. Lamb, K. L. Helsh, and R. J. Batchelor**. 1981. Association between HLA-DR antigens and helper cell activity in the control of dental caries. Nature (London) **292**:770-772.
48. **Lehner, T., J. M. A. Wilton, S. J. Challacombe, and L. Ivanyi**. 1974. Sequential cell-mediated immune responses in experimental gingivitis in man. Clin. Exp. Immunol. **16**:481–492.
49. **Lehner, T., J. M. A. Wilton, L. Ivanyi, and J. D. Manson**. 1974. Immunological aspects of juvenile periodontitis (periodontosis). J. Periodontal Res. **9**:261–272.
50. **Lewicki, W. J., L. W. Long, and J. R. Edwards**. 1971. Determination of the structure of broth dextran produced by a cariogenic streptococcus. Carbohydr. Res. **17**:175–182.
51. **Mackler, B. F.** 1975. Plaque dialysate effects on human lymphocyte blastogenesis and inflammatory responses. Arch. Oral Biol. **20**:423–428.
52. **Mackler, B. F., L. C. Altman, S. Wahl, D. L. Rosenstreich, J. J. Oppenheim, and S. E. Mergenhagen**. 1974. Blastogenesis and lymphokine synthesis by T and B lymphocytes from patients with periodontal disease. Infect. Immun. **10**:844–850.
53. **Mackler, B. F., K. B. Frostad, P. B. Robertson, and B. M. Levy**. 1977. Immunoglobulin bearing lymphocytes and plasma cells in human periodontal disease. Lymphoid cells in periodontal disease. J. Periodontal Res. **12**:37–45.
54. **Mackler, B. F., T. L. Waldrop, P. Schur, P. B. Robertson, and B. M. Levy**. 1978. IgC subclasses in human periodontal disease. I. Distribution and incidence of IgC subclass bearing lymphocytes and plasma cells. J. Periodontal Res. **13**:109–119.
55. **McDougall, W. A.** 1974. Plaque studies. IV. Levans in plaque. Aust. Dent. J. **9**:1–15.
56. **McGregor, D. D., and S. P. Logie**. 1974. The mediator of cellular immunity. VII. Localization of sensitized lymphocytes in inflammatory exudates. J. Exp. Med. **139**:1415–1430.
57. **Melvaer, K. L., K. Helgeland, and G. Rolla**. 1974. A charged component in purified polysaccharide preparations from Streptococcus mutans and Streptococcus sanguis. Arch. Oral Biol. **19**:589–595.
58. **Miranda, J. J., H. Zola, and J. G. Howard**. 1972. Studies on immunological paralysis. X. Cellular characteristics of the induction and loss of tolerance to levan (polyfructose). Immunology **23**:843–855.
59. **Nobreus, N., and R. Attstrom**. 1974. Experimental contact hypersensitivity in the gingiva of dogs. J. Periodontal Res. **9**:245–254.
60. **Nobreus, N., R. Attstrom, and J. Egelberg**. 1974. Effect of antithymocyte serum on development of gingivitis in dogs. J. Periodontal Res. **9**:227–235.

61. **Nobreus, N., R. Attstrom, and J. Egelberg.** 1974. Effect of antithymocyte antiserum on chronic gingival inflammation in dogs. J. Periodontal Res. **9:**236–244.
62. **Page, R. C., P. Davies, and A. C. Allison.** 1973. Effects of dental plaque on the production and release of lysosomal hydrolases by macrophages in culture. Arch. Oral Biol. **18:**1481–1495.
63. **Page, R. C., and H. E.. Schroeder.** 1976. Pathogenesis of inflammatory periodontal disease. A summary of current work. Lab. Invest. **33:**235–249.
64. **Patters, M. R., N. Sedransk, and R. J. Genco.** 1977. Lymphoproliferative response during resolution and recurrence of naturally occurring gingivitis. J. Periodontol. **48:**373–380.
65. **Payne, W. A., R. C. Page, A. L. Ogilvie, and W. B. Hall.** 1975. Histopathologic features of the initial and early stages of gingivitis in man. J. Periodontal Res. **10:**51–64.
66. **Reed, M. J., M. E. Neiders, and R.J. Genco.** 1976. Synergistic effects on DNA synthesis in peripheral blood lymphocytes of mitogens and dental plaque sonicates in man and Macaque monkeys. Arch. Oral Biol. **21:**441–445.
67. **Rolla, G., B. Melsen, and T. Sonju.** 1975. Sulphated macromolecules in dental plaque in the monkey Macaca irus. Arch. Oral Biol. **20:**341–343.
68. **Rylander, H., J. Lindhe, and S. Ahlstedt.** 1976. Experimental gingivitis in immunised dogs. J. Periodontal Res. **11:**339–348.
69. **Schroeder, H. E.** 1977. Histopathology of the gingival crevice, p. 43–103. *In* T. Lehner (ed.), The borderland between caries and periodontal disease. Academic Press, London.
70. **Seymour, G. J., H. M. Dockrell, and J. S. Greenspan.** 1978. Enzyme differentiation of lymphocyte subpopulations in sections of human lymph nodes, tonsils and periodontal disease. Clin. Exp. Immunol. **32:**169–178.
71. **Seymour, G. J., and M. F. Greaves.** 1980. Identification of cells expressing T and p28,33 (Ia-like) antigens in sections of human chronic inflammatory periodontal disease. J. Periodontal Res. **15:**453–161.
72. **Shapiro, L., F. M. Lodato, P. R. Courant, and R. E. Stallard.** 1971. Endotoxin determinations in gingival inflammation. J. Periodontol. **42:**591–596.
73. **Skapski, H., and T. Lehner.** 1976. A crevicular washing method for investigating immune components of crevicular fluid in man. J. Periodontal Res. **11:**19–24.
74. **Smith, N. P., and N. P. Lang.** 1977. Lymphocyte blastogenesis to plaque antigens in human periodontal disease. II. The relationship to clinical parameters. J. Periodontal Res. **12:**310–317.
75. **Smith, S., P. H. Bick, G. A. Miller, R. R. Ranney, P. L. Rice, J. H. Lalor, and J. G. Tew.** 1980. Polyclonal B-cell activation: severe periodontal disease in young adults. Clin. Immunol. Immunopathol. **16:**354–366.
76. **Spitznagel, J. K., and A. C. Allison.** 1970. Mode of action of adjuvants: retinol and other lysosome-labilizing agents as adjuvants. J. Immunol. **104:**119–127.
77. **van der Hoeven, J. S.** 1980. Microbial interactions in the mouth, p. 215–226. *In* T. Lehner and G. Cimasoni (ed.), The borderland between caries and periodontal disease, vol. 2. Academic Press, London.
78. **Waerhaug, J.** 1966. Epidemiology of periodontal disease. Review of literature, p. 181–203. *In* S. P. Ramfjord, D. A. Kerr, and M. M. Ash (ed.), World workshop in periodontics. University of Michigan Press, Ann Arbor.
79. **Waldman, H., and A. Munro.** 1975. The inter-relationship of antigenic structure, thymus independence and adjuvanticity. IV. A general model for B-cell induction. Immunology **28:**509–522.
80. **Walker, D. M.** 1977. Lymphocytes and macrophages in the gingiva, p. 185–198. *In* T. Lehner (ed.), The borderland between caries and periodontal disease. Academic Press, London.
81. **Wicken, A. K., and K. W. Knox.** 1975. Lipotechoic acids: a new class of bacterial antigens. Science **187:**1161–1167.
82. **Wilde, G., M. Cooper, and R. C. Page.** 1977. Host tissue response in chronic periodontal disease. VI. The role of cell-mediated hypersensitivity. J. Periodontal Res. **12:**179–196.
83. **Wilton, J. M. A., and T. Lehner.** 1980. Immunological and microbial aspects of periodontal disease. Recent Adv. Clin. Immunol., vol. 2.
84. **Wilton, J. M. A., H. H. Renggli, and T. Lehner.** 1976. The isolation and identification of mononuclear cells from the gingival crevice in man. J. Periodontal Res. **11:**262–268.
85. **Wilton, J. M. A., D. L. Rosenstreich, and J. J. Oppenheim.** 1975. Activation of guinea pig macrophages by bacterial lipopolysacchrarides requires bone marrow derived lymphocytes. J. Immunol. **114:**388–393.
86. **Wood, J. M.** 1967. The amount distribution and metabolism of soluble polysaccharides in human dental plaque. Arch. Oral Biol. **12:**849–858.

Lymphoid Cell Responsiveness and Human Periodontitis

ROY C. PAGE

*Center for Research in Oral Biology and
Departments of Pathology and Periodontics, Health Sciences Center,
University of Washington, Seattle, Washington 98195*

For more than a decade, periodontal research has focused upon the nature of the interaction between bacterial substances and various host defense mechanisms in an effort to understand the basis of the observed tissue destruction and alveolar bone resorption that are characteristic of periodontitis. Since lymphocytes and plasma cells predominate in the diseased tissues in human periodontitis (although this is not the case in many other animal species) (32), a central role for these cells in the pathogenesis has been postulated. The great bulk of periodontal research done in the past decade has focused on this hypothesis. The key questions have related to assessment of the relative importance of cell-mediated versus humoral immunity and hypersensitivity, the specific role of B versus T lymphocytes, whether activation of B cells is a specific antigenic or a nonspecific polyclonal phenomenon, the role of the immune system in tissue destruction, and whether activation of the immune system is protective or detrimental. A wealth of data has been obtained by use of experimental animals, cell culture studies, and human experimentation. Although definitive answers are not available, facts are emerging that give us a clearer picture of the role played by the lymphoid cells.

In a series of reports beginning in 1970, Ivanyi and Lehner and their colleagues (12–14) showed that cultures of peripheral blood mononuclear cells from individuals with gingivitis and moderately severe periodontitis, incubated in vitro in the presence of homogenates of a panel of bacteria from periodontal pockets or of microbial plaque, responded by undergoing blastogenesis and producing lymphokines, whereas comparable cultures from normal control subjects did not respond. Since, at that time, a blastogenic response to antigen preparations by peripheral blood mononuclear cells in culture was considered to be an in vitro correlate of the cell-mediated hypersensitivity reaction and only T cells were thought to produce lymphokines, an important role for T lymphocytes and delayed hypersensitivity in the pathogenesis of chronic gingivitis and periodontitis was postulated. The idea was supported by the observation that administration of levamisole, a drug which stimulates cell-mediated immune responses, promotes the development of gingivitis and aggravates the severity of established gingivitis (15). Additional support was provided by the studies of Wilde, Cooper, and Page (43), who demonstrated that typical early lesions can be created in the gingival tissues of rats and monkeys previously sensitized to skin contact antigens and then challenged at the gingival margin with the same antigen. A specific T-cell mechanism is involved, because sensitization could be transferred to unsensitized animals by means of lymphocytes from the sensitized animals but not by the serum. Additional support was provided by other investigators (18, 21, 34), who reported that cultures of peripheral blood

217

mononuclear cells from individuals undergoing experimental gingivitis exhibit an enhanced blastogenic response.

In spite of the above, other observations appear to argue against an important role for cell-mediated hypersensitivity in periodontitis. First, investigators had thought that only activated T cells produce lymphokines, the mediators of cell-mediated hypersensitivity. However, Mackler et al. (23) showed that substances from plaque bacteria activate both T and B cells and that B lymphocytes are better producers of lymphokines than are T cells; furthermore, in human periodontitis the cell population is predominantly B lymphoctes and plasma cells, not T lymphocytes and macrophages as is the case in delayed hypersensitivity reactions.

The nature of the infiltrating leukocytes in normal gingival tissue and in tissue specimens taken from individuals with gingivitis and periodontitis has been thoroughly studied (24, 37, 38). Normal gingival tissues contain a few T lymphocytes, but B lymphocytes and plasma cells are not seen in significant numbers. As gingivitis develops, there is a two- to threefold increase in the number of lymphocytes in the tissues, and a few plasma cells appear, especially in the periphery of the infiltrate. In mild gingivitis, i.e., early lesions, most of the lymphocytes are T cells. However, as the severity of gingivitis increases, B lymphocytes come to predominate over T lymphocytes, and the number of plasma cells increases. In periodontitis, the number of plasma cells and lymphocytes is much greater than in gingivitis, and the plasma cells outnumber lymphocytes. Most of the lymphocytes (approximately 78%) are B cells. In active lesions large numbers of polymorphonuclear neutrophilic leukocytes are also seen. It is interesting to note that the events occurring in the tissues as a result of successful periodontal therapy appear to be essentially the reverse of those observed during the development of periodontitis (22).

Although lymphoid cells do predominate in the diseased tissues in humans, dogs, and some nonhuman primates, this is not the case in some other animals who develop periodontitis with extensive tissue destruction and tooth exfoliation (32). For example, plasma cells are extremely rare in severely diseased periodontal tissues of marmosets, and plasma cells and lymphocytes are seen only infrequently in periodontal tissues in minks and rodents with periodontal disease. There is a remarkable lack of evidence of lymphoid cell participation in the lesions of rats infected with gram-negative bacteria, and the same is true for animals infected with gram-positive bacteria, at least up to the final stages of the disease. The same can be said for other rodents, particularly mice and hamsters. In all these species as well as in humans, the destructive lesions are characterized by an influx of polymorphonuclear neutrophilic leukocytes and acute inflammation, and the dormant or inactive lesions are characterized by decreased numbers of polymorphonuclear neutrophilic leukocytes and reduced inflammation.

In humans, T cells appear to be important in the day-to-day host response to bacteria and other substances to which the gingiva is exposed. As indicated by the experiments of Ivanyi and Lehner (15) and Wilde et al. (43) and by extensive clinical observations made on immunodeficient and immunosuppressed patients (29, 35), T cells and cell-mediated hypersensitivity may play a role in the development of the early lesion, a mild stage of gingivitis in which tissue damage is reversible and almost negligible, but at all subsequent stages, B lymphocytes and plasma cells predominate and cell-mediated hypersensitivity is not likely to play an important role. In fact, it has been suggested that conversion from a T-cell infiltrate to a B-cell infiltrate is the harbinger of impending tissue destruction and the major event in the conversion of stable established lesions into destructive lesions (39). This is not the case, because established lesions in which B cells and plasma cells predominate can form and remain stable without progression for indefinite periods (31, 36). Indeed, B-cell activity is not essential; in some animals (rodents, minks) periodontitis resulting in tooth exfoliation can occur in the virtual absence of lymphoid cells from the gingival tissue.

Differentiation of lymphocytes in the gingival tissue is driven by substances from bacteria located in the gingival or periodontal pocket. Whether the lymphocytes are activated specifically by bacterial antigens or nonspecifically by bacterial polyclonal activators is an extremely important question for practical as well as conceptual reasons. If activation is monoclonal, specific antibody will be produced in the diseased gingival tissue and immune complex deposition can be expected to occur. Immune complexes have the capacity to activate complement and to interact with polymorphonuclear neutrophilic leukocytes and monocytes in initiating and perpetuating inflammation and tissue destruction. If such specific sensitization is reflected by circulating lymphoid cells, responsiveness of peripheral blood mononuclear cells to plaque-related antigens should relate to the periodontal condition of the cell donor. In contrast, if B-cell activation is polyclonal, large quantities of immunoglobulin with a broad spectrum of antigenic specificities to both plaque-related and non-plaque-related antigens would be produced in the diseased gingiva. Under these conditions, little or no immune complex formation would be expected and the responsiveness of peripheral blood mononuclear cells to activation by substances from plaque bacteria would be unlikely to correlate with periodontal status. This is not to imply that, in the latter case, lymphocytes and plasma cells are unrelated to the observed pathological alterations. Cells activated mitogenically as well as those activated antigenically produce lymphokines such as lymphotoxin, chemotactic factors, and osteoclastic-activating factor, which may be keystones to tissue destruction.

As previously noted, in a series of reports beginning in 1970 Ivanyi and Lehner and their colleagues (12–14) showed that cultures of lymphoid cells from some individuals with gingivitis and periodontitis, incubated in vitro in the presence of homogenates of a panel of bacteria from periodontal pockets or microbial plaque, respond by undergoing blastogenesis and producing lymphokines, whereas comparable cultures from normal control subjects do not so respond to the same homogenates. The observed response was considered to be a specific antigenic response, in contrast to a nonspecific mitogenic response, although evidence to support this assumption was not presented. Cells from individuals with gingivitis and mild-to-moderate periodontitis responded blastogenically, but those from individuals with severe periodontitis failed to respond. Evidence was provided that failure to respond was dependent upon which cell function was measured and upon the presence of modulating factors in the serum (11). Numerous investigators have repeated and extended the original experiments of Ivanyi and Lehner or modifications thereof. The first of these were Horton, Leikin, and Oppenheim (10), who found a direct positive correlation between the magnitude of the blastogenic response by cells from patients with periodontitis to substances from microbial plaque and the presence and severity of gingivitis and periodontitis. A similar positive correlation was reported by Baker et al. (1), and additional confirming observations were reported by Patters et al. (33) and Lang and Smith (19, 42). For reasons that are not clear, in almost all of these experiments, cultures of peripheral blood mononuclear cells from some of the normal control individuals responded blastogenically, whereas cultures of cells from some patients with periodontitis, regardless of the severity of disease, failed to respond.

Another unusual feature of the studies on lymphoid cell responsiveness is that the exact nature of the activating substances does not appear to be critical. In the original experiments of Ivanyi and Lehner (12), whole homogenates of a panel of microorganisms suspected of association with chronic gingivitis or periodontitis, along with nonoral bacteria as controls, were used as activators. Autologous and heterologous microbial plaque and sediment harvested from homogenates of pure cultures of bacteria are, however, equally effective (1, 10, 13). The same is true of soluble extracts from homogenized microbial plaque (10), extracts from previously boiled, homogenized plaque (19, 42), and even whole saliva (10). The picture was further clouded when Ivanyi and Lehner (14) demonstrated that cultures of peripheral blood mononuclear cells from some but not all patients and control subjects respond to B-cell mitogens such as lipopolysaccharide, dextran, and levan.

The results of in vitro studies reported by Budtz-Jörgensen et al. (6) differ somewhat from those of other investigators. These authors assessed the capacity of peripheral blood mononuclear cells from large groups of patients to respond to preparations of plaque bacteria by production of the lymphokine leukocyte migration inhibition factor. Cells from patients with moderate periodontitis reponded to the bacterial preparations, but those from patients with severe periodontitis did not respond to any of the activators. The latter observation differs from that of Lehner (20), who reported a positive response by cells from patients with severe periodontitis when lymphokines such as macrophage migration inhibition factor and cytotoxic factor were measured. Page et al. (30) failed to find differences between normal individuals and patients with adult periodontitis in the magnitude of responsiveness of peripheral blood mononuclear cells to preparations of plaque bacteria, although they did detect differences between normal individuals and those with juvenile periodontitis. Kiger, Wright, and Creamer (16) found no correlation between blastogenesis and any measure of disease status in a group of patients with periodontitis.

The most compelling evidence supporting the idea that the blastogenic responsiveness of peripheral blood mononuclear cells from patients with chronic gingivitis and periodontitis to preparations of bacteria is specifically antigenic, as opposed to polyclonal, comes from three observations, all of which now seem questionable. (i) Blood lymphocytes from umbilical cord, which could not have previously encountered antigens of plaque bacteria, should not respond when exposed to these substances, and they do not. It was assumed that these cells would respond if the preparations contained polyclonal activators. It is now known that preparations of cord blood mononuclear cells contain many potent suppressor T cells, which can suppress or block blastogenic responses to both antigens and mitogens (26, 28, 34, 44). (ii) There is a great deal of variation in blastogenic responsiveness of cells, from patients with periodontitis and control subjects, activated with substances from plaque bacteria. It has been assumed that, if this response were polyclonal, cells from all subjects and patients would respond in a reasonably uniform manner. This assumption too is invalid. Individuals vary greatly from one to another and from time to time in the responsiveness of their lymphocytes to polyclonal activators (8, 14, 17, 25). (iii) Finally, it has been assumed that specific antigenic responses become maximal at 5 days of incubation and polyclonal responses become maximal at 3 days. In cultures established from most but not all periodontitis patients and activated with preparations of plaque bacteria, maximal blastogenesis is seen at 5 to 7 days. It is true that in most experiments using human peripheral blood leukocytes mitogenic responsiveness to plant lectins occurs at around 3 days, whereas that induced with antigenic substances requires 5 days or more. However, in their response to polyclonal activators present in bacteria, they behave very differently. With these substances, the maximal polyclonal response usually is not seen until after 5 to 7 days (17, 25, 41).

Several recent reports indicate that B-cell activation by substances from plaque bacteria is, at least in major part, polyclonal. Periodontally diseased tissue contains very large amounts of immunoglobulin (4, 5, 7), the bulk of which is nonspecific antibody which does not react specifically with antigenic determinants of plaque bacteria or with altered tissue components (5, 7). Bacterial substances from the periodontal pocket have ready access to the diseased gingival tissue. If significant quantities of specific antibody were present, deposits of immune complex should be readily demonstrable. Clagett and Page (7) were unable to demonstrate their presence in significant amounts, in spite of intensive efforts. Although Berglund (3) found small amounts of antibody specific to plaque-related bacterial antigens, it is more significant that he also found in the tissues from all five patients studied antibody specific to the determinants of *Escherichia coli,* which is clearly not an oral bacterium. Along the same lines, Smith et al. (41), using the plaque-forming cell assay, found that human B lymphocytes activated in vitro with preparations of suspected periodontopathogens produced antibody to unrelated antigens, in this case sheep erythrocytes. Thus, it appears that activation of B cells, either within the gingival tissue or in vitro, with substances from pocket or plaque bacteria results in the production of immunoglobulin with a broad spectrum of antibody specificities, as is expected of polyclonal activation.

Banck and Forsgrën (2) found that 18 of 30 bacterial species tested induced mitogenesis in human B-lymphocyte cultures, and Miller et al. (25) and Kunori et al. (17) demonstrated that lipopolysaccharide, a component of all gram-negative bacteria, has a potent mitogenic effect on the B lymphocytes from human peripheral blood. Cells from asymptomatic subjects vary greatly in the magnitude of their response to lipopolysaccharide (17). The suspected periodontopathogens contain potent polyclonal B-cell activators. *Actinomyces viscosus, Fusobacterium,* and *Capnocytophaga* all evoke a strong mitogenic response in murine B cells, and some of these are equally effective in activating peripheral blood mononuclear cells from normal human subjects (9).

The above observations can account in major part for the fact that mononuclear cell cultures from normal individuals with no history of periodontal disease usually respond blastogenically to preparations of plaque bacteria and that the magnitude of the response varies greatly from one individual to another. Other recent data help to account for the very large range of responsiveness observed in cultures from patients with periodontitis and for the fact that cells from many of these individuals do not respond significantly.

Cells from nonresponder patients and control subjects can be made to respond, simply by altering the culture conditions—for example, by increasing the cell concentration (40; J. B. Suzuki, T. Sims, J. A. Clagett, and R. C. Page, Program Abstr. American Association for Dental Research, abstr. 251, 1980). Additional experiments (R. C. Page, S. Osterberg, T. Sims, and B. Williams, Program Abstr. International Association for Dental Research, abstr. 747, 1981) have shown the blastogenic response to autologous plaque and to the bacterial preparations to be significantly greater after completion of initial therapy (curettage) than before treatment. In some cases the magnitude of the increase was two- to fourfold. After surgical therapy, responsiveness to the bacterial preparations either remained high or increased to even higher levels, whereas responsiveness to the patients' own plaque had begun to decrease in some cases. These observations indicate that patients do in fact have the capacity to react systemically to pocket bacteria and that relatively minor manipulations such as probing, scaling, and curettage can affect the magnitude of the blastogenic response in a major way. These facts and the variation from one laboratory to another in the details of patient processing and management may account in major part for the very large variance in the published data on blastogenesis.

In spite of the rather large body of evidence that most if not all of the suspected periodontal pathogens contain potent polyclonal activators of human B cells and that antibody produced locally in the diseased gingiva and by cells activated in vitro with substances from plaque bacteria is polyclonal, some specificity in immune responsiveness to oral microorganisms exists. Several investigators have demonstrated the presence of circulating antibody to oral microorganisms. Recently, there has been a flurry of reports indicating that individuals with certain kinds of periodontitis have high antibody titers to suspected periodontal pathogens (27). For instance, individuals with generalized, rapidly progressive periodontitis have high serum titers of antibody to antigenic determinants of *Bacteroides asaccharolyticus*. In contrast, individuals with juvenile periodontitis have very low titers of antibody to *B. asaccharolyticus* but high antibody titers to antigenic determinants of *Actinobacillus actinomycetemcomitans* (Y4).

Taken together, the data support the idea that the lymphoblast transformation occurring in the gingival tissues of patients with gingivitis and periodontitis is mainly polyclonal and results from mitogens derived from pocket bacteria. The systemic response to these bacterial preparations, as manifested by blastogenesis of peripheral blood mononuclear cells, is probably a mixture of polyclonal activation and specific monoclonal or antigenic stimulation. The ratio of monoclonal to polyclonal activity may depend upon the characteristics of the microorganism involved and the genetic make-up of the responding host.

SUMMARY

For more than a decade, periodontal research has focused upon the role of host defense mechanisms, especially the immune system, in the pathogenesis of periodontitis, and a great deal of information now exists. In humans, the diseased tissues are infiltrated predominantly with B lymphocytes, plasma cells, and neutrophils, not with T lymphocytes and macrophages as is expected at sites affected by delayed hypersensitivity. Preparations of most periodontal pocket bacteria activate B lymphocytes maintained in culture to produce immuno-

immunoglobulin without specificity for the activating substance, and the bulk of immunoglobulin present in periodontally diseased tissues does not exhibit specificity for antigenic determinants of pocket bacteria. Immune complexes are not commonly found within the affected tissue. These are characteristics of polyclonal in contrast to specific monoclonal B-cell activation. In spite of this, the blastogenic responsiveness of peripheral blood lymphoid cells from patients with adult periodontitis becomes enhanced during successful treatment by curettage and scaling, and the serum of patients with some kinds of periodontitis contains high titers of antibody specific for some antigens of pocket bacteria. In addition, immunization of animals appears to confer protection against, not contribute to, periodontal destruction. Immunodeficiency and immunosuppression have little or no effect on the periodontium. In marked contrast, functional abnormalities of the phagocytic leukocytes, especially the neutrophils, uniformly predispose humans and animals to severe, early-onset periodontitis.

ACKNOWLEDGMENTS

Some of the work described was supported by Public Health Service grants DE-02600 and DE-07063 from the National Institute of Dental Research.

LITERATURE CITED

1. **Baker, J. J., S. P. Chan, S. S. Socransky, J. J. Oppenheim, and S. E. Mergenhagen.** 1976. Importance of *Actinomyces* and certain gram-negative anaerobic organisms in the transformation of lymphocytes from patients with periodontal disease. Infect. Immun. 13:1363–1368.
2. **Banck, G., and A. Forsgrën.** 1978. Many bacterial species are mitogenic for human blood B lymphocytes. Scand. J. Immunol. 8:347–354.
3. **Berglund, S. E.** 1971. Immunoglobulins in human gingiva with specificity for oral bacteria. J. Periodontol. 42:546–551.
4. **Brandtzaeg, P.** 1972. Local formation and transport of immunoglobulins related to the oral cavity, p. 116–150. *In* T. MacPhee (ed.), Host resistance to commensal bacteria. Churchill Livingstone, Edinburgh.
5. **Brandtzaeg, P., and K. Tolo.** 1977. Immunoglobulin systems of the gingiva, p. 145-183. *In* T. Lehner (ed.), The borderland between caries and periodontal disease. Academic Press, London.
6. **Budtz-Jörgensen, E., J. Kelstrup, T. D. Funder-Nielsen, and A. M. Knudsen.** 1977. Leukocyte migration inhibition by bacterial antigens in patients with periodontal disease. J. Periodontal Res. 12:21–29.
7. **Clagett, J. A., and R. C. Page.** 1978. Insoluble immune complexes and chronic periodontal disease in man and the dog. Arch. Oral Biol. 23:153–165.
8. **Dorey, F., and J. Zighelboim.** 1980. Immunologic variability in a healthy population. Clin. Immunol. Immunopathol. 16:406–415.
9. **Engel, D., J. A. Clagett, R. C. Page, and B. Williams.** 1977. Mitogenic activity of actinomyces viscosus. I. Effects on murine B and T lymphocytes and partial charcterization. J. Immunol. 118:1466–1471.
10. **Horton, J. E., S. Leikin, and J. J. Oppenheim.** 1972. Human lympho-proliferative reaction to saliva and dental plaque deposits. An in vitro correlation with periodontal disease. J. Periodontol. 43:522–527.
11. **Ivanyi, L., S. Challacombe, and T. Lehner.** 1973. The specificity of serum factors in lymphocyte transformation in periodontal disease. Clin. Exp. Immunol. 14:491–500.
12. **Ivanyi, L., and T. Lehner.** 1970. Stimulation of lymphocyte transformation by bacterial antigens in patients with periodontal disease. Arch. Oral Biol. 15:1089–1096.
13. **Ivanyi, L., and T. Lehner.** 1971. Lymphocyte transformation by sonicates of dental plaque in human periodontal disease. Arch. Oral Biol. 16:1117–1121.
14. **Ivanyi, L., and T. Lehner.** 1974. Stimulation of human lymphocytes by B-cell mitogens. Clin. Exp. Immunol. 18:347–356.
15. **Ivanyi, L., and T. Lehner.** 1977. The effect of levamisole on gingival inflammation in man. Scand. J. Immunol. 6:219–226.
16. **Kiger, R. D., W. H. Wright, and H. R. Creamer.** 1977. The significance of lymphocyte transformation responses to various microbial stimulants. J. Periodontol. 45:780–785.
17. **Kunori, T., O. Ringden, and E. Moller.** 1978. Optimal conditions for polyclonal antibody secretion and DNA synthesis in human blood and spleen lymphocytes by lipopolysaccharide. Scand. J. Immunol. 8:451–458.

18. **Lang, N. P., and F. N. Smith.** 1976. Lymphocyte response to T-cell mitogen during experimental gingivitis in humans. Infect. Immun. **13**:108–113.
19. **Lang, N. P., and F. N. Smith.** 1977. Lymphocytes blastogenesis to plaque antigens in human periodontal disease. I. Populations of varying severity of disease. J. Periodontal Res. **12**:298–309.
20. **Lehner, T.** 1972. Cell-mediated immune responses in oral disease: a review. J. Oral Pathol. **1**:39–58.
21. **Lehner, T., J. M. A. Wilton, S. J. Challacombe, and L. Ivanyi.** 1974. Sequential cell-mediated immune responses in experimental gingivitis in man. Clin. Exp. Immunol. **16**:481–492.
22. **Lindhe, J., R. Parodi, B. Liljenberg, and J. Fornell.** 1978. Clinical and structural alterations characterizing healing gingiva. J. Periodontal Res. **13**:410–424.
23. **Mackler, B. F., L. C. Altman, S. Wahl, D. L. Rosenstreich, J. J. Oppenheim, and S. E. Mergenhagen.** 1974. Blastogenesis and lymphokine synthesis by T and B lymphocytes from patients with periodontal disease. Infect. Immun. **10**:844–850.
24. **Mackler, B. F., K. B. Frostad, P. B. Robertson, and B. Levy.** 1977. Immunoglobulin bearing lymphocytes and plasma cells in human periodontal disease. J. Periodontal Res. **12**:37–45.
25. **Miller, R. A., S. Gartner, and H. S. Kaplan.** 1978. Stimulation of mitogenic responses in human peripheral blood lymphocytes by lipopolysaccharide: serum and T-helper cell requirements. J. Immunol. **121**:2160–2164.
26. **Morito, T., A. D. Bankhurst, and R. C. Williams.** 1979. Studies of human cord blood and adult lymphocyte interactions with in vitro immunoglobulin production. J. Clin. Invest. **64**:990–995.
27. **Mouton, C., P. G. Hammond, J. Slots, and R. J. Genco.** 1981. Serum antibodies to oral *Bacteroides asaccharolyticus (Bacteroides gingivalis):* relationship to age and periodontal disease. Infect. Immun. **31**:182–192.
28. **Oldstone, M. A. B., A. Tishon, and L. Moretta.** 1977. Active thymus derived suppressor lymphocytes in human cord blood. Nature (London) **269**:333–335.
29. **Oshrain, H. I., S. Mender, and I. D. Mandel.** 1979. Periodontal status of patients with reduced immunocapacity. J. Periodontol. **50**:185–188.
30. **Page, R. C., J. A. Clagett, L. D. Engel, G. Wilde, and T. Sims.** 1978. Effects of prostaglandin on the antigen- and mitrogen-griven responses of peripheral blood lymphocytes from patients with adult and juvenile periodontitis. Clin. Immunol. Immunopathol. **11**:77–87.
31. **Page, R. C., and H. E. Schroeder.** 1976. Pathogenesis of chronic inflammatory periodontal disease. A summary of current work. Lab. Invest. **33**:235–249.
32. **Page, R. C., and H. E. Schroeder.** 1981. Periodontitis in man and animals. Karger, Basel.
33. **Patters, M. R., R. J. Genco, M. J. Reed, and P. A. Mashino.** 1976. Blastogenic response of human lymphocytes to oral bacterial antigens: comparison of individuals with periodontal disease to normal and edentulous subjects. Infect. Immun. **14**:1213–1220.
34. **Patters, M. R., N. Sedransk, and R. J. Genco.** 1979. The lymphoproliferative response during human experimental gingivitis. J. Periodontal Res. **14**:269–278.
35. **Robertson, P. B., B. F. Mackler, T. E. Wright, and M. M. Levy.** 1980. Periodontal status of patients with abnormalities of the immune system. II. Observations over a 2-year period. J. Periodontol. **51**:70–72.
36. **Schroeder, H. E., and J. Lindhe.** 1975. Conversion of established gingivitis in dog into destructive periodontitis. Arch. Oral Biol. **20**:775–782.
37. **Seymour, G. J., H. M. Dockerell, and J. S. Greenspan.** 1978. Enzyme differentiation of lymphocytes subpopulations in sections in human lymph nodes, tonsils and periodontal disease. Clin. Exp. Immunol. **32**:169–178.
38. **Seymour, G. J., and J. S. Greenspan.** 1979. The phenotypic characterization of lymphocyte subpopulations in established human periodontitis. J. Periodontal Res. **14**:38–46.
39. **Seymour, G. J., R. N. Powell, and W. I. R. Davies.** 1979. Conversion of a stable T-cell lesion to a progressive B-cell lesion in the pathogenesis of chronic inflammatory periodontal disease: an hypothesis. J. Clin. Periodontol. **6**:267–277.
40. **Sims, T., J. A. Clagett, and R. C. Page.** 1978. Effects of cell concentration and exogenous prostaglandin on the interaction and responsiveness of human peripheral blood lymphocytes. Clin. Immunol. Immunopathol. **12**:150–161.
41. **Smith, S., P. H. Bick, G. A. Miller, R. R. Ranney, P. L. Rice, J. H. Lalor, and J. G. Tew.** 1980. Polyclonal B-cell activation: severe periodontal disease in young adults. Clin. Immunol. Immunopathol. **16**:354–366.
42. **Smith, F. N., and N. P. Lang.** 1977. Lymphocyte blastogenesis to plaque antigens in human periodontal disease. II. The relationship to clinical parameters. J. Periodontal Res. **12**:310–317.
43. **Wilde, G., M. Cooper, and R. C. Page.** 1977. Host tissue response in chronic periodontal disease. IV. The role of cell-mediated hypersensitivity. J. Periodontal Res. **12**:179–196.
44. **Williams, R. C., and S. J. Korsmeyer.** 1978. Studies of human lymphocyte interactions with emphasis on soluble suppressor activity. Clin. Immunol. Immunopathol. **9**:335–349.

Mononuclear Cell-Mediated Alterations in Connective Tissue

SHARON M. WAHL

*Laboratory of Microbiology and Immunology, National Institute of Dental Research,
Bethesda, Maryland 20205*

INTRODUCTION

The inflammatory process invariably leads to some nonspecific tissue injury. Inflammatory cells contribute to this destruction through the release of inflammatory mediators and enzymes. Development of an inflammatory reaction is accompanied by the emigration and accumulation of neutrophils. These neutrophils, which are short-lived end cells, attempt to contain the causative agent and finally disintegrate and release their content of lysosomal enzymes into the surrounding tissues. Following the onset of acute inflammation, neutrophils are gradually replaced by mononuclear phagocytic cells. These cells are of hematogenous origin, and as they traverse the blood capillaries, they assume the morphological and biochemical properties characteristic of mature macrophages.

In chronic inflammation, it is these macrophages which predominate and are the primary source of such mediators of tissue destruction as lysosomal enzymes, plasminogen activator, collagenase, elastase, and prostaglandins. As the inciting inflammatory agent is eliminated, the inflammatory process subsides and tissue repair commences. The repair of the tissue injury, which may be extensive in chronic inflammation, results in irreversible replacement of the original tissue by collagen. The collagen production and fibrosis which serve to repair damaged tissue may, therefore, also cause fibrotic organ damage. Thus, the inflammatory process has a significant influence on local connective tissue metabolism, both in its breakdown and in its reconstruction. Furthermore, certain connective tissue diseases may be the consequence of the inflammatory process. Recent evidence suggests that the inflammatory cells themselves may regulate these extensive changes in the connective tissue through the release of biologically active mediators.

Macrophages not only produce collagenase but also are capable of stimulating the production of this enzyme by synovial cells. Activated monocyte macrophages release a soluble factor (mononuclear cell factor) which can stimulate adherent synovial cells to produce more collagenase and prostaglandin E_2 (PGE_2) (2). Through the release of this factor, macrophages can regulate synovial cell secretion of PGE_2 and collagenase, amplifying the destruction of the extracellular matrix in rheumatoid arthritis.

DESTRUCTION OF CONNECTIVE TISSUE IN INFLAMMATION

The processes of cellular immunity are the basis for the development of certain chronic inflammatory diseases. These chronic inflammatory lesions, which are characterized by an infiltrate of mononuclear cells, may be destructive to the surrounding connective tissue as in rheumatoid arthritis and periodontal disease. Although cellular immune mechanisms have been

TABLE 1. *Functions of activated macrophages*

Adherence and spreading	Monokine synthesis
Transport and metabolism of glucose	Lymphocyte-activating factor
Respiratory activity	Mononuclear cell factor
Phagocytosis	Fibroblast chemotactic factor
Acid hydrolase activity	Fibroblast-activating factor
Cathepsins	Colony-stimulating factor
Amylase	Interferon
Lipase	Complement components
β-Glucuronidase	C1, 4, 2, 3, 5
Peroxidase	Factor B
Ribonuclease	Factor D
Deoxyribonuclease	Properdin
Acid phosphatase	C3b inactivator
Lysozyme	β1H
Secretion of neutral proteases	Prostaglandin synthesis
Plasminogen activator	Thromboxane
Elastase	Leukotriene
Collagenase	Hydroxy-eicosatetraeneoic acids
Reactive metabolites of oxygen	Endogenous pyrogen
Superoxide	Fibronectin
Hydrogen peroxide	Enzyme inhibitors
Hydroxyl radical	Plasmin inhibitors
	α2 macroglobulin

implicated in the pathogenesis of these lesions, it is not known how the pathways for connective tissue degradation are initiated. Sensitized lymphocytes when activated by specific antigen release a variety of soluble products (lymphokines) involved in the expression of the effector functions of cell-mediated immunity. The changes in the surrounding connective tissue may be mediated by the local production and release of these lymphokine molecules. Although antigen activation of lymphocytes may initiate the process, the destruction is actually brought about by inflammatory macrophages through the production and release of proteolytic and tissue-degrading enzymes. Lymphokine-like molecules have been isolated from chronically inflamed tissue such as the synovium (10) in which destructive changes are occurring. Conversely, synovitis can be induced by the injection of lymphokines into normal joints of experimental animals (1). That lymphocytes can attract macrophages to an inflammatory site through the release of a chemotactic factor, hinder their migration away from the inflammatory foci by the secretion of macrophage inhibitory factor, and activate the macrophages (macrophage-activating factor) to generate neutral proteases including collagenase (13) implicates such a pathway in connective tissue destruction. Collagenase is the rate-limiting enzyme in the degradation of collagen. Furthermore, the breakdown of collagen results in the release of products chemotactic for macrophages (8), promoting further accumulation of macrophages. The lymphokine-enhanced production of acid hydrolases (6) also enables degradation of collagen, basement membrane, and other components of connective tissue.

In addition to the lymphocyte-driven pathway of collagenase release, the macrophages can also be activated by bacteria or bacterial products such as lipopolysaccharide endotoxin and the synthetic adjuvant N-acetyl-muramyl-L-alanyl-D-isoglutamine (15). Not only do these activated macrophages produce collagenase, but also they acquire elevated levels of many enzymes and inflammatory mediators (Table 1) which can contribute to the degradation of surrounding connective tissues. The inflammatory mediator PGE_2, a product of activated macrophages (Fig. 1), contributes to the inflammation (4) and also regulates the production of collagenase (12). Prostaglandins act synergistically with endotoxin to stimulate macrophage secretion of collagenase. This synergistic effect has been analyzed in cultures of macrophages obtained from guinea pig peritoneal exudates. Blockage of PGE_2 synthesis by the prostaglandin synthetase inhibitor indomethacin inhibits collagenase production (Fig. 1b). Enzyme synthesis can be restored by adding exogenous PGE_2 to the indomethacin-treated macrophages. Furthermore, in the absence of PGE_2, the addition of pharmacological agents which directly elevate macrophage levels of cyclic adenosine $3',5'$-monophosphate (Fig. 1a) can reinstate collagenase synthesis. When macrophage cultures are activated with lipopolysaccharide and no indomethacin is added, these cyclic adenosine $3',5'$-monophosphate active agents effectively enhance collagenase production. Thus, the pathway for collagenase stimulation (Fig. 1) appears to require a primary signal (lipopolysaccharide, macrophage-activating factor, N-acetyl-muramyl-L-

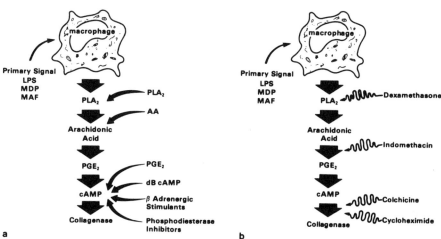

FIG. 1. *Regulation of macrophage collagenase production. The pathway for collagenase synthesis requires a primary signal to the macrophage which stimulates phospholipase A_2 (PLA_2) activity, resulting in an increased supply of arachadonic acid (AA) which enables enhanced PGE_2 production. PGE_2 stimulates cyclic adenosine $3',5'$-monophosphate (cAMP), which then modulates the synthesis of collagenase. (a) Positive regulation of collagenase synthesis. By increasing PGE_2 levels, either by adding PLA_2 or exogenous AA, collagenase synthesis can be increased. Similarly, agents which elevate intracellular levels of cAMP in the presence of the primary signal will modulate enhanced collagenase output by the macrophages. (b) Negative regulation of collagenase synthesis. Interference with the chain of events in collagenase synthesis results in decreased macrophage production of the enzyme. Dexamethasone inhibits PLA_2. Indomethacin blocks PGE_2 synthesis. Colchicine interrupts the sequence of events after PGE_2 synthesis, and cycloheximide, which does not affect PGE_2, blocks protein synthesis. LPS, lipopolysaccharide; MDP, N-acetyl-muramyl-L-alanyl-D-isoglutamine; MAF, macrophage-activating factor.*

alanyl-D-isoglutamine, etc.) which initiates PGE_2 synthesis, causing an enhancement of intracellular cyclic adenosine 3′,5′-monophosphate, which then serves as a trigger for the biosynthetic pathway leading to collagenase production.

INHIBITION OF MACROPHAGE COLLAGENASE PRODUCTION BY ANTI-INFLAMMATORY AGENTS

In addition to indomethacin, which is a nonsteroidal anti-inflammatory drug, collagenase synthesis can be inhibited by other anti-inflammatory agents. The anti-inflammatory steriod dexamethasone inhibits PGE_2 production, presumably by stimulating the release of inhibitors of phospholipase A_2 (3). Steroidal inhibition of PGE_2 production consequently blocks the production of collagenase (Fig. 1b). The ability of dexamethasone to inhibit phospholipase A_2, causing a decrease in PGE_2 levels, can be reversed through the addition of exogenous phospholipase A_2 to the macrophages. This phospholipase A_2-mediated reversal of the inhibition of PGE_2 synthesis in dexamethasone-treated cultures also resulted in the restoration of collagenase synthesis (L. Wahl et al., manuscript in preparation).

In contrast, colchicine, which is also used as an anti-inflammatory agent, does not abrogate PGE_2 production, but does inhibit the production of collagenase. The ability of colchicine to interfere with collagenase production may be a consequence of its microtubule-disruptive potential, since lumicolchicine, a derivative of colchicine which does not affect microtubules, did not interrupt collagenase production or release (Wahl et al., manuscript in preparation). Colchicine may inhibit the transmission of a microtubule-dependent activation signal which occurs subsequent to PGE_2 production, rather than inhibiting the release of collagenase as might be anticipated. Evidence to support such a mechanism stems from the inability to extract collagenase from within cells which have been treated with lipopolysaccharide and colchicine and which are not elaborating collagenase into the medium. Additionally, colchicine needed to be added early after lipopolysaccharide stimulation to effectively block collagenase synthesis and was not effective when added during the time of collagenase release. Thus, it appears that, through their influence on collagenase or prostaglandins, or both, certain anti-inflammatory agents may ameliorate the tissue destructive potential of the inflammatory response.

In addition to collagenase, which is a primary mediator in the degradation of collagen, activated macrophages have an armamentarium of destructive agents including the lysosomal acid hydrolases (Table 1) which can function intracellularly or alternatively can be secreted to degrade collagen, basement membrane, and other constituents of the connective tissue. The activated macrophages also secrete oxidizing agents which can further destroy connective tissue. These oxidizing agents, including superoxide, hydrogen peroxide, and hydroxyl radicals (Table 1), can oxidize enzyme thiol groups, disrupt proteins, lipids, and nucleic acids, and precipitate free radical formation. By such mechanisms, activated macrophages can propagate the damage to surrounding tissue structures.

FIBROSIS AND INFLAMMATION

During the inflammatory response, the appearance of fibroblasts becomes evident. Little is known of the factors that attract fibroblasts to inflammatory lesions and regulate their functions. At the site of a nonspecifically induced inflammatory response, macrophages are the most apparent inflammatory cell. Macrophages have been shown to be instrumental in tissue repair after injury and inflammation. Depletion of macrophages in an experimental animal inhibits wound repair (5) as is evidenced by decreased fibroblast numbers and fibrosis. This suggested that macrophages must influence recruitment and division of fibroblasts as well as collagen synthesis at an inflammatory site. Recent studies have indeed shown macrophages to be capable of contributing to the appearance of enhanced numbers of fibroblasts through the release of soluble factors which influence fibroblast function. When activated, macrophages not only generate enhanced levels of enzymes, but also manufacture and secrete biologically active mediators classified as monokines (Table 1). One of these monokines is capable of initiating fibroblast-directed migration (11). Supernatants from macrophages activated in vitro by N-acetyl-muramyl-L-alanyl-D-isoglutamine or lipopolysaccharide were assayed for their ability to attract dermal fibroblasts across a filter with 8-μm pores. Activated macrophages released a soluble mediator which caused fibroblasts to migrate toward the highest concentration of the macrophage supernatant (Fig. 2). Production of this macrophage-derived chemotactic factor for fibroblasts required activation of the macrophages in vivo or in vitro and de novo protein synthesis. This fibroblast chemotactic activity could be removed from the macrophage supernatants by a fibronectin-specific affinity column and was inhibited in the presence of antibodies to fibronectin. Restoration of chemotactic activity in the depleted macrophage supernatants could be achieved by the addition of exogenous fibronectin. Macrophage supernatants were also found to contain fibronectin by an enzyme-linked immunoassay for fibronectin. These findings indicated that activated macrophages release a chemoattractant for fibroblasts which appears to be the glycoprotein fibronectin. Fibronectin has numerous other biological activities (17), including the promotion of cellular aggregation and cell–substrate adhesiveness. It serves as an opsonin and interacts with macromolecules such as collagen, fibrin, and heparin.

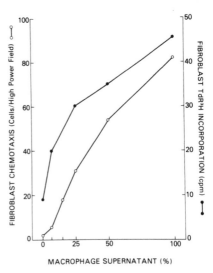

FIG. 2. *Macrophage production of fibroblast chemotactic factor and fibroblast activation factor. Adherent macrophage cultures were stimulated with lipopolysaccharide and the supernatants were assayed for their ability to attract fibroblasts through an 8-μm pore filter in a modified Boyden chamber (11). Data represent the mean of cells which have migrated through the filter per high-power field of triplicate filters. Portions of the supernatants were dialyzed and tested for stimulation of tritiated thymidine (TdR^3H) incorporation by quiescent dermal fibroblasts (14). Data represent the mean counts per minute of triplicate cultures.*

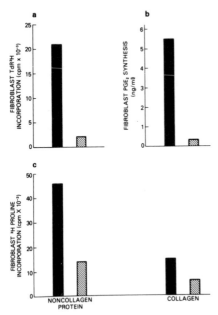

FIG. 3. *Lymphocyte regulation of fibroblast function. Supernatants from control (□) and antigen-activated (■) sensitized, T-enriched lymphocytes were prepared and added to quiescent dermal fibroblast cultures. The fibroblasts were then assayed for: (a) fibroblast proliferation (after 48 h the fibroblast cultures were pulsed with 1 µCi of tritiated thymidine [TdR³H] per ml and processed for determination of TdR³H incorporation into deoxyribonucleic acid [counts per minute] [15]), (b) PGE₂ synthesis (media from 24-h fibroblast cultures were harvested and assayed for PGE₂ by direct radioimmunoassay [12]), and (c) collagen and noncollagen protein syntheses (after 20 h of incubation with lymphocyte supernatants, 2 µCi of [³H]proline per ml was added to the fibroblast cultures for 6 h, and collagen and noncollagen protein syntheses were determined on the basis of susceptibility to collagenase [14]).*

The production of fibronectin by activated macrophages may thus serve as an inflammatory mediator which, in addition to its other functions, can recruit fibroblasts to an area of damaged tissue where they can proliferate and form the scar tissue necessary for tissue repair.

In addition to this mediator of fibroblast chemotaxis, the supernatants of activated macrophages contain a fibroblast-activating factor (14) which stimulates quiescent dermal fibroblasts into active proliferation (Fig. 2). Fibroblast proliferation was determined both by an increased uptake of tritiated thymidine into trichloroacetic acid-precipitable deoxyribonucleic acid and by an increase in numbers of fibroblast cells in culture. This growth-promoting activity was found in the supernatants of macrophage cultures within the first 4 h after stimulation and continued to increase over a 48- to 72-h period. The early appearance and the sustained increase in activity, coupled with the inability of cycloheximide to totally block its appearance, suggested that a preformed or precursor molecule was initially secreted after activation, with subsequent synthesis of additional factor. Once released, this molecule, which has been characterized in the guinea pig as a protein with a molecular weight of 40,000 to 60,000, induces fibroblast proliferation.

Production of this fibroblast-activating factor was independent of prostaglandin regulation, since indomethacin did not block its appearance. Although the same primary signal may initiate production of both collagenase (Fig. 1) and fibroblast-activating factor (Fig. 4) by macrophages, the subsequent chains of events leading to their release may be divergent. In addition to the ineffectiveness of indomethacin in blocking production of fibroblast-activating factor, the anti-inflammatory steroid dexamethasone also does not interrupt elaboration of fibroblast-activating factor, whereas it does block collagenase (Fig. 1b). This dichotomy may be of consequence, since interruption of the inflammatory process by anti-

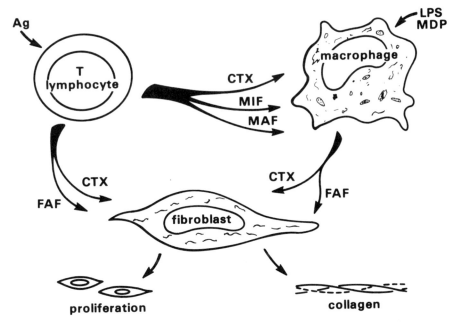

FIG. 4. *Schematic representation of the regulation of fibroblast function by lymphocyte and macrophage mediators. Lymphocytes activated by specific antigen (Ag) produce a chemotactic factor (CTX) for fibroblasts and a fibroblast-activating factor (FAF) which controls fibroblast proliferation and protein synthesis. The lymphocytes also produce lymphokines, including macrophage migration inhibitory factor, macrophage-activating factor, and CTX which attract and activate macrophages, thereby amplifying the response. Macrophages, in turn, whether activated by lymphokines or by agents such as lipopolysaccharide (LPS), also produce CTX and FAF molecules which recruit and stimulate fibroblasts, resulting in the fibrotic response associated with the inflammatory reaction.*

inflammatory drugs minimizes tissue destruction, yet enables repair to proceed in terminating the inflammation.

Thus, the increased numbers of fibroblasts which become evident as an inflammatory process progresses may be accounted for by migration and recruitment, as well as by enhanced proliferation. Macrophages which have been activated can mediate these fibroblast responses and may be a primary source of such stimuli, especially in a nonspecifically induced inflammatory lesion. However, in an antigen-triggered delayed hypersensitivity response, another level of control may contribute to the fibrotic process. T lymphocytes, when activated by specific antigen, not only produce lymphokines (macrophage inhibitory factor, macrophage-activating factor, colony-stimulating factor) which subsequently act upon macrophages to activate them, but the lymphocytes also produce lymphokines which can directly affect fibroblast behavior (Fig. 3). Human lymphocytes produce a soluble molecule (molecular weight, 22,000) which directly causes fibroblast migration (9). Another lymphokine, fibroblast-activating factor, induces fibroblasts to proliferate (14; Fig. 3). Thus, lymphocytes can directly orchestrate the fibroplasia which accompanies a cellular immune response through the release of chemotactic and proliferative factors, or it can amplify the response through the macrophage circuit (Fig. 4). Production of macrophage-active lymphokines enables the macrophage, in turn, to generate those agents in its repertoire which can effectively regulate fibroblast behavior. By these pathways, the inflammatory cells may be instrumental in the accumulation of fibroblasts needed to form the scar tissue and repair the tissue damaged as a consequence of the inflammatory process.

Formation of the collagen which forms the scar tissue appears also to be enhanced by products of activated mononuclear cells (14; Fig. 3). In the presence of either activated lymphocyte or macrophage supernatant factors, fibroblasts can generate enhanced levels of protein, including collagen. This elevation in protein synthesis appears to be independent of fibroblast proliferation and concurrent with elevations in the release of PGE_2 (Fig. 3). The mononuclear cell products appear generally to stimulate enhanced metabolic levels in the responder fibroblasts. Fibrosis associated with inflammatory lesions may be the consequence of lymphokines and monokines that cause fibroblast migration, proliferation, and protein synthesis, all of which are essential in the fibrotic response. By their ability to secrete collagenase, the macrophages may also participate in remodeling this newly formed collagen. These in vitro findings indicate that lymphocytes and macrophages may have decisive roles in determining the amount of tissue injury, the reversibility and extent of fibrosis, and the degree of pathological manifestations.

REGULATION OF FIBROSIS IN
CHRONIC INFLAMMATORY DISEASES

The in vitro ability of lymphocyte and macrophage mediators to initiate fibroplasia and collagen synthesis implicated such a mechanism in the fibrotic repair of injured tissue associated with wounds or acute inflammation, and also in the extensive and often pathophysiological fibrosis which may occur in chronic inflammatory lesions. Granulomas represent chronic inflammatory responses that often are associated with extensive fibrosis. Granulomatous diseases of diverse etiologies, including tuberculosis, schistosomiasis, rheumatoid arthritis, sarcoidosis, and silicosis, are characterized as complex inflammatory responses to tissue injury induced by non-biodegradable agents. Granulomas are mediated through the accumulation and proliferation of monocytes, epithelioid cells, giant cells, lymphocytes, and fibroblasts. The formation of granulomas depends upon the maturation and activation of the mononuclear phagocytic system, and many of these granulomas may involve the development of cellular immune reactions which initiate additional recruitment and activation of monocytes through the lymphokines produced by T cells in response to the slowly degradable antigens. One such hypersensitivity granuloma is found in schistosomiasis, which leads to extensive fibrosis. It is this irreversible fibrotic replacement of liver parenchyma which is the major component of the pathology and morbidity of schistosomiasis. Recent evidence has shown that the constituent cells of the granuloma can modulate the fibrotic course of this disease (16). Granulomas were isolated from the livers of *Schistosoma mansoni*-infected mice. The granulomas were cultured, and the soluble products released from these granulomas were assayed for their influence on fibroblasts. Souble products from the granulomas, which contained primarily lymphocytes and macrophages, were found to stimulate significant proliferation of fibroblasts in culture.

It appears that this mechanism of inflammatory cell-mediated regulation of fibroblast function may be operational in the intact inflammatory foci. Further analysis of specific cellular sources of fibroblast-activating factor in the granuloma are in progress. Granulomas serve to sequester and degrade the foreign body which provoked the response. Finally, collagen production and fibrosis terminate the inflammaton. Although fibrosis is a normal repair process following tissue injury, in chronic inflammation, the irreversible fibrosis can lead to pathophysiological organ damage. Since these host responses to an irritant or antigen resulting in fibroplasia and collagen secretion may have deleterious consequences, it is important to understand the mechanisms leading to such fibrosis as a preliminary step in modulating the potentially harmful outcome of such a response.

In another chronic inflammatory lesion, periodontal disease, it appears that bacterial agents initiate the sequence of inflammation, bone loss, and connective tissue destruction around the teeth. In addition to the destruction of gum tissue by bacterial and inflammatory cell enzymes, histological evidence suggests that fibroblast proliferation and granulation tissue also occur in the gingival tissues (7). Because of the difficulty in obtaining cellular components of this inflammatory lesion, the contributions of the cell populations in the local tissue reaction have not been dissected. However, it is possible that the lymphocytes and macrophages in these inflammatory foci also contribute to the fibroplasia through the release of soluble, biologically active mediators.

SUMMARY

Although additional effector mechanisms are surely involved, it appears that lymphocytes and macrophages may consititute one important pathway in causing the alterations in connective tissue associated with inflammation. Macrophages involved in the host's defense against microbial and other pathogens may coincidently destroy surrounding connective tissue. This tissue destruction appears to be the consequence of the release of macrophage lysosomal enzymes, prostaglandin, and neutral proteases, including collagenase. If the inflammation has an immunological basis, the sensitized lymphocytes release lymphokines which can act as an additional trigger for setting in motion macrophage tissue destruction. As the inciting inflammatory agent is sequestered or degraded, tissue repair begins, and it appears that lymphocytes and macrophages can regulate this process through the release of lymphokines and monokines. These mediators may be responsible for expanding the fibroblast population by mobilizing fibroblasts from adjacent connective tissue and by stimulating fibroblast proliferation. Collagen synthesis is enhanced, resulting in repair and scar formation. In chronic lesions, the continued triggering of lymphocytes and macrophages may result in extensive scarring and impaired function. These conditions may be the expression of defective cellular control mechanisms.

LITERATURE CITED

1. **Andreis, M., P. Stastny, and M. Ziff.** 1974. Experimental arthritis produced by injection of mediators of delayed hypersensitivity. Arthritis Rheum. **17**:537–551.
2. **Dayer, J. M., J. Bréard, L. Chess, and S. M. Krane.** 1979. Participation of monocyte-macrophages and lymphocytes in the production of a factor which stimulates collagenase and prostaglandin release by rheumatoid synovial cells. J. Clin. Invest. **64**:1386.

3. **Hirata, F., E. Schiffman, K. Venkatasubramanian, D. Salomon, and J. Axelrod.** 1980. A phospholipase A_2 inhibitory protein in rabbit neutrophils induced by glucocorticoids. Proc. Natl. Acad. Sci. U.S.A. **77:**2533–2536.
4. **Kuehl, F. A., and R. W. Egan.** 1980. Prostaglandins, arachidonic acid and inflammation. Science **210:**978–984.
5. **Leibovich, S. J., and R. Ross.** 1975. The role of the macrophage in wound repair. A study with hydrocortisone and antimacrophage serum. Am. J. Pathol. **78:**71–100.
6. **Nathan, C. F., H. W. Murray, and Z. A. Cohn.** 1980. The macrophage as an effector cell. N. Engl. J. Med. **303:**622–626.
7. **Page, R. C., and H. E. Schroeder.** 1973. Biochemical aspects of the connective tissue alterations in inflammatory gingival and periodontal disease. Int. Dent. J. **23:**455–463.
8. **Postlethwaite, A. E., and A. H. Kang.** 1976. Collagen and collagen peptide-induced chemotaxis of human blood monocytes. J. Exp. Med. **143:**1299–1307.
9. **Postlethwaite, A. E., R. Snyderman, and A. H. Kang.** 1976. The chemotactic attraction of human fibroblasts to a lymphocyte-derived factor. J. Exp. Med. **144:**1188–1203.
10. **Stastny, P., M. Rosenthal, M. Andreis, and M. Ziff.** 1975. Lymphokines in the rheumatoid joint. Arthritis Rheum. **18:**237–243.
11. **Tsukamoto, Y., W. E. Helsel, and S. M. Wahl.** 1981. Macrophage production of fibronectin, a chemoattractant for fibroblasts. J. Immunol. **127:**673–678.
12. **Wahl, L. M., C. E. Olsen, A. L. Sandberg, and S. E. Mergenhagen.** 1977. Prostaglandin regulation of macrophage collagenase production. Proc. Natl. Acad. Sci. U.S.A. **74:**4955–4958.
13. **Wahl, L. M., S. M. Wahl, S. E. Mergenhagen, and G. R. Martin.** 1975. Collagenase production by lymphokine-activated macrophages. Science **187:**261–263.
14. **Wahl, S. M., and L. M. Wahl.** 1981. Modulaton of fibroblast growth and function by monokines and lymphokines. Lymphokines **2:**179–201.
15. **Wahl, S. M., L. M. Wahl, J. B. McCarthy, L. Chedid, and S. E. Mergenhagen.** 1979. Macrophage activation by mycobacterial water soluble compounds and synthetic muramyl dideptide. J. Immunol. **122:**2226–2231.
16. **Wyler, D. J., S. M. Wahl, and L. M. Wahl.** 1978. Hepatic fibrosis in schistosomiasis: egg granulomas secrete fibroblast stimulatory factor in vitro. Science **202:**438–440.
17. **Yamada, K. M.** 1980. Fibronectin: transformation-sensitive cell surface protein. Lymphokine Rep. **1:**231–254.

Periodontal Diseases and Neutrophil Abnormalities

T. E. VAN DYKE, M. J. LEVINE, AND R. J. GENCO

Departments of Oral Biology and Periodontology and
The Periodontal Disease Clinical Research Center,
State University of New York at Buffalo School of Dentistry, Buffalo, New York 14226

INTRODUCTION

The tissues of the periodontium are in constant contact with a wide variety of microorganisms that colonize the tooth and mucosal surfaces. The primary host resistance factor preventing overwhelming infection is the phagocytic cell, especially the neutrophil or polymorphonuclear leukocyte. This is true of resistance to infection by many organisms, as demonstrated by the high incidence of bacterial infection and severe morbidity in individuals with impaired neutrophil function. Two general questions are posed which will serve as the framework for this review of the role of the neutrophil: (i) What are the specific functions of the neutrophil? (ii) What happens when these functions are impaired?

HOW DOES THE NEUTROPHIL FUNCTION?

Accumulation of neutrophils in the connective tissue and junctional epithelium of the periodontium is a characteristic feature of chronic periodontal disease (24). Upon leaving the circulation, the neutrophil has to locate, identify, ingest, and kill the invading microorganisms. The specific steps in this process are as follows.

Location: chemotaxis. The first suggestion that phagocytic cells are specifically attracted by bacteria or bacterial products was made in 1887 by Metchnikoff (20). Dold, in 1914, demonstrated that contact between serum and bacteria produced chemotactic activity (11). More recently, considerable effort has been directed toward the identification and characterization of agents which attract neutrophils. Ward et al. (37) studied the production of chemotactic factors by bacteria and found that dialyzable small-molecular-weight molecules produced by various strains of staphylococci, streptococci, pneumococci, and gram-negative organisms were chemotactic. In fact, very few of the organisms tested did not elaborate some chemotactic factor. Schiffman et al. (27) partially characterized chemotactic factors from a strain of *Escherichia coli* and found them to be small-molecular-weight peptides containing aspartic acid, serine, glutamic acid, alanine, and glycine residues.

Subsequently, a series of small formyl-methionyl peptides were synthesized and shown to be potent chemoattractants for neutrophils and macrophages (28). Formylmethionine was chosen because it is a compound characteristic of procaryotic metabolism. Since eucaryotic cells initiate protein synthesis with N-formylated methionine, it was reasoned that the chemotactic bacterial factors could be explained in part by these molecules. The synthesis of these peptides laid the groundwork for rapid advances in the study of neutrophil functions.

Activation of the complement system by either the classical or alternate pathways can cause the production of chemotactically active proteins from serum. In humans, complement activation by substances such as antigen-antibody complexes or endotoxin lead to the generation of the fragments C5a and C567, which are chemotactic (see 25 for review). Additionally, chemotactic activity is generated by Hageman factor (factor XII) activation. Kallikrein, plasminogen activator, and fibrin degradation products are also known to be chemotactic (see 16 for review). Other immunocompetent cells of the lymphocyte series elaborate chemotactic lymphokines (1), and the neutrophil itself elaborates a chemotactic factor (10).

To generate motion, the mature neutrophil contains in its cytoplasm a cytoskeleton composed of microtubules and microfilaments which is believed to be the mechanical apparatus through which directed migration occurs. Microfilaments, which are readily observed in subcortical regions, particularly in lamellopodia of advancing cells, are thought to provide the "muscle" for cell movement (31). Microtubules impart directionality. Hence, the neutrophil responds to a concentration gradient of chemotactic factor with directed movement toward the source of that factor. A more detailed analysis of chemotaxis follows later in this paper.

Identification and ingestion: phagocytosis. The neutrophil does not recognize all foreign objects as such because of their surface properties. Often microbes, especially pathogenic strains, have antiphagocytic components on their surface. These antiphagocytic components are neutralized by the binding of specific immunoglobulin G antibody or the complement fragment C3b on the particle surface (opsonization). By having specific receptors for the Fc portion of immunoglobulin G and C3b (30) on its surface, the neutrophil can now identify those opsonized substances. The physiochemical properties of the particle are also changed. As it becomes more hydrophobic, the charge repulsion between phagocyte and particle is reduced (36).

The mechanism by which neutrophils ingest microbes and enclose them in phagosomes is presumably membrane movement around the particle, resulting from the contraction of microfilaments against a microtubule-stabilized cell skeleton. A local increase in membrane fluidity accompanies these phenomena and is thought to result from the interaction of the cell surface with specific opsonic molecules (13).

Bactericidal activity. The ingestion of a microbe is associated with the release of granule contents and a burst of oxidative metabolism. The contents of the granules and the products of oxidative metabolism are secreted into the phagosome and also extracellularly. This is believed to be triggered by the interaction of chemotactic factors and opsonins with specific receptors on the cell surface. The oxidative burst is characterized by increased oxygen consumption by the chemotaxis and increased activity of the hexose monophosphate shunt (30). The active metabolites of oxygen that are produced, including superoxide, hydroxyl radical, hydrogen peroxide, and singlet oxygen, combine with granule contents (myeloperoxidase, H_2O_2, and halide ions) to form a potent microbicidal system (17).

NEUTROPHIL DYSFUNCTION AND PERIODONTAL DISEASE

The role of the neutrophil in periodontal disease is suggested by the finding of severe periodontitis in patients with impaired neutrophil function. Humans and animals with depressed neutrophil function such as those with cyclic neutropenia (9), drug-induced agranulocytosis (5), the Chediak–Higashi syndrome (14, 33), the "lazy leukocyte syndrome" (21), and diabetes mellitus (15, 22) show gingival inflammation, severe loss of alveolar bone supporting the teeth, and often ulceration of the gingiva and oral mucosa. Further evidence for the protective role of the neutrophil in periodontal disease comes from the study of patients with localized juvenile periodontitis (LJP), most of whom have depressed neutrophil chemotaxis (7, 8, 18, 34) and depressed neutrophil phagocytosis (7). In most of these patients monocyte chemotaxis appears normal (7), although occasional patients exhibit depressed monocyte as well as neutrophil chemotaxis (12).

Evidence for the participation of the neutrophil in protection against the potentially periodontopathogenic microflora in animals comes from the experiments of Ättstrom and Schroeder (3). They showed that in normal dogs subgingival plaque develops in the gingival sulcus and proceeds along the root surface at a relatively slow rate. However, in dogs made neutropenic by the administration of antineutrophil serum, bacteria extended more rapidly into the sulcus and along the root surface. Although these experiments lasted only a few days, they point to a role for the neutrophil in suppression of apical migration of subgingival plaque.

Neutrophils may also play a role in tissue destruction, particularly subsequent to secretion of their lysosomal enzymes, many of which can destroy tissues (32), as is seen in chronic, long-standing disease where etiological factors persist. The bulk of evidence obtained from the study of patients with neutrophil disorders and severe periodontal disease suggests that the net effect of neutrophils in periodontal disease is protective; however, in exerting their protective effects, extracellular granule contents and oxygen radicals may contribute to local periodontal destruction.

LJP. Defective neutrophil chemotaxis seen in patients with LJP is of special interest. This form of periodontal disease was selected because of its early development and rapid progression, which are analogous to the periodontal destruction seen in systemic neutrophil disorders. The disease is described as having early onset ($\sim$13 years of age) and is characterized by rapid alveolar bone loss, limited primarily to first molars and incisors, with minimal clinical inflammation (4). The tendency for multiple members of a family to be affected suggests a genetic predisposition. There is also a generalized form of this disease, which has a lower incidence, in which there is no localization of bone loss. The relationship of the localized form and the generalized form is unknown.

TABLE 1. *Defective neutrophil chemotaxis in LJP*

No. of patients/total	Reference
9/9	Cianciola et al. (7)
7/9	Clark et al. (8)
12/17	Lavine et al. (18)
26/32	Van Dyke et al. (34)
17/26	Van Dyke et al. (submitted for publication)
6/10	Owens et al. (Abstr. Annu. Meet. Int. Assoc. Dent. Res. 1981)
77/103 (75%)	Total

Interestingly, there is a reduction of in vitro neutrophil chemotaxis in most patients with either localized or generalized juvenile periodontitis (34). (See Table 1.)

Analysis of neutrophil locomotion in vitro. In an effort to further characterize the nature of the chemotactic defect of neutrophils from patients with LJP, a new method of analysis of in vitro chemotaxis was developed (35). This method, called regression line analysis, makes use of the distribution of neutrophils within the filter in the Boyden chamber assay to obtain information relating to the rate of cell migration and the number of migrating cells in a given cell population. The assay is based upon analysis of linearized data (regression lines) obtained from counts of the neutrophils at preset levels within the filter. On the basis of studies using pharmacological inhibitors of neutrophil chemotaxis, it was determined that the slope of the regression varies with the *rate* of neutrophil migration and that the elevation of the regression line along the y-axis varies with the *number* of cells entering the filter (35).

Regression line analysis was used to evaluate random migration (unstimulated migration), chemotaxis (directed migration in a gradient of

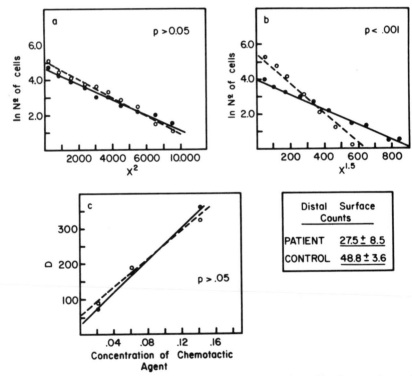

FIG. 1. *Regression line analysis of (a) random migration, (b) chemotaxis, and (c) chemokinesis. Neutrophils from LJP (○) and control (●) are compared statistically by analysis of covariance. The natural logarithm of the number of neutrophils counted at specified distances into the filter is plotted against a decrease in the rate of neutrophil migration. Random migration and chemotaxis are not different from control. Ln, natural logarithm; X, distance; D, diffusion function. Inset: Distal surface counts of chemotaxis experiment in which neutrophils migrated to the bottom of the filter in the Boyden chamber. Data are the mean ± one standard deviation of 10 high-power fields.*

chemotactic factor), and chemokinesis (stimulated migration in the absence of a gradient) in LJP patients. As is illustrated in Fig. 1, in all LJP patients tested, random migration was normal (Fig. 1a) whereas the *rate* of chemotaxis was depressed as compared with the control (Fig. 1b). Additional experiments revealed that chemokinesis was also normal in the the LJP group (Fig. 1c). Hence, these data suggest that the cytoskeletal migratory "apparatus" of the cell is intact, as indicated by normal random migration and chemokinesis, and that there is *not* a shift to a larger subpopulation of nonmotile neutrophils, as illustrated by the number of cells entering the filter in chemotaxis experiments. The defect of neutrophil locomotion in LJP is characterized by a decrease in the rate of cell migration, reflecting an inability to sense or respond to the chemical gradient.

Characterization of the chemotaxis defect in LJP. Several other parameters have been investigated to further describe the nature of the chemotactic defect. The serum of LJP patients was tested for the presence of cell-directed inhibitors of chemotaxis (heat-stable substances which interact directly and reversibly with neutrophils to block chemotaxis) (19) and chemotactic factor inhibitors (heat-labile substances that irreversibly inactivate chemotactically active complement fragments and bacterial factors) (38). These were found in only a few isolated cases (12). The depressed chemotactic function was not reversible by prolonged incubation of neutrophils from LJP patients with normal serum or buffer (12). In addition, two findings indicate that defective neutrophil chemotaxis in LJP patients is not a transient phenomenon:

TABLE 2. *Characterization of neutrophil locomotion in juvenile periodontitis (JP)*

Property or function of neutrophils	Reference(s)
Chemotaxis depressed in 77/103 or 75% of LJP patients	See Table 1 for references
Adherence normal or slightly elevated	Genco et al. (12)
Deformability normal	Genco et al. (12)
Random migration normal	Van Dyke et al. (34; submitted for publication)
Chemotaxis is depressed to a variety of chemotactic factors	Van Dyke et al. (34), Genco et al. (12)
Decreased locomotion of cells due to lack of response to a gradient, i.e., a true chemotaxis defect	Van Dyke et al. (34; submitted for publication)
Locomotion defect intrinsic to the cell in most patients	Lavine et al. (18), Van Dyke et al. (34)
Chemotaxis defect long lasting; found in post-LJP and not reversed by therapy	Clark et al. (8), Van Dyke et al. (34)
Chemotactic defect seen in nondiseased siblings of JP patients	Genco et al. (12)
Binding of fMLP to chemotactically defective cells is reduced	Van Dyke et al. (Biochem. Biophys. Res. Commun., in press)

(i) the defect is not reversed after treatment of the disease and (ii) adults who previously had LJP (post-LJP patients) still exhibit neutrophil chemotaxis abnormalities (34).

It was considered possible that the defect may be a result of an impairment of the deformability of the cell, thereby preventing migration through the small pores of the filter. An example of this phenomenon is the Pegler-Huet anomaly in which the cell nucleus fails to segment. It was found that the LJP patients' neutrophils exhibited depressed chemotaxis at comparable levels when filters of 3-, 5-, or 8-μm pore size were used, suggesting that there is no defect in deformability of the LJP neutrophil (12). Adherence of the neutrophils to a substrate was next evaluated by using a nylon-wool assay (12). There was no reduction, but a slight increase, in adherence of LJP neutrophils to nylon wool as compared with the control (12). Hence, studies of the nature of the neutrophil chemotaxis dysfunction in LJP revealed a defect which was intrinsic to the cell, was demonstrable with several chemotactic factors, was long lasting, and affected chemotaxis but not random migration, adherence, or deformability. A summary of neutrophil functional parameters in LJP is presented in Table 2.

Molecular basis of neutrophil chemotaxis. The findings which suggest that the mechanism of the reduction in chemotaxis in this patient group is uniform between patients points out the potential value of these individuals as a model group for studying human neutrophil function. Studies were undertaken to gain insight into the molecular basis of reduced chemotaxis in LJP to further our understanding of the subcellular mechanisms of chemotaxis and ultimately to provide a clue as to the appropriate treatment modality.

The stages of chemotaxis can be conveniently divided into three component parts as suggested by Zigmond (40). These are (i) the sensory mechanism or detection of the stimulus and gradient by the cell membrane, (ii) transduction of the signal across the membrane, and (iii) the effector mechanism, the

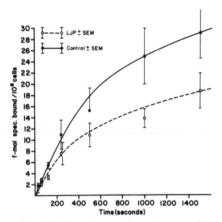

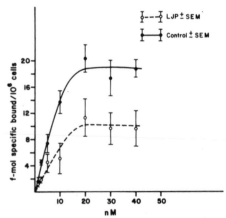

FIG. 2. *Kinetic experiment comparing the binding of fMLP³ᴴ (30 nM) to neutrophils from patients with LJP and controls after incubation for increasing time periods. Each data point represents the mean of at least seven separate experiments. SEM, Standard error of the mean.*

FIG. 3. *Saturation curves comparing fMLP³ᴴ binding to neutrophils from LJP patients and control subjects. Each data point is the mean of seven separate experiments. SEM, Standard error of the mean; 10 fmol ∿ 1,000 cpm.*

cytoskeletal elements and biochemical events that set the cell in motion. Attention will now be focused upon studies of the sensory mechanism since the earlier data suggest that the LJP neutrophil is unable to sense the chemotactic gradient.

The study of neutrophil chemotaxis in general and the sensory mechanisms of the neutrophil membrane were greatly advanced by the work of Schiffman et al. (28), who synthesized a series of peptides which are chemotactic for neutrophils. These peptides, believed to be analogous to the chemotactic factors elaborated by certain bacteria, have provided a valuable tool for the study of chemotactic mechanisms. Subsequently, several groups were able to radiolabel these peptides and demonstrate specific binding sites on the surface of the neutrophil (2, 23, 39). These studies, in conjunction with functional (chemotaxis, degranulation) studies, suggest the presence of specific receptors on the neutrophil surface for chemotactic agents.

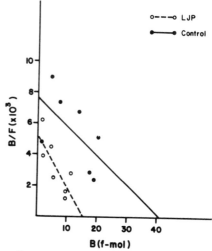

FIG. 4. Scatchard plots of data from equilibrium experiments comparing LJP and control subjects. Regression lines were fit by using least squares regression. Statistical analysis showed the slopes not to be different (P > 0.05) and intercepts to be different (P > 0.001) (analysis of covariance). B, Bound ligand in femtomoles; F, free ligand.

To evaluate binding of chemotactic agent to receptors on LJP neutrophils, we made use of the tritiated chemotactic peptide formyl-methionyl-leucyl-phenylalanine-[^{3}H] (fMLP^{3H}). Briefly, the assay was performed by incubation with fMLP^{3H} in the presence or absence of a 1,000-fold excess of unlabeled fMLP at room temperature. The reaction was terminated by rapid filtration and the amount of radioactivity remaining in the filter was quantitated by liquid scintillation spectroscopy.

The kinetics of peptide binding to LJP and control neutrophils are illustrated in Fig. 2. These experiments were performed at a final concentration of fMLP^{3H} of 30 nM ± 1,000-fold excess of unlabeled fMLP. The incubation time was varied from 30 to 1,500 s. As can be seen, there is approximately 40% reduction in binding to the LJP neutrophils as compared with those from normal subjects.

TABLE 3. Correlation of chemotaxis of neutrophils in response to fMLP and binding of fMLP^{3H} to the neutrophil surface in LJP patients and normal controls[a]

Group	Cells/HPF	fMLP^{3H} bound
Patient	12.6 ± 6.5	9.9 ± 2.4
Control	27.7 ± 9.1	18.8 ± 1.3

[a]Chemotaxis is represented as the number of cells per high-power field (HPF) that have migrated to the distal surface of a micropore filter in the Boyden chamber assay. Values are means ± standard deviation. Binding is represented as femtomoles of fMLP^{3H} specifically bound per 10^6 cells. Values are mean ± standard error of the mean.

Equilibrium experiments were also performed with fMLP^{3H} concentrations of 1.25 to 40 nM incubated for 30 min at 22°C. Figure 3 illustrates results similar to that of the kinetic experiments, namely, a 50% reduction in binding of fMLP^{3H} to LJP neutrophils at saturation. Scatchard analysis of these data (26) revealed that the K_D for binding of fMLP^{3H} to LJP and control neutrophils (Fig. 4) was essentially the same (1.4×10^{-8} M and 1.1×10^{-8} M, respectively); however, the number of binding sites on LJP neutrophils was markedly reduced, being only 9,200 sites per cell, whereas the normal cell exhibited approximately 20,000 sites per cell.

An important aspect of these findings is the correlation of the reduction in fMLP^{3H} binding with a reduction in chemotaxis. As is illustrated in Table 3, there is approximately 50% reduction in chemotaxis of LJP neutrophils and approximately 50% reduction in fMLP^{3H} binding at saturation.

These studies clearly correlate reduced receptor density with a reduced rate of chemotaxis. This finding is consistent with studies suggesting that the defect is intrinsic to the cell, expressed as a reduced ability to respond to a chemotactic gradient, and not a defect in random migration. It is unknown, however, whether the receptor density is the only physical abnormality of the LJP neutrophil; neither is it known whether other receptor-mediated functions of the neutrophil are likewise reduced in LJP.

DISCUSSION

The questions that now require investigation are, What is the cause of the reduction in fMLP^{3H} binding in LJP and will this cause, when identified, account for the reduction in chemotaxis in LJP neutrophils? At this point, one can only speculate on the basis of prior information.

The cause(s) of the reduction in binding sites on LJP neutrophils can be thought of under two major headings: endogenous origin or exogenous origin.

Endogenous origin. It is entirely possible that the reduction in binding sites on LJP neutrophils is genetically predetermined. In fact, there are several lines of evidence supporting this idea. One is, as mentioned earlier, the persistence of the chemotactic defect into adult life and after treatment of the disease. Another line of evidence comes from the study of the siblings and families of patients with LJP. In our series of patients, there is a high prevalence of LJP in certain families, and neutrophil chemotaxis defects are found in many unaffected siblings (12).

Exogenous origin. The opposite view is that the chemotaxis defect and reduction in binding sites are mediated by environmental factors. The most likely factors of this type would be of bacterial or viral origin. Again, there is precedent in the literature for this point of view. Shurin and co-workers (29) and Church and Nye (6) have demonstrated an in vitro reduction in chemotaxis directly mediated by bacteria. We also have shown that most gram-negative anaerobic staining bacteria are capable of inhibiting chemotaxis in vitro, although our data suggest that the effect in vivo is largely local.

Investigation of the mechanism by which the receptor density on the neutrophil is reduced presents many possibilities, which include: (i) blocking of receptors, (ii) homospecific down regulation of receptors, (iii) heterospecific down regulation of receptors, (iv) protease or oxygen radical degradation of receptors or ligand, (v) inhibition of neutrophil function by bacterial metabolites, and (vi) genetic predisposition of the neutrophil to bacterial effects.

Further possibilities for exogenous inhibitors include immune complexes formed with antibody to bacterial antigens or some unidentified antigen or autoantibody to the neutrophil surface.

The questions that are of importance to the clinical practitioner, however, are: What do these in vitro findings mean? Does the reduced rate of neutrophil chemotaxis contribute to more severe disease? Is the reduction in receptor density important clinically and can it be reversed? The significance of neutrophil impairment in LJP may be that the patient is in some way rendered more susceptible to the pathogens. On the basis of the evidence presented here, we suggest that the neutrophil plays a pivotal role in the pathogenesis of periodontal disease. Impairment of neutrophil function, either systemically as in LJP or locally by products of periodontopathogenic bacteria, will result in more rapid, more severe destruction of the periodontal tissues. As our understanding of neutrophil function increases, the likelihood of treatment modalities aimed at restoring neutrophil function increases and the answers to these questions become more feasible.

The focus of this paper has been neutrophil chemotaxis in LJP. However, there are other cellular functions stimulated by chemotactic factors, including bactericidal functions such as degranulation, superoxide production, and enhanced phagocytosis. If, in fact, the decrease in receptor density observed is reflected in a decrease in some of these related responses, the ability of the neutrophil to combat the bacterial insult may be significantly compromised. This, of course, would lead to increased or altered susceptibility to disease. These additional parameters are under investigation.

Although considerable progress has been made in defining the nature of the chemotaxis defect in the LJP neutrophil, it is clear that discussion of the cause of the defect is, at this time, mostly speculation. However, the nature of the disease affecting these patients and the consistency and similarity of the defect between patients provides the researcher with a human model for the study of the molecular basis and biological significance of neutrophil function.

SUMMARY AND CONCLUSIONS

These investigations of the role of the neutrophil in periodontal disease can be summarized as follows:

1. The neutrophil is primarily a protective cell in periodontal disease.
2. Patients with LJP exhibit reduced neutrophil chemotaxis.
3. There is a reduced number of fMLP[3H] binding sites on neutrophils from patients with LJP. This correlates well with the reduction of chemotaxis measured in vitro.
4. LJP is a model (i) for the study of neutrophil function due to the high incidence and homogeneity (i.e., in decreased rate) of the chemotaxis defect and (ii) for the study of the role of neutrophil in the pathogenesis of periodontal disease.

ACKNOWLEDGMENT

This work was supported in part by Public Health Service grant DE04898 from the National Institute for Dental Research.

LITERATURE CITED

1. **Altman, L. C., R. Snyderman, J. J. Oppenheim, and S. E. Mergenhagen.** 1973. A human mononuclear leukocyte chemotactic factor: characterization, specificity and kinetics of production from homologous leukocytes. J. Immunol. **110:**801–810.

2. **Aswanikumar, S., B. Corcoran, E. Schiffman, A. R. O'Day, R. J. Freer, H. J. Showell, E. L. Becker, and C. D. Pert.** 1977. Demonstration of a receptor on rabbit neutrophils for chemotactic peptides. Biochem. Biophys. Res. Commun. **74**:810–817.
3. **Åttstrom, R., and H. E. Schroeder.** 1979. Effect of mechanical plaque control on development of subgingival plaque and initial gingivitis in neutropenic dogs. Scand. J. Dent. Res. **87**:279–287.
4. **Baer, P. N.** 1971. The case for periodontosis as a clinical entity. J. Periodontol. **42**:516–520.
5. **Bauer, W. H.** 1946. The supporting tissues of the tooth in acute secondary granulocytosis (Arsphenamin neutropenia). J. Dent. Res. **25**:501–508.
6. **Church, J. A., and C. A. Nye.** 1979. Inhibition of polymorphonuclear leukocyte chemotaxis by streptokinase-streptodornase. Ann. Allergy **43**:333–336.
7. **Cianciola, L. J., R. J. Genco, M. R. Patters, J. McKenna, and C. J. Van Oss.** 1977. Defective polymorphonuclear leukocyte function in a human periodontal disease. Nature (London) **265**:445–447.
8. **Clark, R. A., R. C. Page, and G. Wilde.** 1977. Defective neutrophil chemotaxis in juvenile periodontitis. Infect. Immun. **18**:694–700.
9. **Cohen, D. W., and A. L. Morris.** 1961. Periodontal manifestation of cyclic neutropenia. J. Periodontal Res. **32**:159–168.
10. **Cornely, H. P.** 1966. Reversal of chemotaxis in vitro and chemotactic activity of leukocyte fractions. Proc. Soc. Exp. Biol. **122**:831–835.
11. **Dold, H.** 1914. Die Bedeutung einiger neurer serologischer Forschungsergebnisse fur die Pathologie. Arb. Belbal. Pathol. Anat. Inst. Tubingen (Leipz.) **9**:30–38.
12. **Genco, R. J., T. E. Van Dyke, B. Park, and H. U. Horozewicz.** 1980. Neutrophil chemotaxis impairment in juvenile periodontitis: evaluation of specificity, adherence, deformability and serum factor. RES J. Reticuloendothel. Soc. **28**(Suppl.):815–915.
13. **Griffin, F. M., Jr., J. A. Griffin, and S. C. Silverstein.** 1976. Studies on the mechanisms of phagocytosis. II. The interaction of macrophages with anti-immunoglobulin IgG coated bone marrow derived lymphocytes. J. Exp. Med. **133**:788–809.
14. **Hamilton, R. E., and J. S. Giansanti.** 1974. Chediak-Higashi syndrome: report of a case and review of the literature. Oral. Surg. **37**:754–761.
15. **Hill, H. R., H. S. Sauk, J. L. Detloff, and P. G. Quie.** 1974. Impaired leukotactic responsiveness in patients with juvenile diabetes mellitus. Clin. Immunol. Immunopathol. **2**:395–403.
16. **Kay, A. B., and A. P. Kaplan.** 1975. Chemotaxis and haemostasis. Br. J. Haematol. **31**:417–422.
17. **Kelbanoff, S. J.** 1975. Antimicrobial mechanisms in neutrophillic polymorphonuclear leukocytes. Semin. Haematol. **12**:117–142.
18. **Lavine, W. S., E. G. Maderazo, J. Stolman, P. A. Ward, R. B. Cogan, I. Greenblatt, and P. B. Robertson.** 1979. Impaired neutrophil chemotaxis in patients with juvenile and rapidly progressing periodontitis. J. Periodontal Res. **14**:10–19.
19. **Maderazo, E. G., P. A. Ward, and R. Quintiliani.** 1975. Defective regulation of chemotaxis in cirrhosis. J. Lab. Clin. Med. **85**:621–630.
20. **Metchnikoff, E.** 1887. Sur la lutle des cellules de l'organisme contre l'invasion. Ann. Inst. Pasteur Paris **1**:321–336.
21. **Miller, M. E., F. A. Oski, and M. B. Harris.** 1971. Lazy leukocyte syndrome, a new disorder of neutrophil function. Lancet **i**:665–669.
22. **Mowat, A. G., and J. Baum.** 1971. Chemotaxis of polymorphonuclear leukocytes from patients with diabetes mellitus. N. Engl. J. Med. **284**:621–627.
23. **Neidel, J., S. Wilkenson, and P. Cuatracases.** 1979. Receptor-mediated uptake and degradation of ^{125}I chemotactic peptide by human neutrophils. J. Biol. Chem. **254**:10700–10706.
24. **Page, R., and H. Schroeder.** 1976. Pathogenesis of inflammatory periodontal disease. J. Lab. Invest. **33**:235–242.
25. **Ruddy, S., I. Gigli, and F. Austin.** 1972. The complement system in man. N. Engl. J. Med. **287**:489–495, 545–549, 592–596, 642–646.
26. **Scatchard, G.** 1946. The attraction of proteins for small molecules and ions. Ann. N.Y. Acad. Sci. **51**:660–672.
27. **Schiffman, E., B. A. Corcoran, and S. M. Wahl.** 1975. N-formylmethionyl peptides as chemoattractants for leukocytes. Proc. Natl. Acad. Sci. U.S.A. **72**:1059–1062.
28. **Schiffman, E., H. J. Showell, B. A. Corcoran, P. A. Ward, E. Smith, and E. L. Becker.** 1975. The isolation and partial characterization of neutrophil chemotactic factor from *Escherichia coli*. J. Immunol. **114**:1831–1837.
29. **Shurin, S. B., S. S. Socransky, E. Sweeney, and T. P. Stossel.** 1979. A neutrophil disorder induced by *Capnocytophaga*, a dental microorganism. N. Engl. J. Med. **301**:849–854.
30. **Stossel, T. P.** 1974. Phagocytosis. N. Engl. J. Med. **290**:717–780, 833–838.
31. **Stossel, T. P.** 1977. Contractile proteins in phagocytosis: an example of cell surface to cytoplasm communication. Fed. Proc. **36**:2181–2184.
32. **Taichman, N. S.** 1970. Mediation of inflammation by the polymorphonuclear leukocyte as a sequela of immune reactions. J. Periodontol. **41**:228–231.
33. **Temple, T. R., Kimball, H. R., S. Kakehashi, and C. R. Amen.** 1972. Host factors in periodontal disease; periodontal manifestation of Chediak-Higashi Syndrome. 2nd International Conference on Periodontal Research, Denmark. J. Periodontal Res., Suppl. 10.

34. **Van Dyke, T. E., H. U. Hososzewicz, L. J. Cianciola, and R. J. Genco.** 1980. Neutrophil chemotaxis dysfunction in human periodontitis. Infect. Immun. **27:**124–132.
35. **Van Dyke, T. E., A. A. Reilly, and R. J. Genco.** 1981. Regression line analysis of neutrophil chemotaxis. Immunopharmacology, in press.
36. **Van Oss, C. J.** 1978. Phagocytosis as a cell surface phenomenon. Annu. Rev. Microbiol. **32:**19–39.
37. **Ward, P. A., I. H. Lepow, and L. H. Newman.** 1968. Bacterial factors chemotactic for polymorphonuclear leukocytes. Am. J. Pathol. **52.:**725–736.
38. **Ward, P. A., and R. C. Talarum.** 1973. Deficiency of the chemotactic factor inactivator in human sera with α-1 antitrypsin deficiency. J. Clin. Invest. **52:**516–519.
39. **Williams, L. T., R. Snyderman, M. C. Pike, and R. J. Lefkowitz.** 1977. Specific receptor sites for chemotactic peptides on human polymorphonuclear leukocytes. Proc. Natl. Acad. Sci. U.S.A. **74:**1204–1028.
40. **Zigmond, S. H.** 1978. Chemotaxis by polymorphonuclear leukocytes. J. Cell Biol. **77:**269–287.

Polymorphonuclear Leukocytes of the Human Gingival Crevice: Clinical and Experimental Studies of Cellular Function in Humans and Animals

J. M. A. WILTON

Department of Oral Immunology and Microbiology, Guy's Hospital Medical and Dental Schools, London SE1 9RT, United Kingdom

INTRODUCTION

The association of bacterial plaque with human gingival and periodontal disease has been well established. (35, 37, 62). The precise basis for the pathogenicity of dental plaque is, however, still not understood. Although the present evidence suggests that there is no single causative microorganism for any of the clinical forms of human periodontal disease, the use of recent techniques of anaerobiosis in the study of pocket and plaque bacteria has identified previously undescribed bacteria (50). It is possible therefore that future studies may provide evidence for the association of specific bacteria or groups of bacteria with different forms or stages of periodontal disease. One disadvantage of current research is the lack of an appropriate animal model of naturally developing disease. Although some information has been gained from rodents, particularly the gnotobiotic rat (28), and from some primate studies (57) regarding the ability of individual plaque bacteria to cause periodontal disease, the form of the disease is acute and atypical, and its relevance to human infection remains uncertain.

Early studies on the pathogenic potential of dental plaque bacteria incriminated gram-negative organisms, especially *Bacteriodes melaninogenicus*, as being essential to the formation of experimental skin lesions (reviewed in 18). Gram-positive bacteria, particularly *Actinomyces* species, are also pathogenic, producing bone loss when inoculated into gnotobiotic rats and hamsters (29). The injection of lipids extracted from *A. naeslundii* into rats gave an acute inflammatory reaction with subsequent bone loss (26). Bone loss can also be induced in vivo in monkeys by injection of *B. asaccharolyticus* (57). An essential component of periodontal disease in humans is the loss of alveolar bone, and any model of the disease must take this into account.

Much of the early work on the pathogenesis of periodontal disease concentrated on the part played by bacterial lipopolysaccharide (LPS) endotoxin, and the early work on the serology and pathogenicity of LPS from oral bacteria has been reviewed (40). One important function of LPS is the ability of this material to activate the alternate pathway of complement, with the generation of biologically active fragments such as anaphylatoxins, chemotaxins, and opsonins (for reviews see 14, 42, 43).

The polymorphonuclear leukocyte (PMN) is the predominant cell of the acute inflammatory response. These cells are phagocytic, and this process is enhanced by immunoglobulin G (IgG) and IgM antibodies and the activated complement

246

component C3b, which act as opsonins via receptors for Fcγ and C3b. PMNs also have an Fcα receptor for both serum and secretory IgA, but the role of this receptor is unclear. IgA can modulate the functions of the PMN by depressing the chemotactic (75) and phagocytic (79) actions of the cells. Whatever the direct toxic effect of bacterial plaque constituents on the components of the gingival tissues, one important mechanism by which plaque could induce inflammation would be by attracting PMNs and macrophages into the gingival tissue and crevicular space. Although these cells are necessary for the integrity of the tissues against bacterial invasion and should be regarded as protective under most circumstances, the continuous emigration of inflammatory cells and fluid components such as complement could also lead to tissue damage (20, 63). The PMN is the principal cell of the gingival crevicular and pocket exudate (1, 55, 83). The enzymes of PMNs and macrophages are capable of causing tissue damage, and such enzymes can be released from these cells by plaque and plaque bacteria both without accompanying phagocytosis by binding to the cell membrane and during the phagocytosis of bacteria (3, 38, 47, 65–67, 72).

Plaque contains both chemotaxins for rabbit and mouse PMNs in vitro and in vivo (15, 31, 41, 70, 77) and chemotaxinogens, such as LPS, which are capable of activating complement via the alternative pathway and producing the chemotactic fragment C5a (58, 78). LPS from oral bacteria has been extensively investigated and was found to be capable of attracting inflammatory cells in both humans and animals in vivo (27, 81) and in vitro in studies using rabbit PMNs (61). The topical application of human plaque filtrate to the gingival crevice of normal dogs and monkeys causes an increased number of PMNs to accumulate (24). An early component of experimental dental plaque adhering to plastic strips is the PMN (5). PMNs were attracted to the gingival crevice by casein in both rats and humans (22). PMNs are found in smears from both healthy and inflamed gingivae (52), and in fluid collected from inflamed gingivae PMNs comprised 98.6% of the cells present (13). When a plastic strip was inserted into the gingival crevice and the adherent cells were collected, 97% of the cells were PMNs (1). In this study it was also found that, although increased numbers of PMNs were seen in patients with gingivitis, the proportion of PMNs was the same as in healthy subjects. None of these studies was able to assess the viability or function of the cells, but this was made feasible when a washing technique for sampling the crevicular fluid from normal subjects was developed (55). This showed that 81% of the cells were viable, and viability increased to 99% with sequential washing, supporting the concept that the emigration of PMNs is a continuous process even in clinically healthy gingivae. Biting increased the number of cells collected by 50%, which suggested that the flow of cells can be modified by physiological as well as pathological processes. The PMNs comprised 91.5% of the cells collected, and this lower figure is probably more accurate than those obtained in other studies since all the cells were sampled, not just those which adhered to plastic. This predominance of PMNs in crevicular fluid was confirmed in a further series of normal subjects, the PMNs accounting for 91.2% of the cells collected (83).

The development of a washing technique made it possible to study the functional capacity of crevicular PMNs from normal crevicular fluid in humans, with peripheral blood PMNs from the same individual used for comparison. It was shown that fewer crevicular PMNs phagocytosed latex beads and *Candida albicans* blastospores when compared with blood PMNs; in addition, fewer *C.*

TABLE 1. *Phagocytosis and killing of* C. albicans *(CA) blastospores by PMNs from crevicular washings in autologous serum and crevicular washings from 14 subjects with clinically healthy gingiva*

Incubation time (min)	% Phagocytosis		No. of CA cells/PMN		% CA cells killed	
	30% serum	Crevicular washings	30% serum	Crevicular washings	30% serum	Crevicular washings
10	57.4 ± 14.9^a	77.1 ± 4.7^b	2.45 ± 0.42	2.79 ± 0.24	6.8 ± 4.2	13.2 ± 9.1^b
60	61.2 ± 18.0	78.6 ± 5.0^b	3.05 ± 0.85	3.54 ± 0.51^b	11.6 ± 2.1	23.3 ± 7.1^b

[a]Mean ± standard deviation.
[b]Significantly different compared with PMNs + serum by Student's *t* test for paired samples.

albicans organisms were taken up by crevicular fluid cells, but the killng capacity of the two populations was the same (85). The opsonic requirements for both types of cell were specific antibody and complement, as removal of one or the other opsonin inhibited phagocytosis. These experiments were performed in 20% autologous serum, and when the function of the crevicular PMNs was assayed in both serum and the crevicular washings, it was found that the crevicular PMN function was consistently greater in the diluted gingival exudate fluid than in 30% autologous serum (Table 1). It can be seen that this increase was most marked when the killing of the ingested fungus was measured. It therefore appears that the gingival crevicular PMNs can function in the inflammatory exudate from which they were collected, and this observation led me to study the in vivo phagocytosis of human crevicular PMNs.

TABLE 2. *Phagocytosis and intracellular IgG, IgA, IgM, and C3 in gingival crevicular PMNs from clinically healthy subjects*

Subject no.	% Cells staining with:				% Cells phagocytosing
	Anti-IgG	Anti-IgA	Anti-IgM	Anti-C3	
1	45	21	25	12	51
2	17	0	8	7	24
3	22	28	18	24	55
4	12	22	13	15	42
5	15	10	8	17	20
6	12	8	5	14	21
7	8	2	2	1	40
8	8	4	2	7	18
9	19	9	7	12	62
10	17	33	44	18	36
11	6	5	8	11	41
12	18	33	12	19	70
13	41	23	17	24	58
14	59	22	14	28	30
Mean	21.35	15.85	13.1	14.9	40.6
SD[a]	15.75	11.35	11.0	7.4	16.8
Membrane	80	<5	35	45	

[a]Standard deviation.

The deficient phagocytosis of crevicular PMNs was due to functional blocking of the C3b receptor on the PMN, and a similar defect could be conferred on blood PMNs by preincubation in crevicular fluid (84). Both crevicular PMNs and crevicular fluid-treated blood PMNs carried membrane-bound IgG, C3, and IgM, but not IgA, and it was concluded that complement-activating antigen–antibody complexes were probably responsible for the phagocytic defect. It is also possible, however, since plaque organisms and their constituents can activate complement by the alternative pathway (78), that C3b generated by this mechanism would also inhibit phagocytosis.

When the PMNs collected from the clinically healthy gingival crevice were immediately fixed by collecting them into buffered glutaraldehyde to inhibit further phagocytosis, it was evident that in vivo the PMNs had taken up bacteria (Table 2). Phagocytosis was assayed by both acridine orange staining and Gram staining, and only PMNs containing at least one morphologicaly recognizable bacterium were counted. The PMNs were also stained for IgG, IgM, IgA, and C3b, and they contained all three isotypes of immunoglobulin and C3b complement. There was no correlation between phagocytosis and the staining for any one isotype or C3b or any combination of isotype and C3b. I have added to Table 2 the figures for membrane-bound immunoglobulin and C3 (83), and it can be seen that there are differences between the intracellular and membrance staining patterns, principally in that IgA was present intracellularly in 15.85% of the cells whereas less than 5% of cells showed membrane-bound IgA. The data shown here support the concepts that PMNs may bind immune complexes, possibly causing degranulation, and phagocytose immune complexes. The absence of a correlation between phagocytosis and immunoglobulin or C3b staining might imply that phagocytosis of bacteria by crevicular PMNs can occur without opsonization.

Some patients with juvenile periodontitis may have defects of PMN chemotaxis and phagocytosis (7, 10, 33). PMNs from patients with juvenile periodontitis appeared to have a chemotactic defect when tested with *Escherichia coli* chemotaxin, activated complement, and a leukocyte-derived chemotactic factor. Phagocytosis of opsonized *Staphylococcus pyogenes* cells was also defective, but no defect could be found in two age-matched patients with a clinically different form of rapidly advancing periodontal disease (7). This defect of PMN chemotaxis in patients with juvenile periodontitis was confirmed and further investigated with C5a used as chemotaxin (10). The defect was one of chemotaxis, not simply of disordered random PMN migration, in 85% of patients studied, and the defect was intrinsic to the cell in most patients with juvenile periodontitis. Among adults with rapidly progressive disease, 50% also had chemotactic defects, but in these patients the majority were due to serum factors, either cell-directed inhibitors of α chemotaxis or heat-labile complement factor inactivators. In contrast to the findings in adults (7), no defect in phagocytosis or PMN bacterial activity for *S. pyogenes* was found in patients with juvenile periodontitis (10). A serum factor which inhibited normal PMN chemotaxis in vitro was also found in some adult patients with periodontitis (33), but this differed from that described for juvenile periodontitis (10) since it was heat stable and even enhanced by heating (23).

It is difficult to see how a generalized systematic defect of chemotaxis in these patients does not predispose to an increased frequency of more severe infections, which are known to occur in patients with PMN chemotactic defects (32).

Murray and Patters (44) showed that the number of PMNs at the site of the lesion in patients with periodontal disease is actually greater than the numbers at unaffected sites. These workers also showed that the phagocytic capacity of the PMNs from the lesion was severely depressed when compared with nonlesion PMNs. I have confirmed these findings in collaboration with Roy Gillett of London Hospital, London, United Kingdom, and extended them to include electron microscopic evaluation of the crevicular PMNs from the lesions and from the unaffected sites in the same mouth, in addition to comparing both to the appearance of normal crevicular PMNs (unpublished data).

Polymorphs from control subjects showed a complete spectrum from entire cells free from bacteria to phagocytic involvement with microorganisms with degranulation, as might be expected from cells whose life in the crevice may have ranged from seconds to hours. Most cells showed phagocytic involvement with normal lysosomal degranulation and phagolysosome formation. What was never seen in the PMNs from control subjects was phagocytosis without obvious granule depletion. In PMNs from the lesions of juvenile periodontitis patients, the same range of phagocytic involvement and degranulation was observed. However, in this group very many more of the cells remained uninvolved with the bacteria around them, and degranulation was markedly reduced even when phagocytosis had occurred. Some cells even showed evidence of the phagocytosis of bacteria without any detectable lysosomal degranulation.

In this study no clear difference emerged between cells from lesion and nonlesion sites in the juvenile periodontitis group, although both were clearly very different from controls. The ultrastructural findings regarding phagocytosis confirm the functional studies performed on the crevicular cells from the same patients. The greater cell numbers in juvenile periodontitis lesions show that, whatever defects of chemotaxis may have been displayed in peripheral blood PMNs by other workers, PMN accumulation was not defective at the site of the injury. Thus it is unlikely that these defects have a bearing on the pathogenesis of the disease. Biopsy material from the gingiva of one of these patients showed abnormally large numbers of neutrophils in the junctional epithelium, presumably on their way to the crevice, and this passage through the junctional epithelium seemed to be an active process.

We seem to have shown a clear, pronounced defect in neutrophil phagocytosis in vivo at the focal site, and we have confirmed the study of Murray and Patters (44) by in vitro studies on crevicular PMNs from the same patients. We have also found a defect of degranulation in vivo in the crevicular PMNs from these patients, and our preliminary studies with blood PMNs suggest that the defective degranulation may also be found in blood cells stimulated with *B. asaccharolyticus* and *Actinobacillus actinomycetemcomitans*, but not *Actinomyces viscosus, C. albicans,* or IgC-coated latex beads (Wilton and Gillet, unpublished data).

Our data on cell accumulation confirm that, in the lesion, PMN adherence, random migration, and chemotaxis must at least be normal. We have shown a reduction in both phagocytosis and degranulation in cells from the lesion and have reason to believe that these may also be systematic defects. Together, these defects would presumably depress effective microbial killing by these cells and could also allow the establishment of a specific pathogenic flora (56) in the gingival crevices of certain teeth during or just after eruption. Two such pathogens have been implicated, namely, *Capnocytophaga* species (46) and *A.*

actinomycetemcomitans (45). *Capnocytophaga* has recently been shown to produce a dialyzable agent which affects the mobility of the plasmalemma of neutrophils (54). Such an agent could also further reduce PMN phagocytic activity, and this would enhance bacterial accumulation at the lesion site. *C. sputigena* was shown to produce a fibroblast proliferation inhibitor (60) which could, via a reduction in fibroblast collagen synthesis, then account for the rapid loss of attachment of the tooth and the rapid formation of a deep pocket.

Inevitably, the normal loss of viability of PMNs in the crevice, if not preceded by effective bacterial killing, would lead to a release of viable organisms and a proliferation of the microflora (both specific and nonspecific bacteria), which in turn would lead to additional PMN death. This mortality would be further enhanced if another of the implicated pathogens, the *Actinobacillus* Y4, was

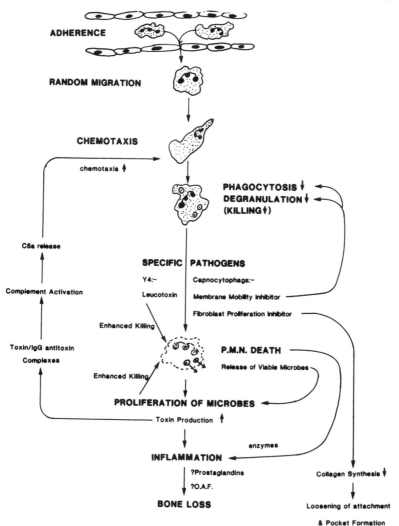

FIG. 1. *Hypothesis for the etiology and pathology of the periodontal lesion of juvenile periodontitis.*

present because this organism has been shown to elaborate a leukotoxin active against circulating PMNs (2, 73) and gingival crevicular PMNs (68). In this respect the organism may be said to have the ability to avoid phagocytosis and is unique since it can only kill PMNs and macrophages. This is an important virulence marker, and this topic has recently been reviewed (80).

Proliferation of Y4 in the pocket would increase the local toxin concentration, and if this were to combine with specific antibody (76), the toxin/antitoxin complexes formed would activate complement, liberating the PMN chemotactic factor C5a and thus increasing the recruitment of PMNs to the lesion. The net effect of these mechanisms would be an enhanced inflammatory response which would proceed to cause the rapid bone loss observed clinically. If the specific causative organisms are removed from the pocket, one could expect at least a partial resolution of the condition in spite of the persistence of any innate neutrophil defect. I therefore propose a hypothesis to account for the etiology and pathology of juvenile periodontitis (Fig. 1) which combines our own experimental data with the results of others.

During the course of the study of juvenile periodontitis, a consistent finding in the material taken from the normal gingival crevice was a number of nonkeratinized ephithelial cells to which bacteria were attached. These bacteria were covered by a neutrophil and enclosed by the processes of the phagocyte but did not appear to lie in phagosomes. The overlying PMN was markedly degranulated, and the appearance of the cell walls of the bacteria indicated that the cell wall might have been damaged. It was reasonable to assume that the lysosomal enzymes of the PMNs might have contributed to this damage. It is known that PMNs can kill *Streptococus mutans* organisms without first phagocytosing them (49). These observations, taken together with the wide variation in the phagocytic capacity of the normal crevicular PMNs in vivo and the depressed phagocytic capacity of these cells in vitro, raised the possibility that PMNs and their lysosomal enzymes might modulate plaque formation by mechanisms other than phagocytosis.

I have devised a model system which allows the study of the interaction

TABLE 3. *Detachment of bacteria from glass surfaces induced by human peripheral blood (PB) PMNs and lysates from PB and synovial fluid (SF) PMNs collected in heparin (HEP) or ethylenediamenetetraacetate (EDTA)*

Prepn	S. mutans			A. viscosus			V. alcalescens		
	t^a	df	P	t	df	P	t	df	P
SF HEP lysate vs PB HEP lysate	1.70	12	NS[b]	0.69	12	NS	0.90	6	NS
SF EDTA lysate vs PB HEP lysate	1.60	10	NS	1.08	12	NS	ND[c]	ND	ND
PB HEP PMNs vs SF EDTA lysate	0.49	17	NS	1.30	22	NS	ND	ND	ND
SF HEP lysate vs SF EDTA lysate	2.60	13	<0.02	1.80	12	NS	ND	ND	ND
PB HEP PMNs vs SF HEP lysate	1.20	31	NS	2.70	34	<0.01	1.97	10	NS
SF HEP lysate vs saline	6.30	10	<0.001	2.20	10	<0.05	2.30	10	NS
SF EDTA lysate vs saline	6.10	8	<0.001	0.72	10	NS	2.82	10	<0.02
PB HEP lysate vs saline	5.40	10	<0.001	3.33	10	<0.01	6.10	14	<0.001
PB HEP PMNs vs saline	6.90	18	<0.001	0.53	18	NS	2.64	14	<0.02

[a]Paired *t* test.
[b]Not significant.
[c]Not done.

TABLE 4. *Killing of bacteria detached from glass by human peripheral blood (PB) PMNs and lysates from PB and synovial fluid (SF) PMNs collected in heparin (HEP) or ethylenediaminetetraacetate (EDTA)*

Prepn	S. mutans		A. viscosus		V. alcalescens	
	% Killing ± SD[a]	P[b]	% Killing ± SD	P	% Killing ± SD	P
PB PMNs	94.3 ± 4.6	<0.001	98.4 ± 2.7	<0.001	99.1 ± 3.4	<0.001
PB PMN lysate	74.8 ± 16.4	<0.001	70.6 ± 12.1	<0.001	90.6 ± 8.7	<0.001
SF HEP lysate	79.2 ± 17.1	<0.001	84.3 ± 11.7	<0.001	98.1 ± 6.4	<0.001
EDTA lysate	84.1 ± 12.1	<0.001	78.6 ± 6.9	<0.001	97.2 ± 8.1	<0.001
Saline	14.2 ± 20.3	—	3.4 ± 4.6	—	2.1 ± 3.1	—

[a]Standard deviation.
[b]Paired *t* test probability.

between glass-adherent plaque bacteria and viable PMNs or their lysosomal enzymes (J. M. A. Wilton and J. J. Jarvis, Bull. Inst. Pasteur Paris, in press). Basically, plaque bacteria are made adherent to glass surfaces by a low-speed $(70 \times g)$ centrifugation, and PMNs or PMN lysates are added to these bacterial films and incubated at 37°C. At specific time intervals, the number of bacteria which become detached are counted, and their viability is assessed by conventional microbiological techniques. We were also able with this model to study the ability of bacteria to adhere to glass after treatment with lysosomal enzymes and PMNs. Finally, the effects of various fluid-phase components such as serum, immunoglobulins, LPS, and dextran were studied because these are an important feature of the gingival environment in vivo.

Peripheral blood PMNs and PMN lysates derived from normal subjects or PMN lysates prepared from synovial fluid PMNs from patients with rheumatoid arthritis removed bacteria attached to glass (Table 3). Phagocytosis under these conditions was not well marked and did not exceed 40% for any organism tested. There were no statistically significant differences between the removal of bacteria by PMNs and that by PMN lysates. *S. mutans* organisms were removed by peripheral blood PMNs collected in heparin and by all three lysates to a significantly greater degree than by saline $(P < 0.001)$. Significant numbers of *A. viscosus* organisms were removed by the lysates from synovial fluid PMNs collected in heparin $(P < 0.05)$ and by lysates from peripheral blood PMNs $(P < 0.01)$ but not by peripheral blood PMNs collected in heparin or lysates from synovial fluid PMNs collected in ethylenediaminetetraacetate. In the case of *Veillonella alcalescens*, significant numbers of organisms were removed by peripheral blood PMNs collected in heparin $(P < 0.02)$ and lysates of peripheral blood PMNs $(P < 0.001)$ but not by lysates of synovial fluid PMNs collected in heparin. There was no difference between the abilities of the lysates from synovial fluid PMNs collected in heparin and in ethylenediaminetetraacetate to remove bacteria except for *S. mutans* $(P < 0.02)$, indicating that the anticoagulant used to collect the cells did not affect the removal process. When the killing of the organisms detached from glass by PMN or PMN lysates was measured, significant killing of all three organisms was found (Table 4). *S. mutans* was killed to some extent by saline, but significant killing by PMN and PMN lysates $(P < 0.001)$ could still be demonstrated. *A. viscosus* and *V. alcalescens* were not killed by saline, and the killing of organisms by PMN preparations ranged from 74 to 98%, *V. alcalescens* clearly being the most susceptible of three organisms tested.

We have also shown that plaque components such as LPS will enhance this removal of bacteria by PMNs whereas dextran will inhibit removal. When the ability of PMNs or their lysosomal enzymes to inhibit the attachment of bacteria to glass was investigated, we found that all three organisms studied were inhibited from attaching after treatment for as little as 5 min (Wilton and Jarvis, in press). This inhibition of attachment was dose dependent, and an effect could be shown with the lysate from as few as 2×10^4 PMNs. Inhibition of attachment was optimal after treatment with PMN lysates for 30 min. PMN and macrophage enzymes are present in gingival crevicular fluid (8, 9, 30), and Taichman (63) has postulated that release of these enzymes is secondary to the binding and phagocytosis of plaque bacteria and immune complexes by PMNs. As we have already shown (84), there are immune complexes on the surface of the crevicular PMNs, and these cells have also phagocytosed bacteria and immune complexes in vivo. Lysosomal enzyme release without death of the cell was induced by plaque components (3, 38, 65–67, 72); LPS released peroxidase and lysozyme from PMNs (71) and can also activate the alternative complement pathway to cause degranulation indirectly via the binding of C3b and C5a to PMNs and macrophages (47, 50). Surface-bound IgG immune complexes (25) and dextran-coated bacteria (65) also cause PMNs to degranulate without the death of the cell. Gallin (16, 17) has shown that PMN degranulation is associated with a decrease in the negative charge of the cell, and a correlation appears to exist between surface charge, neutrophil aggregation, and increased adhesiveness of the cells to a surface.

The ability of PMNs and PMN lysosomal enzymes to remove adherent bacteria or to prevent the attachment of bacteria that would normally adhere may be an important modulating mechanism for the control of plaque formation in vivo. There are obvious differences among the bacteria chosen for this study. S. mutans is a primary colonizer whereas A. viscosus is a secondary colonizer (4) with weak adhesive properties, which would account for the high background counts of removal with saline. V. alcalescens colonizes epithelial cells and is normally found in protected areas of the mouth, but it can be found in the more exposed areas when detachment is prevented by a coating of extrinsic extracellular polysaccharide produced by other bacteria (36, 39). V. alcalescens attached poorly to glass and was easily removed by washing with saline. The glass model may not be appropriate for measuring the adherent properties of soft tissue colonizers and their removal by phagocytic cells, and we are currently studying this by using buccal epithelial cells. Future investigations will examine the precise nature of the PMN enzymes responsible for the detachment and killing of other bacterial species and mixed populations of oral microorganisms.

We have not yet used our model to study the interactions of plaque bacteria, which play such an important role in colonization. Such interactions would include the release of hydrogen peroxide by bacteria, the competition between bacteria for nutrients, and the availability of binding sites in the enamel pellicle and on other organisms (75). In collaboration with Daniel Fine of Columbia University, I have shown that the bacteria used in this model are also removed from enamel and cement surfaces by PMNs.

It has been observed in vivo (51) that phagocytosis of plaque is minimal. It is therefore possible that the exocytosis of enzymes occurs to a greater extent than does phagocytosis. Since mature plaque is probably presented as a unit, simulating a non-phagocytosable surface, rather than individual organisms, the in vivo observations of reduced phagocytosis would be in agreement with the results obtained in this model.

Since the PMNs are an important component of the gingival inflammatory response, any defect of the maturation, delivery, adherence to vascular endothelium, migration, and function of these cells will predispose to severe periodontal disease. In the absence of a sufficient number of competent PMNs, the gingival tissue becomes ulcerated and necrotic, but this process should not be confused with the common form of periodontal disease. Patients with defects of PMN function such as those of Chediak-Higashi syndrome (69) or with quantitative deficiencies of PMNs such as cyclical neutropenia (11) are susceptible to an acute form of ulcerative periodontal disease. In the Chediak-Higashi syndrome there are multiple PMN defects of chemotaxis, phagocytosis, and intracellular killing of microorganisms (12). Such rapid tissue breakdown suggests that PMNs are important for the integrity of gingival tissue, and in this respect, the periodontal tissue is no different from other tissues in the body. There is, however, evidence that release of hydrolytic enzymes by PMNs in response to local environmental factors such as plaque, immune complexes, and complement may be damanging (20, 63, 64, 78, 82). Any consideration of the part played by PMNs in periodontal disease should consider both the cells found in the tissues and those found in the inflammatory exudate, the crevicular or pocket fluid. The precise part played by PMN enzymes in tissue damage is still unclear (21), and it should be remembered that plaque inhibitors such as α-1 antitrypsin might render the PMN enzymes ineffective outside the cell.

The various chemotaxins and chemotaxinogens present in plaque and the gingival crevicular fluid will be critical determinants for the attraction of PMNs to the site of inflammation. A new technique has recently been reported for studying PMN chemotaxins in human gingival crevices (22). Reference has already been made to animal models, and these are also valuable (for reviews see 81, 82). Little attention has been paid to the comparative effects of plaque and its components in the animal studies. We have used the murine peritoneal cavity to study the effect of plaque, individual plaque bacteria, and constituents of plaque bacteria on the chemotactic ability of PMNs and macrophages (81). A summary of these results is shown in Fig. 2. It can be seen that there is a wide spectrum of activity, with plaque soluble extract active at a dose of 12.0 μg and *Veillonella* LPS active at a dose of 5.0 μg. In contrast, lipoteichoic acid is not active at a dose of 50 μg, and mutan II from *S. mutans* has no effect at a dose of 500 μg. The chemotactic effect of the plaque extract was largely abolished by removal of LPS, but there was some residual activity. We also studied the ability of these substances to cause vascular permeability and found that the chemotactic ability of the test substance was correlated with an increase in the levels of immunoglobulin and complement in the exudate fluid.

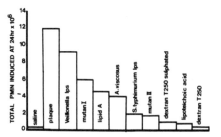

FIG. 2. *Accumulation of PMNs in the peritoneal cavity of CD-1 mice 24 h after the injection of dental plaque soluble extract and a variety of bacterial products.*

We have extended these studies to compare more directly the chemotactic and edema-producing properties of plaque components (O. P. Almeida and J. M. A. Wilton, unpublished data). *Veillonella* LPS induces both PMN migration and edema formation on the rat paw, and levan and dextran, which are not chemotactic, are potent inducers of edema. Mutan I (99% α-1→3 linkages) is chemotactic and also causes edema, but mutan II (90% α-1→3 and 10% α-1→6 linkages) has little effect in either system. It appears from this study that dental plaque components may differ in their effects on individual components of the acute inflammatory response.

Both immunoglobulins and complement are present in human gingival exudate fluid (53, 78, 82), and both are bound to crevicular PMNs (84) and are also ingested. The association of chemotaxis and an increased opsonic capacity of the fluid might enhance the uptake and destruction of bacteria containing LPS via the alternative and classic complement pathways. Activated C3 is known to bind directly to cell wall polysaccharide from *Salmonella abortus,* and polysaccharides isolated from IgG and LPS can also activate the classic complement pathway (43). The macrophages and PMNs in mice challenged with LPS in our study contained IgG and C3, and the macrophages had an enhanced phagocytic capacity. Such a mechanism might occur in the human gingival crevice or pocket. It is also possible that this would result in increased tissue damage as a result of enzyme release by the phagocytic cells and by the mechanisms already discussed. It is known that some of the substances used in the mouse model can modulate immune responses, acting either as adjuvant or as suppressive agents (34, 82). Although PMNs are not known to be important for the induction of the immune response, the macrophage is an essential cell in this process (74). PMNs are the predominant cells in the gingival crevice at all stages of disease and in health (48, 82) and could be protective by phagocytosis of bacteria and immune complexes (82, 84) or by removal of adherent bacteria (Wilton and Jarvis, in press), or they could cause tissue damage as a result of the release of enzymes (51, 66, 67, 72). The complement system has an important regulatory effect on the function of both PMNs and macrophages (for reviews see 78, 82), and our studies have substantiated the importance of C3 in chemotaxis and phagocytic function.

Gingival inflammation is a destructive process, and it is likely that gingival damage is due to a combination of humoral and cellular factors which can interact in many different ways. The attraction of inflammatory cells and increased vascular permeability can be achieved by nonimmune specific mechanisms, as shown in our studies, but antigen–antibody complexes, complement, and cell-mediated immunity can also cause inflammation. Complement activation plays a central role in each of these mechanisms as a chemotaxin, opsonin, anaphylatoxin, and inducer of lysosomal enzyme release. Whatever the relative importance of the different mechanisms, whether in inducing or in sustaining inflammation, the end result will be the tissue destruction of periodontal disease.

SUMMARY

The PMNs are the predominant cells in the healthy gingival crevice and gingival pocket in periodontal disease. In this review I have attempted to assess their importance for the maintenance of gingival health by showing that they are phagocytic cells, both in vivo and in vitro, and that they are capable of removing adherent plaque bacteria by nonphagocytic mechanisms, probably by releasing lysosomal enzymes. PMN enzymes are also capable of inhibiting the attachment of normally adherent bacteria. I have also presented a hypothesis to account for the periodontal lesions of juvenile periodontitis. Since these patients have defects of phagocytosis and chemotaxis and there appears to be an association of certain bacteria with lesions, the maintenance of inflammation is probably a combination of a systematic PMN defect, a local pathogenic plaque flora, and specific antigen–antibody complexes activating complement. Finally, the use of an animal model to study the ability of plaque and plaque constituents to induce PMN and macrophage chemotaxis and initiate vascular permeability was discussed. The studies reported here support the hypothesis that the gingival crevicular PMNs are an important component in the defense of the gingival tissues against the pathogenic effects of dental plaque.

ACKNOWLEDGMENTS

I acknowledge the fruitful collaboration of Heinz Renggli, Oslei de P. Almeida, D. C. Fine, R. Gillett, and J. Jarvis in the studies reported here. The work of Dr. Almeida was supported by FASPESP grant 771 066V, and the studies of phagocytic modulation of bacterial detachment are supported by the Medical Research Council (U.K., no. 480/0414 6SB).
I also thank T. Lehner for much fruitful discussion and support in all the work presented in this review.

LITERATURE CITED

1. **Attstrom, R.** 1970. Presence of leukocytes in crevices of healthy and inflamed gingivae. J. Periodontal Res. 5:42–47.
2. **Baehni, P., C. C. Tsai, W. P. McArthur, B. F. Hammond, and N. S. Taichman.** 1979. Interaction of inflammatory cells and oral microorganisms. VIII. Detection of leukotoxic activity of a plaque-derived gram-negative microorganism. Infect. Immun. 24:233–243.
3. **Baehni, P., C. C. Tsai, N. S. Taichman, and W. P. McArthur.** 1978. Interaction of inflammatory cells and oral microorganisms. V. Electron microscopic and biochemical study on the mechanisms of release of lysosomal constituents from human polymorphonuclear leukocytes exposed to dental plaque. J. Periodontal Res. 13:333–348.
4. **Bourgeau, G., and B. C. McBride.** 1976. Dextran-mediated interbacterial aggregation between dextran-synthesizing streptococci and *Actinomyces viscosus*. Infect. Immun. 13:1228–1234.
5. **Brecx, M., A. Ronstrom, J. Theilade, and R. Attstrom.** 1981. Early formation of dental plaque on plastic films. 2. Electron microscopic observations. J. Periodontal Res. 16:213–227.
6. **Capel, P. J. A., D. Groenboer, G. Grosveld, and K. W. Pondman.** 1978. The binding of activated C3 to polysaccharides and immunoglobulins. J. Immunol. 121:2566–2572.
7. **Ciancola, L. J., R. T. Genco, M. R. Patters, J. McKenna, and C. J. Van Oss.** 1977. Defective polymorphonuclear leukocyte function in a human periodontal disease. Nature (London) 265:445–447.
8. **Cimasoni, G., I. Ishikawa, and F. Jaccard.** 1977. Enzyme activity in the gingival crevice, p. 13–41. *In* T. Lehner (ed.), The borderland between caries and periodontal disease. Academic Press, London.
9. **Cimasoni, G., and Y. Kowashi.** 1980. Poteinases of the gingival crevice and their inhibitors, p. 31–49. *In* T. Lehner and G. Cimasoni (ed.), The borderland between caries and periodontal disease II. Academic Press, London.
10. **Clark, R. A., R. C. Page, and G. Wilde.** 1977. Defective neutrophil chemotaxis in juvenile periodontitis. Infect. Immun. 8:694–700.
11. **Cohen, D. W., and A. C. Morris.** 1961. Periodontal manifestations of cyclical neutropenia. J. Periodontol. 32:159–167.
12. **Davis, W. C., and S. D. Douglas.** 1972. Defective granule formation and function in the Chediak-Higashi syndrome in man and animals. Semin. Hematol. 9:431–450.
13. **Egelberg, J.** 1963. Cellular elements in gingival pocket fluid. Acta Odontol. Scand. 21:283–287.
14. **Elin, R. J., and S. M. Wolff.** 1976. Biology of endotoxin. Annu. Rev. Med., p. 127–141.
15. **Engel, D., D. van Epps, and J. Clagett.** 1976. In vivo and in vitro studies on possible pathogenic mechanisms of *Actinomyces viscosus*. Infect. Immun. 14:548–554.
16. **Gallin, J. I.** 1980. Degranulating stimuli decrease the negative surface charge and increase the adhesiveness on human neutrophils. J. Clin. Invest. 65:298–306.
17. **Gallin, J. I., D. G. Wright, and E. Schiffman.** 1978. Role of secretory events in modulating human neutrophil chemotaxis. J. Clin. Invest. 62:1364–1374.

18. **Gibbons, R. J.** 1964. Aspects of the pathogenicity and ecology of the indigenous oral flora of man, p. 168–285. *In* A. Barlow, R. D. Deliann, V. R. Dowall, and L. B. Gaze (ed.), Anaerobic bacteria: role in disease. Charles C Thomas, Publisher, Springfield, Ill.
19. **Gibbons, R. J., and J. Van Houte.** 1975. Bacterial adherence in oral microbial ecology. Annu. Rev. Microbiol. **29:**19–44.
20. **Goldstein, I. M.** 1974. Lysosomal hydrolases and inflammatory materials, p. 51–84. *In* G. Weissman (ed.), Mediators of inflammation. Plenum Press, New York.
21. **Goldstein, I. M., H. B. Kaplan, A. Radin, and M. Frosch.** 1976. Independent effects of IgG and complement upon human polymorphonuclear function. J. Immunol. **117:**1282–1287.
22. **Golub, L. M., V. J. Iacono, G. Nicoll, N. Ramamurthy, and R. S. Kaslick.** 1981. The response of human sulcular leukocytes to a chemotactic challenge. J. Periodontal Res. **16:**171–179.
23. **Gothier, D. E., H. R. Gaumer, B. L. Philstrom, and L. E. A. Folke.** 1975. Evaluation of a serum component in periodontal disease capable of modulating chemotactic infiltration. J. Periodontal Res. **10:**65–72.
24. **Hellden, L., and J. Lindhe.** 1973. Enhanced emigration of crevicular leukocytes mediated by factors in dental plaque. Scand. J. Dent. Res. **81:**123–129.
25. **Henson, P. M.** 1971. The immunologic release of constituents from neutrophil leucocytes. I. The role of antibody and complement on nonphagocytosable surfaces or phagocytosable particles. J. Immunol. **107:**1535–1546.
26. **Irving, J. T., M. G. Newman, S. S. Socransky, and J. D. Heeley.** 1975. Histological changes in experimental periodontal disease in rats monoinfected with a Gram-negative organism. Arch. Oral Biol. **20:**219–220.
27. **Jensen, S. B., F. U. Jackson, and S. E. Mergenhagen.** 1964. Alterations in the type and bactericidal activity of mouse peritoneal phagocytes after intraperitoneal administration of endotoxin. Acta Odontol. Scand. **22:**71–93.
28. **Johnson, D. A., C. H. Chen, J. C. Dombrowski, and A. Nowotny.** 1976. Role of bacterial products in periodontitis. I. Endotoxin content and immunogenicity of human plaque. J. Periodontal Res. **11:**349–359.
29. **Jordan, H. V., P. H. Keyes, and S. Bellack.** 1972. Periodontal lesions in hamsters and gnotobiotic rats injected with *Actinomyces* of human origin. J. Periodontal Res. **7:**21–28.
30. **Kowaskaki, Y., F. Jaccard, and G. Cimasoni.** 1979. Increase of free collaganase and neutral protease activities in the gingival crevice during experimental gingivitis in man. Arch. Oral Biol. **24:**645–650.
31. **Kraal, J. H., and W. V. Loesche.** 1974. Rabbit polymorphonuclear leukocyte migration *in vitro* in response to dental plaque. J. Periodontal Res. **9:**9–19.
32. **Kramer, N., H. D. Perez, and I. M. Goldstein.** 1980. An immunoglobulin (IgG) inhibitor of polymorphonuclear leukocyte motility in a patient with recurrent infection. N. Engl. J. Med. **303:**1253–1258.
33. **Lavine, W. S., E. G. Maderazo, J. Stolman, P. A. Ward, R. B. Cogen, I. Greenblatt, and P. B. Robertson.** 1979. Impaired neutrophil chemotaxis in patients with juvenile and rapidly progressing periodontitis. J. Periodontal Res. **14:**10–19.
34. **Lehner, T.** 1977. Immunology of the gut. Ciba Found. Symp. **46** (new series):135–159.
35. **Lehner, T., J. M. A. Wilton, S. J. Challacombe, and L. Ivanyi.** 1974. Sequential cell-mediated immune responses in experimental gingivitis in man. Clin. Exp. Immunol. **16:**481–492.
36. **Liljemark, W. F., and R. J. Gibbons.** 1971. Ability of *Veillonella* and *Neisseria* species to attach to oral surfaces and their proportions present indigenously. Infect. Immun. **4:**264–268.
37. **Loe, H., E. Theilade, and S. B. Jensen.** 1965. Experimental gingivitis in man. J. Periodontol. **36:**177–187.
38. **McArthur, W. P., and N. S. Taichman.** 1976. Interaction of inflammatory cells and oral microorganisms. II. Modulation of rabbit polymorphonuclear leukocyte hydrolase release by polysaccharides in response to *Streptococcus mutans* and *Streptococcus sanguis*. Infect. Immun. **41:**1309–1314.
39. **McCabe, R. M. and J. A. Donkersloot.** 1977. Adherence of *Veillonella* species mediated by extracellular glycosyltransferase from *Streptococcus salivarius*. Infect. Immun. **18:**726–734.
40. **Mergenhagen, S. E.** 1967. Nature and significance of somatic antigens of oral bacteria. J. Dent. Res. **46:**46–52.
41. **Miller, R. L., L. E. A. Folke, and C. R. Umana.** 1975. Chemotactic ability of dental plaque upon autologous or heterologous human polymorphonuclear leukocytes. J. Periodontol. **46:**409–414.
42. **Morrison, D. C., and J. L. Ryan.** 1979. Bacterial endotoxins and host immune responses. Adv. Immunol. **28:**293–450.
43. **Morrison, D. C., and R. J. Ulevich.** 1978. The effects of bacterial endotoxins on host mediation systems. Am. J. Pathol. **93:**527–617.
44. **Murray, P. A., and M. R. Patters.** 1980. Gingival crevice neutrophil function in periodontal lesions. J. Periodontal Res. **15:**463–469.
45. **Newman, M. G., and S. S. Socransky.** 1977. Predominant cultivable microbiota in periodontosis. J. Periodontal Res. **12:**120–128.
46. **Newman, M. G., S. S. Socransky, E. Savitt, D. Propas, and A. Crawford.** 1976. Studies of the microbiology of periodontosis. J. Periodontol. **47:**373–379.

47. **Page, R. C., P. Davies, and A. C. Allison.** 1973. Effects of dental plaque on the production and release of lysosomal hydrolases by macrophages in culture. Arch. Oral Biol. **18:**1481–1495.
48. **Page, R. C., and H. E. Schroeder.** 1976. Pathogenesis of inflammatory periodontal disease. A summary of current work. Lab. Invest. **33:**235–249.
49. **Passo, S. A., C. C. Tsai, W. P. McArthur, C. Leifer, and N. S. Taichman.** 1980. Interaction of inflammatory cells and oral microorganisms. IX. The bactericidal effects of human polymorphonuclear leucocytes on isolated plaque microorganisms. J. Periodontal Res. **15:**470–482.
50. **Schorlemmer, H. U., and A. C. Allison.** 1976. Effects of activated complement components on enzyme secretion by macrophages. J. Immunol. **31:**781–788.
51. **Schroeder, H. E., and R. Attstrom.** 1980. Pocket formation; an hypothesis, p. 99–123. *In* T. Lehner and G. Cimasoni (ed.), The borderland between caries and periodontal disease II. Academic Press, London.
52. **Sharry, J. J., and B. Krasse.** 1960. Observations on the origins of salivary leukocytes. Acta Odontol. Scand. **18:**347–358.
53. **Shillitoe, E. J., and T. Lehner.** 1972. Immunoglobulins and complement in crevicular fluid, serum and saliva in man. Arch. Oral Biol. **17:**241–247.
54. **Shurin, S. B., S. S. Socransky, E. Sweeney, and T. P. Stossel.** 1979. A neutrophil disorder induced by *Capnocytophaga*, a dental microorganism. N. Engl. J. Med. **301:**849–854.
55. **Skapski, H., and T. Lehner.** 1976. A crevicular washing method for investigating immune components of crevicular fluid in man. J. Periodontal Res. **11:**19–24.
56. **Slots, J.** 1976. The predominant cultivable organisms in juvenile periodontitis. Scand. J. Dent. Res. **84:**1–10.
57. **Slots, J., and E. Hausmann.** 1979. Longitudinal study of experimentally induced periodontal disease in *Macaca arctoides;* relationship between microflora and alveolar bone loss. Infect. Immun. **23:**260–269.
58. **Snyderman, R., H. Gewurz, and S. E. Mergenhagen.** 1968. Interactions of the complement system with endotoxic lipopolysaccharide. Generation of a factor chemotactic for polymorphonuclear leucocytes. J. Exp. Med. **128:**259–275.
59. **Socransky, S. S.** 1977. Microbiology of periodontal disease—present status and future considerations. J. Periodontol. **48:**497–504.
60. **Stevens, R. H., M. N. Sela, J. Shapira, and B. F. Hammond.** 1980. Detection of a fibroblast proliferation inhibitory factor from *Capnocytophaga sputigena.* Infect. Immun. **27:**271–275.
61. **Sveen, K.** 1977. The capacity of lipopolysaccharides from *Bacteroides, Fusobacterium* and *Veillonella* to produce skin inflammation and the local and generalised Schwartzmann reaction in rabbits. J. Periodontal Res. **12:**340–350.
62. **Syed, S. A., and W. J. Loesche.** 1978. Bacteriology of human experimental gingivitis: effect of plaque age. Infect. Immun. **21:**821–829.
63. **Taichman, N. S.** 1970. Mediation of inflammation by polymorphonuclear leucocytes as a sequela of immune reactions. J. Periodontal Res. **41:**228–231.
64. **Taichman, N. S., H. L. Freedman, and T. Uriuhara.** 1966. Inflammation and tissue injury. I. The response to intradermal injections of human dentogingival plaque in normal and neutropenic rabbits. Arch. Oral Biol. **11:**1385–1392.
65. **Taichman, N. S., B. F. Hammond, C.-C. Tsai, P. C. Baehni, and W. P. McArthur.** 1978. Interaction of inflammatory cells and oral microorganisms. VII. In vitro polymorphonuclear leukocyte responses to viable bacteria and to subcellular components of avirulent and virulent strains of *Actinomyces viscosus.* Infect. Immun. **21:**594–604.
66. **Taichman, N. S., and W. P. McArthur.** 1976. Interaction of inflammatory cells and oral bacteria: release of lysosomal hydrolases from rabbit polymorphonuclear leukocytes exposed to Gram-positive plaque bacteria. Arch. Oral Biol. **21:**257–263.
67. **Taichman, N. S., C.-C. Tsai, P. C. Baehni, N. Stoller, and W. P. McArthur.** 1977. Interaction of inflammatory cells and oral microorganisms. IV. In vitro release of lysosomal constituents from polymorphonuclear leukocytes exposed to supragingival and subgingival bacterial plaque. Infect. Immun. **16:**1013–1023.
68. **Taichman, N. S., and J. M. A. Wilton.** 1981. Leukocytotoxicity of an extract from *Actinobacillus actinomycetemcomitans* for human gingival polymorphonuclear leukocytes. Inflammation **5:**1–12.
69. **Tempel, T. R., H. R. Kimball, S. Kakehashi, and C. R. Amen.** 1972. Host factors in periodontal disease: periodontal manifestations of the Chediak-Higashi syndrome. J. Periodontal Res. **7**(Suppl. 10):26–27.
70. **Tempel, T. R., R. Snyderman, H. U. Jordan, and S. E. Mergenhagen.** 1970. Factors from saliva and oral bacteria chemotactic for polymorphonuclear leukocytes; their possible role in gingival inflammation. J. Peridontol. **41:**71–80.
71. **Thorne, K. J. I., R. C. Oliver, and J. Lackie.** 1977. Changes in the surface properties of rabbit polymorphonuclear leucocytes induced by bacteria and bacterial endotoxin. J. Cell Sci. **27:**213–228.
72. **Tsai, C.-C., B. F. Hammond, P. Baehni, W. P. McArthur, and N. S. Taichman.** 1978. Interaction of inflammatory cells and oral microorganisms. VI. Exocytosis of PMN lysosomes in response to Gram-negative plaque bacteria. J. Periodontal Res. **13:**504–512.

73. **Tsai, C.-C., W. P. McArthur, P. C. Baehni, B. F. Hammond, and N. S. Taichman.** 1979. Extraction and partial characterization of a leukotoxin from a plaque-derived gram-negative microorganism. Infect. Immun. **25**:427–439.
74. **Unanue, E. R.** 1972. The regulatory role of macrophages in antigenic stimulation. Adv. Immunol. **15**:95–165.
75. **Van der Hoeven, J. S.** 1980. Microbial interactions in the mouth, p. 215–226. *In* T. Lehner and G. Cimasoni (ed.), The borderland between caries and periodontal disease II. Academic Press, London.
76. **Van Swol, R. L., A. Gross, J. A. Setterstrom, and S. M. D'Alessandro.** 1980. Immunoglobulins in periodontal tissues. II. Concentrations of immunoglobulins in granulation tissue from pockets of periodontosis and periodontitis patients. J. Periodontol. **51**:20–24.
77. **Wennstrom, J., L. Heijl, J. Lindhe, and S. Socransky.** 1980. Migration of gingival leukocytes mediated by plaque bacteria. J. Periodontal Res. **15**:363–372.
78. **Wilton, J. M. A.** 1977. The function of complement in crevicular fluid, p. 223–247. *In* T. Lehner (ed.), The borderland between caries and periodontal disease. Academic Press, London.
79. **Wilton, J. M. A.** 1978. Suppression by IgA of IgG-mediated phogocytosis by human polymorphonuclear leukocytes. Clin. Exp. Immunol. **34**:423–428.
80. **Wilton, J. M. A.** 1981. Microbial interference with inflammation and phagocyte function. *In* F. O'Grady (ed.), Microbial perturbation of host defences. Academic Press, London.
81. **Wilton, J. M. A., and O. P. Almeida.** 1980. The comparative inflammatory effect of dental plaque, lipopolysaccharide, lipoteichoic acid, dextran and levan on leucocytes in the mouse peritoneal cavity, p. 83–97. *In* T. Lehner and G. Cimasoni (ed.), The borderland between caries and periodontal disease II. Academic Press, London.
82. **Wilton, J. M. A., and T. Lehner.** 1980. Immunological and microbial aspects of periodontal disease, p. 146–181. *In* R. A. Thompson (ed.), Recent advances in clinical immunology. Churchill Livingstone, Edinburgh.
83. **Wilton, J. M. A., H. H. Renggli, and T. Lehner.** 1976. The isolation and identification of mononuclear cells from the gingival crevice in man. J. Periodontal Res. **2**:262–268.
84. **Wilton, J. M. A., H. H. Renggli, and T. Lehner.** 1977. The role of Fc and C3b receptors in phagocytosis by inflammatory polymorphonuclear leucocytes in man. Immunology **32**:955–961.
85. **Wilton, J. M. A., H. H. Renggli, and T. Lehner.** 1977. A functional comparison of blood and gingival inflammatory polymorphonuclear leucocytes in man. Clin. Exp. Immunol. **27**:152–158.

Leukocidal Mechanisms of
Actinobacillus actinomycetemcomitans

N. S. TAICHMAN, W. P. McARTHUR, C.-C. TSAI, P. C. BAEHNI, B. J. SHENKER,
P. BERTHOLD, C. EVIAN, AND R. STEVENS

*University of Pennsylvania School of Dental Medicine, Center for Oral Health Research,
Philadelphia, Pennsylvania 19104*

INTRODUCTION

We have been interested in gaining information on the functions of polymorphonuclear neutrophils (PMNs) in the periodontal environment. These cells constantly migrate into the healthy or diseased gingival crevice, forming an interface between the plaque microbiota and underlying host tissues. It is likely that PMN interactions with plaque components reflect an antibacterial defense system as well as a mechanism of promoting inflammatory tissue injury (see discussion in 8). We have previously defined some of the ways in which plaque organisms stimulate PMN responses in vitro: we found that numerous plaque bacteria activate PMN phagocytosis, lysosome release, etc. But these reactions were not associated with morphological or biochemical evidence of deleterious effects on PMN viability. Recently, we discovered that *Actinobacillus actinomycetemcomitans* destroyed PMNs (1); thus far, this is the only known plaque organism to kill PMNs (Table 1). Since *A. actinomycetemcomitans*

TABLE 1. *Leukotoxic and nonleukotoxic plaque bacteria*[a]

Leukotoxic organisms

A. actinomycetemcomitans

Nonleukotoxic organisms

Whole plaque (gingivitis/periodontitis)[b]
Actinomyces propionicus
A. israelii
A. naeslundii
A. viscosus
Bacteroides melaninogenicus
Capnocytophaga
Eikenella corrodens
Leptotrichia buccalis
Haemophilus aphrophilus
Rothia dentocariosa
Streptococcus mutans
S. sanguis

[a]Several strains of freshly harvested organisms (5 to 200 per PMN) were incubated with PMNs at 37°C for up to 2 h. Leukotoxic organisms caused the release of lactic dehydrogenase into the culture medium, but PMNs exposed to nonleukotoxic bacteria retained lactic dehydrogenase.
[b]Whole plaque refers to heterogeneous bacterial deposits collected from supragingival areas in patients with early gingivitis or advanced periodontitis.

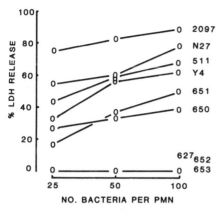

FIG. 1. *Extracellular release of lactic dehydrogenase (LDH) from human peripheral blood PMNs exposed to different strains of* A. actinomycetemcomitans *isolated from juvenile periodontitis plaque. Incubations were carried out for 60 min at 37°C in serum-free Hanks balanced salt solution (1).*

organisms are found in relative abundance in plaque samples of juvenile periodontitis patients (9, 10, 13), it is conceivable that their leukotoxic effect may be pertinent in the etiology of this disorder. The purpose of this paper is to highlight current results of some of our experiments pertaining to the leukotoxic mechanisms of *A. actinomycetemcomitans.*

We have tested several strains of *A. actinomycetemcomitans* and found that the majority rapidly kill human PMNs in vitro (Table 2; 1; P. C. Baehni, C. C. Tsai, W. P. McArthur, B. F. Hammond, B. J. Shenker, and N. S. Taichman, Arch. Oral Biol., in press). The organisms were from the American Type Culture Collection or from juvenile periodontitis plaque samples (kindly given to us by S. S. Socransky, Forsyth Dental Center, Boston, Mass.). Various ratios of freshly cultured bacteria were incubated with PMNs for up to 2 h; at the end of the experiment, PMN death was estimated by measuring lactic dehydrogenase or ^{51}Cr release (from prelabeled leukocytes) in the culture medium (Fig. 1). The leukotoxic reaction was not dependent upon ingestion of *A. actinomycetemcomitans* by PMNs, as it occurred under environmental conditions which obviated phagocytosis (1). It is important to point out that leukotoxicity was completely abolished by preheating organisms (e.g., at 56°C for 30 min), indicating the lipopolysaccharides (endotoxin) were not responsible for this phenomenon.

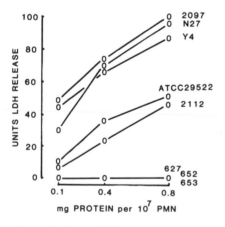

FIG.. 2. *Extracellular release of lactic dehydrogenase (LDH) from human peripheral blood PMNs incubated for 60 min (37°C) with various amounts of sonic extracts obtained from leukotoxic and nonleukotoxic strains of* A. actinomycetemcomitans.

LEUKOTOXIC ACTIVITY OF SONIC EXTRACTS

Sonication of leukotoxic (but not nonleukotoxic) *A. actinomycetemcomitans* strains yields a soluble, heat-labile substance(s) which destroys human blood PMNs (14), monocytes (11), and gingival crevice PMNs (12) (Fig. 2). A variety of other human cells, as well as leukocytes from rabbits, rats, mice, and guinea pigs, are not susceptible to the leukotoxin (Table 3), but within the past few months, we have found that monkey (*Macaca fascicularis*) PMNs are sensitive to the leukotoxin (L. T.

TABLE 2. *Leukotoxic activity of* A. actinomycetemcomitans

Strain	Activity[a]
ATCC strains	
29522	+
29523	V
29524	+
Plaque isolates	
Y4	+
N27	+
511	+
650	+
651	+
2043	+
2097	+
2112	+
627	−
652	−
653	−

[a]Symbols: +, leukotoxic organisms; −, nonleukotoxic organisms; V, variable.

Glickman, B. F. Hammond, W. P. McArthur, B. J. Shenker, R. Stevens, N. S. Taichman, and C.-C. Tsai, unpublished data). The availability of a species closely related to man with similar reactions to the toxin offers promise for expanded observation on host-*A. actinomycetemcomitans* interrelationships. In this connection, we have been able to isolate the organism from monkey plaque and have also found that infected animals have antibodies capable of neutralizing its leukotoxin.

We are currently trying to purify the *A. actinomycetemcomitans* leukotoxin. As mentioned earlier, the toxin is heat labile. It is also inactivated by treating sonic extracts with a variety of proteolytic enzymes (14). A significant portion of the toxin is probably localized within surface membrane vesicles of leukotoxic organisms (which also contain "LG antigen") (C. H. Lai, M. A. Listgarten, and B. F. Hammond, J. Periodontal Res., in press). These vesicles are abundant in most leukotoxic strains and appear to be shed from the organisms during all phases of growth (see B. F. Hammond and R. H. Stevens, this volume).

TABLE 3. *Sensitivities of different mammalian cells to* A. actinomycetemcomitans *leukotoxin*

Leukotoxin-sensitive target cells
Human blood PMNs and monocytes
Human gingival crevice PMNs
Monkey blood PMNs and mononuclear cells

Leukotoxin-resistant target cells
Human lymphocytes (T and B cells), erythrocytes, platelets, fibroblasts and epithelium
Rabbit, rat, mouse, and guinea pig blood PMNs, mononuclear cells, and peritoneal macrophages.

MECHANISM OF ACTION OF THE LEUKOTOXIN

Binding of A. actinomycetemcomitans leukotoxin to cell membranes of PMNs (14) or monocytes (11) appears to be a prerequisite event in the cytotoxic reaction. Several lines of evidence support this conclusion. In preliminary experiments we have been able to localize A. actinomycetem-comitans antigens on the surface of PMNs by immuno-electron microscopic procedures (P. Berthold, W. P. McArthur, N. S. Taichman, and C.-C. Tsai, unpublished data). Leukotoxic factors can be removed from crude sonic bacterial extracts by absorption with either PMN or monocyte membranes but not readily with erythrocyte membranes (erythrocytes are resistant to the toxin) (11, 14). PMN membranes coated with leukotoxic components can be employed as immunogens in rabbits to produce antisera which neutralize A. actinomycetemcomitans leukotoxin. In contrast, PMN membranes pretreated with sonic extracts of nonleukotoxic strains do not give rise to neutralizing antibodies. Kinetic studies demonstrate that the leukotoxin rapidly associates (in less than 5 min) with target cells, which cannot be rescued by repeated washing to remove toxic components (11).

We are exploring ways of interfering with the binding of the leukotoxin to target cells. α-Methyl-D-mannoside can partially inhibit killing if pre-incubated with monocytes prior to addition of toxin (11). Presumably, this compound prevents access of leukotoxin to carbohydrate moieties on the cell membrane. Phosphatidic acid and certain related derivatives can also inhibit cell death if either the leukocytes or the leukotoxin is preincubated with these compounds (P. Baehni, C. C. Tsai, I. Ginsburg, N. S. Taichman, and W. P. McArthur, J. Dent. Res. Spec. Issue A, vol. 60, abstr. 857, 1981). Protection in such instances may be the result of phospholipids blocking membrane-binding components of the toxin or competing or interfering with the toxin-binding areas on cell membranes. Complete neutralization of A. actinomycetemcomitans leukotoxin can be achieved by treating leukotoxic strains or sonic extracts with antibodies. These can be produced by immunizing rabbits with leukotoxic strains or sonic extracts (7). Furthermore, the sera from patients with juvenile periodontitis contain immunoglobulin G antibodies which inhibit A. actinomycetemcomitans leukotoxicity (see below). It is likely that antitoxin antibodies also interfere with the toxin binding to the cell membrane.

Once associated with the leukocyte membrane, it is not known how the leukotoxin actually kills the cells. Although albumin or high-molecular-weight dextran both inhibit extracellular discharge of LDH, the cells are still irreversibly damaged (1, 14). Thus, osmotic lysis is not the primary mechanism of cytotoxicity. Cell death also occurs under conditions which minimize endocytosis (e.g., in the presence of cytochalasin B or at 4°C in the case of monocytes) (11). Inhibition of protein synthesis or energy metabolism or pretreatment of cells with different anti-inflammatory drugs has thus far been without effect on the cytotoxic response (11).

EFFECT OF HUMAN SERA ON LEUKOTOXIC ACTIVITY

As mentioned earlier, antibodies against leukotoxic strains of A. actinomyce-temcomitans can completely abolish killing of PMNs (7). We have screened a large number of human sera to determine whether toxin-neutralizing activity is a feature of juvenile periodontitis. In these studies, A. actinomycetemcomitans leukotoxin was preincubated with sera from normal individuals or from persons with various inflammatory disorders; the mixtures were then tested with peripheral blood PMNs (C. C. Tsai, W. P. McArthur, P. C. Baehni, C. Evian, R. J. Genco, and N. S. Taichman, J. Clin. Periodontol., in press) or with gingival crevicePMNs (12). In both instances it was clear that the vast majority (>90%) of juvenile periodontitis sera neutralized the leukotoxin (Fig. 3). On the other hand, normal sera or sera from patients with other diseases usually amplified leukotoxicity. Some non-juvenile periodontitis sera did exhibit toxin-neutralizing potential, but usually at significantly lower titers than that seen with juvenile periodontitis sera. We have yet to positively identify the leukotoxin-exhancing factor(s) in normal serum, but it is not immunoglobulin, α_1 antitrypsin, or α_2 macroglobulin (7).

We have been studying immuno-logical interactions of sonic extracts of A. actinomycetemcomitans with juvenile periodontitis sera or with rabbit antisera against specific A. actinomycetemcomitans strains. All strains seem to share common anti-

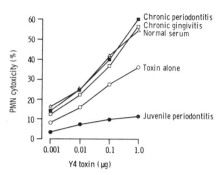

FIG. 3. *Effects of different sera on the killing of gingival crevice PMNs exposed to various concentrations of sonic extracts prepared from* A. actinomycetemcomitans *strain Y4. The experiments were conducted as outlined by Taichman and Wilton (12).* A. actinomycetemcomitans *leukotoxin was preincubated (37°C, 15 min) with different heat-inactivated (56°C, 30 min) sera (5.0% vol/vol). Gingival crevice PMNs were then added to the mixtures for an additional 15 min (37°C), and cell killing was quantitated as the percentage of cells which no longer excluded trypan blue. It is apparent that juvenile periodontitis sera inhibit leuko-toxicity, whereas other sera amplify killing of PMNs.*

gens, but based upon immunodiffusion and immunoelectrophoresis data we believe that there are at least four different A. actinomycetemcomitans serotypes (Table 4) (Baehni et al., Arch. Oral Biol., in press; C. C. Tsai, W. P. McArthur, P. Baehni, and N. S. Taichman, J. Dent. Res. Spec. Issue A, vol. 60, abstr. 856, 1981). Within the leukotoxic groups it is apparent that there are at least two unique antigens associated with these organisms. The first antigen is seen in all leukotoxic strains and the second appears in group 2 organisms, as represented by strain 511. It is significant that most juvenile periodontitis sera (44 of 50)

TABLE 4. *Serotypes of* A. actinomycetemcomitans[a]

Antigenic group	Toxicity	Strains
1	Leukotoxic strains	ATCC 29522, ATCC 29524, Y4, N27, KB, 650, 651, 2043, 2097
2	Leukotoxic strains	511
3	Nonleukotoxic strains	ATCC 29523, 627
4	Nonleukotoxic strains	652, 653

[a]Data based on immunodiffusion and immunoelectrophoretic analyses of sonic extracts of A. *actinomycetemcomitans* with specific rabbit antisera or with juvenile periodontitis sera.

TABLE 5. *Relative antibody titers to sonic extracts of*
A. actinomycetemcomitans *in juvenile periodontitis* [a]

	Bacterial sonic extracts			
Age group (yr)	Y4	511	627	652
9–12 ($n = 5$)	24.8 ± 28.6	3.3 ± 2.2	3.9 ± 2.3	0.4 ± 0.2
13–20 ($n = 13$)	6.9 ± 9.3	3.4 ± 2.8	9.6 ± 13.3	1.0 ± 0.8
21–25 ($n = 7$)	4.9 ± 4.9	4.2 ± 3.5	3.8 ± 2.0	1.0 ± 1.0
26–31 ($n = 6$)	2.5 ± 2.5	3.6 ± 3.5	7.4 ± 6.0	0.5 ± 0.3
Adult periodontitis ($n = 7$)	1.6 ± 1.1	1.9 ± 1.9	3.3 ± 2.6	0.4 ± 0.3

[a]Results (mean ± standard deviation) expressed as the ratio of antibody titer in juvenile periodontitis sera when compared to the titer in a reference pool of normal human serum. The titers were determined by the microenzyme-linked immunosorbent assay procedure: optimal amounts (3.8 µg of protein per well) of sonic extracts from different strains were absorbed onto microtiter plates. Serial dilutions of serum were added followed by peroxidase-conjugated goat anti-human immunoglobulins. Chromogenic peroxidase reaction products were developed and monitored at 492 nm.

have antibodies directed to the more common leukotoxic antigen, whereas only 6 of 50 show reactions to the antigen of group 2. Of this smaller population, 4 of 6 sera were secured from persons in the same family; thus, this family seemed to have been infected by and immunized to the same serotype. It will be interesting to ascertain whether similar relationships exist in other families with juvenile periodontitis.

We are quantitating antibody titers to *A. actinomycetemcomitans* in juvenile periodontitis sera by a micro-enzyme-linked immunosorbent assay. In comparison with anti-*A. actinomycetemcomitans* activity in a pool of normal serum, preliminary data indicate that juvenile periodontitis patients have elevated antibody titers to antigens in sonic extracts of leukotoxic and nonleukotoxic *A. actinomycetemcomitans* (Table 5). This is in general agreement with findings reported by other groups (4; R. J. Genco, N. S. Taichman, and C. A. Sodowski, J. Dent. Res. Spec. Issue A, vol. 59, abstr. 246, 1980; P. A. Murray and R. J. Genco, J. Dent. Res. Spec. Issue A, vol. 59, abstr. 245, 1980). Of particular interest is the fact that our youngest patients (9 to 12 years) seem to have the highest levels of antibodies against leukotoxic strain Y4 when compared with older patients. If this observation is substantiated with larger numbers of sera, it may indicate that the humoral immune response to Y4 and related leukotoxic *A. actinomycetemcomitans* strains may be critical during very early stages in the development of juvenile periodontitis.

SPECULATION ON THE ROLE OF *A. ACTINOMYCETEMCOMITANS* IN JUVENILE PERIODONTITIS

The results of our studies and the observations of others support the premise that *A. actinomycetemcomitans* strains may be etiological agents during some phase in the development of juvenile periodontitis. Since these organisms are found in relative abundance in the gingival crevice of patients with this disorder, it is conceivable that they continually release leukotoxic substances into the environment. If such materials retain activity in vivo, a local depletion of PMNs and monocytes (macrophages) may ensue, thereby compromising antibacterial defense in the vicinity. This might be followed by continued proliferation of *A. actinomycetemcomitans* or result in the establishment of other plaque organisms which are normally excluded from the area, or both.

Several key issues must still be addressed before we can completely define the interrelationships of *A. actinomycetemcomitans* and juvenile periodontitis. First, we have to determine when the organisms gain access to the gingival crevice: does this occur during the "initial" or during the relatively "advanced" stages of the disorder? We suspect that infection occurs in the earliest phases because young children with juvenile periodontitis seem to have higher antibody titers to leukotoxic strains when compared with adolescents or young adults (Table 5). The basis for susceptibility to infection by *A. actinomycetemcomitans* is not understood, and several potential determinants merit investigation. Since a significant proportion of juvenile periodontitis patients have a chemotactic dysfunction (2, 3, 6, 15), this could represent a mechanism to place the crevice at risk to colonization by leukotoxic strains. The formation of leukotoxin-neutralizing antibodies may be imperative to the outcome of infection in such instances. If sufficient antibodies are delivered to the crevice fast enough, the disease might regress spontaneously. If the immune response is not sufficiently potent during the initial stages of infection, the lesion might become "established" and continue to progress because of proliferation of *A. actinomycetemcomitans* or the addition of other pathogenetic organisms, or both. Such areas would not heal of their own accord, but more generalized infection by *A. actinomycetemcomitans* would be minimized because the host had already produced ample antibody to prevent the spread of the organism to, or to neutralize its leukotoxins at, virgin gingival sites. Thus, the localized forms of juvenile periodontitis may reflect an immune reaction which is adequate to restrict infection to primary sites of colonization (e.g., the first permanent molars and incisors). But the more diffuse forms of the disease may mirror a breakdown in or a relatively inefficient immune reaction to offending organisms.

Various elements of this hypothesis can be tested, and we are directing considerable effort to this end. For example, it should be possible to get some information on the time and sites of initial infection by *A. actinomycetem-comitans* and to document the kinetics of the immune response in susceptible persons. It should also be possible to correlate whether infection with leukotoxic as opposed to nonleukotoxic strains is pertinent to the development of disease in one person versus another and in healthy sites versus diseased areas. The acquisition of such data may be facilitated by an agar well immunotargeting technique which is presently under development in our laboratory (N. S. Taichman, R. Stevens, B. Hammond, C. C. Tsai, P. Baehni, and W. P. McArthur, J. Dent. Res. Spec. Issue A, vol. 60, abstr. 855, 1981). This procedure attempts to identify both leukotoxic and nonleukotoxic strains in plaque samples streaked onto agar plates containing semiselective growth media for these organisms. At the end of a 4- to 5-day growth period, holes are punched in the agar approximately 4 to 5 mm from bacterial colonies. Subsequently, rabbit antisera to different *A. actinomycetemcomitans* groups are added to the well, and immunoprecipitin reactions are read within 24 h. With this method, we can identify at least three major serogroups of laboratory strains (groups 1, 2, and 3; Table 4), and preliminary results with clinical plaque samples have thus far yielded encouraging results. We are hopeful that this procedure will allow for rapid monitoring of *A. actinomycetemcomitans* serotypes in plaque samples, providing important information on the dynamics of the infectious process.

At this point we want to caution against overstating or overinterpreting a role for *A. actinomycetemcomitans* leukotoxin in the etiology of juvenile periodontitis. The story is still unfolding, and it is becoming apparent that *A. actinomycetemcomitans* strains have other potent biological properties besides leukotoxic potentials. Even after neutralization of leukotoxicity, for example, these organisms can stimulate PMN reactions leading to extracellular secretion of inflammatory mediators (W. P. McArthur, et al., this volume). Both leukotoxic and non-leukotoxic strains possess heat-labile (B. Shenker, W. McArthur, C. C. Tsai, P. Baehni, and N. S. Taichman, J. Dent. Res. Spec. Issue A, vol. 60, abstr. 858, 1981) and heat-resistant (P. Chen, B. C. Nair, and R. J. Genco, J. Dent. Res. Spec. Issue A, vol. 60, abstr. 859, 1981) factors which modulate lymphoid functions. Further, leukotoxic strains contain endotoxic (5) as well as nonendotoxic (A. Nowotny, U. H. Behling, B. Hammond, C. H. Lai, M. Listgarten, P. H. Pham, and F. Sanavi, J. Dent. Res. Spec. Issue A, vol. 60, abstr. 851, 1981) substances that activate bone resorption in vitro. Lastly, it is also important to emphasize that *A. actinomycetemcomitans* may be only one of many potential "pathogenic" organisms in juvenile periodontitis. Periodontal disease has an uncanny and somehow predictable way of embarrassing the unwary researcher who overfocuses on a single organism or abnormal host response as the all-encompassing etiological denominator. These conditions occur in constantly changing microenvironments which are not programmed to respond to or respect all of our hypotheses.

SUMMARY

A. actinomycetemcomitans may conceivably be one of the etiological agents in juvenile periodontitis. These organisms are found in high proportions in subgingival plaque of juvenile periodontitis patients, and most strains synthesize a heat-labile exotoxin which destroys human PMNs or monocytes. The leukotoxin rapidly binds to target cells and produces irreversible cell injury within moments. These cytopathic changes can be inhibited by specific antibodies which neutralize the toxin. Such antibodies are found in high titers in sera from the vast majority of juvenile periodontitis patients. We hypothesize that infection by *A. actinomycetemcomitans* may occur during the very early stages in the development of juvenile periodontitis and that leukotoxin production in the gingival crevice may deplete the area of an essential host defense mechanism. The kinetics and potency of the humoral immune response to *A. actinomycetemcomitans* leukotoxin may be crucial in determining whether infection resolves spontaneously or develops into an established clinical lesion.

ACKNOWLEDGMENTS

We are grateful to Janet Klass and Ann Stephenson for skillful technical assistance and to Rosalie Lillie for help in preparing the manuscript.

Our studies are supported by Public Health Service grants DE-02623 and DE-03995 from the National Institute of Dental Research.

LITERATURE CITED

1. **Baehni, P. C., C. C. Tsai, W. P. McArthur, B. F. Hammond, and N. S. Taichman.** 1979. Interaction of inflammatory cells and oral microorganisms. VIII. Detection of leukotoxic activity of a plaque-derived gram-negative microorganism. Infect. Immun. 24:233–243.
2. **Ciancola, L. K., R. T. Genco, M. R. Patters, J. McKenna, and C. J. VanOss.** 1977. Defective polymorphonuclear leukocyte function in a human periodontal disease. Nature (London) 265:445–447.
3. **Clark, R. A., R. C. Page, and G. Wilde.** 1977. Defective neutrophil chemotaxis in juvenile periodontitis. Infect. Immun. 18:694–700.
4. **Ebersole, J. L., D. E. Frey, M. A. Taubman, and J. J. Smith.** 1980. An ELISA for measuring serum antibodies to *Actinobacillus actinomycetemcomitans*. J. Periodontal Res. 15:621–632.
5. **Kiley, P., and S. C. Holt.** 1980. Characterization of the lipopolysaccharide from *Actinobacillus actinomycetemcomitans* Y4 and N27. Infect. Immun. 30:862–873.
6. **Lavine, W. S., E. G. Maderazo, J. Stolman, P. A. Ward, R. B. Cogen, I. Greenblatt, and P. B. Robertson.** 1979. Impaired neutrophil chemotaxis in patients with juvenile and rapidly progressing periodontitis. J. Periodontal Res. 14:10–19.
7. **McArthur, W. P., C. C. Tsai, P. C. Baehni, R. J. Genco, and N. S. Taichman.** 1981. Leukotoxic effects of *Actinobacillus actinomycetemcomitans*. Modulation by serum components. J. Periodontal Res. 16:159–170.
8. **Newman, H. N.** 1980. Neutrophils and IgG at the host-plaque interface on children's teeth. J. Periodontol. 51:642–651.
9. **Newman, M. G., and S. S. Socransky.** 1977. Predominant cultivable microbiota in periodontosis. J. Periodontal Res. 12:120–128.
10. **Slots, J., H. S. Reynolds, and R. J. Genco.** 1980. *Actinobacillus actinomycetemcomitans* in human periodontal disease: a cross-sectional microbiological investigation. Infect. Immun. 29:1013–1020.
11. **Taichman, N. S., R. T. Dean, and C. J. Sanderson.** 1980. Biochemical and morphological characterization of the killing of human monocytes by a leukotoxin derived from *Actinobacillus actinomycetemcomitans*. Infect. Immun. 28:258–268.
12. **Taichman, N. S., and J. M. A. Wilton.** 1981. Leukotoxicity of an extract from *Actinobacillus actinomycetemcomitans* for gingival polymorphonuclear leukocytes. Inflammation 5:1–12.
13. **Tanner, A. C. R., R. C. Haffer, G. T. Bratthall, R. A. Visconti, and S. S. Socransky.** 1979. A study of the bacteria associated with advancing periodontitis in man. J. Clin. Periodontol. 6:278–307.
14. **Tsai, C.-C., W. P. McArthur, P. C. Baehni, B. F. Hammond, and N. S. Taichman.** 1979. Extraction and partial characterization of a leukotoxin from a plaque-derived gram-negative microorganism. Infect. Immun. 25:427–439.
15. **van Dyke, T. E., H. J. Horoszewicz, L. J. Cianciola, and R. J. Genco.** 1980. Neutrophil chemotaxis dysfunction in human periodontitis. Infect. Immun. 27:124–132.

EFFECTOR SYSTEMS—SPECIFIC AND NONSPECIFIC

Relation Between Periodontal Disease Activity and Serum Antibody Titers to Oral Bacteria

KÅRE TOLO AND PER BRANDTZAEG

Department of Periodontology, Dental Faculty, and Histochemical Laboratory, Institute of Pathology, Rikshospitalet, University of Oslo, Oslo, Norway

INTRODUCTION

Immunoglobulins are released into the circulation from various sites of production, and the serum antibody levels reflect the overall humoral immune responses, including the local ones that are not involved in the secretory immune system. The gingival pattern of inflammatory cell infiltrate developing in response to dental plaque is suggestive of local antigenic stimulation (21, 24, 38). Bacterial antigens have been detected in gingival phagocytes by Takeuchi et al. (50) and Ranney (41). We found such antigens in macrophages close to the gingival crevice, and local plasma cells producing immunoglobulin IgG antibodies to the same antigens were also observed (4).

Bacterial lipopolysaccharides and polysaccharides are known to be potent B-cell mitogens (23), and the dental plaque probably exerts a topical mitogenic effect in addition to being a source of antigens. Much attention has been given to the proliferative response of peripheral blood lymphocytes to preparations of oral bacteria (22, 27, 39), but mitogens may have contributed to the observed blastogenesis (7, 12). However, several gram-negative anaerobic organisms have elicited statistically more frequent positive results in subjects with periodontitis than in those with normal gingiva (39), indicating sensitization to bacterial antigens. Moreover, results of tissue culture experiments have suggested gingival synthesis of antibodies to *Fusobacterium* (2) and to *Bacteroides asaccharolyticus* (W. B. Clark, B. J. Mansheim, W. J. Lucas, M. B. Hall, J. E. Beem, and M. L. Strenstrøm, Int. Assoc. Dent. Res., 59th General Session, abstr. 706, 1981).

More than 50% of the circulating IgG and IgA are normally distributed extravascularly (29, 56), and immunofluorescence studies of inflamed gingiva have demonstrated that the connective tissue ground substance is permeated by serum-derived immunoglobulins which diffuse into the crevicular epithelium (3, 4). The increased permeability in inflamed gingiva makes it likely that the interstitial immunoglobulin levels approach those of serum. The levels of IgG, IgA, and IgM in crevicular fluid from severely inflamed gingiva averaged 70 to 85% of the respective serum concentrations (45). Regardless of their site of origin, therefore, serum antibodies to gram-negative anaerobic bacteria will influence the local host–parasite relationship during the development of periodontal disease.

We have previously discussed the possibly protective and adverse effects of antibodies in the gingival area and pointed out that the balance between the complement-activating immunoglobulins (IgG and IgM) and the antiphlogistic IgA may be of importance (4). The way antibody influences mucosal antigen penetration is of special interest since this event may be related to the initial phase of periodontal disease. In an in vitro test model with rabbit sublingual mucosa, we found that human albumin and transferrin penetrated the membrane at rates corresponding to the respective molecular weights of the two test proteins (52). With membranes from animals immunized with human albumin, the influx of this protein was apparently retarded as a result of the formation of immune complexes; however, the concurrent penetration of transferrin was significantly enhanced (52). Application of antigen in the gingival crevice of sensitized animals has likewise been reported to lead to immune complex formation in the crevicular epithelium (32), and application of antigen on epithelial surfaces of sensitized animals stimulates local emigration of neutrophils (1). Immune complexes enhance the release of lysosomal enzymes (10) through a mechanism that can be triggered by extremely low antigen concentrations (8). Thus, IgG and IgM antibodies to antigens from gram-negative anaerobic bacteria probably maintain complement activation in the crevicular area and may, therefore, indirectly impair the epithelial barrier function. The phlogistic effects of IgG and IgM antibodies may also be relevant to activation of latent collagenase (57). Altogether, enhanced penetration of bacterial lipopolysaccharides and other antigens is most likely involved in the conversion of a relatively stable established lesion of gingivitis to a progressive lesion of periodontitis.

It is of interest to map the humoral immune response pattern to plaque bacteria for two reasons. First, organisms responsible for the most significant changes in antibody titers are probably closely associated with the development of periodontal disease. Second, identification of the most immunogenic bacterial antigens is necessary to elucidate the immunopathological mechanisms involved in the periodontal lesion.

ASSAYS FOR ANTIBACTERIAL ACTIVITY OF SERUM IMMUNOGLOBULINS

Passive hemagglutination based on sheep erythrocytes coated with bacterial cells or bacterial antigen preparations was previously used in studies of serum antibodies to oral bacteria (19, 25, 27). Unfractionated serum is usually tested by this method, and IgG, IgA, and IgM may all contribute to the result; information about the isotype of the antibodies is, therefore, not obtained unless the test includes a step of enhancement with class-specific heteroantisera or reduction to inhibit IgM activity.

Indirect immunofluorescence based on incubation of bacterial smears with human serum has also been extensively used. Bacterial cells from pure cultures and isotype-specific fluorescent conjugates are required to obtain definite information. An important pitfall is the presence of antibacterial activities in the fluorescent conjugates, and control smears incubated with saline instead of human serum are always necessary (37). A certain element of subjectivity is obviously involved in the determination of endpoint titers of positive sera. Gilmour and Nisengard (17) stated that indirect immunofluorescence gives lower titers than several other tests, the sensitivity being 1% of that obtained with passive hemagglutination. However, Ebersole et al. (11) obtained similar titers with the two methods. Differences in the antigen binding to erythrocytes and different antigenicity of the coats may explain variability in hemagglutination, and differences in the secondary conjugates affect the sensitivity of indirect immunofluorescence tests.

TABLE 1. *Reciprocal serum antibody titers to anaerobic oral bacteria in subjects with clinically normal gingiva or periodontal disease*

Bacterium	Assay[a]	No. of sera	Controls	Gingivitis	Periodontitis	References
Actinomyces israelii	IIF (IgG)	40		40	**110**[b]	Nisengard and Beutner (36)
A. israelii	IIF (IgG)	39		<30	40	Gilmour and Nisengard (17)
A. naeslundii	IIF (IgG)	40		40	**110**	Nisengard and Beutner (36)
A. naeslundii	IIF (IgG)	39		<40	**80**	Gilmour and Nisengard (17)
A. viscosus	HA	23		56	91[c]	Lehner et al. (27)
A. viscosus	IIF (IgG)	9	55		40	Williams et al. (58)
Bacterionema matruchotii	IIF (IgG)	39		<50	>40	Gilmour and Nisengard (17)
Bacteroides melaninogenicus	HA	54	20[d]	<20[e]		Hofstad (19)
B. melaninogenicus	HA	23	10	5	10[c]	Lehner et al. (27)
Bacteroides A41	IIF (IgG)	9			5	Williams et al. (58)
B. fragilis	HA	54	40[d]	40[e]		Hofstad (19)
Fusobacterium fusiforme	HA	23		7	12[c]	Lehner et al. (27)
F. nucleatum	HA	54	20[d]	80[e]		Hofstad (19)
Fusobacterium polymorphum	BA	11	456		**2,644**	Evans et al. (15)
Fusobacterium H31	IIF (IgG)	9	<4		<8	Williams et al. (58)
Fusobacterium F4	IIF (IgG)	53		50[f]		Ørstavik and Brandtzaeg (37)
Leptotrichia buccalis	H	9		<100		Merhagen et al. (33)
L. buccalis	H	6			>128	Falkler and Hawley (16)
L. buccalis	HA	6			>32	Falkler and Hawley (16)
L. buccalis	IIF (IgG)	90	20[g]	120[h]		Mashimo et al. (31)
L. buccalis	IIF (IgM)	90	<20[g]	<40[h]		Mashimo et al. (31)
Selenomonas E14	IIF (IgG)	19	<4	10	20	Gilmour and Nisengard (17)
Veillonella	IIF (IgG)	9			<4	Williams et al. (58)
Veillonella	HA	23		50	80[c]	Lehner et al. (27)
Veillonella	IIF (IgG)	9	<4		<4	Williams et al. (58)
Veillonella	IIF (IgG)	53		80		Ørstavik and Brandtzaeg (37)

[a] IIF, Indirect immunofluorescence; HA, passive hemagglutination; H, hemolysis test; BA, bactericidal test.
[b] Boldface figures represent statistically significant increase ($P < 0.05$) of titer compared with gingivitis group or controls.
[c] Subjects with juvenile periodontitis.
[d] Healthy children.
[e] Blood donors.
[f] Army recruits.
[g] Children 6 to 12 years of age.
[h] Adults, 25 to 45 years of age.

Passive hemolysis is more sensitive than passive hemagglutination (16, 33), but IgA antibodies cannot be measured by this method. The hemolysis test is based on antigen-coated sheep erythrocytes that are incubated first with complement-inactivated human serum and then with a standard preparation of guinea pig complement. Bactericidal assays (15) are also complement dependent, and their sensitivity is approximately 10 times that of passive hemagglutination (9).

Introduction of heteroantibodies labeled with radioactive tracers or enzymes has largely increased the sensitivity of assays for human antibodies. Sanford and Smith (44) reported that a radioimmunoassay (RIA) for quantitation of serum antibody to *Escherichia coli* and *F. polymorphum* was, on the average, 27 times more sensitive than indirect immunofluorescence. The authors also pointed out that the RIA detected quantitative differences between sera not apparent by indirect immunofluorescence, and the reproducibility was good, showing a coefficient of variation of 5%. RIA is a rapid method, and labeled reagents specific for human immunoglobulins are now commercially available. Obvious drawbacks are the requirement for an expensive scintillation counter and the possibility of contaminating the environment with radioactivity.

An enzyme-linked immunosorbent assay (ELISA) was introduced by Engvall and Perlemann (14) and has become a popular method for quantitation of antibodies to bacterial antigens. The sensitivity of the ELISA is equal to that of the RIA (13), the immunological reagents are relatively inexpensive and are stable for months, and no radiation hazards are involved. In our hands the reproducibility of the ELISA is similar to that reported for the RIA, giving a coefficient of variation of less than 10% in six parallel tests (53). A major advantage with both the RIA and the ELISA is that the readings are objective and digital results are obtained.

In all types of assay for antibodies to bacteria, the preparation of bacterial cells or bacterial components is fundamental; the standardization of such preparations is a major problem. Intact cells, formalinized bacteria, and more or less purified fractions of bacterial proteins or polysaccharides have been used to test human sera for antibodies to oral bacteria. These antigen preparations necessarily have different binding properties to erthrocytes and to the solid phases used in the RIA and ELISA. Bruins et al. (5) reported that bacterial polysaccharides were detached form polystyrene by washing with 0.05% Tween 20, which has been routinely used in the ELISA. Fc receptors for IgG and IgA may contribute to nonspecific binding to gram-positive cocci (35), and it is possible that similar nonspecific results can occur with other organisms. Binding to Fc receptor is presumably a greater problem with intact bacterial cells than with coats of antigen fractions.

NATURAL SERUM ANTIBODIES TO ANAEROBIC ORAL BACTERIA

The subgingival microbiota in periodontal disease is dominated by gram-negative rods, most of which are obligate anaerobes (51). *Actinomyces* species are predominant in older plaques associated with gingivitis (49), but gram-negative organisms also account for a large proportion of the gingival microbiota in this group of patients.

In Table 1 we have summarized some of the studies of serum antibodies to anaerobic oral bacteria reported over the past 15 years. Highly varying titers to different organisms of the subgingival microbiota have been observed. We agree with Mashimo et al. (31) that natural antibodies to organisms of dental plaque are present in most adults, although few data have been based on sera of subjects with a healthy periodontium. Most control sera have been obtained from blood donors, army recruits, and other subjects in whom the periodontal conditions have not been strictly defined. In light of the prevalence of gingivitis in the general population, it is probably correct to refer these studies to the gingivitis group rather than to the group with healthy gingiva.

The level of antibodies observed in subjects with a defined clinically healthy gingiva forms a base line for evaluation of the humoral response to anaerobic oral bacteria in subjects with periodontal disease. At present, little information is available about this level, but according to our results it is lower than that observed in the gingivitis group (K. Tolo, K. Schenck, and P. Brandtzaeg, in preparation).

SERUM ANTIBODIES TO ANAEROBIC ORAL BACTERIA IN PERIODONTAL DISEASE

In 14 of 20 comparative studies, the titers of specific activity to various anaerobic bacteria were reported to be increased in subjects with periodontal disease (Table 1). In three studies the titers were lower in subjects with periodontal disease, and in another three no difference was observed. Two of the three studies that showed a reduced titer in the periodontitis group included only four subjects with periodontal disease and five subjects in the control group, and the variation between individuals was considerable. Subjects with periodontal disease had significantly increased levels of serum antibody to *Actinomyces israelii* and *A. naeslundii* (17, 36), *B. melaninogenicus* (27), *F. polymorphum* (15), and *Leptotrichia buccalis* (17).

METHODOLOGICAL CONSIDERATIONS

The range of levels of antibody to different anaerobic bacteria observed in subjects with periodontal disease is very wide. A large number of sera therefore have to be examined to reveal characteristics of the immune response clearly associated with the disease. The number of bacterial species in the subgingival microbiota, not to mention the number of bacterial antigens, makes it necessary to carry out a substantial amount of experimentation before the humoral immune response can be mapped completely.

The introduction of immunoassays based on microtiter plates has facilitated simultaneous testing of several antigen systems, and automatically operated washing devices and multichanneled reading machines have made it possible to handle a large number of sera in a reasonably short time. The progress that can be made in this field will now depend mainly on ability to culture the bacteria of the subgingival microbiota and to extract and purify relevant antigen fractions from such cultures. Initially, crude fractions have to be tested with an adequate number of human sera to identify the most immunogenic bacteria and their major antigens. Further antigen purification will be needed to obtain detailed information about the immunopathology of the periodontal lesion.

CLINICAL VARIABLES

A meaningful search for correlations between gingival condition and the level of serum antibody to oral bacteria requires that the clinical variables be evaluated with precision and satisfactory reproducibility. It appears that in most published studies, more attention was given to the immunological method than to the clinical description of the periodontal condition.

In 7 of 10 studies of serum antibodies (Table 1), no criteria were given for the diagnosis of gingivitis or for the grading of the degree of gingival inflammation. Unfortunately, all clinical index systems proposed are more or less dependent on the subjective interpretation of the criteria. Estimation of gingival fluid flow by staining of filter paper strips placed in the gingival crevice or by a gingival fluid meter can be made with good reproducibility, showing a coefficient of variation of 4% for the paper strips and 3% for the fluid meter according to Suppipat (48). A more practicable method for scoring of gingival inflammation is to count the number of gingival crevices that show bleeding on gentle probing; probes that can be set to a predetermined level of pressure are available and may improve the reproducibility of this method (54).

Loss of supporting periodontal tissues has traditionally been estimated by measuring periodontal pockets with graded periodontal probes. It has been shown that the level of intact periodontal fibers can be determined by probing with a force of 0.75 N (18, 28, 54). Glavind and Løe (18) reported that the method of error in such measurements was less than 0.5 mm, and the means obtained by each observer showed a standard error of ± 0.12 mm. However, systematic measurements require 45 min per patient (18). Recent studies have indicated that the precision obtained by radiographic estimation of the alveolar bone level is approximately ± 0.2 mm. Lang and Hill (26) stated that periodic identical radiographs may be a valuable adjunct to supplement data on the progression of periodontitis, which may be a more relevant clinical indicator of disease activty than accumulated loss of attachment.

STUDIES OF RELATIONS BETWEEN SERUM ANTIBODIES AND PERIODONTAL CONDITION

Data from other laboratories. Attempts made during the past decade to correlate the humoral immune response to subgingival bacteria with the severity and type of periodontal disease were largely inconclusive. The fact that the immunological methods used provided data of limited value in quantitative terms and incomplete information about the immunoglobulin isotypes involved resulted in only a fragmentary mapping of the immune response (Table 1). Moreover, in several studies too little attention was given to the clinical variables used to characterize the subjects from whom the sera were obtained.

The introduction of the ELISA seemed to revive the research activity in this field (Table 2). Ebersole et al. (11) studied the levels of serum antibodies to *Actinobacillus actinomycetemcomitans* in nine subjects with various periodontal conditions. Antibacterial activity was determined by ELISA, indirect immuno-fluorescence, passive hemagglutination, and direct bacterial agglutination. The results showed that the ELISA titers correlated well with the titers obtained by the other methods. The ELISA proved to have increased sensitivity combined with ability to detect quantitative differences not revealed by the other methods. The ELISA coats were made with bacterial suspensions, and the same approach was used by Magee (30). Surface antigens are probably well represented in this type of coat, but other relevant antigens may not be represented. Moreover, the coating reproducibility may be poorer than that obtained with solutions of antigens, and the results of Ebersole et al. (11) indicated a relatively high background with a correspondingly low signal-to-noise ratio. Thus, there seems to be an increased nonspecific binding to coats of intact bacterial cells compared with coats prduced by antigens in solution.

A comprehensive study of the serum antibodies to *B. asaccharolyticus* (oral subspecies of *B. melaninogenicus*) in subjects with various periodontal

TABLE 2. *Serum antibody activity to anaerobic oral bacteria measured by an ELISA*[a]

Bacterium	Immuno-globulin class	Normal	Gingivitis	Perio-dontitis	Reference
A. actinomycetem-			$n = 5$[b]	$n = 3$	
comitans	IgG		12	60	Ebersole et al. (11)
B. asaccharolyticus			$n = 56$	$n = 35$	
	IgG		56 ± 64	258 ± 468	Mouton et al. (34)
	IgA		1.8 ± 1.7	2.3 ± 2.9	
	IgM		3.4 ± 3.5	2.9 ± 2.5	
B. asaccharolyticus		$n = 13$	$n = 11$	$n = 35$	
	IgG	66 ± 46	118 ± 60[c]	142 ± 54	Tolo et al. (in
	IgA	42 ± 43	81 ± 62	92 ± 61	preparation)
	IgM	17 ± 12	19 ± 14	34 ± 27[d]	
B. oralis	IgG	88 ± 33	86 ± 42	77 ± 32	
	IgA	26 ± 17	27 ± 18	32 ± 25	
	IgM	17 ± 11	19 ± 20	31 ± 33[d]	
C. ochracea	IgG	10 ± 7	18 ± 13	20 ± 18	
	IgA	9 ± 5	12 ± 9	14 ± 9	
	IgM	4 ± 3	3 ± 4	9 ± 10[d]	
F. nucleatum strain 1	IgG	42 ± 25	45 ± 28	42 ± 21	
	IgA	10 ± 10	11 ± 11	16 ± 12	
	IgM	6 ± 8	4 ± 6	15 ± 21[d]	
F. nucleatum strain 2	IgG	19 ± 14	37 ± 32	25 ± 20	
	IgA	13 ± 10	15 ± 14	13 ± 8	
	IgM	3 ± 2	2 ± 3	7 ± 10[d]	
Fusobacterium	IgG	31 ± 20	66 ± 34	51 ± 35	
	IgA	12 ± 12	26 ± 29	31 ± 35	
	IgM	4 ± 5	7 ± 4	12 ± 15[d]	
S. sputigena	IgG	46 ± 23	67 ± 27	60 ± 34	
	IgA	18 ± 10	24 ± 15	25 ± 16	
	IgM	19 ± 8	20 ± 10	30 ± 20[d]	
Veillonella	IgG	39 ± 19	50 ± 24	47 ± 27	
	IgA	19 ± 11	22 ± 14	24 ± 13	
	IgM	23 ± 14	18 ± 8	31 ± 24[d]	

[a]Results are given in optical density units (mean $\pm$ standard deviation).

[b]Number of sera tested.

[c]Boldface figures represent a significant increase compared with normal ($P < 0.05$). Student's test, two-tailed.

[d]Significantly increased compared with gingivitis group ($P < 0.05$). Student's test, two-tailed.

conditions was recently published by Mouton et al. (34). The specific activity of serum IgG, IgA, and IgM was determined by an ELISA based on coats made with a crude saline extract of homogenized cells from an oral strain. A pool of positive human sera was used as antibody reference, and standard curves were established for the three isotypes. The specificity of the assay was verified by absorption of the positive serum with bacterial cells. Interestingly, absorption with a nonoral strain of *B. melaninogenicus* removed little of the serum activity, indicating the presence of antigens specific for the oral serotype.

Mouton et al. (34) found that the development of serum antibodies to *B. asaccharolyticus* followed the general immune response pattern; in the first months of life there was a rapid increase of IgM activity, followed by IgG and after 6 months also by IgA. Adults with periodontal disease had five times higher levels of IgG antibodies than controls, and the isotype balance was strikingly altered. Thus, the IgG-to-IgA antibody ratio was 30 in controls but 110 in subjects with periodontal disease. IgA antibodies probably compete with IgG antibodies when antigens penetrate the crevicular epithelium, and since IgA lacks complement-activating properties its function may have an anti-phlogistic potential. Thus, disproportionate increase of the IgG titer may be of immunopathological relevance. It may be argued that the age distribution of the periodontitis group was different from that of the controls, but we have observed only a moderate increase of IgG antibody levels to *B. asaccharolyticus* with increasing age in adulthood (Tolo, Schenck, and Brandtzaeg, in preparation).

Data from our laboratory. We have recently established an ELISA for determination of antibody activities of human IgG, IgA, and IgM to eight strains of oral bacteria (53). The strains were sampled from periodontal pockets of subjects with periodontitis and included *B. asaccharolyticus, Capnocytophaga ochracea,* two strains of *F. nucleatum,* one unidentified *Fusobacterium* strain, *B. oralis, Selenomonas sputigena,* and a *Veillonella* strain. After pure cultures were obtained, growth was propagated in a peptone–yeast–glucose medium (20) in which Trypticase was replaced by peptone. The cultures were stored at $-90°C$ with 8.75% dimethyl sulfoxide. Classification was based on Gram staining, motility, end product analyses of volatile acids, carbohydrate fermentation, nitrate reduction, indole reaction, and presence of catalase (6, 20).

Monocultures were grown for 14 days in 0.5-liter portions of the deoxygenated peptone medium; incubation took place at $37°C$ in an anaerobic glove box in an atmosphere of 85% nitrogen, 10% hydrogen, and 5% carbon dioxide and in the presence of a palladium catalyst. Purity was confirmed by subculturing on blood agar plates. Cultures free from contaminants were centrifuged at $10,000 \times g$ for 30 min at $4°C$, and the supernatant fluid was removed. The cells were washed twice in 100 ml of phosphate-buffered saline and centrifuged as above, and the washings were added to the culture fluid. Cloudy supernatants were passed through a sterilized 0.22-μm filter (Millipore Corp.). *B. asaccharolyticus* grew poorly in the peptone medium and was therefore propagated on blood agar. Colonies from 10 plates were collected, suspended in 13 ml of phosphate-buffered saline, and crushed in a cell-disrupting press. The suspension was centrifuged, and the supernatants were collected as above and stored at $-20°C$.

Supernatant fluids from each of the eight bacterial strains were transferred aseptically to dialysis tubing disinfected by boiling in aqueous glycerol for 30 min before use. Dialysis was performed against running tap water for 3 days, and the dialysate was lyophilized if no contaminants were detected by plating on

OD$_{405}$

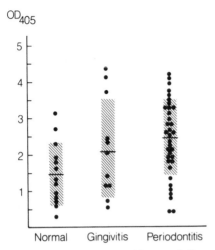

FIG 1. *Specific activity of human IgG to eight strains of gram-negative, anaerobic bacteria isolated from subgingival plaque. The sera were tested by an ELISA at a dilution of 1:100, and each point represents cumulative class-specific antibody activity to the eight strains. The shaded areas indicate the 95% confidence intervals. The means were significantly higher in the gingivitis and periodontitis groups than in normal controls ($P<0.05$).*

OD$_{405}$

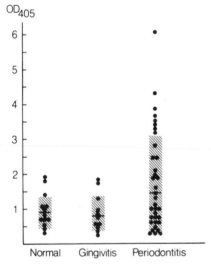

FIG. 2. *Specific activity of human serum IgM to eight bacterial strains tested and recorded as described in Fig. 1. The mean of the periodontitis group was significantly higher than those of the gingivitis group and the controls ($P < 0.05$).*

blood agar. The powders were dissolved in deionized water and filtered through a Sephade G-75 column eluted with deionized water. Fractions corresponding to the void volume peak were pooled, lyophilized, and stored at $-70°C$.

The optimal coating concentrations for the ELISA were determined for the eight antigen fractions, and standard curves were established on the basis of pooled serum from 10 subjects with periodontal disease (53). The specific antibacterial activities of IgG, IgA, and IgM were then measured in the sera of 59 subjects who received a complete dental examination including dental radiographs, medical history, and oral examination with registration of gingival pocket depths and number of bleeding points (Tolo, Schenk, and Brantzaeg, in preparation). Subjects with prior periodontal therapy, those with systemic disease, and those taking medication that might influence the immune response were excluded. The subjects were divided into three groups: normal periodontium (no gingival pockets >4 mm, bleeding index <0.1, attachment level >95%), gingivitis (no gingival pockets >4 mm, bleeding index >0.1, attachment level >95%), and periodontitis (gingival pockets >4 mm, bleeding index >0.1, attachment level <95%).

All subjects had specific IgG activity to antigens from the eight bacterial strains, but considerable individual differences were seen with regard to the level of activity (Table 2). The specific activity of IgA and IgM was below the detection limit in a few sera. A significantly increased level of serum IgG to *B. asaccharolyticus, C. ochracea, F. nucleatum* strain 2, and the unidentified *Fusobacterium* strain was observed in the gingivitis group compared with the normal group. With regard to *S. sputigena,* the increase in IgG activity was smaller, and no significant increase of the IgG activity to *B. oralis, F. nucleatum* strain 1, and *Veillonella* was observed in the gingivitis group. The specific activity of IgA was significantly increased only to *B. asaccharolyticus* and the *Fusobacterium* strain, and IgM activity showed no increase to any strain in the gingivitis group (Table 2).

In the periodontitis group the level of IgG and IgA activity was significantly increased to *B. asaccharolyticus, C. ochracea,* and the unidentified *Fusobacterium* strain compared with normal levels, and the IgA activity was in addition increased to *F. nucleatum* strain 1. The specific IgM activity was significantly increased to all organisms except *Veillonella,* when compared with both the normal group and the gingivitis group (Table 2).

The differences among the three groups when the antibody titers to all eight bacterial strains are collectively taken into account are illustrated in Fig. 1 and 2 with regard to serum IgG and IgM activities, respectively.

DISCUSSION

Our observation of specific activities of serum immunoglobulins to oral bacteria in subjects with a normal periodontium is in accordance with the concept of "natural antibodies" supported by several earlier studies (Table 1). The fact that increased IgG activity was observed to three of eight strains in both gingivitis and periodontitis indicates that some, but not all, of the bacteria of the subgingival microbiota are immunologically associated with the development of periodontal disease.

The increased IgG titer to *B. asaccharolyticus* agrees with the observations of Mouton et al. (34) and Clark et al. (Int. Assoc. Dent. Res., 59th General Session, abstr. 706, 1981), and circumstantial evidence has previously pointed toward a special role of this organism in periodontal disease (40, 46, 51).

The increased titer to *Fusobacterium* is in accordance with the reports of Evans et al. (15) and Berglund (2). Kristoffersen and Hofstad (25) did not observe any correlation between the level of hemagglutinating antibodies to antigens from fusobacteria and the presence of periodontal disease, but the limited quantitative efficiency of passive hemagglutination compared with the ELISA (11) might have contributed to this discordance. However, in the periodontitis group we did not find an increased IgG activity to two of the three strains of *Fusobacterium.* Tanner et al. (51) reported that fusobacteria were the most common isolates in subgingival samples from periodontitis patients, and it was apparent that major morphological and physiological differences existed between the strains. Our experience with classification of fusobacteria supports the view of Tanner et al. (51), and the different levels of antibody activity to our three strains indicate that a thorough taxonomic review of fusobacteria is needed.

The raised IgG activity to *C. ochracea* in the periodontitis group accords with the report of Tanner et al. (51) that this strain increased from a mean of 0.6% of the cultivable bacteria from sites with normal gingiva to a mean of 3.6% from sites with moderate gingival inflammation.

In contrast to the general trend of data indicating an increased serum IgG activity to some gram-negative anaerobic bacteria in periodontal disease, one recent study reported decreased activity to *B. asaccharolyticus, C. ochracea,* and

F. nucleatum (S. L. Doty, D. E. Lopatin, and F. N. Smith, Int. Assoc. Dent. Res., 59th General Session, abstr. 750, 1981). No details of the study were given in the abstract, and at present no explanation can be offered to explain this discrepant observation.

In the periodontitis group we observed a striking increase in IgM activity to all eight strains tested except for *Veillonella*. This result has to be interpreted with caution, since we have not yet analyzed the sera for rheumatoid factor, which may interfere with IgM determinations in the ELISA (43, 55). The concentration of serum IgM is approximately 10% of the corresponding concentration of IgG, and the extravascular proportion of IgM in the gingiva may be even smaller. The complement-activating capacity of IgM is, however, remarkably increased compared with IgG. In a system of erythrocytes, it has been calculated that it takes 800 IgG molecules to create a binding site for C1 whereas only one IgM molecule is neccessary. Our observation of increased IgM activity to *Fusobacterium* may agree with the report of Evans et al. (15), who demonstrated that the increased bactericidal serum activity to *F. polymorphyum* observed in subjects with periodontal disease was associated with IgM.

The selective increase of IgG activity to *B. asaccharolyticus* observed by Mouton et al. (34) in patients with periodontitis was not confirmed in our study since we also noticed a significantly raised IgA titer. This discrepancy may depend on differences in patient groups or in methods. In addition, we found that the IgG increase to *C. ochracea* and *Fusobacterium* was paralleled by a raise IgA activity. However, there were large individual differences, and further studies are needed to evaluate the relation between changes in IgG to IgA antibody ratios and disease severity. The continuous phlogistic effect of a persisting antibacterial IgG response is an attractive explanation for the chronicity of periodontal disease. Indeed, when the humoral response to all eight strains of anaerobic bacteria tested is considered collectively, the most striking feature is a raised IgG titer in both patients with gingivitis and patients with perodontitis. Moreover, regardless of whether the consistently increased IgM titers seen in the latter patients represent true antibodies to the eight strains or an induced rheumatoid factor activity, this observation may, in immunopathological terms, be highly relevant to the conversion of the periodontal lesion from gingivitis to progressive periodontitis.

SUMMARY

Assays for serum antibodies to bacterial antigens were briefly discussed, and results of studies relevant to the oral microbiota were sumarized. Meaningful correlations between periodontal disease activity and serum titers to gram-negative anaerobic oral bacteria require representative antigen preparations, and both the clinical and the immunological variables have to be determined with high sensitivity and good reproducibility. Recent results based on an ELISA were reviewed. These studies indicate that subjects with periodontal disease respond to a selection of the subgingival organisms with a relatively high proportion of complement-activating immunoglobulins. This may result in a disturbed immunological homeostasis in the gingival area and contribute to conversion of the relatively stable lesion of gingivitis to the progressive lesion of periodontitis.

LITERATURE CITED

1. **Belamy, J. E. C., and N. O. Nielsen.** 1974. Immune-mediated emigration of neutrophils into the lumen of the small intestine. Infect. Immun. **9:**615–619.
2. **Berglund, S. E.** 1971. Immunoglobulins in human gingiva with specificity for oral bacteria. J. Periodontol. **42:**546–551.
3. **Brandtzaeg, P.** 1966. Local factors of resistance in the gingival area. J. Periodontal Res. **1:**19–42.
4. **Brandtzaeg, P., and K. Tolo.** 1977. Immunoglobulin systems of the gingiva, p. 145–183. *In* T. Lehner (ed.), The borderland between caries and periodontal disease. Academic Press, London.
5. **Bruins, S. C., I. Ingwer, M. L. Zeckel, and A. C. White.** 1978. Parameters affecting the enzyme-linked immunosorbent assay of immunoglobulin G antibody to a rough mutant of *Salmonella minnesota*. Infect. Immun. **21:**721–728.
6. **Buchanan, R. E., and N. E. Gibbons (ed.).** 1974. Bergey's manual of determinative bacteriology, 8th ed. The Williams & Wilkins Co., Baltimore.
7. **Burckhardt, J. J., B. Guggenheim, and A. Hefti.** 1977. Are *Actinomyces viscosus* antigens B-cell mitogens? J. Immunol. **118:**1460–1465.
8. **Cardella, C. J., P. Davies, and A. C. Allison.** 1974. Immune complexes induce selective release of lysosomal hydrolases from macrophages. Nature (London) **247:**46–48.
9. **Carlsson, H. E., and A. A. Lindberg.** 1978. Immunochemistry of Salmonella O-antigens: characterization of the antibody response to tyvelose 1→3 mannose→1 bovine serum albumin representative of Samonella O-antigen 9. Acta Pathol. Microbiol. Scand. Sect. C **86:**237–244.
10. **Cochrane, C.** 1975. Herman Beerman Lecture. The participation of cells in the inflammatory injury of tissue. J. Invest. Dermatol. **64:**301–306.
11. **Ebersole, J. L., D. E. Frey, M. A. Taubman, and D. Smith.** 1980. An ELISA for measuring serum antibodies to *Actinobacillus actinomycetmcomitans*. J. Periodontal Res. **15:**621–632.
12. **Engel, D., J. Clagett, R. Page, and B. Williams.** 1977. Mitogenic activity of *Actinomyces viscosus*. I. Effects on murine B and T lymphocytes, and partial characterization. J. Immunol. **118:**1466–1471.
13. **Engvall, E., and H. E. Carlsson.** 1976. Enzyme-linked immunosorbent assay, ELISA, p. 135–147. *In* G. Feldman et al. (ed.), First International Symposium on Immunoenzymatic Techniques. INSERM symposium no. 2. North-Holland Publishing Co., Amsterdam.
14. **Engvall, E., and P. Perlemann.** 1972. Enzyme-linked immunosorbent assay, ELISA. III. Quantitation of specific antibodies by enzyme-labeled anti-immunoglobulin in antigen-coated tubes. J. Immunol. **109:**129–135.
15. **Evans, R. T., S. Spaeth, and S. E. Mergenhagen.** 1966. Bactericidal antibody in mammalian serum to obligatory anaerobic Gram-negative bacteria. J. Immunol. **97:**112–119.
16. **Falkler, W. A., Jr., and C. E. Hawley.** 1975. Antigens of *Leptotrichia buccalis*. I. Their serologic reaction with human sera. J. Periodontal Res. **10:**211–215.
17. **Gilmour, M. N., and R. J. Nisengard.** 1974. Interactions between serum titres to filamentous bacteria and their relationship to human periodontal disease. Arch. Oral Biol. **19:**959–968.
18. **Glavind, L., and H. Løe.** 1967. Errors in the clinical assessment of periodontal destruction. J. Periodontal Res. **2:**180–184.
19. **Hofstad, T.** 1974. Antibodies reacting with lipopolysaccharides from *Bacteroides melaninogenicus*, *Bacteroides fragilis*, and *Fusobacterium* in serum from normal human subjects. J. Infect. Dis. **129:**349–351.
20. **Holdeman, L. V., E. P. Cato, and W. E. Moore.** 1977. Anaerobe laboratory manual, 4th ed. Virginia Polytechnic Institute Anaerobe Laboratory, Blacksburg.
21. **Hopps, R. M., and N. W. Johnson.** 1976. Cell dynamics of experimental gingivitis in macaques. Cell proliferation within the inflammatory infiltrate. J. Periodontal Res. **11:**210–217.
22. **Horton, J. E., S. Leiken, and J. Oppenheim.** 1972. Human lymphoproliferative reaction to saliva and dental plaque-deposits. An *in vitro* correlation with periodontal disease. J. Periodontol. **43:**522–527.
23. **Ivanyi, L.** 1977. Immune responses to dextrans, levans and lipopolysaccharides in man, p. 199–209. *In* T. Lehner (ed.), The borderland between caries and periodontal disease. Academic Press, London,
24. **Johnson, N. W., and R. M. Hopps.** 1975. Cell dynamics of experimental gingivitis in macaques. The nature of the cellular infiltrate with varying degrees of gingivitis. J. Periodontal Res. **10:**177–190.
25. **Kristoffersen, T., and T. Hofstad.** 1970. Antibodies in humans to an isolated antigen from oral fusobacteria. J. Periodontal Res. **5:**110–115.
26. **Lang, N. P., and R. W. Hill.** 1977. Radiographs in periodontics. J. Clin. Periodontol. **4:**16–28.
27. **Lehner, T., J. M. A. Wilton, L. Ivanyi, and J. D. Mason.** 1974. Immunological aspects of juvenile periodontitis (periodontosis). J. Periodontal Res. **9:**261–272.
28. **Listgarten, M. A.** 1980. Periodontal probing: What does it mean? J. Clin. Periodontol. **7:**165–176.
29. **Lønsnap Poulsen, H.** 1974. Interstitial fluid concentrations of albumin and immunoglobulin G in normal men. Scand. J. Clin. Lab. Invest. **34:**119–122.
30. **Magee, J. T.** 1980. An enzyme-labelled immunosorbent assay for *Brucella abortus* antibodies. J. Med. Microbiol. **13:**167–172.

31. **Mashimo, P. A., R. J. Genco, and S. A. Ellison.** 1976. Antibodies reactive with *Leptotrichia buccalis* in human serum from infancy to adulthood. Arch. Oral Biol. **21:**277–283.

32. **McDougall, W. A.** 1974 The effect of topical antigen on the gingiva of sensitized rabbits. J. Periodontal Res. **9:**153–164.

33. **Mergenhagen, S. E., W. C. de Araujo, and E. Varah.** 1965. Antibody to *Leptotrichia buccalis* in human sera. Arch. Oral Biol. **10:**29–33.

34. **Mouton, C., P. G. Hammond, J. Slots, and R. J. Genco.** 1981. Serum antibodies to oral *Bacteroides asaccharolyticus* (*Bacteroides gingivalis*): relationship to age and periodontal disease. Infect. Immun. **31:**182–192.

35. **Myhre, E. B., and G. Kronvall.** 1977. Heterogeneity of nonimmune immunoglobulin Fc reactivity among gram-positive cocci: description of three major types of receptors for human immunoglobulin G. Infect. Immun. **17:**475–482.

36. **Nisengard, R. J., and E. H. Beutner.** 1970. Immunologic studies of periodontal disease. V. IgG type antibodies and skin test responses to Actinomyces and mixed oral flora. J. Periodontol. **41:**149–152.

37. **Ørstavik, D., and P. Brandtzaeg.** 1977. Serum antibodies to plaque bacteria in subjects with dental caries and gingivitis. Scand. J. Dent. Res. **85:**106–113.

38. **Page, R. C., and H. E. Schroeder.** 1976. Pathogenesis of inflammatory periodontal disease. A summary of current work. Lab. Invest. **33:**235–249.

39. **Patters, M. R., P. Chen, J. McKenna, and R. J. Genco.** 1980. Lymphoproliferative responses to oral bacteria in humans with varying severities of periodontal disease. Infect. Immun. **28:**777–784.

40. **Patters, M. R., R. J. Genco, M. J. Reed, and P. A. Mashimo.** 1976. Blastogenic response of human lymphocytes to oral bacterial antigens: comparison of individuals with periodontal disease to normal and edentulous subjects. Infect. Immun. **14:**1213–1220.

41. **Ranney, R. R.** 1978. Immunofluorescent localization of soluble dental plaque components in human gingiva affected by periodontitis. J. Periodontal Res. **13:**99–108.

42. **Refshauge, N., and J. Tolderlund.** 1978. Periodic identical intraoral radiographs. Oral Surg. Oral Med. Oral Pathol. **45:**311–316.

43. **Salonen, E. M., A. Vaheri, J. Suni, and O. Wager.** 1980. Rheumatoid factor in acute viral infections: interference with determination of IgM, IgG and IgA antibodies in and enzyme immunoassay. J. Infect. Dis. **142:**250–255.

44. **Sanford, B. A., and K. O. Smith.** 1977. Radioimmunoassay procedure for quantitating bacterial antibody in human sera. J. Immunol. Methods **14:**313–323.

45. **Schenkein, H. A., and R. J. Genco.** 1977. Gingival fluid and serum in periodontal desease. I. Quantitative study of immunoglobulins, complement components and other plasma proteins. J. Periodontol. **48:**772–777.

46. **Socransky, S. S., R. J. Gibbons, A. C. Dale, L. Bortnick, E. Rosenthal, and J. B. MacDonald.** 1964. The microbiota of the gingival crevice area of man. I. Total microscopic and viable counts and counts of specific organisms. Arch. Oral Biol. **8:**275–280.

47. **Socransky, S. S., S. C. Holt, E. R. Leadbetter, A. C. R. Tanner, E. Savitt, and B. F. Hammond.** 1979. Capnocytophaga: new genus of gram-negative gliding bacteria. III. Physiological characterization. Arch. Microbiol. **122:**29–33.

48. **Suppipat, N.** 1977. Evaluation of an electronic device for gingival fluid quantitation. J. Periodontol. **48:**388–394.

49. **Syed, S. A., and W. J. Loesche.** 1978. Bacteriology of human experimental gingivitis: effect of plaque age. Infect. Immun. **21:**821–829.

50. **Takeuchi, H., M. Sumitani, K. Tsubakimoto, and M. Tsutsui.** 1974. Oral microorganism in the gingiva of individuals with periodontal disease. J. Dent. Res. **53:**132–136.

51. **Tanner, A. C. R., C. Haffer, G. T. Bratthall, R. A. Visconti, and S. S. Socransky.** 1979. A study of the bacteria associated with advancing periodontitis in man. J. Clin. Periodontol. **6:**278–307.

52. **Tolo, K., P. Brantzaeg, and J. Jonsen.** 1977. Mucosal penetration of antigen in the presence or absence of serum-derived antibody. An in vitro study of rabbit oral and intestinal mucosa. Immunology **33:**733–743.

53. **Tolo, K., K. Schenck, and P. Brandtzaeg.** 1981. Enzyme-linked immunosorbent assay for human IgG, IgA and IgM antibodies to antigens from anaerobic cultures of seven oral bacteria. J. Immunol. Methods **45:**27–40.

54. **van der Velden, U., and J. H. de Vries.** 1978. Introduction of a new periodontal probe: the pressure probe. J. Clin. Periodontol. **5:**188–197.

55. **Vejtorp, M.** 1980. The interference of IgM rheumatoid factor in enzyme-linked immunosorbent assays of rubella IgM and IgG antibodies. J. Virol. Methods **1:**1–9.

56. **Waldman, T. A., and W. Strober.** 1969. Metabolism of immunoglobulins. Prog. Allergy **13:**1–110.

57. **Werb, Z.** 1978. Pathways for the modulation of macrophage collagenase activity, p. 213–228. *In* J. F. Horton, Tarpley, and Davis (ed.), Proceedings, Mechanisms of Localized Bone Loss (a special supplement to Calcified Tissue Abstracts).

58. **Williams, B. L., R. M. Pantalone, and J. C. Sherris.** 1976. Subgingival microflora and periodontitis. J. Periodontal Res. **11:**1–18.

Association Between Systemic and Local Antibody and Periodontal Diseases

M. A. TAUBMAN, J. L. EBERSOLE, AND D. J. SMITH

Department of Immunology, Forsyth Dental Center, Boston, Massachusetts 02115

FEATURES OF HUMAN PERIODONTAL DISEASE

A consistently observed feature in human periodontal tissues is the presence of a dense inflammatory infiltrate consisting almost totally of plasma cells and lymphocytes (23, 28). Recent findings also suggest that the inflammatory infiltrate in periodontosis consists of more than 70% plasma cells and blast cells (17). The inflammatory component is also associated with the very early stages of gingival disease (27). There is substantial evidence that human B lymphocytes (2, 15) and T lymphocytes (14) are sensitized to various products of oral microorganisms, suggesting that these products gain access to immunocompetent cells. Subsequent immune reactions may then contribute to the pathogenesis of periodontal disease (13). There has been continuing discussion of the potential of the host immune response as a protective or destructive factor in the genesis of periodontal disease. In the past decade, many investigations have provided evidence that immunopathological reactions brought about by lymphocytes, macrophages, immune complexes, or neutrophils were or could be responsible in whole or in part for the type of tissue destruction seen in periodontal disease.

CELLULAR ASPECTS OF PERIODONTAL DISEASE(S)

Mackler and his co-workers (18–20) found that mild gingivitis was characterized by lymphocytes lacking surface immunoglobulins, presumably thymus (T)-dependent cells, and that periodontitis lesions contained predominantly immunoglobulin-positive lymphocytes and plasma cells. They suggested that the cellular infiltrate present during the most destructive stage of periodontal disease was primarily composed of bone marrow (B)-derived cells. Others found that a majority of lymphoid cells in lesions of established chronic inflammatory periodontal disease were immunoglobulin M (IgM)-bearing B lymphocytes; few T cells were identified (30). Still others found a preponderance of T lymphocytes in surgical specimens of the gingiva after an extensive regimen of scaling and plaque control for at least 2 months (32). The progressive B-lymphocyte nature of the lesion has also been observed in a germfree rat system, where gingival lymphocytes were characterized (34). Introduction of ovalbumin (of approximate size to penetrate gingival tissues; 22) resulted in gingival cell sensitization and periodontal bone loss in rats. Therefore, cells of the B-lymphocyte series can be found in the periodontal tissues. Consistent with these findings are several new suggestions as to the importance of these cells and their products in the pathogenesis of periodontal diseases.

POLYCLONAL ACTIVATION AND PERIODONTAL DISEASE

A recent suggestion involves theoretical considerations of "polyclonal activation." Smith and his co-workers (33) have shown that sonic extracts from various oral organisms stimulate human peripheral blood lymphocytes to produce plaque-forming cells against fluorescein isothiocyanate-conjugated sheep erythrocytes. Sonic extracts from *Escherichia coli*, *Bacteroides melaninogenicus*, *Actinomyces naeslundii*, and *A. viscosus* were shown to be as effective in polyclonal activation as pokeweed mitogen (L. Lariscy, G. Miller, P. Bick, R. Ranney, and J. Tew, J. Dent. Res. Spec. Issue A **59**:325, abstr. 230, 1980). These investigators hypothesize that polyclonal B-cell activators stimulate B cells to produce antibody or lymphokines, or both. Osteolytic or calcium-mobilizing factors from plasma cells (osteoclast-activating factor) may be responsible for the loss of the alveolar bony support seen in periodontal diseases. Although the proposed hypothesis is quite interesting, there is at present little direct evidence to support a major role for polyclonal activation in destructive periodontal disease.

Recently, the concept of the protective nature of the immune response has regained ascendancy. One aspect involves the neutrophil as a protective cell. Evidence was derived from the fact that systemic neutrophil disorders are often associated with severe periodontal disease and the laboratory demonstration that neutrophil function is defective in localized juvenile periodontitis (periodontosis) patients. Further experiments (21) have shown that patients

TABLE 1. *Comparison of the sensitivity of the ELISA procedure with bacterial agglutination (BA), passive hemagglutination (PHA), and indirect immunofluorescence (IIF)*

A. Antibody to intact *A. actinomycetemcomitans* (strain Y4) comparative titers (IIF of each patient normalized to 1)

Serum	ELISA	BA	IIF
A	18.7	3.2	1
B	12.7	1.2	1
C	2.3	0.2	1
D	>15.5	>2.4	1
E	3.9	0.6	1
F	5.6	1.6	1
G	>4.9	>0.8	1
H	>4.0	>0.4	1
I	2.6	>0.4	1

B. Antibody to sonic extract antigens of *A. actinomycetemcomitans* comparative titers (PHA of each patient normalized to 1)

Serum	ELISA	PHA
A	39.0	1
B	20.4	1
C	46.7	1
D	25.8	1
E	19.0	1
F	10.6	1
H	9.0	1
G	27.8	1
I	>7.0	1

with juvenile periodontitis have antibodies which neutralize the leukotoxin produced by *Actinobacillus actinomycetemcomitans*.

SERUM ANTIBODIES AND PERIODONTAL DISEASE(S)

The presence of serum antibodies to important periodontopathic organisms has been confirmed as these organisms have been recognized (11, 24, 26; J. L. Ebersole, M. A. Taubman, D. J. Smith, R. J. Genco, and D. E. Frey, Clin. Exp. Immunol., in press). Generally, attempts to correlate antibody levels to oral bacteria with the development and severity of periodontal disease have been inconclusive because many of the potentially periodontopathic organisms were not enumerated at the times the attempts were made. A second reason is that methodology has not been available to measure disease activity. Therefore, the relationship between periodontal disease and host immune response remains to be clarified.

ENZYME-LINKED IMMUNOSORBENT ASSAY (ELISA)

The ELISA procedure has been used in our laboratories to detect and measure isotype-specific antibodies directed to a variety of defined antigens including dinitrophenylated proteins (9), *Streptococcus mutans* antigens (35), ovalbumin (34), and sheep erythrocytes. This procedure has been particularly useful for detecting the small quantities of antibody present in secretions and has enabled us to investigate functional aspects of the secretory immune system. We adopted this procedure to analyze antibodies to intact periodontal disease-associated microorganisms.

The organisms were grown in chemically defined or complex media and then formalinized. Initially, various dilutions of each organism were bound to microtiter plates and tested to determine the optimal bacterial concentration for binding to the plates. Optimal dilutions of rabbit anti-human IgG, IgA, or IgM and the enzyme conjugate (goat anti-rabbit IgG conjugated with alkaline phosphatase) were also determined on the basis of optical density at 400 nm after subtraction of background (8).

ORGANISMS

A battery of oral microorganisms was selected on the basis of previous association with periodontal disease or culturing from sites of disease (present or past). The organisms used were *Actinobacillus actinomycetemcomitans* Y4, *A. actinomycetemcomitans* ATCC 29523, *Actinomyces naeslundii* I, *A. viscosus* T14Av, *A. viscosus* T14V, *Bacteroides gingivalis* 381, *B. melaninogenicus* subsp. *intermedius* 581, *Campylobacter concisus* 484 (ATCC 33237), *Capnocytophaga gingivalis* 27, *C. ochracea* 6, *C. sputigena* 4 (ATCC 33123), *Eikenella corrodens* 373, *E. corrodens* 1073, *Eubacterium brachy*, *Fusobacterium nucleatum* 364, *Selenomonas sputigena* 5, *Streptococcus mutans* Ingbritt, *S. sanguis* 254, *Wolinella* sp. (anaerobic vibrio) 286, *W. recta* 371, and *W. succinogenes* 9584.

SENSITIVITY

As mentioned, the ELISA assay has been shown to have the sensitivity to detect antibodies in secretions. Such an assay would be ideal, because of the ease of performance, for testing sera and the small amounts of gingival crevice fluid available.

We compared the sensitivity of the ELISA procedure with bacterial agglutination, passive hemagglutination, and indirect immunofluorescence (26). As shown in Table 1, the ELISA is from 2.3 to 46.7 times as sensitive as other immunological assays that have been employed for antibody detection. This technique has been shown to be as sensitive as radioimmunoassay (10). Certain individuals apparently lacked reactivity when the conventional techniques were used, but the ELISA was able to detect the presence of serum antibodies of the IgG isotype. The ELISA can also be used to determine isotype-specific antibodies with relative ease compared with other procedures.

Experimental sera and salivas were tested under the optimal conditions. The results are expressed as ELISA units. These were determined by relating optical density values from each experimental sample to a reference serum or saliva (that sample with high reactivity to each individual organism) which was assigned a value of 100 ELISA units. Thus, comparisons of reactivity between organisms and isotypes cannot be made; however, comparisons of the individual reactions to an organism can be made among the groups of individuals tested.

PATIENT SAMPLES

All serum and saliva samples were obtained from the patient populations of Forsyth Dental Center and the State University of New York at Buffalo. Blood was drawn by venipuncture, and lemon drop-stimulated parotid saliva was collected by use of a standard Curby cup. Individuals were divided into six groups (36) including: localized juvenile periodontitis (LJP), generalized juvenile periodontitis (GJP), acute necrotizing ulcerative gingivitis (ANUG), adult periodontitis (AP), edentulous, and normal. The LJP group was composed of 38 patients who had alveolar bone loss that was on the molars and incisors and involved not more than two additional teeth (<14 teeth). The mean age of the group was 19.3 years, with a range of 14 to 29. The GJP group ($n = 11$) had severe alveolar bone loss on ≥ 14 teeth with no definite pattern of localized disease. The mean age of the group was 22.0 years, with a range of 13 to 29. The AP group consisted of 39 patients who exhibited severe alveolar bone loss with numerous vertical defects in the bone support. This group had a mean age of 32.4 years, with a range of 27 to 63. The ANUG group ($n = 9$) had a mean age of 23.3 years, with a range of 17 to 29. The edentulous group had six patients with ages greater than 50 years. The normal group consisted of 24 healthy individuals with a mean age of 24.6 years and a range of 18 to 37. These patients had no evidence of bone loss or periodontal disease other than mild gingivitis.

SPECIFICITY: REPRESENTATIVE ADSORPTION STUDIES

In these studies, we established the lack of cross-reaction among the rabbit anti-human isotyping sera and the specificity of these sera (8). Antibody in patients' serum was shown to be specific for the *Actinobacillus*. Virtually no cross-reactivity was observed between this organism and other commonly isolated plaque organisms (Fig. 1). Even another strain of *Actinobacillus* (*A. actinomycetemcomitans* 29523) which produces little leukotoxin demonstrated minimal cross-reactivity, establishing the specificity of antibody to these organisms (Ebersole et al., in press). Similar specificity studies have been performed for *Bacteriodes* species, *Capnocytophaga* species, and *Wolinella* species.

Serum IgG

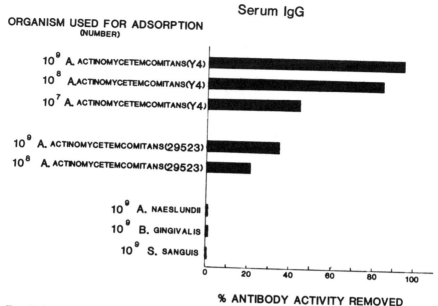

ORGANISM USED FOR ADSORPTION
(NUMBER)

% ANTIBODY ACTIVITY REMOVED

FIG. 1. *Specificity of serum antibodies to* A. actinomycetemcomitans *strain Y4. Five sera were adsorbed with various numbers of formalinized microorganisms. Subsequently, the unadsorbed and adsorbed sera were tested in an ELISA for antibody activity against A.* actinomycetemcomitans *Y4. The data are expressed as $100 - (\bar{x}$ ELISA units adsorbed $/ \bar{x}$ ELISA units unadsorbed$) \times 100 = \%$ of antibody activity removed. Mean antibody activity (ELISA units) was determined from triplicate analyses of each treatment sample, and the standard errors for each test were no greater than 9%.*

ANTIBODIES TO PERIODONTAL DISEASE-ASSOCIATED MICROORGANISMS: SYSTEMIC RESPONSES

Sera from 38 LJP (periodontosis), 11 GJP, 38 AP, 9 ANUG, 6 edentulous, and 24 normal patients were screened for IgG antibodies to the battery of oral microorganisms. In general, four categories of response were noted in the sera of these patients. These categories were determined by comparison among the diseased and normal patients. The four categories were as follows:

Category I. No differences in the level of serum antibodies related to disease.

Category II. Increased levels of serum antibody in certain individual patients with periodontal disease(s) when compared with the normal group.

Category III. Increased levels of serum antibody and increased frequency of response in groups with periodontal disease(s) when compared with the normal group.

Category IV. Reduced level and frequency of response in the group(s) with periodontal disease(s).

Below we describe the findings in each of these categories, which are shown in Fig. 2.

I. No Differences in Immune Response

In general, two subcategories of response (minimal and generalized) could be ascertained which did not differ with respect to disease state. All individuals

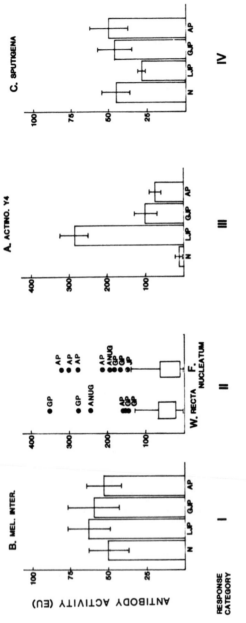

FIG. 2. Response categories of human serum antibody reactions to oral microorganisms. I. Generalized serum response among diseased (LJP, GJP, AP) and normal (N) patients as represented by serum IgG antibody to B. melaninogenicus subsp. intermedius. Bars represent the mean antibody activity (ELISA units, EU) of the group, and the brackets enclose 2 standard errors. II. Extreme serum response in some diseased individuals when compared to the general population samples (N, LJP, GJP, and AP) as represented by serum IgG responses to W. recta strain 371 and F. nucleatum strain 364. The boxes enclose those antibody levels which 50% of the individuals studied exhibit, and the brackets enclose the antibody levels which 95% of the individuals studied exhibit. The closed circles are antibody levels which are significantly greater than 95% of the individuals tested. Each point represents a diseased individual diagnosed as LJP (JP), GJP (GP), AP, and ANUG. III. Serum antibody response that is significantly increased in patients within a disease category as represented by LJP responses to A. actinomycetemcomitans strain Y4. The open bars and brackets are as described for category I. IV. Serum responses to an oral microorganism that are reduced in level and frequency within diseased grouping of patients as represented by responses to Capnocytophaga sputigena strain 4. The open bars and brackets are as described in category I.

responded minimally to *E. brachy*, *W. succinogenes*, and *S. sputigena*. In contrast, there was a generalized response to *E. corrodens*, *B. melaninogenicus* subsp. *intermedius*, *S. mutans* (serotype *c*), *S. sanguis*, *A. viscosus*, and *A. naeslundii*. However, whether or not all individuals responded, no significant differences were noted in the level of serum IgG between the diseased and normal patients to these organisms.

II. Increased Levels of Serum Antibody in Certain Patients with Disease(s)

Increased serum antibody levels were noted in some patients with different forms of periodontal disease compared with the normal group when tested against *Fusobacterium* and the *Wolinella* species (Fig. 2). Virtually all individuals who showed elevated responses to these organisms had some type of disease, but not all (or even a majority) of the disease patients showed elevated responses. Although this category must be extended by further observations, this type of response may be indicative of a unique type of infection or host reaction.

III. Increased Level and Frequency of Response in Group(s) with Disease

This most striking category included responses to two organisms.

Elevated response to *A. actinomycetemcomitans* Y4 in LJP. Nearly 90% of the LJP patients had detectable IgG antibodies to strain Y4. This was significantly different from all other groups (Ebersole et al., in press). Only the GJP group, with 55% positive responders, was also significantly elevated compared with the normal group. As shown in Fig. 2, the levels of IgG antibodies to strain Y4 in the LJP patients were significantly increased compared with all other diseased or nondiseased groups.

Isotypes. We tested for IgM, IgA, and IgE antibody to strain Y4, and the results are summarized in Table 2.

An increased frequency of IgM antibody to strain Y4 was detected in the LJP, GJP, and AP groups ($P < 0.001$). Also, a highly significantly increased level of IgM response was seen in these same groups. Similarly, IgA and IgE serum responses were elevated in level and frequency in the LJP and GJP groups. However, elevations in the AP group response were not as striking. The IgM antibodies may reflect a more generalized cross-reactivity in the AP patients to the gram-negative microorganisms that are found in subgingival plaque.

Antigens. We also examined the human antibody response to antigens from *A. actinomycetemcomitans*, including the response to leukotoxin (IgG), a group

TABLE 2. *Serum antibody to* A. actinomycetemcomitans *strain Y4*

Disease category	% Positive[a]		
	IgM	IgA	IgE
LJP	76[b]	68[b]	76[b]
GJP	82[b]	64[b]	82[b]
AP	62[b]	34	34
ANUG	33	44	11
Edentulous	0	17	33
Normal	33	14	17

[a]Positive samples were determined as >2 standard deviations above the mean antibody activity of four sera extensively adsorbed with homologous organisms.
[b]Significantly different from normal group.

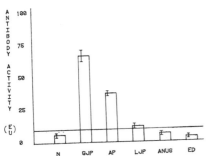

FIG. 3. *Serum IgG antibody responses to* B. gingivalis *strain 381 in normal (N; n = 24), GJP (n = 11), AP (n = 38), LJP (n = 38), ANUG (n = 9), and edentulous (ED; n = 6) patients. The open bars represent the mean antibody activity for each group and the brackets enclose 2 standard errors. The shaded area shows a background serum reaction determined by extensive adsorption of four positive sera with formalinized* B. gingivalis. *The solid line is 2 standard deviations greater than the mean background level from the four adsorbed sera. Any antibody levels greater than this background were considered as positive responses.*

carbohydrate (IgG), and the lipopolysaccharide (IgM). Similar to the level of the response to the intact microorganism, the serum response to these antigens was significantly elevated in the serum of the periodontosis patients. From 67 to 71% of the LJP patients were found to respond to these antigens.

Response to *A. actinomycetemcomitans* ATCC 29523. We found (Ebersole et al., in press) that serum IgG antibody to strain ATCC 29523 did not differentiate between periodontal disease categories as well as antibody to strain Y4. Although levels of antibody to strain 29523 were significantly elevated in LJP and GJP, the frequency of the detection of antibody was not increased in these patients. These results may indicate that important antigenic determinants, present on Y4, are not present on 29523 since absorption with 29523 organisms did not remove antibody to Y4. One important difference is the relative lack of leukotoxin production by strain 29523 (1). *A. actinomycetemcomitans* is the only plaque organism with identified leukotoxic properties.

Elevated response to *B. gingivalis* in AP. The second organism of importance to which we have observed an elevated immune response is *B. gingivalis*. The elevated response was associated with AP and GJP patients, as shown in Fig. 3. Serum IgG antibody levels were significantly higher in the GJP and AP patients when compared with all other groups. In addition, the frequency of positive IgG antibody in GJP (64%) and in AP (73%) groups compared with all other groups was highly significant (Table 3). It is interesting

TABLE 3. *Serum response to* B. gingivalis *cells and* B. gingivalis *lipopolysaccharide (LPS)*

	% Positive	
Patient group	IgG antibody to *B. gingivalis*	IgM antibody to *B. gingivalis* LPS
LJP	35	33
GJP	64[a]	73[a]
AP	73[a]	40
ANUG	11	33
Edentulous	0	17
Normal	8	25

[a]Statistically different from normal.

TABLE 4. *Relative distribution of antibody to* C. sputigena *in LJP and normal subjects[a]*

Antibody level	ELISA units	Antibody to *C. sputigena* (% of subjects in category)	
		LJP group (n = 37)	Normal group (n = 23)
None	<20	45	26
Low	20–50	50	13
Moderate	51–100	5	35
High	>100	0	26

[a]Kolmogorov-Smirnov two-sample test: $P < 0.005$.

to note that virtually all normal and edentulous subjects failed to manifest antibody to *B. gingivalis* whereas all but 26% of AP patients had antibody to this organism.

The IgM serum responses to *B. gingivalis* lipopolysaccharide were also investigated and are shown in Table 3. A significant serum IgM antibody response to the LPS from *B. gingivalis* was found in the GJP group. The serum antibody levels to *B. melaninogenicus* subsp. *intermedius* were also determined (Fig. 2), and no differences were found among the groups. The data thus far suggest that the presence of *B. gingivalis* or the immune response to this organism may be highly significant in the more chronic and generalized types of periodontal disease.

IV. Decreased Level and Frequency of Response in Group(s) with Disease

Decreased level and frequency of response to *Capnocytophaga* in patients with LJP. *Capnocytophaga* species have been identified as prominent members of the flora of periodontosis patients. A consistent pattern in the serum responses to the *Capnocytophaga* species was observed. The LJP patients exhibited a decreased response compared with all other groups, including significantly decreased responses to *C. sputigena* (Fig. 2) and to its associated type or T antigen. Also, there was a decreased frequency of response to *Capnocytophaga* in the LJP group. Ninety-five percent of the patients had a level of antibody to *C. sputigena* that was less than 50 ELISA units. The distribution of antibodies to *C. sputigena* was significantly different between the LJP patients and normal subjects. LJP patients showed an increased frequency of low response (50%) and also an increased frequency of negative response (45%; Table 4). Therefore, although *A. actinomycetemcomitans* and *Capnocytophaga* microorganisms are found in disease-associated plaque in LJP, the systemic humoral response to each is quite different in the LJP patients. The data suggest that *Capnocytophaga* species may be activating suppressor cell networks in LJP patients or that these patients may be tolerant to *Capnocytophaga* species antigens.

Familial Aspects of Serum Response

Thus far, seven families, each with at least one member diagnosed as having a type of juvenile disease, have been examined to determine whether antibody responses to various periodontal disease-associated microorganisms are similar

TABLE 5. *Serum IgG antibody to
A. actinomycetemcomitans
strain Y4 in seven families of
patients with JP disease*

Category	No. of individuals with antibody[a]/ no. in category
Total	10/28 (36%)
LJP	7/8 (88%)
Post-LJP	1/2 (50%)
GJP	2/4 (50%)
Others[b]	0/14 (0%)

[a]Antibody response greater than the mean plus 2 standard deviations above the normal population.
[b]Other family members including siblings and parents.

among the members of a family. If antibody responses to these organisms reflect either a present or past infection, information on the intrafamily distribution of these organisms would be obtained. The results of these analyses are shown in Table 5. Generally, only the family members with juvenile-type disease had high levels of serum antibodies to *A. actinomycetemcomitans* strain Y4; the nondiseased members' antibodies were within the range of a normal population. Furthermore, the juvenile patients did not demonstrate elevated antibody levels to any of the other organisms tested. These results provide support for the possible involvement of *A. actinomycetemcomitans* in periodontosis and also suggest that the response to this organism is quite limited.

Significance of serum antibody

Diagnostic potential. The diagnostic potential of serum or local antibodies is well established for many infectious diseases. However, the use of these antibody criteria for diagnosis is usually unnecessary since the features of the juvenile-type diseases are virtually pathognomonic. As other relationships between antibody and disease are uncovered, some of this information may be useful in diagnosis. However, the potential of antibody in the predictive or prognostic aspects of disease occurrence appear to be more significant.

Predictive potential. We have been interested in this approach and are currently employing several experiment protocols to determine the predictive potential of antibody. Important questions regarding the relationship of the host and the infecting bacterial agent remain to be answered, e.g., At what stage of the infection is antibody detected? Once detected, is it a harbinger of improvement or decline? How is antibody associated with active disease? These questions will have to be approached for individual organisms and the respective immune response. It may be possible to detect early immune responses prior to gross infection. This would enable early institution of therapeutic modalities.

Effect of treatment. An important consideration is the effect of treatment on the immune response to periodontopathic microorganisms. This approach can be particularly important if a portion of the efficacy of certain treatments can be enhanced by the elicitation of an immune response. Such studies are vital precursors to determination of the potential efficacy of a vaccine approach in periodontal disease. Scaling is perhaps the most common form of periodontal therapy. We investigated the serum IgG immune response to various organisms in 10 patients treated by scaling and in 6 patients who were not scaled (Table 6). Of nine organisms tested, responses to seven organisms increased, whereas only two responses increased in patients not treated. In a separate experiment, 3 patients with *A. actinomycetemcomitans* in their flora were sampled before and

TABLE 6. *Changes in serum IgG antibody levels*
to oral microorganisms after scaling

Organism	Treated			Untreated		
	↑ [a]	=	↓	↑	=	↓
A. viscosus T14V	2/10	7/10	1/10	0/6	6/6	0/6
B. gingivalis	3/10	7/10	0/10	0/6	4/6	2/6
B. melaninogenicus						
subsp. intermedius	1/9	8/9	0/9	0/6	6/6	0/6
C. sputigena	3/9	6/9	0/9	1/6	5/6	0/6
E. corrodens 373	4/8	4/8	0/8	0/6	6/6	0/6
F. nucleatum	0/9	8/9	1/9	0/6	6/6	0/6
S. sputigena	0/9	8/9	1/9	0/6	4/6	2/6
S. sanguis	1/9	8/9	0/9	0/6	6/6	0/6
W. recta	2/9	7/9	0/9	1/6	5/6	0/6

[a] A change in antibody was determined as an increase or decrease of 25% or more in antibody as measured by ELISA.

at least twice after scaling over a period of 2 to 3 months. IgG antibody in serum to *A. actinomycetemcomitans* was increased and continued to increase during this period. Salivary antibody also increased. This type of increased immune response after treatment has also been observed on the cellular level (R. C. Page, S. Osterberg, T. Sims, and B. Williams, J. Dent. Res. Spec. Issue A **60**:496, abstr. 747, 1981). The effects of such antibody have yet to be established. However, the presence of elevated antibody to locally pathogenic microorganisms could contribute to the efficacy of this type of therapy.

ANTIBODIES TO PERIODONTAL DISEASE-ASSOCIATED MICROORGANISMS: SALIVARY IgA RESPONSE

Studies in animal model systems have suggested that salivary IgA antibodies may be partially protective in experimental periodontal disease (7). However, little is known concerning the human salivary antibody response to periodontopathic microorganisms. Use of an ELISA procedure has enabled an analysis of antibodies to a number of these organisms and the subsequent correlation of these antibodies with different types of periodontal disease in the fashion previously described. Salivas from 9 LJP, 2 GJP, 22 AP, a normal, and 2 IgA-deficient patients were analyzed for IgA antibodies to the battery of organisms. These correlations are preliminary since only limited numbers of salivas have been analyzed. However, the types of responses observed fell into category I (no differences in the level of salivary IgA antibodies related to disease) or into category III (increased levels of salivary IgA antibody and increased frequency of response in groups with periodontal disease(s) when compared with normal).

I. No Differences Between Organisms

No differences among groups were noted with respect to the salivary response to *A. naeslundii, S. sanguis, S. mutans,* and *Capnocytophaga* species.

III. Elevated Level and Frequency of Response in Disease Groups

Elevated response to *A. actinomycetemcomitans* in LJP. Although patients in a combined juvenile periodontitis group (nine LJP + two GJP) had normal levels of salivary IgA, 91% of these patients had IgA antibody to strain Y4 (Ebersole et al., in press). Only 23% of normal patients had antibody to Y4, and the IgA-deficient salivas showed no antibody. The mean level of salivary IgA antibody in the JP group was more than 13 times greater than in the normal group ($P < 0.01$) (Ebersole et al., in press).

Elevated response to *B. gingivalis* in AP. The IgA levels in the saliva of the AP patients were also in a normal range (Ebersole et al., in press). IgA antibody levels to *B. gingivalis* in the saliva of AP patients were significantly greater than in the normal group ($P < 0.05$). More than 40% of the AP patients exhibited levels of salivary IgA antibody to *B. gingivalis* that were greater than the mean plus 2 standard deviations of the normal population.

The AP patients also showed significantly elevated salivary IgA responses to *F. nucleatum* and *A. viscosus* T14. The presence of salivary IgA antibody to these organisms may indicate that these patients are sensitized by stimulation of gut-associated lymphoid tissue or by direct stimulation of immunocompetent tissue in salivary glands (6). Some generalized periodontosis patients responded quite well to certain of the organisms, and more of these patients must be studied to better define the immune response of this group.

Contributions of Salivary Antibodies to Periodontal Disease(s)

The above data suggest that salivary antibodies have the same potential for diagnostic or predictive aspects of disease assessment as sera. The major advantage would be that saliva is easier to obtain than blood and involves a less invasive procedure.

It has been suggested that the protective potential of IgA antibody could reside in the ability to retard antigen penetration of oral membranes (3). However, in laboratory experiments, penetration by heterologous antigen was enhanced. Possibly the ability of IgG to bind to neutrophils can result in lysosomal enzyme release and disruption of basement membranes, rendering them more penetrable. In this way, IgG antibody may interfere with mucosal integrity, at least to heterologous antigens. In contrast, IgA antibody may be able to restrict development of pathological IgG tissue reactions by elimination of the antigen prior to tissue entry (3).

Antibody in the Gingival Crevice

Many questions arise as to the importance of gingival crevice fluid in periodontal disease. Does this fluid and its antibody possess diagnostic or prognostic significance? We have developed a reproducible method of accurately

TABLE 7. *Relationship of human SCF antibody level to serum antibody level*

Organisms	SCF antibody		
	>Serum	=Serum	<Serum
B. melaninogenicus subsp. *intermedius* *S. mutans* *C. sputigena* *E. corrodens*	0/52	8/52	44/52
A. actinomycetemcomitans Y4 *B. gingivalis* *W. recta* *F. nucleatum*	12/49[a]	13/49	24/49

[a]Kolmogorov-Smirnov two-sample test: $P < 0.005$.

quantitating the fluid which is present in the gingival crevice at any given time. This fluid was called static crevicular fluid (SCF) and may be a combination of saliva and true crevicular fluid. Our approach has been to test SCF antibody from each individual to one organism to which that individual manifests a serum IgG antibody response. After correction for volume, the relationship of SCF antibody to serum antibody was determined as a ratio. In individuals with immune response to periodontopathic organisms (*A. actinomycetemcomitans* Y4, *B. gingivalis*, *F. nucleatum*, or *W. recta*) 27% of the SCF samples had more IgG antibody to the respective organism than was present in serum (Table 7). These were also individuals with disease. In contrast, none of the samples from individuals with elevated serum antibody levels to less periodontopathic organisms had more antibody in SCF than was in serum (Table 7). These patients exhibited indications of previous disease, but at the time of sampling, there was no evidence of active disease. There was a significantly different distribution in the SCF/serum antibody ratio to suspected periodontopathic microorganisms in diseased patients when compared with other individuals. The results show that at selected sites there may exist either a local synthesis and secretion of specific antibody into SCF or a concentration mechanism of the serum antibody. These findings suggest that a local contribution of antibody into SCF may be variable but related to the disease state. This technique may provide insight concerning antibody secretion in the gingival crevice area and may have potential in determining sites of disease activity.

Specific Immune Response in Periodontal Disease

We believe our studies and those of others support the concept of a *specific* immune response to certain organisms in the host's oral microbiota in certain periodontal diseases. One such organism of importance appears to be *A. actimomycetemcomitans*. Recent microbiological studies have demonstrated the high frequency of isolation of *A. actinomycetemcomitans* from dental plaque of patients with periodontosis (J. Slots, H. S. Reynolds, P. M. Lobbins, and R. J. Genco, J. Dent. Res. Spec. Issue A **59**:328, abstr. 244, 1980). Also, only certain strains of *A. actinomycetemcomitans* have been shown to possess leukotoxic activity (P. Baehni, C. C. Tsai, W. McArthur, B. Hammond, S. S. Socransky, and N. Taichman, J. Dent. Res. Spec. Issue A **59**:323, abstr. 223, 1980), and these strains seem to predominate in the periodontosis patients. The importance of the leukotoxic activity in the possible pathogenicity of *A. actinomycetemcomitans* is unknown; however, McArthur and colleagues (21) have found levels of IgG in periodontosis patients' sera that effectively inhibit the activity of the leukotoxin. These findings may be a key to a potential role for the specific antibody in periodontal disease(s).

Protective Potential of Antibody

The neutrophil has also received recent emphasis as a participant in periodontal diseases. These cells are prominent in the gingival crevice and crevicular epithelium (29). It has been noted that patients with some neutrophil chemotactic defects also have associated periodontal disease. Several investigators have shown defective neutrophil chemotaxis in patients with periodontosis (4, 5) or with some types of acute, early-onset periodontal disease (12, 16). In a study of 31 periodontosis patients, it was found that 81% demonstrated a chemotactic defect, and 43% of adult patients with severe periodontitis exhibited defects (36). Several studies have indicated that bacterial factors can affect neutrophils (1, 31). Therefore, the suggestion has been made that the neutrophil is a protective cell in the peridontium and that defective neutrophil function can result in more severe disease. Individuals with this type of defect may be more susceptible to infection with periodontopathic organism(s) (e.g., *A. actinomycetemcomitans*). Infection with *A. actinomycetemcomitans* may further compromise the host's neutrophils and disease may result. It is now clear that 90% of JP patients have *A. actinomycetemcomitans* leukotoxin-neutralizing activity (21). This immune response can restore the balance of necessary protective aspects of the host to interfere with *A. actinomycetem-comitans* infection. Stimulation of B cells by *A. actinomycetemcomitans* either by specific antigen or by nonspecific polyclonal activation could lead to the generation of osteoclast-activating factor or other osteolytic factors giving rise to rapid bone destruction (32). Therefore, antibody, by interfering with biologically detrimental effects of microorganisms and perhaps with penetration of antigens into the gingival area, can be protective in juvenile and adult forms of periodontal diseases.

Antibodies and Juvenile and Adult Disease

Several laboratories have identified serum (Ebersole et al., in press; P. A. Murray and R. J. Genco, J. Dent. Res. Spec. Issue A **59**:329, abstr. 245, 1980; C.-H. Lai and M. A. Listgarten, J. Dent. Res. Spec. Issue A **59**:513, abstr. 975, 1980; R. J. Genco, N. S. Taichman, and C. A. Sadowski, J. Dent. Res. Spec. Issue A **59**:329, abstr. 246, 1980), saliva ((Ebersole et al., in press), and crevicular fluid (P. A. Murray and R. J. Genco, J. Dent. Res. Spec. Issue A **59**:329, abstr. 245, 1980) antibodies to the *A. actinomycetemcomitans* organism and the leukotoxin (Ebersole et al., in press). Dependent upon the immunological procedure used, 60 to 90% of the periodontosis patients exhibited antibody activity to *A. actinomycetemcomitans*. Thus, the available information reinforces the possibility that *A. actinomycetemcomitans* may be a factor in the development of periodontosis. However, further studies are needed to identify the relationship between the acquisition of antibodies to *A. actinomycetemcomitans* and the relative risk of developing periodontosis.

Associations of serum antibody responses with other forms of periodontal disease have also been uncovered. Although the association is as yet not as definitive as with Y4, more than 70% of sera from individuals with generalized periodontosis and adult periodontitis showed elevated levels of IgG antibody activity to *B. gingivalis* strain 381 whole cells and lipopolysaccharide (25; J. L. Ebersole, D. E. Frey, M. A. Taubman, D. J. Smith, J. R. Wetherell, and R. J. Genco. J. Dent. Res. Spec. Issue A **59**:329, abstr. 248, 1980).

Preliminary evidence exists that other immunoglobulin-containing fluids potentially critical to the disease process also demonstrate these relationships. We have shown that salivary IgA antibody levels to Y4 antigens were elevated in periodontosis categories (Ebersole et al., in press). Crevicular fluid IgG antibody also shows this association (Murray and Genco, J. Dent. Res. Spec. Issue A **59**:329, abstr. 245, 1980). Thus, a specific antibody response to microorganisms implicated in periodontal disease seems to exist at the local site as well as systemically. How these responses can be manipulated to the host's advantage will be the subject of future investigations.

SUMMARY

Antibody levels in serum, saliva, and crevicular fluid of periodontal disease patients were examined. Antibodies to a variety of oral microorganisms were measured in sera of patients with LJP, GJP, AP, and ANUG, and in edentulous and normal subjects. Cross-sectional analyses of these antibody levels identified four general categories of humoral responses. Response category I is described by a generalized response to the microorganisms that is not associated with any type of periodontal disease. Category II describes diseased individuals who exhibit an extreme response to an organism that is significantly different from the entire population tested. Category III describes serum responses to an organism that are significantly increased in level and frequency of detection in patients with one type of periodontal disease when compared with all other patient groups. Finally, response category IV describes antibody levels that are significantly decreased in level and frequency in patients with one type of periodontal disease when compared with all other patient groups. Examination of salivary IgA antibodies to these microorganisms showed distribution levels that frequently correlated with the distribution of serum responses. Comparisons were also made between SCF and serum antibody levels in the patients. The results of these studies suggest that fluid obtained from different sites within an individual can vary substantially in content of antibody.

ACKNOWLEDGMENTS

This work was supported in part by Public Health Service grants DE-04881 and DE-03420 from the National Institute of Dental Research. J.L.E. and D.J.S. are recipients of Research Career Development Awards DE-00075 and DE-00024 from the National Institute of Dental Research.

We gratefully acknowledge Robert J. Genco for supplying some of the sera utilized and Benjamin Hammond for supplying some of the antigens tested. We thank Dierdre Frey and Elizabeth Adamson for expert technical assistance and Barbara Connolly for secretarial assistance.

LITERATURE CITED

1. **Baehni, P., C.-C. Tsai, W. P. McArthur, B. F. Hammond, and N. S. Taichman**. 1979. Interaction of inflammatory cells and oral microorganisms. VIII. Detection of leukotoxic activity of a plaque-derived gram-negative organism. Infect. Immun. **24**:233–243.
2. **Brandtzaeg, P.** 1973. Immunology of inflammatory periodontal lesions. Int. Dent. J. **23**:438–454.
3. **Brandtzaeg, P., and K. Tolo.** 1978. Mucosal penetrability enhanced by serum-derived antibodies. Nature (London) **266**:262–263.
4. **Cianciola, L. J., R. J. Genco, M. R. Patters, J. McKenna, and C. J. vanOss.** 1977. Defective polymorphonuclear leukocyte function in a human periodontal disease. Nature (London) **265**:445–447.
5. **Clark, R. A., R. C. Page, and G. Wilde.** 1977. Defective neutrophil chemotaxis in juvenile periodontitis. Infect. Immun. **18**:694–700.
6. **Crawford, J. M., M. A. Taubman, and D. J. Smith**. 1975. Minor salivary glands as a major source of secretory immunoglobulin A in the human oral cavity. Science **190**:1206–1209.
7. **Crawford, J. M., M. A. Taubman, and D. J. Smith**. 1978. The effects of local immunization with periodontopathic microorganisms on periodontal bone loss in gnotobiotic rats. J. Periodontal Res. **13**:445–459.
8. **Ebersole, J. L., D. E. Frey, M. A. Taubman, and D. J. Smith**. 1980. An ELISA for measuring serum antibodies to *Actinobacillus actinomycetemcomitans*. J. Periodontal Res. **15**:621–632.
9. **Ebersole, J. L., M. A. Taubman, and D. J. Smith**. 1979. Thymic control of secretory antibody responses in rats. J. Immunol. **123**:19–24.
10. **Engvall, E., and H. E. Carlsson**. 1976. Enzyme-linked immunosorbent assay (ELISA), p. 135. *In* C. Feldman (ed.), First International Symposium on Immunoenzymatic Techniques. North-Holland Publishing Co., Amsterdam.
11. **Genco, R. J., P. A. Mashimo, G. Krygier, and S. A. Ellison**. 1974. Antibody-mediated effects on the periodontium. J. Periodontol. **45**:330–337.
12. **Gothier, D. E., H. R. Gaumer, B. L. Philstrom, and L. E. A. Folke.** 1975. Elevation of a serum component in periodontal disease capable of modulating chemotactic infiltration. J. Periodontol. **10**:65–72.
13. **Horton, J. E., J. J. Oppenheim, and S. E. Mergenhagen**. 1974. A role for cell-mediated immunity in the pathogenesis of periodontal disease. J. Periodontol. **45**:352–360.
14. **Ivanyi, L., and T. Lehner.** 1970. Stimulation of lymphocyte transformation by bacterial antigens in patients with periodontal disease. Arch. Oral Biol. **15**:1089–1096.

15. **Kagan, J. M.** 1980. Local immunity to *Bacteroides gingivalis* in periodontal disease. J. Dent. Res. **59**(Spec. Issue DI):1750–1756.

16. **Lavine, W. S., E. G. Maderazo, J. Stolman, P. A. Ward, R. B. Cogan, I. Greenblatt, and P. B. Robertson.** 1979. Impaired neutrophil chemotaxis in patients with juvenile and rapidly progressing periodontitis. J. Periodontal Res. **14**:10–19.

17. **Liljenberg, B., and J. Lindhe.** 1980. Juvenile periodontitis. Some microbiological, histopathogical and clinical characteristics. J. Clin. Periodontol. **7**:48–61.

18. **Mackler, B. F., K. B. Frostad, P. B. Robertson, and B. M. Levy.** 1977. Immunoglobulin bearing lymphocytes and plasma cells in human periodontal disease. J. Periodontal Res. **12**:37–45.

19. **Mackler, B. F., T. C. Waldrop, P. Shur, P. B. Robertson, and B. M. Levy.** 1978. IgG subclasses in human periodontal disease. Distribution and incidence of IgG subclass bearing lymphocytes and plasma cells. J. Periodontal Res. **13**:109–119.

20. **Mackler, B. F., J. A. Withers, D. L. Woodson, E. Coker, A. Herrin, L. Friedman, and P. H. O'Neill.** 1979. Human gingival lymphocytes. I. Methodology for the isolation of human gingival lymphocytes. J. Dent. Res. **58**:1946–1952.

21. **McArthur, N. P., C.-C. Tsai, P. C. Baehni, R. J. Genco, and N. S. Taichman.** 1981. Leukotoxic effects of *Actinobacillus actinomycetemcomitans*. Modulation by serum components. J. Periodontal Res. **16**:159–170.

22. **McDougall, W. A.** 1971. Penetration pathways of a topically applied foreign protein into rat gingiva. J. Periodontal Res. **6**:89–99.

23. **McHugh, W. D.** 1963. Some aspects of the development of gingival epithelium. Periodontics **1**:239–244.

24. **Mergenhagen, S. E., W. C. deAraujo, and E. Varah.** 1965. Antibody to *Leptotrichia buccalis* in human sera. Arch. Oral. Biol. **10**:29–33.

25. **Mouton, C., P. G. Hammond, J. Slots, and R. J. Genco.** 1981. Serum antibodies to oral *Bacteroides asaccharolyticus* (*Bacteroides gingivalis*): relationship to age and periodontal disease. Infect. Immun. **31**:182–192.

26. **Nisengard, R. J., and E. H. Beutner.** 1970. Immunologic studies of periodontal disease. V. IgG type antibodies and skin test responses to *Actinomyces* and mixed oral flora. J. Periodontol. **41**:149–152.

27. **Payne, W. A., R. C. Page, A. L. Ogilvie, and W. B. Hall.** 1975. Histopathic features of the initial and early stages of experimental gingivitis in man. J. Periodontal Res. **10**:51–64.

28. **Schroeder, H. E.** 1970. Quantitative parameters of early human gingival inflammation. Arch. Oral Biol. **15**:383–400.

29. **Schroeder, H. E., S. Munzel-Pedrazolli, and R. Page.** 1973. Correlated morphometric and biochemical analysis of gingival tissue in early chronic gingivitis in man. Arch. Oral Biol. **18**:899–923.

30. **Seymour, G. J., and J. S. Greenspan.** 1979. The phenotypic characterization of lymphocyte subpopulations in established human periodontal disease. J. Periodontal Res. **14**:39–46.

31. **Shurin, S. B., S. S. Socransky, E. Sweeney, and T. P. Stossel.** 1979. A neutrophil disorder induced by Capnocytophaga, a dental microorganism. N. Engl. J. Med. **301**:849–854.

32. **Sinden, P. R. V., and D. M. Walker.** 1979. Inflammatory cells extracted from chronically inflamed gingiva. J. Periodontal Res. **14**:467–464.

33. **Smith, S., P. H. Bick, G. A. Miller, R. R. Ranney, P. L. Rice, J. H. Lalor, and J. G. Smith.** 1980. Polyclonal B-cell activation: severe periodontal disease in young adults. Clin. Immunol. Immunopathol. **16**:354–366.

34. **Taubman, M. A., J. M. Buckelew, J. L. Ebersole, and D. J. Smith.** 1981. Periodontal bone loss and immune response to ovalbumin in germfree rats fed antigen-free diet with ovalbumin. Infect. Immun. **32**:145–152.

35. **Taubman, M. A., D. J. Smith, and J. L. Ebersole.** 1978. Antibody binding of glucosyltransferase enzyme preparations from homologous and heterologous serotypes of *S. mutans*. Adv. Exp. Med. Biol. **107**:317–325.

36. **van Dyke, T. E., H. U. Horoszewicz, L. J. Cianciola, and R. J. Genco.** 1980. Neutrophil chemotaxis dysfunction in human periodontitis. Infect. Immun. **27**:124–132.

The Complement System in Periodontal Diseases

HARVEY A. SCHENKEIN

Department of Periodontics, Medical College of Virginia,
Virginia Commonwealth University, Richmond, Virginia 23219

INTRODUCTION

The human complement system is a major humoral effector mechanism that contributes to protective responses against foreign substances and to damage to host tissues (7, 19). Many of the biological effects of this enzyme system result from the release of activation peptides from the parent proteins consequent to limited proteolytic cleavage. Other biologically important phenomena result from the binding of these proteins or their cleavage products to specific receptors found on many cells including neutrophils, platelets, mast cells, macrophages, and erythrocytes. Thus, data have been gathered that implicate the complement system as playing a role in such phenomena as phagocytosis, chemotaxis, alteration of vascular permeability, cytolysis, lymphokine production, antibody synthesis, lysosomal enzyme release, and bone resorption.

The complement system consists of 18 plasma proteins (see Table 1) and can be divided into three major pathways. The classical and alternative pathways provide mechanisms for initiation of the enzymatic systems and share the common purpose of assembling an enzyme capable of cleaving C3, the central

TABLE 1. *Proteins of the complement system*

Factor	Mol wt	Serum concn (μg/ml)	Cleavage products
Classical pathway			
C1q	400,000	70	
C1r	190,000	34	
C1s	174,000	31	
C4	209,000	430	C4a, C4b, C4bi, C4c, C4d
C2	117,000	30	C2a, C2b
Alternative pathway			
P (properdin)	220,000	25	
D	23,500	2	
B	100,000	240	Ba, Bb
C3	185,000	1,300	C3a, C3b, C3bi, C3c, C3d
H (β1H globulin)	150,000	360	
I (C3b INA)	88,000	35	
Terminal sequence			
C5	206,000	75	C5a, C5b
C6	128,000	60	
C7	121,000	55	
C8	151,000	80	
C9	79,000	160	
Control proteins			
C1 INH	105,000	150	
C4 BP	590,000	?	

component of the system. The terminal sequence results in assembly of a cytolytic protein complex. Classical pathway and terminal sequence proteins are called *components* and are symbolized by the letter C followed by a number; alternative pathway proteins are called *factors* and are denoted by letters, e.g., factor B. Cleavage fragments are denoted by lowercase letters following the protein designation (e.g., C3a), and enzymatically active forms are indicated by a bar over the letter or number (e.g., $\overline{D}$).

BIOCHEMISTRY OF THE COMPLEMENT SYSTEM

Classical pathway. The major function of the classical complement pathway is to provide an effector or amplification mechanism consequent to the interaction of specific antibody with antigen. Immune complexes containing immunoglobulin G (IgG) or IgM bind to the C1q subunit of the Ca^{2+}-dependent trimolecular complex containing C1q, C1r, and C1s. This stimulates internal proteolysis of C1r and C1s to form the active enzyme $\overline{C1}$, in which $\overline{C1s}$ bears the active enzymatic site. The substrates of $\overline{C1s}$ are C4 and C2. $\overline{C1s}$ hydrolyzes a peptide bond in C4 to release C4a, and C4b, the major fragment, binds to the immune complex by a labile binding site or is released into the fluid phase. The presence of bound C4b permits binding and cleavage of C2, releasing the C2b fragment. C2a enters a Mg^{2+}-dependent interaction with C4b to form the classical pathway C3 convertase $\overline{C42}$.

There are three major modes of biochemical control of the classical pathway. First, C1 activity is controlled by the C1 inhibitor (C1 INH), which binds irreversibly to the active sites of both C1r and C1s. Patients with hereditary angioedema have a congenital deficiency of C1 INH and demonstrate spontaneous C1 activation and C4 and C2 destruction. Second, C4b is inactivated by two naturally occurring plasma proteins, C4 binding protein (C4BP) and C3b inactivator (C3b INA, alternative pathway factor I). The C4BP combines with C4b and renders it susceptible to proteolytic cleavage by C3b INA to form C4bi and thence to serum proteases, to eventually release the C4c fragment from the C4b molecule, rendering it inactive. Third, the C42 complex is inherently unstable, and inactive C2a rapidly decays from the complex.

Alternative pathway. The alternative pathway differs from the classical pathway in that specific immunity (e.g., antibody) is not required for its activity. C3 convertase activity can be generated in serum deficient in C4 or C2, or in the complete absence of immunoglobulins or classical pathway components.

It is currently thought that the initiating event in alternative pathway activation is the spontaneous hydrolysis of a thioester bond in the third complement component (C3) to form a "C3b-like" molecule. This process occurs at a very slow rate in plasma and may lead to the association of "C3b-like C3" with factor B of the alternative pathway. In the absence of an activating surface or molecule (e.g., a gram-negative bacterium or its endotoxin), this C3B or C3bB complex is dissociated by factor H (β1H globulin), a protein that competes for the factor B binding site on C3b.

When an activating surface is present, however, it provides a site for the covalent interaction of C3 with molecules on its surface, and this bound C3 or C3b provides a privileged or protected binding site for factor B. Access of factor H to B bound to C3b on an alternative pathway activator is relatively restricted, permitting a Mg^{2+}-dependent association of factor B with C3 or C3b. Factor $\overline{D}$, a serine esterase with specificity for factor B, cleaves B into the fragments Ba (which is released) and Bb (which remains bound), forming the alternative pathway convertase C3bBb. This enzyme is also described as the "amplification convertase," since its substrate (C3) is utilized to form new C3b sites on the surface of the activator and thus additional C3 convertase sites. The process of C3 cleavage results in the release of the C3a peptide from C3.

There are several mechanisms which control alternative pathway activity. Properdin (P), the first alternative pathway factor described, acts to stabilize the convertase C3bBb by forming the stabilized C3bBbP. Since C3bBb is subject to decay due to dissociation of Bb, the importance of properdin is to delay such decay. More important, however, is the mechanism for control of the amplification convertase C3bBb. As mentioned above, factor H completes with B for its C3b binding site, and is capable of dissociating Bb from C3bBb. Higher concentrations of factor H are required to accomplish this on an activating surface (e.g., rabbit erythrocytes) than on a nonactivating surface (e.g., sheep erythrocytes). Once factor H is bound to C3b, C3b becomes susceptible to proteolysis by factor I (C3b inactivator) to produce an intermediate form called C3bi. C3bi in turn is degraded by other proteases (e.g., elastase, trypsin, plasmin) to form C3c (which is released into the fluid phase) and C3d (which remains bound).

Terminal sequence. Once the classical or alternative pathway C3 convertases have formed, incorporation of C3b to form C423b or (C3b)nBb alters the specificity of the active sites on C2a or Bb to yield C5-cleaving activity and provides a binding site for the C5 molecule. Thus, the final proteolytic step occurs, yielding C5a (which is released) and C5b, which is bound to the immune complex or alternative pathway activator. C5b complexes with C6 and then with C7 to form the C5b,6,7 complex, the first step in formation of the membrane attack complex. This complex will bind to lipid membranes, including those of bacteria, nucleated cells, and erythrocytes. Incorporation of C8 initiates damage by forming a structural pore or channel through the membrane that permits free ion passage. Incorporation of C9 to form a membrane-bound C5b-9 complex will cause osmotic lysis and cell death.

BIOLOGICAL ACTIVITIES OF THE COMPLEMENT PROTEINS

Many of the biochemical reactions occurring during complement activation give rise to protein fragments or complexes that are active in various biological systems. Many of the effects seen depend upon binding of complement peptides to specific receptors found on many cells. The most well-known interaction, that of C5b-9 to produce cell membrane damage, does not involve specific receptor binding, but rather occurs by insertion of the complex into the lipid membrane. This will occur on artificial liposomes as well as on mammalian cells.

Several inflammatory effects may result from complement activation:

1. *Kinin-like activity.* Changes in vascular permeability following cleavage of C4 and C2 by C1s have been noted, although the basis for this activity has not been determined.

2. *Anaphylatoxins.* The C3a and C5a fragments of C3 and C5 are capable of releasing histamine from mast cells and basophils, as well as inducing smooth muscle contraction. This activity is controlled by serum carboxypeptidase B (anaphylatoxin inactivator), which removes the terminal arginine from C3a and C5a.

3. *Chemotactic factors*. The major complement-derived chemotactic factor is C5a, which attracts monocytes and neutrophils. It also has been demonstrated that C3bBb is chemotactic for neutrophils.

4. *Binding and phagocytosis*. Particles coated with C3b bind to C3b receptors present on neutrophils, monocytes, and macrophages, but do not themselves promote ingestion. However, there is synergy between IgG and C3b in IgG-mediated phagocytosis. One exception to this is the so-called "activated" macrophage, which will bind and ingest C3b-coated particles in the absence of IgG. Macrophages (monocytes) also demonstate C3bi (also called CR3) receptors which promote attachment and enhance (but do not mediate) phagocytosis; neutrophils bear only the C3b (CR1) receptor.

5. *Macrophage spreading and migration inhibition* has been demonstrated for the Bb fragment of factor B.

6. *Leukopenia followed by leukocytosis* has been demonstrated after administration of C3e, a tryptic fragment of C3.

7. *Lymphokine production* by B lymphocytes can be induced in tissue culture by the C3b fragment of C3.

8. *Lymphocyte proliferation*. Mouse B lymphocytes proliferate in response to human C3b, but human cells do not. However, the response of human peripheral lymphocytes to antigens is inhibited in vitro by C3 cleavage products.

9. *Macrophage degranulation*. It has been demonstrated that the binding of C3b to macrophages induces the release of lysosomal enzymes.

10. *Antibody synthesis*. In vivo depletion of C3 appears to prevent the development of primary responses to T-dependent antigens and the development of B memory cells. This may be due to a requirement for C3 in the binding of antigen to dendritic cells of the lymphoid follicles.

11. *Bone resorption*. Certain in vivo systems have demonstrated complement-dependent prostaglandin-mediated bone resorption in the presence of heterologous serum or antisera against bone tissue. This may result from antigen–antibody interaction at the surface of bone cells.

12. *The C3d receptor*. The C3d (or CR2) receptor is present on some B lymphocytes but not on monocytes. No specific function has as yet been described for this receptor or for the C3b receptor also present on some B cells. It has been suggested that C3 receptor-bearing B cells are those that respond to T-dependent antigens.

COMPLEMENT SYSTEM IN PERIODONTAL DISEASES

Complement system of gingival fluid and gingival tissues. Several investigators have attempted to demonstrate a role for complement-mediated reactions in the periodontium, yet evidence accumulated over the past 10 years has been, at best, indirect and circumstantial. One approach that has been particularly ungratifying has been the attempt to demonstrate bound deposits of immunoglobulins and complement components in gingival biopsies. Platt and co-workers (28) attempted to localize C3 in tissues from subjects with gingivitis and periodontitis and found only occasional positive immunofluorescent staining. The staining pattern that was seen bore no relation to immunoglobulin deposition and appeared to be artifactual. Similar studies by Genco and co-workers in 1974 (10) again demonstrated only occasional specimens containing C3 or C4. They showed that extensive washing of gingival tissues reduced detectable C3 and C4, indicating that a great deal of the protein was present as extravasated serum proteins rather than as immune precipitates. This observation was again confirmed by Clagett and Page (6), who could not find insoluble immune complexes in tissues taken from either humans or dogs with chronic periodontitis. These studies demonstrate that classical immune complex–complement deposition is not a major feature of the local periodontal lesion.

A second approach that has provided somewhat more information has been the examination of the inflammatory exudate of the gingival sulcus or periodontal pocket, termed gingival fluid (GF). These studies have been hindered by the small amounts of GF that can be collected, and their interpretations are confounded by the vast array of bacterial and host-derived substances present in the fluid.

GF has been identified as a plasma exudate which contains cellular elements and soluble constituents derived from host tissues and bacteria. Plasma proteins, including immunoglobulins, were first described by Brandtzaeg (5) to be present in GF, and the complement component C3 was first quantitated in GF by Shillitoe and Lehner (34). Since that time, quantitative and qualitative immunochemical and functional determinations have been used in attempts to characterize GF complement.

Attström and co-workers (2) demonstrated that immunochemical measurements of C3 (by electroimmunoassay) were similar in serum and GF from patients with periodontitis, but that C3 was partially converted in GF. C4 in these samples was present at only 50% of the serum concentration, and factor B was also converted. Schenkein and Genco (29), using antibodies reactive only with native C3, demonstrated that native C3 in GF from patients with severe chronic periodontitis was present at less than 25% of the levels found in sera from the same subjects. The implication that C3 conversion had occurred was confirmed by immunoelectrophoresis (30) and by the demonstration of C3d in the gingival exudates. It was further shown that factor B cleavage had occurred in each GF tested, and that C4, although present at only about 60% of serum levels, was converted in only a small percentage of GFs. It is significant that neither study demonstrated any alteration in serum complement components, implicating local mechanisms in the cleavage of complement proteins.

In a parallel study of GFs from patients with localized juvenile periodontitis, we demonstrated cleavage of both C3 and factor B in GF but not in serum (H. A. Schenkein and R. J. Genco, J. Immunol. 120:1796, 1978). In addition, however, C4 cleavage was demonstrable in a majority of GFs from patients with localized juvenile periodontitis. Thus, specific antibody could reach the periodontal tissues via serum. In addition, it has recently been shown that gingival plasma cells synthesize immunoglobulins with specificity for bacterial antigens (17, 31).

Only recently has specific antibody been demonstrated in GF itself. Several investigators have identified IgG, IgA, and IgM in GFs (13, 29, 34). Studies of patients with localized juvenile periodontitis have indicated that high serum and GF antibody levels to *Actinobacillus actinomycetemcomitans*, an organism found in high frequency in this disease. It is conceivable that C4 cleavage observed in GFs from subjects with localized juvenile periodontitis may be a result of antigen–antibody reactions of this sort. It has in fact been demonstrated (22) that subgingival plaque specimens from patients with gingivitis or periodontitis contain bacteria coated in vivo with immunoglobulins or complement (C3), or both.

An alternative approach to the study of the role of complement in periodontal inflammation has been the study of activation of complement by microorganisms associated with periodontal diseases. In 1972, Snyderman (35) discussed the potential role of bacterial endotoxins in tissue destruction. He suggested that one mechanism for periodontal inflammation could be via the interaction of bacterial products and serum complement within tissues, leading to the local generation of chemotactic factors and anaphylatoxins and to local degranulation of neutrophils, macrophages, and mast cells. In that same year, Shapiro and co-workers (33) demonstrated the presence of endotoxin activity in GF, dental plaque, gingival tissue extract, and whole saliva. The endotoxin levels correlated with the degree of gingival inflammation.

These findings raise the question of what mechanisms may be responsible for complement component cleavage in these forms of periodontal disease. It is tempting to speculate that local activation of complement via the classical or alternative pathway, or both, may occur. Classical pathway activation would require the presence of antibody, antigen, and a functional complement system. Functional complement activity has been detected in GF by Courts and co-workers (8). Both C1 hemolytic activity and whole complement hemolytic activity were detected by tube titration techniques. It was found that this activity was destroyed if GF samples were held at room temperature for several minutes and that C1 activity could be destroyed in vitro by whole dental plaque. Thus, a functional classical pathway is probably present in GF, and GF contains anti-complementary activity.

Other techniques have provided indirect evidence for active complement fragments or anticomplementary activity in gingival tissue. Extracts of gingival tissues from patients with periodontal disease have been shown to be chemotactic for human monocytes, and this activity was inhibitable by antibodies to C5 (24). Similar extracts could generate chemotactic factors from serum (25). In addition, GFs have been shown to be bactericidal (32).

Potential mechanisms of complement activation in periodontal disease. There is a great deal of evidence that antibodies reactive with dental plaque microorganisms are present in human sera and in GF. Serum antibodies reactive with species of *Leptotrichia, Fusobacterium, Bacteriodes, Actinomyces*, oral streptococci, *Actinobacillus*, and others have been described (9–11, 18, 20, 27). In addition, antibody activity has been found in extracts of inflamed gingival tissues (3).

Several investigators have demonstrated in vivo complement consumption induced by dental plaque and several species of oral bacteria. Activation of the alternative or classical pathways, or both, has been demonstrated for *Actinomyces viscosus, Streptococcus mutans, S. sanguis, Bacteriodes orales, Veillonella parvula, Propionibacterium acnes, Corynebacterium parvum, B. melaninogenicus,* and others (12, 23, 26, 36). Thus, the variety and abundance of oral gram-positive and gram-negative bacteria capable of activating complement make it attractive to postulate that many of the inflammatory events associated with periodontal inflammation are related to or embellished by the complement system.

It must be added that the mechanism by which complement component cleavage occurs in GF is not known. Since C3 and factor B cleavage have been regularly observed, it is possible that GF contains an intact alternative pathway as it enters the gingival sulcus and that activation occurs as it passes out of the tissue. Since endotoxin has been found in these tissues (33) and may be able to enter the gingiva through sulculus or pocket epithelium, activation of the alternative and classical pathways may occur within the gingiva. A third possibility is that cleavage of complement components occurs by non-complement-mediated proteolysis due to host and bacterial enzymes present in the local lesion. This possibility was verified by Nilsson et al., who demonstrated cleavage of purified C5 by GF (U. R. Nilsson, J. Goultshin, M. E. Norman, J. A. Mapes, W. P. McArthur, and N. S. Taichman, J. Dent. Res. Spec. Issue A **56:**A74, abstr. 125, 1977). It is important to point out that many of these proteases generate biologically active fragments from C3 and C5 and are therefore not trivial in their potential significance.

Studies of complement-mediated reactions in experimental animals. The persisting lack of an acceptable animal model of periodontal disease has limited studies of the role of complement in experimental periodontitis and gingivitis. A limited number of interesting studies have been done.

Nisengard and co-workers (21) induced experimental Arthus reactions in the gingivae of immunized monkeys. They observed that injections of homologous antigen into the gingiva induced both an inflammatory infiltrate and alveolar osteoclastic bone resorption reminiscent of periodontitis. Deposits of IgG and C4 were observed in perivascular areas, indicating that Arthus-type reactions could induce lesions similar to those seen in periodontitis.

A second approach has been to assess various parameters of gingival response to plaque in dogs that have been decomplemented. Administration of carrageenan (an inhibitor of C1) failed to influence the migration of neutrophils and monocytes into the gingival crevice (1). Administration of cobra venom factor (CVF), a C3b analog and alternative pathway activator, to dogs challenged with plaque extract decreased the influence of plaque extract on vascular changes, but failed to alter the attraction of neutrophils into the gingival crevice (14). However, when dogs were immunized with plaque extract, it was found that neutrophil migration and vascular exudation diminished (15). Recently, it was shown that, when extracts from pure cultures of *Actinomyces viscosus* and *Capnocytophaga ochracea* are applied to the gingivae of dogs decomplemented with CVF, there is diminished accumulation of leukocytes in the junctional epithelium (37). The implications of these studies are that chemotactic attraction of leukocytes induced in vivo by dental plaque is complement dependent and that this process may contribute to the initiation of gingivitis in a healthy periodontium.

Studies of this nature have always been difficult to interpret because of the short-term effect of the decomplementation relative to the chronicity of human disease, as well as the suspect purity of the decomplementing reagents. For example, CVF is strongly immunogenic, leading to a primary antibody response within a few days after administration and clearance. This makes long-term decomplementation by this means impossible. In addition, most CVF preparations contain phospholipase activity, and unless the effect of this enzyme is carefully controlled or excluded, the biological consequences of CVF administration cannot be attributed to decomplementation alone. Nevertheless, this approach to short-term effects of decomplementation can be useful and interesting.

Saliva–complement interactions. One potentially important interaction in the oral cavity, as demonstrated by Boakle and co-workers (4), is that between saliva and complement proteins. It has been known for several years that despite the fact that there is no detectable C3 in parotid saliva, there are IgA antibodies reactive with C3 (immunoconglutinins) in parotid secretions (16). Thus, there is probably no functional complement system in saliva itself. However, salivary secretions interact with complement to enhance its hemolytic activity by optimizing ionic strength requirements for certain early complement components such as $C\overline{1}$ (4).

Other factors interacting with complement are also present in saliva. It has recently been reported that a purified parotid-derived proline-rich protein inhibits C1 reactivity with C2, thus possibly providing a control mechanism for enhancement of complement activation due to ionic strength effects (R. J. Boakle and J. Vesely, J. Dent. Res. Spec. Issue A **60:**652, abstr. 1372, 1981).

It is conceivable that salivary factors enter the gingival crevice and affect GF complement activity therein. Such effects may aid in coating crevicular bacteria with C3 and permit salivary immunoconglutinins to agglutinate bacteria that are present subgingivally.

Conclusions. It is apparent that a central role for the complement system in periodontal diseases has not been established, although evidence has accumulated which indicates that the potential for the occurrence of complement-mediated phenomena in the periodontium does exist.

One issue yet to be resolved is whether activation of complement occurs within the periodontal tissues. Although immune complex deposition is not necessarily a major feature of chronic periodontitis or gingivitis, it is likely that soluble bacterial products capable of fluid-phase alternative pathway activation (e.g., endotoxins) can enter the tissues through the damaged crevicular epithelium. These reactions may not be detectable by immunofluorescence or immunoenzyme techniques.

A second issue is the significance of sulcular activation of GF complement. One potentially important interaction in the sulcus may be between sulcular phagocytes, mainly neutrophils, and bacteria opsinized with IgG antibody and C3b. Phagocytosis of bacteria may serve both as a first line of defense against access of bacteria to the underlying tissues and as a mechanism for initiation of tissue damage by host-derived histiolytic enzymes. Another important consequence of complement activation in the sulcus may be the maintenance of vascular and cellular inflammatory phenomena via release of active products. Such processes may include chemotaxis, anaphylatoxin activity, and cytotoxicity to host and bacterial cells.

It is also of interest to consider the potential for the influence of complement proteins on cellular constituents of the immune response. It is thought that cellular immune reactions, local antibody synthesis, and cell-mediated cytotoxic phenomena may contribute to tissue destruction in periodontal diseases. Certain interactions between complement and lymphoid cells may be of significance. For example, lymphokine synthesis by B cells induced by C3b may occur in the periodontium. Similarly, C3 cleavage products produced by bacterium–complement interactions may inhibit cell-mediated immune reactions induced by bacterial antigens, thus acting as a modulator of cellular immunity and possibly of antibody production. It has also been proposed that C3b induces release of lysosomal enzymes by macrophages and thus provides an additional mechanism for destruction of connective tissue.

SUMMARY

The role of the complement system in the pathogenesis of periodontal disease is not well established. The presence of complement proteins and their cleavage products, as well as activators of the complement pathways, in the gingival environment has made it attractive to postulate that complement may contribute to the inflammatory process observed. Numerous and complex biological effects of complement proteins have been described, yet the importance of these effects in human periodontal diseases is not known.

ACKNOWLEDGMENT

This work was supported in part by Public Health Service grant RR-05724 from the National Institutes of Health.

LITERATURE CITED

1. **Attström, R., and U. Larsson.** 1974. Effect of decomplementation by carragheenan on the migration of neutrophils and monocytes into dog gingival crevices. J. Periodontal Res. 9:165–175.
2. **Attström, R., A. B. Laurell, V. Lahsson, and A. Sjoholm.** 1975. Complement factors in gingival crevice material from healthy and inflammed gingiva in humans. J. Periodontal Res. 10:19–27.
3. **Berglund, S. F.** 1971. Immunoglobulins in human gingiva with specificity for oral bacteria. J. Periodontol. 42:546–551.
4. **Boakle, R. J., K. M. Pruitt, M. S. Silverman, and J. L. Glymph.** 1978. The effects of human saliva on the hemolytic activity of complement. J. Dent. Res. 57:103–110.
5. **Brandtzaeg, P.** 1965. Immunochemical comparison of proteins in human gingival pocket fluid, serum and saliva. Arch. Oral Biol. 10:795–803.
6. **Clagett, J. A., and R. C. Page.** 1978. Insoluble immune complexes and chronic periodontal diseases in man and the dog. Arch. Oral Biol. 23:153–165.
7. **Cooper, N. R.** 1976. The complement system, p. 158. In H. H. Fudenberg, D. P. Sites, J. L. Caldwell, and J. V. Wells (ed.), Basic and clinical immunology. Lange Medical Publishers, San Francisco.
8. **Courts, F. J., R. J. Boakle, H. H. Fudenberg, and M. S. Silverman.** 1977. Detection of functional complement components in gingival crevicular fluid from humans with periodontal disease. J. Periodontal Res. 56:327–331.
9. **Evans, R. T., S. Spaeth, and S. E. Mergenhagen.** 1966. Bacteriocidal antibody in mammalian serum to obligatory anaerobic gram-negative bacteria. J. Immunol. 97:112–179.
10. **Genco, R. J., P. A. Mashimo, G. Kryggier, and S. A. Ellison.** 1974. Antibody-mediated effects on the periodontium. J. Periodontol. 45:330–337.
11. **Gilmour, M. N., and R. J. Nisengard.** 1974. Interactions between serum titers and filamentous bacteria and their relationship to human periodontal disease. Arch. Oral Biol. 19:959–968.
12. **Hawley, C. E., and W. A. Falkler.** 1978. The anticomplementary activity of lipopolysaccharide preparations and sonicates from a strain of Fusobacterium nucleatum. J. Periodontal Res. 13:24–36.
13. **Holmberg, K., and J. Killander.** 1971. Quantitative determination of immunoglobulin (IgG, IgA, and IgM) and identification of IgA-type in the gingival fluid. J. Periodontal Res. 6:1–8.
14. **Kahnberg, K. E., J. Lindhe, and R. Attström.** 1976. The role of complement in initial gingivitis. I. The effect of decomplementation by cobra venom factor. J. Periodontal Res. 11:269–278.
15. **Kahnberg, K. E., J. Lindhe, and R. Attström.** 1977. The effect of decomplementation by caragheenan on experimental initial gingivitis in hyperimmune dogs. J. Periodontal Res. 12:479–490.
16. **Lachman, P. J., and R. A. Thomson.** 1970. Immunoconglutinins in human saliva—a group of unusual IgA antibodies. Immunology 18:157–169.
17. **Lally, E. T., P. C. Baehni, and W. P. McArthur.** 1980. Local immunoglobulin synthesis in periodontal disease. J. Periodontal Res. 15:159–164.
18. **Mansheim, B. J., M. L. Stenstrom, S. B. Low, and W. B. Clarke.** 1980. Measurement of serum and salivary antibodies to the oral pathogen Bacteriodes asaccharolyticus in human subjects. Arch. Oral Biol. 25:553–557.
19. **Müller-Eberhard, H. J.** 1978. Chemistry and function of the complement system. Hosp. Pract. 12:33.
20. **Nisengard, R. J., and E. H. Beutner.** 1970. Immunologic studies of periodontal disease. IgG type antibodies and skin test responses to Actinomyces and mixed oral flora. J. Periodontol. 41:149–152.
21. **Nisengard, R., E. H. Beutner, N. J. Neugeboren, M. Neiders, and J. Asaro.** 1977. Experimental induction of periodontal disease with Arthus-type reactions. Clin. Immunol. Immunopathol. 8:97–104.
22. **Nisengard, R., and C. Jarrett.** 1976. Coating of subgingival bacteria with immunoglobulin and complement. J. Periodontol. 47:518–521.

23. **Nygren, H., G. Dahlen, and L. A. Nilsson**. 1979. Human complement activation by lipopolysaccharides from *Bacteriodes oralis, Fusobacterium nucleatum,* and *Veillonella parvula.* Infect Immun. **26:**391–396.
24. **Okada, H., and M. S. Silverman**. 1979. Chemotactic activity in periodontal disease. I. The role of complement in monocyte chemotaxis. J. Periodontal Res. **14:**20–25.
25. **Okada, H., and M. S. Silverman**. 1979. Chemotactic activity in periodontal disease. II. The generation of complement derived chemotactic factors. J. Periodontal Res. **14:**147–152.
26. **Okuda, K., and I. Takazoe**. 1980. Activation of complement by dental plaque. J. Periodontal Res. **15:**232–239.
27. **Orstavik, D., and P. Brandtzaeg**. 1977. Serum antibodies in subjects with dental caries and gingivitis. Scand. J. Dent. Res. **35:**106–113.
28. **Platt, D., R. G. Crosby, and M. H. Dalbrow**. 1970. Evidence for the presence of immunoglobulin and antibodies in inflamed periodontal tissues. J. Periodontol. **41:**215–222.
29. **Schenkein, H. A., and R. J. Genco**. 1977. Gingival fluid and serum in periodontal diseases. I. Quantitative study of immunoglobulins, complement and other plasma proteins. J. Periodontol. **48:**772–777.
30. **Schenkein, H. A., and R. J. Genco**. 1977. Gingival fluid and serum in periodontal diseases. II. Evidence for cleavage of complement components C3, C3 pro-activator (factor B) and C4 in gingival fluid. J. Periodontol. **48:**778–784.
31. **Schonfeld, S. E., and J. M. Kagan**. 1908. Determination of the specificity of plasma cells for bacterial antigens in situ. Infect. Immun. **27:**947–952.
32. **Sela, M. N., G. Natan, M. Lahav, I. Ginsburg, and T. Dishon**. 1980. Bacteriolytic activity of human gingival exudate. Inflammation **4:**195–203.
33. **Shapiro, L., F. M. Lodato, O. R. Courant, and R. E. Stallard**. 1972. Endotoxin determinations in gingival inflammation. J. Periodontol. **43:**591–596.
34. **Shillitoe, E. J., and T. Lehner**. 1972. Immunoglobulins and complement in crevicular fluid, serum, and saliva in man. Oral Biol. **17:**241–247.
35. **Snyderman, R.** 1972. Role for endotoxin and complement in periodontal tissue destruction. J. Dent. Res. **51**(Suppl.):356–361.
36. **Tsai, C. C., U. R. Nilsson, W. P. McArthur, and N. S. Taichman**. 1977. Activation of the complement system by some gram-positive oral bacteria. Arch. Oral Biol. **22:**309–312.
37. **Wennström, J., L. Heijl, J. Lindhe, and S. Socransky**. 1980. Migration of gingival leukocytes mediated by plaque bacteria. J. Periodontal Res. **15:**363–372.

Humoral and Cellular Mediation
of Bone Resorption

ANN L. SANDBERG

*Laboratory of Microbiology and Immunology, National Institute of Dental Research,
Bethesda, Maryland 20205*

INTRODUCTION

The persistence of inflammation which ultimately leads to the loss of bone in periodontal disease is probably, in part, the result of activation of both the humoral and the cellular immune systems in response to metabolic products, endotoxins, chemotactic factors, and antigenic constituents of oral microorganisms. The inflammatory effects of the humoral components, which include immunoglobulins and complement, are extensive, and their participation in the periodontal disease process is implicated by the finding of antibody-producing cells (plasma cells) in the periodontal tissues and immunoglobulins, as well as fragments of the complement components, in the crevicular fluid (18, 19). The apparent activation of complement in inflamed gingival tissue and in the synovial fluid of patients with rheumatoid arthritis suggests that complement may be directly involved in the destruction of bone associated with these two pathological states. The infiltration of the diseased periodontal tissue with the immunologically competent macrophages and lymphocytes also provides a potential source of inflammatory mediators such as monokines, lymphokines, and effector molecules (e.g., prostaglandins) which influence the loss of bone. The localization of lymphocytes and macrophages adjacent to bone-resorbing surfaces suggests their involvement in this pathological event.

The following in vitro studies indicate that both cellular and humoral mechanisms may contribute to the resorption of bone, and it is conjectured that they function similarly in vivo to produce the bone loss observed in advanced periodontal disease.

HUMORAL IMMUNE MECHANISMS OF BONE RESORPTION

The inflammatory consequences of activation of the complement system have been extended to include the destruction of connective tissue. Earlier histological evidence had indicated a role for complement in the breakdown of cartilage, increased bone resorption, and impaired bone growth (10). A quantitative assay based on the release of previously incorporated ^{45}Ca from fetal rat long bones (radii and ulnae) in organ cultures was used to verify these findings and partially delineate the mechanism(s) of complement-dependent bone resorption (16, 17). The addition of high concentrations (50%) of normal rabbit serum, which served as the complement source, to organ cultures of fetal rat long bones stimulated the release of ^{45}Ca into the supernatant culture medium to a significantly greater extent than heated (complement-deficient) serum (Table 1). After 6 days of culture in the presence of complement, marked histological changes including loss of matrix and enhanced numbers of

309

TABLE 1. *Complement-mediated bone resorption and PGE synthesis*

Serum	^{45}Ca release (cpm/ml)	Medium PGE_2 (ng/culture)
Heated normal	$2,280 \pm 160$	0.1 ± 0.1
Unheated normal	$3,390 \pm 200^a$	3.3 ± 0.4^a
Unheated normal + indomethacin	$1,860 \pm 170$	1.0 ± 0.6
C6 deficient	$1,990 \pm 120$	0.8 ± 0.5
C6 deficient + C6	$2,970 \pm 190^b$	4.0 ± 1.2^b
C6 deficient + C6 + indomethacin	$1,760 \pm 230$	0.6 ± 0.5

[a] Significantly different from heated normal serum, $P < 0.05$.
[b] Significantly different from C6-deficient serum, $P < 0.05$.

osteoclasts were observed in the bones. Complement was identified as the heat-labile bone-resorbing activity by the finding that serum from rabbits genetically lacking the sixth component of complement (C6) did not support resorption. This biological activity was, however, restored by the addition of functionally purified C6 (Table 1). Thus, the late-acting complement components at least through C6 were required. As expected, the anaphylatoxins, C3a and C5a, were ineffective.

The complement-induced resorptive response was delayed compared with that initiated by parathyroid hormone or vitamin D metabolites and suggested the synthesis of a mediator by the bone tissue. This mediator was found to be prostaglandin E_2 (PGE_2) (Table 1), a potent agent of bone resorption (9) with kinetics similar to those initiated by complement. Indomethacin, an inhibitor of prostaglandin synthesis, blocked complement-dependent bone resorption, and levels of PGE_2 in the supernatants of cultures containing normal serum or C6-deficient serum reconstituted with C6 were elevated above those of supernatants of cultures containing heat-inactivated serum or C6-deficient serum, as determined by radioimmunoassay. Marked variability was observed in the concentrations of several pools of rabbit sera that induced in vitro bone resorption, suggesting that the limiting factor might be antibody since antibodies which agglutinated rat erythrocytes were detected in these pools. Adsorption of normal serum with rat spleen cells markedly decreased the synthesis of PGE_2 and the release of ^{45}Ca from the bones, indicating that antibodies reactive with cell surface antigens initiated the complement-mediated destruction of bone. Additional evidence for the requirement of antibody was obtained by the finding that PGE_2 synthesis and the resorptive activity could be restored to the adsorbed complement source by the addition of the 19S or 7S fractions of rabbit anti-rat erythrocyte or anti-sonicated rat bone sera. Activation of either the classical complement pathway by intact immunoglobulin G molecules or the alternative pathway by the $F(ab')_2$ fragments of these antibodies resulted in enhanced PGE_2 synthesis and bone resorption. The antibodies or antibody fragments reactive with cellular antigens apparently direct the action of complement to the cell surface, an absolute requirement for enhanced PGE_2 synthesis and bone resorption. These two biological effects did not occur in complement-containing cultures to which unreleated immune complexes (human serum albumin–anti-human serum albumin) were added.

Complement may influence the loss of bone through one or more of several mechanisms. Its ability to stimulate phospholipid metabolism (3) as well as to release lipids from cell membranes (8, 20) may provide a source of the prostaglandin precursor, arachidonic acid. In addition, complement-induced alterations of the cell membrane may enhance the accessibility of arachidonic acid to the enzymes of the cyclooxygenase pathway of prostaglandin synthesis or indirectly affect the metabolic activity of this enzyme system. Experimental evidence clearly indicates that complement does alter the response of bone to arachidonic acid. In the presence of complement and antibodies, the exogenous addition of arachidonic acid to bone cultures markedly elevated both prostaglandin synthesis and the release of ^{45}Ca from the bones. This is attributable to an enhanced incorporation of arachidonic acid into PGE_2 with a

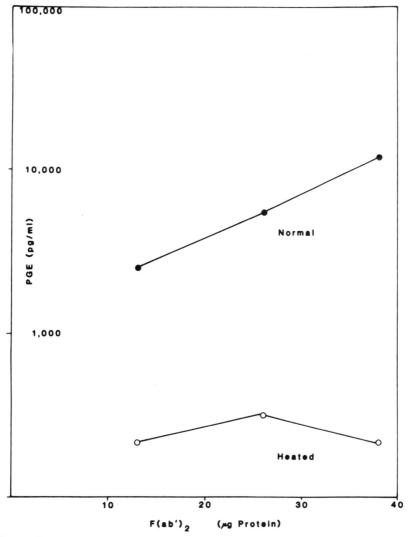

FIG. 1. *Complement-mediated synthesis of PGE_2 by rat peritoneal macrophages in culture. Cultures contained 4×10^6 macrophages, 30% normal or heated rabbit serum, and the indicated concentrations of anti-rat erythrocyte $F(ab')_2$ fragments.*

resultant increase in bone resorption since both effects were inhibited by indomethacin. Other unrelated inhibitors such as hydrocortisone and RO 20-5720 also blocked the complement-mediated response of bone to arachidonic acid. The stimulation of prostaglandin synthesis and ^{45}Ca release from bone by arachidonic acid was dependent on an intact complement system since the prostaglandin precursor was ineffective when added to cultures containing C6-deficient rabbit serum. Restoration of the complement system by functionally purified C6 allowed full expression of the stimulatory activity of arachidonic acid.

In view of the increased number of osteoclasts observed in the bones treated with complement, it is possible that these are the cells which respond to complement. Another cell of the monocytic series, the macrophage, synthesizes enhanced levels of PGE_2 when cultured in the presence of anti-rat erythrocyte $F(ab')_2$ fragments and complement (Fig. 1). Like the previously described effects of complement on bone, the activation of macrophages requires the late complement components, at least through C6, since minimal prostaglandin synthesis was detected in the supernatants of macrophages cultured in the presence of C6-deficient serum. Another similarity observed between the macrophage and bone cultures was the response to arachidonic acid. In C6-deficient serum supplemented with C6, arachidonic acid was a potent stimulator of PGE_2 synthesis, an effect which was inhibited by indomethacin. If, as suspected, the macrophage, which has been shown to resorb bone in vitro by a proataglandin-mediated mechanism (1), is analogous to the osteoclast, the latter cell may well be the cell in bone that is stimulated by complement activation to produce PGE_2, which in turn induces bone resorption.

The complement system may exert a second effect on bone metabolism in that it inhibits the synthesis of new connective tissue. The addition of antibodies and complement to cultures of fetal rat calvaria markedly inhibited the synthesis of collagen by the bones (as detected by the incorporation of [^{3}H]proline into collagenase-digestible protein) but had relatively little effect on noncollagen protein (B. E. Kream, L. G. Raisz, and A. L. Sandberg, Calcif. Tissue Int., in press). These findings cannot be ascribed to an enhanced degradation of collagen since only a minimal increase in the amount of [^{3}H]proline in the media of the cultures containing complement was observed; rather, they favor the hypothesis that complement selectively inhibits osteoblastic collagen synthesis. Serum which is heat inactivated to destroy the complement activity or lacks C6 is incapable of inhibiting collagen synthesis. This complement-dependent effect is not mediated by PGE_2. PGE_2 synthesis was elevated in the cultures of calvaria which contained complement and exhibited decreased collagen synthesis. However, the addition of indomethacin, RO 20-5720, acetylsalicylic acid, and flufenemic acid, all of which completely inhibited PGE_2 synthesis by the calvaria, did not restore normal collagen synthesis. Thus, complement may function in a dual capacity in influencing connective tissue metabolism. Activation of this mediator system stimulates the resorption of bone by enhancing PGE_2 synthesis and inhibits bone growth via a PGE_2-independent mechanism (Fig. 2).

CELLULAR IMMUNE MECHANISMS OF BONE RESORPTION

The cellular immune system may also be a major participant in localized bone loss via the generation of the lymphokine osteoclast-activating factor (OAF)

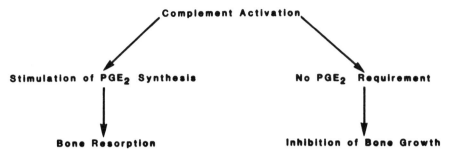

FIG. 2. *Dual function of complement in the regulation of bone metabolism.*

which was identified by its ability to cause the release of ^{45}Ca from prelabeled fetal rat bones in organ culture (7). This mediator is produced by leukocytes which have been activated by mitogens, antigenic material in dental plaque, or allogeneic stimulation, as well as by lymphoid cell lines derived from patients with multiple myeloma and Burkitt's lymphoma. It has also been detected in the sera of myeloma patients and in the supernatants of cultures of bone marrow from patients with this neoplasm. Although clearly a lymphocyte product, as was suggested by the radiosensitivity of the responding cell population and established later with cultures of separated cells, the presence of macrophages or macrophage products is an absolute requirement for OAF production. Macrophage–lymphocyte contact was initially considered to be essential, but more recent evidence indicates that lymphocytes supplemented with conditioned medium from cultures of macrophages release OAF (21, 22). The macrophage dependence is attributable to the production of PGE_2 by these cells since several inhibitors of prostaglandin synthesis, including indomethacin, flufenemic acid, and RO 20-5720, abolish both the production of OAF and the appearance of prostaglandins in the supernatants of activated leukocyte cultures. These inhibitors were effective only when added at the initiation of culture. Although indomethacin blocked the appearance of OAF in the cultures of mitogen-stimulated leukocytes, it had no effect on mitogenesis or protein synthesis, dissociating these two latter responses from the production of the bone-resorbing mediator. Further identification of the macrophage product as PGE was attained by the exogenous addition of PGE_1 or PGE_2 to enriched activated lymphocyte cultures (Table 2). The supernatants from these cultures, after diafiltration to remove prostaglandins, which directly cause bone resorption,

TABLE 2. *Elaboration of OAF by enriched lymphocytes to which*
PGE_1 or PGE_2 was exogenously added[a]

Enriched lymphocytes	PGE_1	PGE_2	OAF production, ^{45}Ca release (experimental/control ratio)
+	−	−	0.93 ± 0.07
+	+	−	1.86 ± 0.24[b]
+	−	+	1.36 ± 0.03[b]
−	+	−	0.92 ± 0.12
−	−	+	0.95 ± 0.13

[a]From reference 22.
[b]Significantly greater than 1.0, $P < 0.05$.

contained OAF activity, whereas supernatants of cultures maintained in the absence of prostaglandins were inactive, demonstrating that prostaglandins can replace the macrophages required for the production of OAF. The generation of OAF, therefore, appears to be unlike that of other lymphokines, e.g., migration inhibition factor and colony-stimulating factor, which are inhibited by prostaglandins. Thus, in addition to its direct action, PGE_2 contributes indirectly to bone resorption by initiating the production of OAF by appropriately stimulated lymphocytes. Several laboratories are in agreement that, once generated, OAF acts directly on bone, an event which is not mediated by prostaglandins. Indomethacin does not block the release of ^{45}Ca from bones cultured in the presence of OAF. The anti-inflammatory steroid dexamethasone does, however, inhibit this response when added to cultures simultaneously with OAF; it is ineffective if added 24 h after OAF pretreatment. When treated with OAF, the collagen content of cultured bones is decreased, and large numbers of osteoclasts are present. Conventional histological techniques do not readily distinguish whether this latter finding reflects an influx of osteoclasts or an increased size of preexisting cells. Although this area remains controversial, recent quantitative morphological examination of OAF-treated bones indicates that this lymphokine, as well as PGE_2 and vitamin D metabolites, acts primarily by increasing the size of the osteoclasts, and this finding supports the theory that the resorption is mediated by increased activity of the existing osteoclasts (5).

The intracellular events which trigger the resorptive process remain largely undefined. As with many other biological systems, cyclic adenosine 3',5'-monophosphate has been implicated as a mediator in the response of bone to OAF and other bone-resorbing agents (12). OAF, as well as parathyroid hormone (PTH), stimulates the early (5 min) accumulation of cyclic adenosine 3',5'-monophosphate in cultures of mouse cranial bones which are later resorbed. However, a causal relationship between these two effects has not been established since there is an apparent dissociation of resorption and cyclic adenosine 3',5'-monophosphate accumulation in cultures containing high levels of OAF.

In addition to its resorptive effects, OAF, at concentrations that stimulate bone resorption, also inhibits collagen synthesis in fetal rat calvaria in organ cultures. The synthesis of noncollagen protein is less affected. That this inhibitory effect can, indeed, be ascribed to OAF is supported by the finding that it and the bone-resorptive activities persist through two stages of OAF purification.

The in vitro effects of OAF are similar to those of native PTH. The dose-response curve and time course of OAF-induced ^{45}Ca release from cultured bones resemble those of PTH but differ from those of PGE_2. PGE_2 does not exhibit as steep a dose-response curve as OAF or PTH, and the release of ^{45}Ca from bones exposed to PGE_2 is slower (5 days) than is that induced by the other two mediators (2 days).

OAF has the characteristics of a protein in that it is susceptible to inactivation by trypsin and pronase but not by ribonuclease or neuraminidase. Papain, which inactivated PTH, did not inactivate OAF. Several criteria further distinguish OAF from PTH and other known bone-resorbing agents. In contrast to PTH, OAF is heat and acid labile. OAF fails to cross-react with conventional antibodies reactive with PGE and native PTH and is not extracted from activated leukocyte supernatants by lipid solvents which remove PGE_2 and vitamin D metabolites. As determined by molecular sieve column chromatography, OAF elutes in a molecular-weight range of 11,000 to 25,000 (6, 14). If the leukocytes are cultured in the presence of serum, an additional peak of OAF activity is found associated with albumin. Under dissociating conditions (socium dodecyl sulfate and urea), OAF obtained from cultures of human tonsils has been reported to migrate as a 9,000-molecular-weight protein on polyacrylamide gels (11). These studies indicate a molecular weight of 17,000 under non-dissociating conditions. These findings raise the possibility that OAF may exist in monomeric or dimeric forms. An additional species of OAF ("little OAF") has been described which elutes from a Bio-Gel P6 column between 1,330 and 3,500 (15). OAF with a molecular weight of approximately 18,000 was converted to "little OAF" by equilibration in 1 M NaCl or 2 M urea, and "little OAF" self-associated to the larger-molecular-weight molecule after equilibration in buffers of low ionic strength. "Little OAF" may represent a subunit of the more commonly described larger-molecular-weight OAF. Although papain did not inactivate the native OAF, "little OAF" was susceptible to digestion by this enzyme as well as by trypsin. "Little OAF" had presumably escaped earlier detection because it is present in low concentrations and exhibits a steep biphasic dose-response curve requiring multiple dilutions for its assay. In addition, its activity is lost after a few weeks of storage at $-20°C$. Although OAF derived from tonsils has been reported to have been purified to homogeneity, as evidenced by its association with a single band in polyacrylamide gel electrophoresis and the finding of a single terminal amino acid (glutamic acid or glutamine) (11), other investigations reveal contamination of peripheral blood leukocyte-derived OAF with other lymphokine activities. As with may of the other lymphokines, the definition of OAF as a discrete molecular entity awaits further analysis.

The most specific and straightforward approach to distinguishing OAF from other lymphokines and its detection in clinical samples would be the utilization of immunochemical techniques. A monoclonal antibody has been produced to the tonsil-derived OAF (13). This antibody, the immunoglobulin nature of which has been verified by its reactivity with anti-mouse immunoglobulin and staphylococcal protein A, neutralizes the biological activity of OAF but does not interfere with that of PTH, PGE, or vitamin D metabolites. More recently, a monoclonal antibody against the active amino acid sequence of bovine parathyroid hormone (amino acids 1 through 34) has been obtained (P. Stashenko, S. Offenbacher, and J. M. Goodson, J. Dent. Res. Spec. Issue A **60**:498, abstr. 754, 1981; P. Stashenko, T. A. Binder, and J. M. Goodson, J. Dent. Res. Spec. Issue A **60**:498, abstr. 755, 1981). This antibody inhibits bone resorption initiated by peripheral blood-cell derived OAF but not that due to PGE_2. When insolubilized, this monoclonal antibody removed the bone-resorbing activity from a preparation of OAF, and complexes of OAF and the anti-1−34 PTH antibody were dissociated at low pH. These latter findings raise the very interesting possibility that there is primary structure homology between OAF and the active fragment of PTH. Although, as stated previously, conventional antiserum to PTH did not inhibit bone resorption initiated by OAF, it is highly possible that this antiserum reacts only with antigenic determinants outside the domain of the active region of PTH. These reagents will be invaluable for investigating the possible similarities between OAF and other lymphokines, demonstrating the participation of OAF in bone destruction, and dissecting its effects from those of other known bone resorbers.

SUMMARY

It is apparent that multiple mechanisms may be involved in the bone loss associated with periodontal disease. As summarized in Fig. 3, both the humoral and the cellular immune systems probably contribute to and may, in fact, interact in the initiation and amplification of this pathological process. By extrapolation from in vitro studies, alveolar bone resorption may be mediated by localized antibody-dependent activation of complement or by the lymphocyte-derived OAF. Common to both of these immunological mechanisms of bone destruction is the production of prostaglandins of the E series. These potent resorbing agents, elevated levels of which have been detected in inflamed gingival tissues and dental cysts (2, 4), are produced by a cellular constituent of bone after exposure to antibody specific for a cell surface antigen and complement. Presumably, the osteoclast is the cell that responds to these components of the humoral immune system since another cell of the monocytic series, the macrophage, synthesizes and secretes prostaglandins when cultured with antibodies and complement. In addition to providing evidence for the cellular source of the prostaglandins in bone, these latter findings suggest that complement stimulation of macrophages adjacent to bone may also enhance prostaglandin-mediated bone resorption. PGE not only exerts a direct resorptive effect on bone, but also has been identified as the macrophage product required

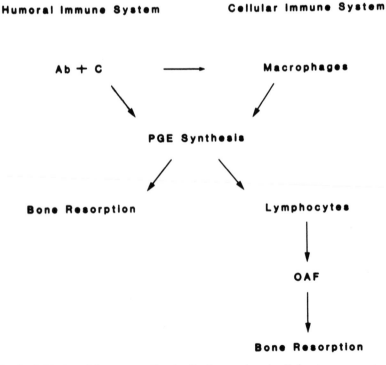

FIG. 3. Initiation of bone resorption by the humoral and cellular immune systems.

for the production of OAF by appropriately stimulated lymphocytes. Once generated, this lymphokine resorbs bone via a prostaglandin-independent mechanism. The deleterious effects of the humoral and cellular immune systems on bone are not limited to enhanced resorption; they also include the impairment of bone growth by selective inhibition of collagen synthesis. Precise delineation of the participation of humoral and cellular factors in alveolar bone loss awaits further sophisticated investigations, some of which will be greatly facilitated by the application of immunochemical techniques utilizing the recently described monoclonal antibodies reactive with OAF.

LITERATURE CITED

1. **Dominquez, J. H., and G. R. Mundy**. 1980. Monocytes mediate osteoclastic bone resorption by prostaglandin production. Calcif. Tissue Int. **31**:29–34.
2. **Goodson, J. M., F. E. Dewhirst, and A. Brunetti**. 1974. Prostaglandin E_2 levels and human periodontal disease. Prostaglandins **6**:81–85.
3. **Güttler, F.** 1972. Phospholipid synthesis in HeLa cells exposed to immunoglobulin G and complement. Biochem. J. **128**:953–960.
4. **Harris, M., M. V. Jenkins, A. Bennett, and M. R. Wills**. 1973. Prostaglandin production and bone resorption by dental cysts. Nature (London) **245**:213–215.
5. **Holtrop, M. E., and L. G. Raisz**. 1979. Comparison of the effects of 1,25-dihydroxycholecalciferol, prostaglandin E_2, and osteoclast-activating factor with parathyroid hormone on the ultrastructure of osteoclasts in cultured long bones of fetal rats. Calcif. Tissue Int. **29**:201–205.
6. **Horton, J. E., W. J. Koopman, J. J. Farrar, J. Fuller-Bonar, and S. E. Mergenhagen**. 1979. Partial purification of a bone-resorbing factor elaborated from human allogeneic cultures. Cell. Immunol. **43**:1–10.
7. **Horton, J. E., L. G. Raisz, H. A. Simmons, J. J. Oppenheim, and S. E. Mergenhagen**. 1972. Bone resorbing activity in supernatant fluid from cultured human peripheral blood leukocytes. Science **177**:793.
8. **Inoue, K., T. Kinoshita, M. Okada, and T. Akiyama**. 1977. Release of phospholipids from complement-mediated lesions on the surface structure of Escherichia coli. J. Immunol. **119**:65–72.
9. **Klein, D. C., and L. G. Raisz**. 1970. Prostaglandins: stimulation of bone resorption in tissue culture. Endocrinology **86**:1436–1440.
10. **Lachmann, P. J., R. R. A. Coombs, H. B. Fell, and J. T. Dingle**. 1969. The breakdown of embryonic (chick) cartilage and bone cultivated in the presence of complement-sufficient antisera. 3. Immunologic analysis. Int. Arch. Allergy Appl. Immunol. **36**:469–485.
11. **Luben, R. A.** 1978. Purification of a lymphokine: osteoclast activating factor from human tonsil lymphocytes. Biochem. Biophys. Res. Commun. **84**:15–22.
12. **Luben, R. A., M. C. Chen, D. M. Rosen, and M. A. Mohler**. 1979. Effects of osteoclast activating factor from human lymphocytes on cyclic AMP concentrations in isolated mouse bone and bone cells. Calcif. Tissue Int. **28**:23–32.
13. **Luben, R. A., M. M. Mohler, and G. E. Nedwin**. 1979. Production of hybridomas secreting monoclonal antibodies against the lymphokine osteoclast activating factor. J. Clin. Invest. **64**:337–341.
14. **Luben, R. A., G. R. Mundy, C. L. Trummel, and L. G. Raisz**. 1974. Partial purification of osteoclast-activating factor from phytohemagglutinin-stimulated human leukocytes. J. Clin. Invest. **53**:1473–1480.
15. **Mundy, G. R., and L. G. Raisz**. 1977. Big and little forms of osteoclast activating factor. J. Clin Invest. **60**:122–128.
16. **Raisz, L. G., A. L. Sandberg, J. M. Goodson, H. A. Simmons, and S. E. Mergenhagen**. 1974. Complement-dependent stimulation of prostaglandin synthesis and bone resorption. Science **185**:789–791.
17. **Sandberg, A. L., L. G. Raisz., J. M. Goodson, H. A. Simmons, and S. E. Mergenhagen**. 1977. Initiation of bone resorption by the classical and alternative C pathways and its mediation by prostaglandins. J. Immunol. **119**:1378–1381.
18. **Schenkein, H. A., and R. J. Genco**. 1977. Gingival fluid and serum in periodontal diseases. J. Periodontol. **48**:772–777.
19. **Schenkein, H. A., and R. J. Genco**. 1977. Gingival fluid and serum in periodontal diseases. J. Periodontol. **48**:778–784.
20. **Schlager, S. I., S. K. Ohanian, and T. Borsos**. 1978. Stimulation of the synthesis and release of lipids in tumor cells under attack by antibody and C. J. Immunol. **120**:895–901.
21. **Yoneda, T., and G. R. Mundy**. 1979. Prostaglandins are necessary for osteoclast-activating factor production by activated peripheral blood leukocytes. J. Exp. Med. **149**:279–283.
22. **Yoneda, T., and G. R. Mundy**. 1979. Monocytes regulate osteoclast-activating factor production by releasing prostaglandins. J. Exp. Med. **150**:338–350.

Roles of Lysozyme in the Host Response to Periodontopathic Microorganisms

VINCENT J. IACONO, BRUCE J. MacKAY, JERRY J. POLLOCK, PAUL R. BOLDT, STEVEN LADENHEIM, BARBARA L. GROSSBARD, AND MARY L. ROCHON

Department of Periodontics and Department of Oral Biology and Pathology, State University of New York at Stony Brook, Stony Brook, New York 11794

INTRODUCTION

The development of the periodontal lesion is generally thought to include interactions of bacteria, their products, and various components of the immune system (27, 87, 91). The result is a clinically apparent and histologically detectable inflammatory response which itself is the outcome of a series of complex reactions (69). The cellular sources of components which play major roles in inflammation are the polymorphonuclear leukocyte (PMN) or neutrophil and the mononuclear phagocyte or macrophage (6). These cells possess a variety of potential antimicrobial substances and hydrolytic enzymes distributed within their cytoplasmic granules (16, 33). The macrophage has been reported to be abundant in the inflamed gingiva of humans (25, 69, 80) and is the most conspicuous cell observed within the gingival lamina propria (26). Plaque bacteria and their components have been shown to induce macrophage enzyme release (1, 40, 67, 99), and lysosomal enzymes are present in significantly greater amounts in inflamed gingivae than in healthy gingivae of humans (41). The potential role(s) for PMNs in the pathogenesis of inflammatory periodontal diseases is also receiving great attention (28). The neutrophil is the predominant cell type in the gingival sulcus during the initiation and progression of these diseases (3, 42, 70, 79), and some observations suggest the potential for PMN enzyme release to mediate tissue damage (36, 88, 90). The influx of neutrophils into the gingival sulcus is thought to be due to complement activation and to the production of chemotactic substances produced by microbial plaque (43, 93). The preponderance of B cells observed in the gingival tissues of patients with advanced disease may be due in part to the release of PMN neutral serine proteases which are polyclonal B-cell activators (5, 55). These findings point to the possibility that tissue damage during periodontitis is neutrophil mediated. However, clinical observations indicate that PMNs may serve a protective role in the periodontium (29, 95).

The continued presence of large numbers of neutrophils in the junctional epithelium and pseudopockets during gingivitis (69) may reflect the individual's ability to respond adequately to the microbial challenge and prevent further periodontal destruction. It is conceivable that a chronic nonprogressive gingivitis may be considered as successful host resistance against the microflora and their toxic products. Indeed, it has been suggested that a dysfunction of the neutrophil barrier, either through intrinsic mechanisms (14) or extrinsically by microbial factors (85, 94), may be partially responsible for severe and rapid progressive periodontal disease. The physical barrier of the junctional epithelium and the presence of soluble and cellular elements of the immune system most likely play a significant role in the prevention of the penetration of

318

intact microogranisms into the periodontal tissues during most kinds of periodontal disease (30). However, it is generally regarded that bacterial components and their products do penetrate the tissues and mediate periodontal pathology either directly or through interactions with various segments of the host defense system (1, 48, 59, 67). The prominent inflammatory cell present in the affected tissues is the mononuclear phagocyte or macrophage (69). Since the macrophage would normally not be expected to come in contact with microorganisms in the periodontal connective tissue, it most likely responds to their products (62, 68, 89, 99). The ability of this inflammatory cell to neutralize the effects of bacterial components may therefore partially determine the extent of tissue destruction. Alternatively, the stimulated macrophage is known to secrete a number of soluble substances which contribute to the development of chronic inflammation (19). Macrophages release lysozyme, lysosomal hydrolases, neutral proteases (e.g., plasminogen activator, collagenase, and elastase), prostaglandins and other arachidonic acid oxygenation products, complement components (C1q, C2, and C4) and all factors of the alternative pathway, at least two phospholipases, and various factors affecting cell proliferation and the immune response (19, 23).

Several treatises would be required for a comprehensive discussion of the antibacterial properties and tissue-damaging effects of the many neutrophil and mononuclear phagocyte components which participate in the defense against dental plaque and the products of the subgingival microflora. The focus of this review is on lysozyme, a cationic protein which is found in both the azurophil specific granules of neutrophils (10, 53) and which is the major secretory product of macrophages (19). Gordon and co-workers observed that lysozyme was released from monocytes on a constitutive basis and found that it was secreted in amounts approximating 1% of the cellular protein content every 24-h period (32). As has been observed for other inflammatory exudates (47, 82), lysozyme is present in large amounts in gingival crevicular fluid, and its concentration increases with the severity of periodontal inflammation (8). This report includes discussions of the growth-inhibitory, aggregating, and lytic effects of the enzyme on oral microorganisms and of studies of its interaction with mammalian cells. Since the molecule's role in host resistance still remains unclear, selective isolation of lysozyme from its biological sources will be required to determine its function as an individual factor and as part of a total antibacterial system. A technique for the selective removal, quantitative recovery, and one-step purification of human lysozyme (HL) will therefore also be presented.

EFFECTS ON MICROBIAL GROWTH

The environment of the oral cavity is one of constant changes in microbial growth conditions (83). In addition to variation in physical parameters and available nutrients, the presence of numerous antibacterial factors limits the growth rate of many oral microorganisms to two or three cell divisions per day (76). Since lysozyme is found in significant amounts in saliva and crevicular fluid (56) and has been considered to be the major PMN antibacterial factor for gram-positive microorganisms (61), we examined its effects on several oral bacteria, in particular the seven serotypes of *Streptococcus mutans* (45). Strains of *S. mutans* were inoculated into a chemically defined medium (87) containing various amounts of hen egg white lysozyme (HEWL), and growth was monitored spectrophotometrically. Serotype a (AHT) and b (BHT and FA-1) strains were

TABLE 1. *Effect of HEWL on growth of* S. mutans

Strain	% Inhibition[a] by HEWL at indicated concn								
	25[b]	50	75	100	160	320	500	1,000	5,000
AHT (a)[c]	47	97	NG						
BHT (b)	57	99	NG						
FA-1 (b)	56	93	NG						
GS-5 (c)	7	7	14	44	89	91	93	91	91
B13 (d)	15	15	15	15	42	54	64	78	78
LM-7 (e)								CG	85
OMZ-174 (f)								CG	53
6715 (g)							CG	30	77

[a]Inhibition is expressed as the percent reduction in absorbance of cultures containing HEWL compared with the non-enzyme-containing cultures at that incubation time when the latter reached stationary phase. NG, no growth; CG, complete growth.

[b]HEWL amounts represent the final concentration in micrograms per milliliter of chemically defined medium (87).

[c]Strains of S. mutans representing each of the known seven serotypes (a–g) (71).

the most susceptible to lysozyme (Table 1). Significant growth inhibition of these serotypes was effected by as little as 25 μg of HEWL per ml, and total inhibition of these serotypes occurred with just over 50 μg of lysozyme per ml. The serotype e and f strains were the most resistant of S. *mutans* cultures, and serotypes c and d were intermediate in their susceptibility to the enzyme. These observed differences could be related to the ability of lysozyme to gain access to the cell wall peptidoglycan or to other structures such as the cytoplasmic membrane and components of an endogenous autolytic enzyme system. In support of this possibility, we observed that an antigen extract of S. *mutans* LM-7 blocked the growth-inhibitory properties of lysozyme (V. J. Iacono, B. J. MacKay, S. DiRienzo, J. J. Pollock, and J. M. Zuckerman, J. Dent. Res. Spec. Issue B **59**:910, abstr. 89, 1980), and we have isolated lipoteichoic acid as a lysozyme-binding component of S. *mutans* BHT by affinity chromatography (Iacono et al., submitted for publication). In addition, it has been shown that lysozyme binds to pure acylated lipoteichoic acid of S. *mutans* BHT in vitro, which inhibits this amphiphilic molecule's hemagglutinating potential (L. I. Katona et al., *in* A. J. Wicken and G. D. Shockman, ed., *Chemistry and*

TABLE 2. *Comparison of the effects of HL and HEWL on the growth of the human isolates of serotype c* S. mutans

Strain	% Inhibition[a] by indicated concn (μg/ml) of:							
	HEWL					HL		
	100	250	500	750	1,000	60	200	500
GS-5	72	86	91	100	100	100	100	100
RMR	21	22	70	81	84			
SB	0	18	21	17	53			
DPR	0	0	0	21	61	53	100	100
DJR	0	0	0	0	10	0	18	64

[a]Inhibition is expressed as the percent reduction in absorbance of cultures containing HEWL or HL compared with the non-lysozyme-containing cultures at that time when the latter reached stationary phase.

TABLE 3. *Dechaining analysis of* S. mutans *grown in the presence of lysozyme*[a]

Strain	HEWL (μg/ml)	No. of chains[b] of different cell number					Mean chain length ± SD[c]
		1–2	3–5	6–8	9–11	12	
GS-5	0	0	9	7	7	11	9.0 ± 2.2
	100	26	19	6	0	0	3.1 ± 0.8
	250	19	23	13	3	1	4.3 ± 0.8
	1,000	48	10	15	0	0	2.4 ± 0.4
DPR	0	43	41	22	10	8	5.1 ± 0.5
	250	116	24	9	3	0	2.5 ± 0.6
	500	80	48	8	5	1	2.9 ± 0.3
	1,000	85	30	5	6	1	3.0 ± 0.4
DJR	0	5	19	18	7	24	9.4 ± 1.0
	250	97	22	14	9	7	5.8 ± 1.1
	500	93	43	16	8	1	3.3 ± 0.5
	1,000	50	44	11	1	1	3.4 ± 0.4

[a]Standardized samples (10 μl) of stationary cultures were Gram stained, and photomicrographs were taken of five randomly selected fields under oil immersion.

[b]Number reflects total number of chains in each range of cell length counted in five fields.

[c]Mean chain length is the total number of cells divided by the number of chains counted in five fields. SD, Standard deviation of the mean.

Biological Activities of Bacterial Surface Amphiphiles, in press). Many recent investigations have revealed that lipoteichoic acids from several bacteria strongly inhibit autolysin activity (15, 44). Should the binding of lysozyme to lipoteichoic acid occur in *S. mutans* in vivo, a deregulation of autolysin activity might occur that would affect cell division and lysis or cause an alteration of a highly organized membrane system, leading to efflux of small molecules, growth inhibition, and cell death. In addition, the binding of lysozyme to released exocellular lipoteichoic acid might block some of the periodontopathic activities attributed to this molecule (40).

Serotype c strains of *S. mutans* are the most prevalent of the detectable serotypes found in human populations (34) and are thought to be the principal microorganisms in caries development (35). When lysozyme was tested for its effects on five serotype c strains (GS-5, RMR, SB, DPR, and DJR), significant differences were detected in the growth inhibition of each strain (Table 2) (T. P. Byrnes, V. J. Iacono, J. J. Pollock, and M. L. Rochon, J. Dent. Res. Spec. Issue A **60:**571, abstr. 1047, 1981). HL had a much greater inhibitory effect than HEWL, but had the same strain specificity (Table 2). When strains escaped the bacteriostatic effects of lysozyme and grew to stationary phase, dechaining was observed with all concentrations of lysozyme (Table 3). When chain length was evaluated, greater than 57% of chains consisted of diplococci and single cells, an increase of more than 100% over non-lysozyme-containing cultures (Table 3). Although the mechanism for dechaining by lysozyme is not known, it has been proposed that it results from an activation and deregulation of autolysin activity (103). Dechaining may be an effector mechanism whereby lysozyme participates in the regulation of the oral microflora. In support of this hypothesis, dechained bacteria were found to survive to a considerably lesser extent than normal chained cultures when exposed to an acidic environment and to further lysozyme treatment (Table 4). Dechaining may partially explain the observation that there is neither a reduction in plaque levels of *S. mutans* nor a major restriction in carbohydrate consumption in subjects who are on fluoride supplements and who have markedly reduced caries experience (96). These individuals might possess dechained *S. mutans* which would not survive as well as normal streptococci when the local pH dropped as a result of carbohydrate consumption.

When tested for its effects on the periodontal pathogen *Actinomyces viscosus* T14(V), growth inhibition was observed with as little as 160 µg of HEWL per ml (45). As can be seen in Fig. 1, large amounts of HEWL continued to suppress the growth of this virulent strain of *A. viscosus* T14 over a 24-h period. Strains of three oral gram-negative rods were also tested: *Eikenella corrodens*, which is commonly found in deep periodontal pockets with minimal clinical imflammation (86); *Capnocytophaga* species, which are among the predominant cultivable microbiota isolated from periodontal lesions (63); and *Actinobacillus actinomycetemcomitans*, which was originally isolated from pockets of individuals with periodontosis (46). Unlike gram-positive microorganisms, *A. actinomycetemcomitans* Y4, *E. corrodens* 4319, and *Capnocytophaga* strain 2010 were totally resistant to the growth-inhibitory properties of HEWL (Fig. 1). This

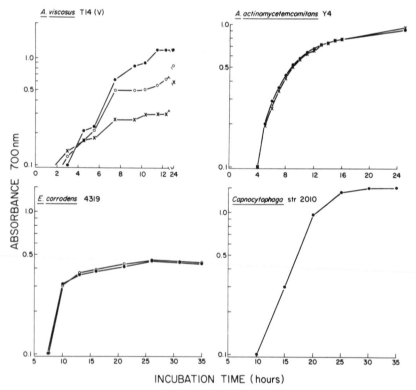

FIG. 1. *Comparison of growth of* A. viscosus *T14(V),* A. actinomycetemcomitans *Y4,* E. corrodens *4319, and* Capnocytophaga *strain 2010 in media containing various amounts of HEWL. Symbols:* ●, *medium alone;* ○, *medium plus 1 mg of HEWL per ml;* ×, *medium plus 5 mg of HEWL per ml.*

TABLE 4. *Effect of low environmental pH on dechained cells[a]*

Strain DPR cells	Culture medium	Absorbance (700 nm) at 24 h
Control	DM	0.95
Control	DM + L	0.43
Dechained	DM	0.26
Dechained	DM +L	No growth

[a]Cells harvested from cultures grown in the presence (dechained) and absence (control) of lysozyme (1,000 μg/ml) were resuspended to the original culture volume in 0.05 M sodium acetate, pH 3.9, and incubated for 5 h at 37°C. Samples (0.2 ml) were then removed and added to fresh defined medium (DM) or DM plus lysozyme (DM + L). Growth was monitored spectrophotometrically.

resistance may be due, in part, to the outer membrane of these bacteria, which serves as a permeability barrier (9, 18). Lysozyme would therefore not be able to gain access to its substrate unless damage to the outer membrane occurred (104). Lysozyme has been shown to bind lipopolysaccharide of *Pseudomonas aeruginosa* (20) and possibly that of *Veillonella* (7). Binding to lipopolysaccharide or other structures might therefore result in damage to the outer membrane which is not apparent when the bacteria are growing in enriched media. This would account for the growth inhibition of *Capnocytophaga* strain 2010 after preincubation of the bacteria in lysozyme prior to transfer to growth medium (Fig. 2). During balanced growth, in which all nutrients are continuously supplied, repair mechanisms may be operative such that irreversible damage is not manifested (84). In support of this possibility, our previous studies with *Veillonella alcalescens* indicated that this gram-negative diplococcus was totally resistant to the bacteriostatic effect of lysozyme (45). Yet, when this microorganism was incubated in a nonnutrient buffer containing lysozyme alone, electron microscopic observation revealed that significant numbers of the cells had lysed (93a). These studies strongly suggest that lysozyme is a highly effective regulator of bacterial growth in the oral cavity, especially since environmental conditions are known to vary widely in available nutrients and physicochemical parameters (83).

MEDIATOR OF MICROBIAL AGGREGATION

Host resistance to potentially harmful bacteria is not always equated with bacteriostatic and bactericidal events. Aggregation or agglutination of bacteria by natural defense factors is also an important mechanism for elimination of potential microbial pathogens (39). Bacterial aggregation can occur by both immunological and non-imunological mechanisms, resulting in the inhibition of adherence and microbial colonization or enhanced phagocytosis, or both (56). In addition to its growth-inhibitory effects, lysozyme has also been shown to act on bacteria by agglutination, thus possibly preparing them for phagocytosis (72, 74). However, too great an agglutination may result in intense phagocytosis with extracellular release of PMN lysosomal enzymes, leading to inflammation (102). It has been demonstrated that lysozyme binds to and aggregates the various serotypes of *S. mutans* (72), and binding is blocked by inhibitors of muramidase activity (72). It was observed that serotype a and b strains bound more enzyme and aggregated to a greater extent than the other serotypes (72). These data suggested that lysozyme binding and bacterial aggregation could

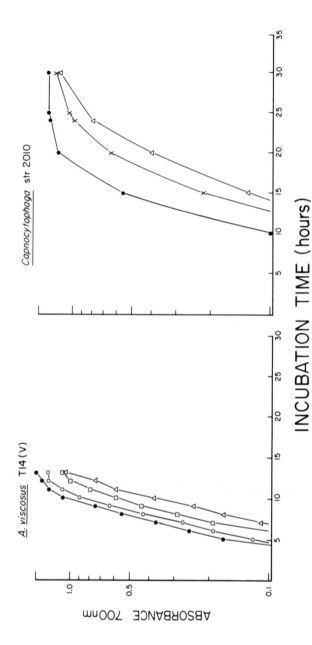

Fig. 2. *Comparison of growth of A. viscosus T14(V) and that of Capnocytophaga strain 2010 after preincubation (30 min) with various amounts of HEWL. Symbols:* ●, *medium alone;* ○, *medium plus 50 µg of HEWL per ml;* ×, *medium plus 167 µg of HEWL per ml;* □, *medium plus 250 µg of HEWL per ml;* △, *medium plus 500 µg of HEWL per ml.*

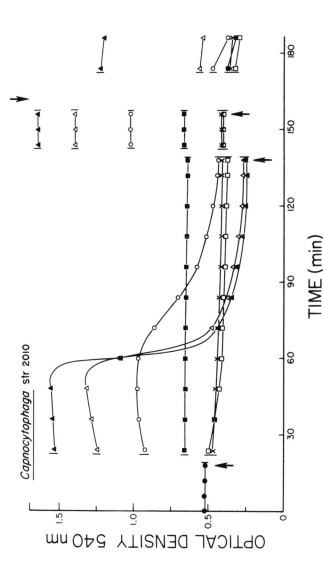

FIG. 3. Aggregation of stationary-phase Capnocytophaga strain 2010 by lysozyme. Analyses consisted of the addition of 100 µl of 0.01 M Tris-hydrochloride, pH 8.0, containing various amounts of HEWL to 900 µl of lyophilized cells in 0.01 M Tris (optical density at 540 nm, 0.520) (first arrow). After the suspensions were incubated for 1 min with stirring, the optical density was monitored at 540 nm for various times to 138 min, at which time the suspensions were stirred for 1 min (second arrow). At 156 min, NaCl was added to a final concentration of 0.12 M (third arrow). The cuvettes were stirred for 1 min at 162 min (fourth arrow), and reactions were monitored to 186 min. Symbols: ●, preincubated cells; ×, 0.01 M Tris-hydrochloride alone; □, 10 µg of HEWL per ml; ■, 50 µg of HEWL per ml; ○, 100 µg of HEWL per ml; △, 250 µg of HEWL per ml; ▲, 5 mg of HEWL per ml.

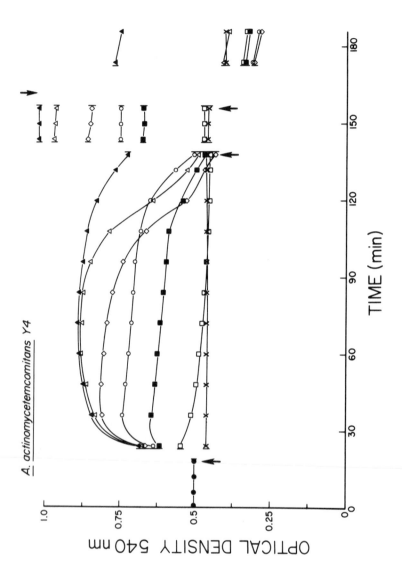

FIG. 4. *Aggregation of stationary-phase A. actinomycetemcomitans Y4 by lysozyme. Assay was performed as described in Fig. 3. Symbols:* ●, *preincubated cells;* ×, *0.01 M Tris-hydrochloride alone;* □, *25 μg of HEWL per ml;* ■, *50 μg of HEWL per ml;* ○, *75 μg of HEWL per ml;* ◇, *100 μg of HEWL per ml;* △, *250 μg of HEWL per ml;* ▲, *5 mg of HEWL per ml.*

occur through interaction of the enzyme's active site with specific surface components. Lysozyme would therefore aggregate bacteria in a "lectin-like" fashion, binding to surface carbohydrate residues at various "receptor" sites (72). This potential binding mechanism does not exclude the possibility that the enzyme's charge or areas other than the active site are involved in aggregation.

Since the sulcular neutrophil is most likely to come in contact with gram-negative microorganisms, we tested three gram-negative rods in our aggregation system (details in legend to Fig. 3). Lysozyme was found to have significant aggregation potential for stationary-phase cells of *Capnocytophaga* strain 2010 (Fig. 3), *A. actinomycetemcomitans* Y4 (Fig. 4), and *E. corrodens* 4319 (Fig. 5). In addition, the degree of aggregation for each microorganism was proportional to the amount of enzyme added, and aggregating amounts of enzyme were found to fall within the range of concentrations of lysozyme in inflammatory exudates (82). Unlike the results observed with *Veillonella*, addition of NaCl to the gram-negative periodontal pathogens did not result in turbidimetric evidence of lysis (Fig. 3–5) (93a). However, biochemical assays which measure nucleic acid release in addition to ultrastructural analyses would have to be done to assess lytic damage, if any, to the cells.

Of interest was the finding that log-phase *E. corrodens* 4319 aggregated to a lesser extent than stationary-phase cells in the presence of similar amounts of lysozyme (Fig. 5 and 6). This could possibly reflect the increased synthesis of lysozyme receptors on the surface of stationary-phase cells. Several investigators have shown that lysozyme can bind to the outer membrane of intact gram-negative bacteria and can interact directly with isolated outer membrane components such as lipopolysaccharide (12, 20, 50, 81). Binding to the outer membrane might take place through both electrostatic and hydrophobic interactions, as well as through "lectin-like" effects (58, 72, 100). The elucidation of the mechanisms of lysozyme binding will of necessity await the isolation of potential receptors.

BACTERIOLYTIC PROPERTIES

The antibacterial property traditionally attributed to lysozyme is its lytic action brought about by hydrolysis of the peptidoglycan which is responsible for the rigidity of the bacterial cell (74). The accessibility of a susceptible peptidoglycan is of importance in the determination of whether a particular microorganism will lyse in the presence of lysozyme. Surface carbohydrate and other structural components may make it difficult for lysozyme to reach its substrate in gram-positive microorganisms. This results in resistance to lysis which can be overcome by the addition of salts (60) or detergents (17). We reported that addition of NaCl to HEWL-aggregated *S. mutans* BHT results in lysis effected by mechanisms independent of the enzyme's muramidase properties (72). Lysis was attributed, in part, to activation of autolytic enzymes (72).

The restricted access of lysozyme to the peptidoglycan is also the explanation given for the resistance of most gram-negative microorganisms to lysis (104). These cells have an outer membrane containing lipopolysaccharide, proteins, and lipids which create a barrier against the entrance of large molecules (75). Unlike most gram-negative microorganisms, however, *Veillonella* species can be lysed in the presence of lysozyme alone (7, 93a). This most likely is due to an

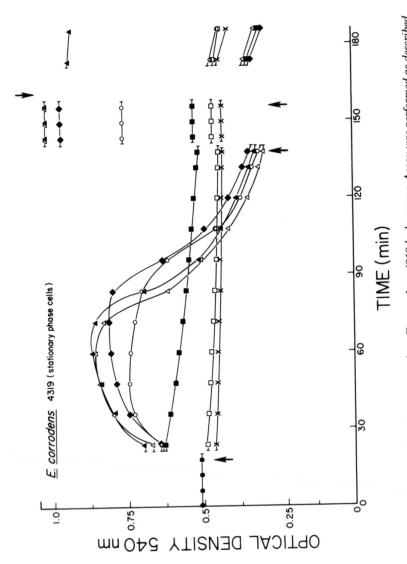

FIG. 5.   *Aggregation of stationary-phase E. corrodens 4319 by lysozyme. Assay was performed as described in Fig. 3. Symbols:* ●, *preincubated cells;* ×, *0.01 M Tris-hydrochloride alone;* □, *10 μg of HEWL per ml;* ■, *50 μg of HEWL per ml;* ○, *100 μg of HEWL per ml;* ◆, *175 μg of HEWL per ml;* △, *250 μg of HEWL per ml;* ▲, *5 mg of HEWL per ml.*

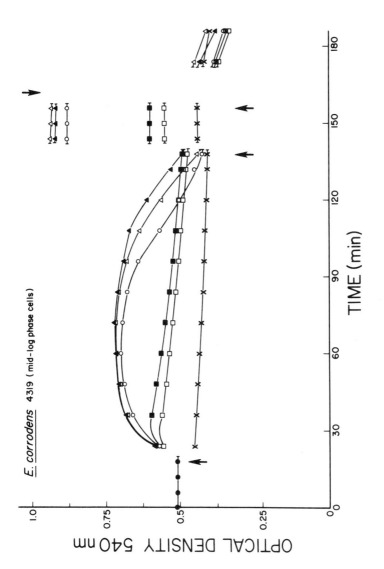

FIG. 6. *Aggregation of mid-log-phase E. corrodens 4319 by lysozyme. Assay was performed as described in Fig. 3. Symbols:* ●, *preincubated cells;* ×, *0.01 M Tris-hydrochloride alone;* □, *25 μg of HEWL per ml;* ■, *50 μg of HEWL per ml;* ○, *100 μg of HEWL per ml;* ▲, *175 μg of HEWL per ml;* △, *250 μg of HEWL per ml.*

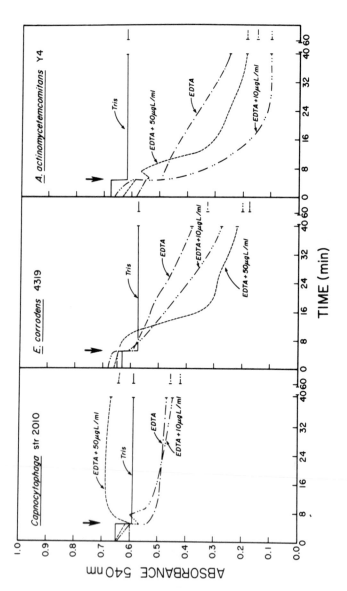

FIG. 7. *Effect of lysozyme on log-phase* Capnocytophaga *strain 2010 (left),* E. corrodens *4319 (middle), and A. actinomycetemcomitans Y4 (right). Analyses consisted of the addition of freshly harvested and washed cells suspended in either 0.01 M Tris-hydrochloride, pH 8.0, or Tris buffer containing 1 mM EDTA (volume, 1.8 ml) to cuvettes and incubation for 5 min at 37°C with stirring (Gilford 2400 spectrophotometer; Spectrostir setting, 6.5). Changes in absorbance were monitored at 540 nm. Vertical arrows indicate addition of 200 μl of Tris or Tris containing HEWL such that the final volume for each suspension was 2.0 ml and HEWL concentrations were 0, 10, or 50 μg/ml.*

ineffective outer membrane barrier. We observed that aggregation, rather than lysis, occurred when lysozyme was added to suspensions of *Capnocytophaga* strain 2010, *E. corrodens*, and *A. actinomycetemcomitans* Y4, and subsequent addition of salts effected deaggregation rather than lysis (Fig. 3–6). However, biochemical and ultrastructural studies would be necessary to rule out the possibility of any cellular damage.

Gram-negative bacteria may be rendered sensitive to the lytic potential of lysozyme in vivo by antibody and complement (2) and by PMN components (21, 101). Several techniques have been reported by Noller and Hartsell (64) to render these microorganisms susceptible to lysis in vitro. All of these procedures apparently alter the outer membrane either structurally or chemically, exposing the rigid peptidoglycan to enzymatic degradation. A common bacteriolytic system includes the addition of ethylenediaminetetraacetate (EDTA) to cell suspensions prior to incubation with lysozyme (73). The addition of EDTA results in the activation of phospholipase A, which weakens hydrophobic interactions between membrane phospholipids and lipopolysaccharide (38), permitting lysozyme access to the peptidoglycan.

We therefore tested the muramidase potential of lysozyme, in amounts likely to be present in the gingival sulcus, on log-phase cells of three periodontopathic bacteria which had been suspended in a tris(hydroxymethyl)aminomethane (Tris)-EDTA buffer (details in legend to Fig. 7). Of the three gram-negative rods, *Capnocytophaga* strain 2010 was the most resistant to the enzyme (Fig. 7). Evidence of lysis was not apparent either turbidimetrically or by visual examination of the cell suspensions. Although a reduction in turbidity was observed in those suspensions containing EDTA alone or EDTA with 10 µg of

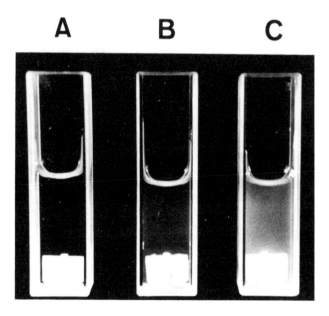

FIG. 8. *Cuvettes illustrating lysis of* A. actinomycetemcomitans *Y4 after incubation for 2 h. Experimental design was as described in Fig. 7. (A) Cells in 0.01 M Tris-hydrochloride, pH 8.0, containing 1 mM EDTA and 10 µg of HEWL per ml. (B) Cells in Tris containing 1 mM EDTA. (C) Cells in Tris only.*

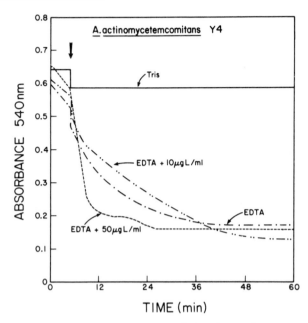

FIG. 9. *Effect of lysozyme on stationary-phase* A. actinomycetemcomitans *Y4. Experimental design was as described in Fig. 7.*

lysozyme per ml, this was probably due to the membrane-destabilizing effects of EDTA, with subsequent release of lipopolysaccharide (38, 54). When lysozyme was added to suspensions containing EDTA, an initial aggregation was observed, which was most pronounced with 50 μg of lysozyme (Fig. 7). This may reflect a greater preference of lysozyme for outer membrane components of this microorganism than for those of the other two gram-negative rods tested. In support of this hypothesis was the finding that *Capnocytophaga* strain 2010 aggregated to the greatest extent in the presence of lysozyme (Fig. 3). *E. corrodens* 4319 was intermediate in its susceptibility to the lytic effects of lysozyme (Fig. 7). Both turbidimetric evidence of lysis and visible clearing of the cell suspensions occurred with 50 μg of lysozyme per ml of Tris-EDTA buffer. After 60 min of incubation, suspensions containing 10 μg of lysozyme per ml showed signs of lysis (Fig. 7). *A. actinomycetemcomitans* Y4 was extremely susceptible to lysozyme (Fig. 7). Clearing was observed within minutes in the presence of just 10 μg of lysozyme per ml. Suspensions containing 50 μg of lysozyme per ml eventually lysed, but only after an initial short period of aggregation (Fig. 7). Although a fall in turbidity occurred in those suspensions containing only EDTA, visible evidence of lysis was not apparent even after 2 h of incubation (Fig. 8). Of interest was the finding that stationary-phase cells were also lysed by lysozyme (Fig. 9). However, in comparison to log-phase cells, 50 μg of lysozyme was more effective than 10 μg of lysozyme (Fig. 7 and 9). This requirement for more enzyme may have been due to the greater barrier effect of the stationary-phase outer membrane.

The dramatic lytic effect of lysozyme for *A. actinomycetemcomitans* Y4 is of interest in light of the fact that this microorganism has been shown to produce a cytotoxin for human PMNs (94). The disruption of neutrophils may just represent a Pyrrhic victory for the microorganism. PMN lysates contain membrane-active proteins, phospholipases, and lysozyme, which can act in concert to destroy the microorganism in the immediate vicinity of the ruptured neutrophil (21, 101). Should this occur in the gingival sulcus, it would represent an important mechanism whereby lysozyme participates in the control of this potentially virulent periodontal pathogen.

The administration of antibiotics, in particular tetracycline derivatives, as adjuncts to periodontal treatment is receiving widespread support (13). However, antibiotics may affect the sensitivity of microorganisms to natural defense mechanisms (24). When *A. actinomycetemcomitans* Y4 was rendered resistant to 20 µg of tetracycline per ml by serial transfer into media containing

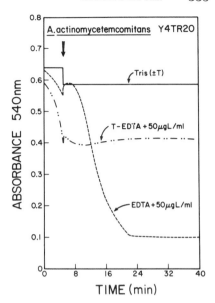

FIG. 10. *Effect of lysozyme on stationary-phase* A. actinomycetemcomitans *Y4 TR20. Experimental design was essentially as described in Fig. 7. T refers to cultures grown in the presence of 20 µg of tetracycline per ml of medium.*

increasing amounts of the antibiotic, this strain (termed Y4TR20) also developed a resistance to the lytic effect of lysozyme (Fig. 10, curve T-EDTA + 50 µg of lysozyme per ml). This resistance, although unexplained, may have been due to the strengthening of membrane permeability barriers, alteration of peptidoglycan structure, or to the presence of inactivating enzymes (105). The possibility also existed that Y4TR20 was resistant to lysis as a result of the continued presence of tetracycline in the cell envelope which effectively blocked the access of lysozyme to its substrate. Y4TR20 was therefore grown in the absence of the antibiotic and was found to lyse in the presence of EDTA and 50 µg of lysozyme per ml (Fig. 10). These findings argue against the continued long-term administration of tetracycline to patients with periodontal diseases.

A zone of bacteriolysis between the apical extent of the subgingival microflora and the wall of advancing PMNs has been observed in electron microscopic studies of the inflamed gingival sulculus region (26). In vitro studies have indicated that neutrophils release hydrolytic enzymes and bactericidal factors when exposed to oral microorganisms (4, 92). These observations, in conjunction with our findings on the lytic potential of lysozyme (72, 93a), suggest that bacteriolysis external to the sulcular neutrophils is due to the conjoint effects of lysozyme and factors which destroy the outer membrane permeability barrier.

NONENZYMATIC PROPERTIES OF HL

The presence of large amounts of lysozyme in PMNs and macrophages (32) and the enzyme's various antibacterial properties (discussed above) are suggestive of a major role for lysozyme in host resistance. In addition to direct effects on microorganisms, recent evidence suggests that lysozyme may serve as a regulator of membrane phenomena, either by binding to specific receptors or through the hydrophobicity of certain segments of the molecule (65). HL, but not HEWL, has been shown to exhibit these effects on mammalian cells (65). These enzymes are known to have similar but not identical active sites (77) and do show significant variation in their amino acid composition (11, 49), as well as major immunological differences (37). We have also shown that HL is a more potent antibacterial factor for oral microorganisms (45, 93a). It is therefore reasonable to expect distinct functions for HL. These additional roles for the molecule may include enhancement of lymphocyte proliferation in mixed lymphocyte cultures (J. Rinehart, H. Jacob, and E. Osserman, Clin. Res. 27:305A, 1979) and a nonenzymatic role in the metabolism, transformation, and mineralization of cartilage and bone (78). This latter function is thought to occur through an effect on proteoglycan turnover, possibly regulating the aggregation state of proteoglycans or modifying enzyme activities which contribute to the degradation of the extracellular matrix (52, 78).

Since lysozyme is secreted continuously by macrophages (32), recent studies have focused on the direct effects of the molecule on the functions of inflammatory cells (31, 51). These nonenzymatic functions are illustrated in Fig. 11. Klockars and Roberts (51) observed that HL in physiological concentrations (10 to 400 µg/ml) had a direct stimulating effect on the phagocytosis of yeast cells by human neutrophils. The initial events that occur during phagocytosis have been shown to be related to a degranulation of specific granules which contain most of the PMN lysozyme (22). Lysozyme is released early and may therefore act back on the cell, enhancing phagocytosis in vivo.

We have begun studies on the phagocytosis and killing of radiolabeled S. mutans and A. viscosus T14(V) by human PMNs in the presence of lysozyme, using the microassay system developed by Verbrugh and co-workers (98). Preliminary data indicate decreased viability when the bacteria were exposed to lysozyme and PMNs rather that PMNs or lysozyme alone.

It has been suggested by Gordon and co-workers (31) that lysozyme, which is continuously secreted by monocytes, might modulate PMN membrane function (Fig. 11). These investigators observed that HL is a potent inhibitor of PMN chemotaxis and of superoxide production by stimulated PMNs (31). HL may therefore function in a negative feedback system, possibly reducing excessive tissue injury and the concomitant inflammatory response observed during PMN phagocytic activity. The wall of neutrophils seen in the gingival sulcus in vivo (26) may in part be affected by the large amount of lysozyme in the gingival fluid (8). However, whether the primary function of HL in the gingival sulcus is antibacterial in nature or is a modulator of inflammation, or whether it functions in both ways, has yet to be determined.

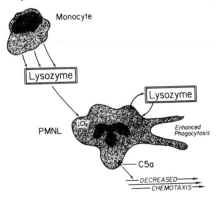

FIG. 11. *Schematic diagram illustrating the modulation of neutrophil function by human lysozyme. Details in text.*

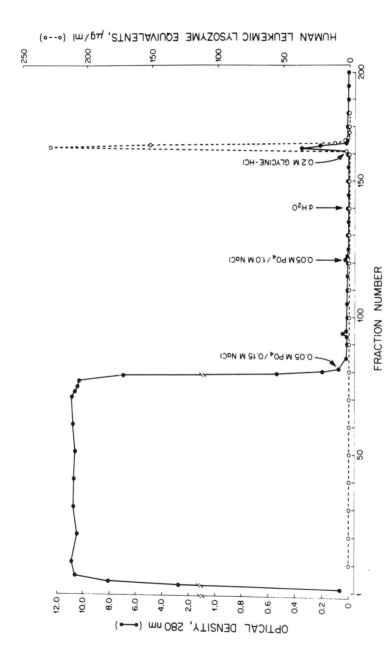

FIG. 12. *Affinity chromatography of lyophilized parotid saliva (2 liters) resuspended in 325 ml of distilled water and applied to a column of sheep immunoglobulin G1 anti-HL coupled to epoxy-activated Sepharose 6B and eluted at a flow rate of 25 ml/h. The arrows indicate where elutions with indicated solvents were started. All fractions were assayed for absorbance at 280 nm (●—●) and for lytic activity with M. lysodeikticus as a substrate (○--○).*

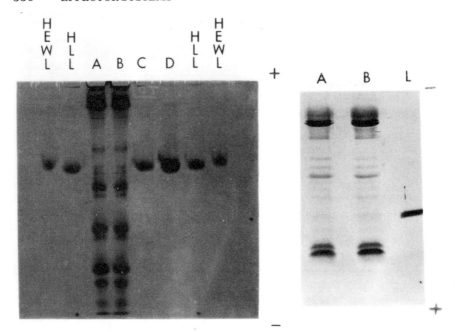

FIG. 13. *Cationic PAGE pattern (left) and sodium dodecyl sulfate-PAGE pattern (right) of the parotid salivary affinity column fractions. Lanes A and B contained parotid saliva and the nonadsorbed material, respectively, both at a concentration of 50 mg/ml. Lanes C and D contained 10 μg and 40 μg of the glycine HCl eluate. Lane L contained 5 μg of the glycine HCl eluate. The remaining lanes contained HEWL and human leukemic lysozyme (HLL) standards, as indicated.*

PURIFICATION OF HL

Our findings indicate that HL is a more potent antibacterial factor than HEWL for oral microorganisms (45). In addition, it has been reported that HL, but not HEWL, may be an important modulator of the inflammatory response (31). These differences between HL and HEWL preclude the use of HEWL in studies which would define the roles of lysozyme in host resistance. However, HL is not easy to obtain in pure form. The urine of leukemia patients excreting lysozyme is a good source for the preparation of HL, but these patients are difficult to obtain (66). In addition, preparative techniques would have to be developed to isolate the enzyme from normal leukocytes, tissues, and secretions which contain relatively low absolute quantities of this protein. Several isolation techniques have been reported which rely on the use of cationic exchangers and chitin affinity columns, as well as the use of lysozyme lysates and bacterial absorbents of *Micrococcus lysodeikticus* cells (57, 97). However, each of these procedures results in poor recovery of lysozyme and, more importantly, they allow for the nonselective removal of other potential antibacterial cationic factors. The elucidation of the functions of HL requires its selective removal from its biological sources followed by reconstitution antibacterial studies. We therefore developed a rapid and effective immunoadsorption procedure for the quantitative recovery, selective removal, and one-step purification of HL (B. J. MacKay, V. J. Iacono, and J. J. Pollock, J.

Dent. Res. Spec. Issue A **60**:654, abstr. 1379, 1981). The immunoadsorbent was prepared by coupling sheep immunoglobulin G1 antibody directed against human leukemic lysozyme to epoxy-activated Sepharose 6B (Pharmacia Fine Chemicals). As shown in Fig. 12, when 2 liters of parotid saliva was applied to the column, virtually all protein failed to bind to the immunoadsorbent, and only those fractions which eluted with glycine-HCl demonstrated lytic activity. Assay of lysozyme activity indicated that 1.97 mg of lysozyme had been applied to and recovered from the column, virtually 100% recovery. As demonstrated by cationic polyacrylamide gel electrophoresis (PAGE) and sodium dodecyl sulfate PAGE, lysozyme was selectively removed from the parotid saliva, and all components detected in the saliva were present in the nonadsorbed fractions (Fig. 13). The homogeneity of the enzyme preparation was confirmed by amino acid analysis, N-terminal amino acid analysis, and sedimentation velocity and sedimentation equilibrium ultracentrifugation (B. J. MacKay, Ph.D. thesis, State University of New York at Stony Brook, 1981). The immunoadsorption procedure was also found to selectively remove lysozyme from submandibular–sublingual saliva. The effectiveness of this isolation technique will allow reconstitution antibacterial studies of saliva to further define the role of lysozyme in the oral cavity.

Studies of the nonenzymatic roles of HL will require large amounts of lysozyme. We have been able to isolate lysozyme selectively from acid extracts of whole PMNs and from neutrophil granules by the immunoadsorption procedure. However, the amounts recovered, although quantitative (approximately 100%), are insufficient for studies of phagocytosis and chemotaxis (<5 mg/10^9 cells) (MacKay, Ph.D. thesis, 1981). We therefore proceeded to isolate lysozyme from crude ammonium sulfate precipitates of human leukemic urine. As shown by

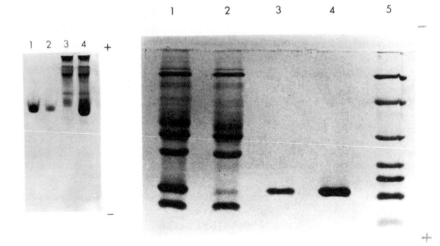

FIG. 14. *Cationic PAGE pattern (left) and sodium dodecyl sulfate PAGE pattern (right) of leukemic urine affinity column fractions. In the pattern on the left, lanes 4 and 3 contained 50 μl of a crude ammonium sulfate precipitate of urine and nonadsorbed material, respectively. Lanes 2 and 1 contained 5 μg and 20 μg of the glycine HCl eluate, respectively. In the pattern on the right, lanes 1 and 2 contained the crude ammonium sulfate precipitate and nonadsorbed material, respectively. Lanes 3 and 4 contained 5 μg and 20 μg of the glycine HCl eluate, respectively. Lane 5 contained sodium dodecyl sulfate PAGE standards.*

the cationic and sodium dodecyl sulfate PAGE patterns in Fig. 14, similar to what was found for saliva and PMN samples, the immunoadsorbent selectively removed lysozyme from a crude ammonium sulfate precipitate, and the elution procedure effected quantitative recovery of the enzyme. Assay of lysozyme activity indicated that 35 mg of lysozyme from 1.1 g of precipitated urine had been applied and recovered from the column. The ability to obtain large amounts of HL will now make it possible to determine the significance of this cationic protein in the host defense against periodontal pathogens and in the regulation of the inflammatory response present in periodontal diseases.

SUMMARY

The growth-inhibitory, aggregating, and lytic properties of lysozyme were investigated with oral microorganisms. This natural defense factor was found to be a highly effective and selective bacteriostatic agent for gram-positive but not gram-negative microorganisms under ideal growth conditions. When S. mutans escaped the bacteriostatic effect of lysozyme, dechaining was observed, and dechained cultures were less resistant than chained streptococci to adverse environmental conditions. Aggregation occurred for all cultures, and it was directly proportional to enzyme concentration. Mechanisms for aggregation were discussed in terms of lysozyme binding to specific receptors such as surface carbohydrate, lipoteichoic acid, and lipopolysaccharide. Lysozyme was an effective lytic factor for S. mutans BHT and Veillonella sp. Lysis of other S. mutans serotypes was effected by the addition of physiological amounts of salt to treated cell suspensions. Lytic mechanisms were discussed in terms of activating autolysins. Of the three gram-negative rods studied, A. actinomycetemcomitans Y4 was the most susceptible to the lytic potential of the enzyme. Of interest was the observation that tetracycline resistance reduced the lytic effect of lysozyme for this periodontal pathogen. HL, but not HEWL, has been shown to have nonenzymatic properties including roles in the mineralization of bone, enhancement of lymphocyte transformation and neutrophil phagocytosis, and inhibition of chemotaxis. Studies to determine the roles of lysozyme in the regulation of periodontal inflammation and in the resistance to products of the subgingival microflora will require large amounts of human enzyme. An immunoadsorption procedure was therefore developed to isolate lysozyme selectively from its human sources.

ACKNOWLEDGMENTS

We thank J. Van Houte, Forsyth Dental Center, for providing us with serotype c strains of S. mutans; R. Stevens, University of Pennsylvania, for A. actinomycetemcomitans Y4; H Bulkascz, Medical College of Georgia, for E. corrodens 4319; and J. Slots, State University of New York at Buffalo, for Capnocytophaga strain 2010. We are also grateful for the superb secretarial assistance of Harriet Sussman.

This work was supported by Public Health Service grant DE-04296 from the National Institute of Dental Research.

LITERATURE CITED

1. **Allison, A. C., P. Davies, and R. C. Page.** 1973. Effects of endotoxin on macrophages and other lymphoreticular cells. J. Infect. Dis. **128**(Suppl.):212–219.
2. **Amano, T., S. Inai, Y. Seki, S. Kashiba, K. Fugikawa, and S. Nishimura.** 1954. Studies on the immune bacteriolysis. I. Accelerating effect on the immune bacteriolysis by lysozyme-like substance of leucocytes and egg-white lysozyme. Med. J. Osaka Univ. **4**:401–418.
3. **Attstrom, R.** 1971. Studies on neutrophil polymorphonuclear leukocytes at the dento-gingival junction in gingival health and disease. J. Periodontal Res. **8**(Suppl.):1–15.
4. **Baehni, P., C. C. Tsai, N. S. Taichman, and W. P. McArthur.** 1978. Electron microscopic and biochemical study on the mechanisms of release of lysosomal constituents from human polymorphonuclear leukocytes exposed to dental plaque. J. Periodontal Res. **13**:333–348.

5. **Baggiolini, M., U. Bretz, B. Dewald, and M. E. Feigenson.** 1978. The polymorphonuclear leukocyte. Agents Actions 8:3–10.
6. **Baggiolini, M., J. Schnyder, and U. Bretz.** 1979. Lysosomal enzymes and neutral proteinases as mediators of inflammation, p. 263–272. In G. Weissman, B. Samuelsson, and R. Paolelli (ed.), Advances in inflammation, vol. 1. Raven Press, New York.
7. **Bladen, H. A., and S. E. Mergenhagen.** 1964. Ultrastructure of Veillonella and morphological correlation of an outer membrane with particles associated with endotoxic activity. J. Bacteriol. 88:1482–1492.
8. **Brandtzaeg, P., and W. V. Mann, Jr.** 1964. A comparative study of the lysozyme activity of human gingival pocket fluid, serum, and saliva. Acta Odontol. Scand. 22:441–455.
9. **Braun, V., and K. Rehn.** 1969. Chemical characterization, spatial distribution and function of a lipoprotein (murein-lipoprotein) of the E. coli cell wall. The specific effect of trypsin on the membrane structure. Eur. J. Biochem. 10:426–438.
10. **Bretz, U., and M. Baggiolini.** 1974. Biochemical and morphological characterization of azurophil and specific granules of human neutrophilic polymorphonuclear leukocytes. J. Cell. Biol. 63:251–269.
11. **Canfield, R. E., S. Kammerman, J. H. Sobel, and F. J. Morgan.** 1971. Primary structures of lysozyme from man and goose. Nature (London) New Biol. 223:16–17.
12. **Chopra, I., T. G. B. Howe, and P. R. Ball.** 1977. Lysozyme-promoted association of protein I molecules in the outer membrane of Escherichia coli. J. Bacteriol. 132:411–418
13. **Ciancio, S. G., M. L. Mather, and J. A. McMullen.** 1980. An evaluation of minocycline in patients with periodontal disease. J. Periodontol. 51:530–534.
14. **Cianciola, L. J., R. J. Genco, M. R. Patters, J. McKenna, and C. J. van Oss.** 1977. Defective polymorphonuclear leukocyte function in a human periodontal disease. Nature (London) 265:445–447.
15. **Cleveland, R. F., J. V. Holtje, A. J. Wicken, A. Tomasz, L. Daneo-Moore, and G. D. Shockman.** 1975. Inhibition of bacterial wall lysis by lipoteichoic acids and related compounds. Biochem. Biophys. Res. Commun. 67:1128–1135.
16. **Cohn, Z. A.** 1975. The role of proteases in macrophage physiology, p. 483-493. In E. Reich, D. B. Rifkin, and E. Shaw (ed.), Proteases and biological control. Cold Spring Harbor conferences on cell proliferation, vol. 2. Cold Spring Harbor Laboratory, Cold Spring Harbor, N.Y.
17. **Coleman, S. E., E. van de Rijn, and A. S. Bleiweis.** 1971. Lysis of cariogenic and noncariogenic oral streptococci with lysozyme. J. Dent. Res. 50:939–943.
18. **Costerton, J. W., J. M. Ingram, and K.-J. Cheng.** 1974. Structure and function of the cell envelope of gram-negative bacteria. Bacteriol. Rev. 38:87–110.
19. **Davies, P., R. J. Bonney, J. L. Humes, and F. A. Kuehl.** 1980. The role of macrophage secretory products in chronic inflammatory processes. J. Invest. Dermatol. 74:292–296.
20. **Day, D. F., M. L. Marceau-Day, and J. M. Ingram.** 1978. Protein-lipopolysaccharide interactions. I. The reaction of lysozyme with Pseudomonas aeruginosa LPS. Can. J. Microbiol. 24:196–199.
21. **Elsbach, P.** 1980. Degradation of microorganisms by phagocytic cells. Rev. Infect. Dis. 2:106–128.
22. **Estensen, R. D., J. G. White, and B. Holmes.** 1974. Specific degranulation of human polymorphonuclear leukocytes. Nature (London) 248:347–348.
23. **Farenčik, M., and J. Štefanovič.** 1979. Lysosomal enzymes of phagocytes and the mechanism of their release. Folia Microbiol. (Prague) 24:503–515.
24. **Fierer, J., and F. Finley.** 1979. Lethal effect of complement and lysozyme on polymyxin-treated, serum-resistant gram-negative bacilli. J. Infect. Dis. 140:581–589.
25. **Freedman, H. L., M. A. Listgarten, and N. S. Taichman.** 1968. Electron microscopic features of chronically inflamed human gingiva. J. Periodontal Res. 3:313–327.
26. **Garant, P. R.** 1976. An electron microscopic study of the periodontal tissues of germ free rats and rats monoinfected with Actinomyces naeslundii. J. Periodontal Res. 15(Suppl.):1–79.
27. **Genco, R. J., R. T. Evans, and S. A. Ellison.** 1969. Dental research in microbiology with emphasis on periodontal disease. J. Am. Dent. Assoc. 78:1016–1036.
28. **Genco, R. J., and S. E. Mergenhagan.** 1979. Summary of a workshop on leukocyte function in bacterial diseases with an emphasis on periodontal disease. J. Infect. Dis. 139:604–612.
29. **Genco, R. J., T. E. Van Dyke, B. Park, M. Ciminelli, and H. Horoszewicz.** 1980. Neutrophil chemotaxis impairment in juvenile periodontitis: evaluation of specificity, adherence, deformability, and serum factors. RES J. Reticuloendothel. Soc. 28(Suppl.):81–91.
30. **Gibson, W. A., and I. C. Shannon.** 1964. Microorganisms in human gingival tissues. Periodontology 2:119–121.
31. **Gordon, L. I., S. D. Douglas, N. E. Kay, O. Yamada, E. F. Osserman, and H. S. Jacob.** 1979. Modulation of neutrophil function by lysozyme. J. Clin. Invest. 64:226–232.
32. **Gordon, S., J. Todd, and Z. A. Cohn.** 1974. In vitro synthesis and secretion of lysozyme by mononuclear phagocytes. J. Exp. Med. 139:1228–1248.
33. **Goren, M. B.** 1977. Phagocytic lysosomes: interactions with infectious agents, phagosomes, and experimental perturbations in function. Annu. Rev. Microbiol. 31:507–533.
34. **Hamada, S., N. Masuda, and S. Kotani.** 1980. Isolation and serotyping Streptococcus mutans from teeth and feces of children. J. Clin. Microbiol. 11:314–318.

35. **Hamada, S., and H. D. Slade.** 1980. Biology, immunology, and cariogenicity of *Streptococcus mutans.* Microbiol. Rev. **44:**331–384.
36. **Hamp, S. E., and L. E. A. Folke.** 1968. The lysosomes and their possible role in periodontal disease. Odontol. Tidskr. **76:**353–375.
37. **Hanke, N., E. M. Prager, and A. C. Wilson.** 1973. Quantitative immunological and electrophoretic compairson of primate lysozymes. J. Biol. Chem. **248:**2824–2828.
38. **Hardaway, K. L., and C. S. Buller.** 1979. Effect of ethylenediaminetetraacetate in phospholipids and outer membrane function in *Escherichia coli.* J. Bacteriol. **137:**62–68.
39. **Harris, R. H., and R. Mitchell.** 1973. The role of polymers in microbial aggregation. Annu. Rev. Microbiol. **27:**27–50.
40. **Harrop, P. J., R. L. O'Grady, K. W. Knox, and A. J. Wicken.** 1980. Stimulation of lysosomal enzyme release from macrophages by lipoteichoic acid. J. Periodontal Res. **15:**492–501.
41. **Hasegawa, K., G. Cimasoni, and P. Vaugnat.** 1975. Inflamed gingivae contain more free lysosomal enzymes. Experientia **31:**765–766.
42. **Heijl, L., B. Rifkin, and H. A. Zander.** 1976. Conversion of chronic gingivitis to periodontitis in squirrel monkeys. J. Periodontol. **4:**710–716.
43. **Hellden, L., and J. Lindhe.** 1973. Enhanced emigration of crevicular leukocytes mediated by factors in human dental plaque. Scand. J. Dent Res. **81:**123–129.
44. **Holtje, J. V., and A. Tomasz.** 1975. Lipoteichoic acid: a specific inhibitor of autolysin activity in *Pneumonococcus.* Proc. Natl. Acad. Sci. U.S.A. **72:**1690–1694.
45. **Iacono, V. J., B. J. MacKay, S. DiRienzo, and J. J. Pollock.** 1980. Selective antibacterial properties of lysozyme for oral microorganisms. Infect. Immun. **29:**623–632.
46. **Irving, J. T., M. G. Newman, S. S. Socransky, and J. D. Heeley.** 1975. Histological changes in experimental periodontal disease in rats monoinfected with a Gram-negative organism. Arch. Oral. Biol. **20:**219–220.
47. **Jenn, R. S., J. G. Tew, and D. M. Donaldson.** 1967. Extracellular β-lysin and muramidase in body fluids and inflammatory exudates. Proc. Soc. Exp. Biol. Med. **124:**545–548.
48. **Johnson, D. A., C. Lo Chen, J. C. Dombrowski, and A. Nowotny.** 1976. Role of bacterial products in periodontitis. I. Endotoxin content and immunogenicity of human plaque. J. Periodonal Res. **11:**549–559.
49. **Jolles, J., and P. Jolles.** 1972. Comparison between human and bird lysozymes. Notes concerning the prevously observed deletion. FEBS Lett. **22:**31–33.
50. **Kamio, Y., and H. Nikaido.** 1977. Outer membrane of *Salmonella typhimurium.* Identification of proteins exposed on the cell surface. Biochim. Biophys. Acta **464:**589–601.
51. **Klockars, M., and P. Roberts.** 1976. Stimulation of phagocytosis by human lysozyme. Acta Haematol. **55:**289–295.
52. **Kuettner, K. E., N. Sorgente, R. L. Croxen, D. S. Howell, and J. C. Pita.** 1974. Lysozyme in preosseous cartilage. VII. Evidence for physiological role of lysozyme in normal endochondral calcification. Biochim. Biophys. Acta **372:**335–344.
53. **Leffell, M. S., and J. K. Spitznagel.** 1972. Association of lactoferrin with lysozyme in granules of human polymorphonuclear leukocytes. Infect. Immun. **6:**761–765.
54. **Leive, L.** 1974. The barrier function of the gram-negative envelope. Ann. N.Y. Acad. Sci. **235:**109–127.
55. **Mackler, B. F., K. B. Frostad, P. B. Robertson, and B. M. Levy.** 1977. Immunoglobulin bearing lymphocytes and plasma cells in human periodontal disease. J. Periodontal Res. **12:**37–45.
56. **Mandel, I. D.** 1979. In defense of the oral cavity, p. 473–491. *In* I. Kleinberg, S. A. Ellison, and I. D. Mandel (ed.), Proceedings: Saliva and Dental Caries (a special supplement to Microbiology Abstracts, vol 3). Information Retrieval Inc., Washington, D.C.
57. **Masuda, N., S. Kobayashi, K. Mizuno, and F. Sakiyama.** 1978. Isolation of human urinary lysozyme. J. Biochem. **84:**971–975.
58. **Mateau, N., F. Capron, V. Luzzah, and A. Billecocq.** 1978. The influence of protein-lipid interactions on the order-disorder conformational transitions of the hydrocarbon chain. Biochim. Biophys. Acta **508:**109–121.
59. **Mergenhagen, S. E., T. R. Tempel, and R. Snyderman.** 1970. Immunologic reactions and periodontal inflammation. J. Dent. Res. **49**(Suppl.):256–261.
60. **Metcalf, R. H., and R. H. Diebel.** 1969. Differential lytic response of enterococci associated with addition order of lysozyme and anions. J. Bacteriol. **99:**674–680.
61. **Modrzakowski, M. C., M. H. Cooney, L. E. Martin, and J. K. Spitznagel.** 1979. Bactericidal activity of fractionated granule contents from human polymorphonuclear leukocytes. Infect. Immun. **23:**587–591.
62. **Moore, R. N., R. Urbaschek, L. M. Wahl, and S. E. Mergenhagen.** 1979. Prostaglandin regulation of colony-stimulating factor production by lipopolysaccharide-stimulated murine leukocytes. Infect. Immun. **26:**408–414.
63. **Newman, M. G., and S. S. Socransky.** 1977. Predominant cultivable microbiota in periodontosis. J. Periodontal Res. **12:**120–129.
64. **Noller, E. C., and S. E. Hartsell.** 1961. Bacteriolysis of *Enterobacteriaceae.* I. Lysis of four lytic systems utilizing lysozyme. J. Bacteriol. **81:**482–491.

65. **Osserman, E. F., M. Klockars, J. Halper, and R. E. Fischel.** 1973. Effects of lysozyme on normal and transformed mammalian cells. Nature (London) 243:331–335.
66. **Osserman, E. F., and D. P. Lawlor.** 1966. Serum and urinary lysozyme (muramidase) in monocytic and monomyelocytic leukemia. J. Exp. Med. 124:921–951.
67. **Page, R. C., P. Davies, and A. C. Allison.** 1973. Effects of dental plaque on the production and release of lysosomal hydrolases by macrophages in culture. Arch. Oral Biol. 18:1481–1495.
68. **Page, R. C., P. D. Davies, and A. C. Allison.** 1974. Pathogenesis of the chronic inflammatory lesion induced by group A streptococcal cell walls. Lab. Invest. 30:563–581.
69. **Page, R. C., and H. C. Schroeder.** 1976. Pathogenesis of inflammatory periodontal disease. A summary of current work. Lab Invest. 33:235–249.
70. **Payne, W., R. C. Page, A. L. Ogilvie, and W. B Hall.** 1975. Histopathologic features of the initial and early stages of experimental gingivitis in man. J. Periodontal Res. 10:51–64.
71. **Perch, B., J. Kjems, and T. Ravn.** 1974. Biochemical and serological properties of *Streptococcus mutans* from various human and animal sources. Acta Pathol. Microbiol. Scand. 82:357–370.
72. **Pollock, J. J., V. J. Iacono, H. Goodman, B. J. MacKay, L. I. Katona, L. B. Taichman, and E. Thomas.** 1976. The binding, aggregation and lytic properties of lysozyme, p. 325–352. *In* H. M. Stiles, W. J. Loesche, and T. C. O'Brien (ed.), Proceedings: Microbial Aspects of Dental Caries (a special supplement to Microbiology Abstracts). Information Retrieval Inc., Washington, D.C.
73. **Repaske, R.** 1946. Lysis of gram-negative bacteria by lysozyme. Biochim. Biophys. Acta 22:189–191.
74. **Salton, M. R. J.** 1957. The properties of lysozyme and its action on microogranisms. Bacteriol. Rev. 20:82–89.
75. **Salton, M. R. J.** 1968. Lytic agents, cell permeability, and monolayer penetrability. J. Gen. Physiol. 52:2275–2525.
76. **Scherp, H. W.** 1971. Dental caries: prospects for prevention. Science 173:1199–1205.
77. **Schindler, M., Y. Assaf, N. Sharon, and D. M. Chipman.** 1977. Mechanism of lysozyme catalysis: role of ground-state strain in subsite D in hen egg-white and human lysozymes. Biochemistry 16:423–431.
78. **Schmidt, A., Y, Rodegerdts, and E. Buddecke.** 1978. Correlation of lysozyme activity with proteoglycan biosynthesis in epiphyseal cartilage. Calcif. Tissue Res. 26:163–172.
79. **Schroeder, H. E., M. Graf-de Beer, and R. Attstrom.** 1975. Initial gingivitis in dogs. J. Periodontal Res. 10:128–142.
80. **Schroeder, H. E., S. Munzel-Pedrozzoli, and R. C. Page.** 1973. Correlated morphometric and biochemical analysis of gingival tissue in early chronic gingivitis in man. Arch. Oral. Biol. 18:899–923.
81. **Scibienski, R. J.** 1979. Cellular parameter of the immunological memory induced by lysozyme-LPS mixtures and complexes. Immunol. Commun. 8:325–336.
82. **Senn, H. J., B. Chu, J. O'Malley, and J. F. Holland.** 1970. Experimental and clinical studies on muramidase (lysozyme). I. Muramidase activity of normal human blood cells and inflammatory exudates. Acta Haematol. 44:65–77.
83. **Shannon, I. L., R. P. Suddick, and F. J. Dowd, Jr.** 1974. Saliva: composition and secretion. Monogr. Oral Sci. 2:3–42.
84. **Shockman, G. D., M. L. Higgins, L. Daneo-Moore, S. J. Mattingly, J. R. DiPersio, and B. Terleckyj.** 1976. Studies of balanced and unbalanced growth of *Streptococcus mutans*. J. Dent. Res. Spec. Issue A 55:10–18.
85. **Shurin, S. B., S. S. Socransky, E. Sweeney, and T. P. Stossel.** 1979. A neutrophil disorder induced by *Capnocytophaga* a dental microorganism. N. Engl. J. Med. 301:849–854.
86. **Slots, J.** 1977. The predominant cultivable microflora of advanced periodontitis. Scand. J. Dent. Res. 85:114–121.
87. **Socransky, S. S.** 1970. Relationship of bacteria to the etiology of periodontal disease. J. Dent. Res. 49(Part 1):203–222.
88. **Taichman, N. S.** 1970. Mediation of inflammation by the polymorphonuclear leukocyte as a sequela of immune reactions. J. Periodontol. 41:228–231.
89. **Taichman, N. S., R. T. Dean, and C. J. Sanderson.** 1980. Biochemical and morpological characterization of the killing of human monocytes by a leukotoxin derived from *Actinobacillus actinomycetemcomitans*. Infect. Immun. 28:258–268.
90. **Taichman, N. S., H. L. Freedman, and T. Uriuhara.** 1966. Inflammation and tissue injury. I. The response to intradermal injections of human dento-gingival plaque in normal and leukopenic rabbits. Arch. Oral Biol. 11:1385–1392.
91. **Taichman, N. S., and W. P. McArthur.** 1975. Current concepts in periodontal disease. Annu. Rep. Med. Chem. 10:228–239.
92. **Taichman, N. S., C.-C. Tsai, P. C. Baehni, N. Stoller, and W. P. McArthur.** 1977. Interaction of inflammatory cells and oral microorganisms. IV. In vitro release of lysosomal constituents from polymorphonuclear leukocytes exposed to suprangingival and subgingival bacterial plaque. Infect. Immun. 16:1013–1023.
93. **Tempel, T. R., R. Snyderman, H. V. Jordan, and S. E. Mergenhagen.** 1970. Factors from saliva and oral bacteria chemotactic for polymorphonuclear leukocytes: their possible role in gingival inflammation. J. Periodontol. 41:71–80.

93a. **Tortosa, M., M.-I. Cho, T. J. Wilkens, V. J. Iacono, and J. J. Pollock.** 1981. Bacteriolysis of *Veillonella alcalescens* by lysozyme and inorganic anions present in saliva. Infect. Immun. **32**:1261–1273.

94. **Tsai, C.-C., W. P. McArthur, P. C. Baehni, B. F. Hammond, and N. S. Taichman.** 1979. Extraction and partial characterization of a leukotoxin from a plaque-derived gram-negative microorganism. Infect. Immun. **25**:427–439.

95. **van Dyke, T. E., H. U. Horoszewicz, L. J. Cianciola, and R. J. Genco.** 1980. Neutrophil chemotaxis dysfunction in human periodontitis. Infect. Immun. **27**:124–132.

96. **Van Houte, J., R. Aasenden, and T. C. Peebles.** 1981. Lactobacilli in human dental plaque and saliva. J. Dent. Res. **60**:2–5.

97. **Vasstrand, E. N., and H. B. Jensen.** 1980. Affinity chromatography of human saliva lysozyme and effect of pH and ionic strength on lytic activity. Scand. J. Dent. Res. **88**:219–228.

98. **Verbrugh, H. A., R. Peters, P. K. Peterson, and J. Verhoef.** 1978. Phagocytosis and killing of staphylococci by human polymorphonuclear and mononuclear leucocytes. J. Clin. Pathol. **31**:539–545.

99. **Wahl, L. M., S. M. Wahl, S. E. Mergenhagen, and G. R. Martin.** 1974. Collagenase production by endotoxin-activated macrophages. Proc. Natl. Acad. Sci. U.S.A. **71**:3598–3601.

100. **Wainwright, P., D. M. Power, E. W. Thomas, and J. V. Davies.** 1978. The interaction of cytochrome C with phospholipids. A pulse-radiolysis study. Int. J. Radiat. Biol. **33**:151–162.

101. **Weiss, J., P. Elsbach, I. Olsson, and H. Odeberg.** 1978. Purification and characterization of a potent bactericidal and membrane active protein from the granules of human polymorphonuclear leukocytes. J. Biol. Chem. **253**:2664–2672.

102. **Weissmann, G., J. E. Smulen, and H. M. Korchak.** 1980. Release of inflammatory mediators from stimulated neutrophils. N. Engl. J. Med. **303**:27–34.

103. **Westmacott, D., and H. R. Perkins.** 1979. Effects of lysozyme on *Bacillus cereus* 569: rupture of chains of bacteria and enhancement of sensitivity to autolysins. J. Gen. Microbiol. **115**:1–11.

104. **Witholt, B., and M. Boekhout.** 1978. The effect of osmotic shock on the accessibility of the murein layer of exponentially growing *Escherichia coli* to lysozyme. Biochim. Biophys. Acta **508**:296–305.

105. **Zimmermann, W.** 1979. Penetration through the gram-negative cell wall: a co-determinant of the efficacy of beta-lactam antibiotics. Int. J. Clin. Pharmacol. Biopharm. **17**:131–134.

Oxygen Radicals in Inflammation and Immunity

J. TERRELL HOFFELD

Cellular Immunology Section, Laboratory of Microbiology and Immunology,
National Institute of Dental Research, Bethesda, Maryland 20205

INTRODUCTION

The bactericidal mechanisms of phagocytic cells have been studied for many years. The increased consumption of oxygen when bacteria were added to leukocytes was first noted in 1933; this "oxidative metabolic burst" was considered to be an enhancement of metabolism which provided more energy for the cells to engulf bacteria (1). It was not until 1959 that it was definitively shown that the excess oxygen taken up by phagocytic cells was being utilized by the hexose monophosphate shunt (29). The first evidence for production of H_2O_2 by phagocytic cells and the first suggestion of a possible bactericidal role of that H_2O_2 were presented in 1961 (16). In 1967, the bactericidal mechanism catalyzed by myeloperoxidase was shown to be H_2O_2-dependent (18). Over the past 14 years, the oxygen-derived metabolites of phagocytic cells have been shown to be one of the most important mechanisms for intracellular killing of bacteria. The economy of nature has not limited the utilization of oxygen merely to respiratory and bactericidal functions. Many of the enzymes involved in redox control mechanisms, as well as many enzymes which directly oxidize substrates, have been shown to involve highly reactive, short-lived oxygen radicals as intermediates. This is of more than academic interest since some of these enzymes release the radical intermediates into the surrounding tissues, producing damage similar to the bactericidal effects of oxygen radicals; others of these enzymes are self-inactivated by the radical intermediates. Thus, oxygen radicals not only cause destruction but also can serve as short-lived mediators of feedback control mechanisms. Some of the enzymes which release reactive oxygen intermediates or produce reactive oxygen products, or both, are

alcohol oxidase
aldehyde oxidase
amine oxidase
glucose oxidase
glycollate oxidase
indoleamine-2,3-dioxygenase
reduced nicotinamide adenine dinucleotide phosphate (NADPH) oxidase
prostaglandin cyclooxygenase
xanthine oxidase

Intercellular and intracellular mediators such as arachidonate derivatives, cyclic nucleotides, divalent cations, and lymphokines were initially studied as independent mechanisms of control, but most of their effects have subsequently been shown to be interrelated. Similarly, the oxygen radicals now appear to be intimately interconnected with the activities of prostaglandins, cyclic nucleotides, ionic calcium, and lymphokines. As a result of the recognition of these interconnections, some of the "fine-tuning" of cellular control mechanisms is finally being elucidated.

OXYGEN RADICALS

If molecular oxygen is reduced by the addition of one electron, the product is the superoxide anion ($O_2^{\cdot-}$):

$$O_2 + e^- \longrightarrow O_2^{\cdot-}$$

In an aqueous environment, especially in the presence of the enzyme superoxide dismutase, superoxide is further reduced to form hydrogen peroxide (H_2O_2):

$$2\,O_2^{\cdot-} + 2\,H^+ \longrightarrow O_2 + H_2O_2$$

Superoxide and hydrogen peroxide can react, especially in the presence of iron, to yield hydroxyl radical ($OH^\cdot$):

$$O_2^{\cdot-} + H_2O_2 \longrightarrow O_2 + OH^- + OH^\cdot$$

In the presence of H_2O_2 and halide ions (usually Cl^- or I^-) and the enzyme myeloperoxidase, a highly reactive hypohalite is formed:

$$H_2O_2 + Cl^- \xrightarrow{\text{Myeloperoxidase}} H_2O + OCl^-$$

The occurrence of another oxygen radical, singlet oxygen ($^1O_2$), in mammalian cells is hotly debated among biophysicists and will not be further considered here.

As mentioned above, a number of enzymes are involved in oxidative processes utilizing oxygen radical intermediates (see list above). The enzyme associated with bactericidal capacity in phagocytic cells, which is apparently responsible for the generation of superoxide, is NADPH oxidase. This enzyme has a transmembranous orientation (10), accepting NADPH on the cytosolic end and releasing $O_2^{\cdot-}$ on the extracellular end. The utility of this orientation is that, as a phagosome is formed around the ingested particle, the $O_2^{\cdot-}$ will be released into the interior of the phagosome (Fig. 1). At the same time, the other enzyme molecules which have not been incorporated into the phagosome are available to release $O_2^{\cdot-}$ into the extracellular environment. The interrelationship of the hexose monophosphate shunt with superoxide production is presented in Fig. 1. The accumulated $NADP^+$ which results from the oxidation of NADPH can be reduced by glucose-6-phosphate dehydrogenase, the controlling enzyme of the hexose monophosphate shunt. Additionally, the excess NADPH provided by the hexose monophosphate shunt can reduce oxidized glutathione to reduced glutathione, a scavenger compound which is important for the protection of cells against damage initiated by oxygen radicals.

The high reactivity of oxygen radicals permits them to damage almost any type of biological molecule to which they have access, including peptides, carbohydrates, nucleic acids, and lipids. It is probably this broad range of substrates which enables oxygen radicals to expose inaccessible bacterial components to degradative enzymes of the phagocytic vacuole. The process of lipid peroxidation appears to be the most damaging effect of the generation of reactive oxygen species. Hydroxyl radical ($OH^\cdot$) is the radical which most effectively initiates lipid peroxidation (12). The reaction of $OH^\cdot$ with unsaturated fatty acids is presented schematically in Fig. 2. Briefly, $OH^\cdot$ attacks an unsaturated carbon, either cleaving the adjacent bond or converting the stable carbon to a carbon radical. This carbon radical can then transfer electrons in an autocatalytic chain reaction along conjugated double bonds with possible cleavage of carbon–carbon bonds at any site. In the presence of molecular oxygen, toxic aldehydes and lipid hydroperoxides may be formed at any of these radical carbons. The release of malondialdehyde from unsaturated fatty acids is considered a cardinal sign of lipid peroxidation (12). This material is mutagenic or toxic, depending on the dose (38). Thus, in the absence of a protective mechanism, a single OH reacting with cell membrane unsaturated lipid can set off a series of autocatalyzed reactions which could conceivably result in the complete breakdown of membrane architecture and the release of toxic byproducts. This activity is useful as a bactericidal mechanism, but of obvious detriment to a cell which is producing constitutive low levels and stimulated high levels of oxygen radicals.

Lipid peroxidation can be prevented or decreased by a number of either endogenous or exogenous agents which can prevent generation of reactive oxygen species, prevent interaction of radicals with membrane lipids, or block autocatalysis of lipid peroxidation.

Blockers of generation of reactive oxygen species
    anaerobiosis
    protease inhibitors
Scavengers of interaction of various radicals with substrates
    α-tocopherol
    β-carotene
    catalase
    diazabicyclooctane
    diphenylfuran
    glutathione/glutathione peroxidase
    mannitol
    sodium benzoate
    superoxide dismutase
Blockers of autocatalysis of lipid peroxidation
    α-tocopherol
    butylated hydroxyanisole
    butylated hydroxytoluene
    diphenyl-p-phenylenediamine
    n-propyl gallate

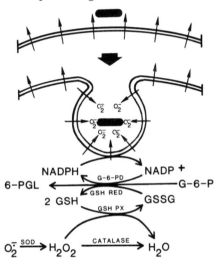

FIG. 1. *Biochemical pathways associated with the oxidative metabolic burst. NADPH oxidase enzyme molecules, represented by the small arrows in the membranes, do not release O_2^- until either a particulate (as presented here) or soluble stimulus initiates that activity. As the phagosome is formed around the particle, NADPH is oxidized, O_2^- is released into the phagosome, and the hexose monophosphate shunt is activated, providing reducing potential for the reduction of both $NADP^+$ and oxidized glutathione. Abbreviations: G-6-P, glucose-6-phosphate; G-6-PD, glucose-6-phosphate dehydrogenase; GSH, reduced glutathione; GSH PX, glutathione peroxidase; GSSG, oxidized glutathione; GSSG RED, glutathione reductase; NADPH, reduced nicotinamide adenine dinucleotide phosphate; $NADP^+$, oxidized nicotinamide adenine dinucleotide phosphate; 6-PGL, 6-phosphogluconolactone; SOD, superoxide dismutase.*

Conversely, inhibition of the activity of or deficiency of any of these protective mechanisms is permissive of lipid peroxidation (3).

Experimental approaches to the study of the role of reactive oxygen species in various processes depends almost entirely on "guilt-by-association" rather than direct proof of action. The high reactivity and short half-lives of most of these molecules dictate that any physicochemical means of measuring local concentrations will diminish the concentration available to react with other substrates. Thus, the phenomenon being observed may be either decreased or blocked totally by the measurement procedure. As a result, correlations between replicates can be shown, but cause and effect is only implied. There are numerous assays available to measure each of the reactive oxygen species:

Measures of enhanced oxidative metabolism
    $^{14}CO_2$ production from [1-^{14}C]glucose
    polarography
Measures of production of reactive oxygen species
    chemiluminescence (luminol enhanced)
    electron spin resonance/spin trapping
    ferricytochrome c reduction
    horseradish peroxidase-catalyzed oxidation of homovanillic acid, phenol red, or
      scopoletin
    nitroblue tetrazolium reduction
    sulfite oxidation
Measures of by-products of lipid peroxidation
    chloroform/methanol-extractable fluorescence
    lipofuscin fluorescence
    production of saturated hydrocarbon gases
    thiobarbituric acid-reactive materials

These assays have the disadvantage of being unable to measure localized concentrations (e.g., intraphagosomal), which may be relevant to the action of these molecules. The measurement of the specific products of the reactions of the various oxygen metabolites with different biochemical substrates can provide evidence of a reactive oxygen-mediated process. These assays also have the disadvantage of differential recovery of product and occasional channelling of reactants to some end product other than the one being measured. The use of the specific scavengers and blockers (see list above) in bioassay systems has provided a great deal of information on the role of reactive oxygen species either in vivo or in vitro. Even these agents have the disadvantages of differential distribution in cells, tissues, and organs and differential availability at relevant reaction sites (especially hydrophilic versus hydrophobic agents). Thus, definitive implication of oxygen radicals in any process usually requires the use of two or more different assay types to correlate and confirm each other.

One very useful experimental approach to the biology of oxygen radicals has been the study of animals or humans who are (i) genetically defective in producing oxygen radicals or (ii) either genetically or nutritionally deficient in scavenging mechanisms.

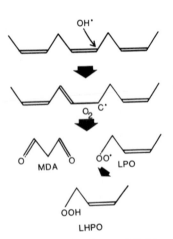

FIG. 2. *General scheme of lipid peroxidation. See text for details. Abbreviations: LHPO, lipid hydroperoxide; LPO, lipid peroxide; MDA, malondialdehyde.*

Examples of some of these disease syndromes are as follows:

Disease syndromes associated with deficiency of oxygen radical production
  chronic granulomatous disease
    initiation defect
    lipochrome histiocytosis
  glucose-6-phosphate dehydrogenase deficiency
  myeloperoxidase deficiency
Disease syndromes associated with deficiency of protective mechanisms
  acatalasemia
  glutathione peroxidase deficiency
  glutathione reductase deficiency
  glutathione synthetase deficiency

In many of these conditions, specific, discrete deficiencies have been identified, and the characteristic pathological syndromes can be adequately explained by that deficiency alone (17). Nutritional supplementation with alternative scavengers of similar specificity has worked well in patients deficient in scavenging mechanisms (3). Thus, therapeutic approaches are being developed on the basis of the increased understanding of these pathoses.

ROLE OF OXYGEN RADICALS
IN ACUTE AND CHRONIC INFLAMMATION

The involvement of phagocytic cells at inflammatory sites was classically considered to be one of engulfment, killing, and debridement. More recently, the response of phagocytic cells to both particulate and soluble proinflammatory stimuli has been better defined. Among the soluble stimuli of enhanced oxidative metabolic activity of phagocytes are the following:

A23187 (Ca^{2+} ionophore)
bacterial lipopolysaccharide
concanavalin A
cytochalasin E
immune complexes
sodium fluoride
surface-active agents
tetradecanoyl phorbol acetate

Each of these stimuli has been shown to initiate both the oxidative metabolic burst and interaction with arachidonate derivatives, divalent cations, cyclic nucleotides and lymphokines (Fig. 3). After initiation of the oxidative metabolic burst, a release of membrane-bound calcium activates a calcium-dependent phospholipase, which cleaves arachidonic acid from the membrane. This arachidonate can serve as substrate for either cyclooxygenase or lipoxygenase. The resultant arachidonate derivatives can modulate cyclic nucleotide levels (27). The proinflammatory soluble and particulate stimuli also cause a release from macrophages of Interleukin 1, a T-cell stimulant (24). The stimulated T lymphocytes can then, in turn, stimulate enhanced macrophage activity (23). The concomitant oxidative metabolic burst can also have a feedback damping effect on the phagocyte activation. Phagocyte-derived reactive oxygen species

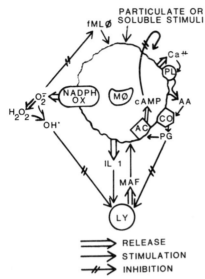

RELEASE
STIMULATION
INHIBITION

FIG. 3. *Interaction of oxidative metabolism with arachidonate derivatives, cyclic nucleotides, calcium ions, and lymphokines. Experimental evidence for each one of these actions has been presented from many laboratories. The actual sequence of actions and relative importance of each action are still under investigation. Abbreviations: AA, arachidonic acid; AC, adenylate cyclase; cAMP, cyclic adenosine monophosphate;   CO,   cyclooxygenase; fMLΦ,   formyl-methionyl-leucyl-phenylalanine; IL 1, Interleukin 1; LY, lymphocyte; MAF, macrophage activating factor; MΦ, macrophage; NADPH OX, NADPH oxidase; PG, prostaglandins; PL, phospholipase.*

have been shown to oxidatively inactivate soluble chemotactic factors such as formyl-methionyl-leucyl-phenylalanine (34), thereby removing an initiating stimulus.

Arachidonate derivatives. The prostaglandins also provide an interesting model for the involvement of oxygen radicals in other enzymatic processes related to inflammation. High doses of α-tocopherol, a potent scavenger of OH and blocker of the autocatalysis of lipid peroxidation, block prostaglandin synthesis through the cyclooxygenase pathway (35). Conversely, low doses of OH scavengers enhance the formation of cyclooxygenase products (25). This seeming paradox has been explained by the finding that the release of a reactive oxygen intermediate in the cyclooxygenase-catalyzed reactions inactivates the enzyme once in every 5,000 reaction cycles (6). Thus, low doses of antioxidant were able to protect the enzyme from autoinactivation, thereby enhancing activity. Conversely, high doses of antioxidant scavenged the reactive intermediates, preventing the reaction from going to completion. The important role of the arachidonate derivatives, not only in both chronic and acute inflammation in general but also in periodontal inflammation and bone resorption specifically, is considered in more detail in papers by P. Goldhaber and L. Rabadjija, R. Snyderman and G. A. McCarty, and S. Wahl (this volume).

Autotoxicity. The presence of a sustained, chronic stimulus or a high dose of an acute stimulus can lead to autolysis of phagocytic cells (26). The constitutive levels of antioxidant defenses such as reduced glutathione, catalase, and superoxide dismutase are inadequate to protect a cell against an acute high-dose stimulant. Thus, high doses of tetradecanoyl phorbol acetate can cause autolysis of phagocytic cells, and lipid peroxidation has been implicated as the lethal process (33). Similarly, chronic stimuli such as silica or streptococcal cell walls lead to chronic degeneration of phagocytes with the accumulation of the lipid peroxidation product lipofuscin intracellularly (37). This process can be inhibited by supplementation with additional antioxidants (37).

Tissue damage. Just as the chronic or hyperacute generation of oxygen radicals from a phagocyte may initiate peroxidation of its own membrane lipids, so too may any cell or tissue in contact with a stimulated phagocyte suffer destructive effects. The outwardly directed NADPH oxidase, as mentioned previously, is distributed over the entire cell membrane, not just the area which becomes a phagosome. Thus, the activation of the hexose monophosphate shunt in one area of the cell can lead to the production of substrate NADPH for NADPH oxidase molecules not involved in the area of the initial stimulus. The nonspecific tissue damage that results from the stimulated phagocyte contacting bystander tissue has been implicated in rheumatoid arthritis, wherein lipid perooxidation products have been detected in joint fluids (20). The local injection of a pharmaceutical preparation of superoxide dismutase into affected rheumatoid joints has proven therapeutic (19). Similarly, the use of this agent in several animal models of inflammation has had an anti-inflammatory effect.

This nonspecific bystander cell damage may also have some useful effects. Some data suggest that the nonspecific killing of tumor cells by macrophages (36) or neutrophils (5) may be due to generation of oxygen radicals by the inflammatory cells. Other data suggest that antibody-dependent cell-mediated cytotoxicity (2) and T cell-mediated cytotoxicity (32) are mediated by reactive oxygen species.

Recent work from my laboratory (Z. Metzger, J. T. Hoffeld, and J. J. Oppenheim, submitted for publication) has shown that proliferation of fibroblasts, in vitro, is also inhibited by macrophage-derived oxygen radicals and one or more non-prostaglandin E arachidonate derivatives. These data suggest that the repair of damaged tissue at a chronic inflammatory site can be delayed as long as the stimulated phagocytes are present.

The likelihood of nonspecific damage is not limited to neighboring cells. Nearby tissue matrices are also subject to oxidative damage in the presence of activated phagocytic cells. In particular, the superoxide anion is capable of both depolymerizing hyaluronate solutions and preventing collagen gelation (11). This action could be of utility to the phagocytes in permitting their movement through tissue matrices. At the same time, however, chronic inflammatory sites would have gross architectural breakdown in the presence of chronically stimulated phagocytes.

Aging effects. Aging has inhibitory effects on the body's capacity to resist infection, repair damaged tissues, and resolve inflammation (e.g., chronic periodontal disease). Other signs of aging include the accumulation of lipofuscin (lipid peroxidation product) (37), the increased expiration of ethane and pentane (by-products of lipid peroxidation) (28), and diminished immune repsonses, the depression of which can be prevented or reversed by antioxidants (13). These observations, and others, have supported a free radical theory of aging. This theory proposes that all cells are continuously exposed to oxidative damage, either from biochemical reactions or simple exposure to atmospheric oxygen (13). Depending on the antioxidative capacity of the individual cell and the degree of exposure to damaging influences, cells will accumulate the toxic products and sustain the physical damage of peroxidation. This cumulative damage decreases cell function, leading to cell death. Thus, in chronic inflammation in an aging host, the functional integrity of both the tissues and the protective infiltrate is compromised, exacerbating destruction.

Inhibition of lymphocyte response. Just as cells are at a greater risk of oxidative damage with aging, so too are lymphocytes endangered by their close proximity to activated macrophages around which they cluster for enhancement of lymphocyte functions. Indeed, we have proposed that the balance between the lymphocyte-stimulatory effect of the macrophage-derived interleukin 1 and the lymphocyte-inhibitory effect of macrophage-derived oxygen radicals may modulate the immune response (14). Antioxidants enhance immune responses either in vitro (13a) or in vivo (31). Antioxidants can also prevent the in vitro inhibition of lymphocyte responses induced by granuloma-inducing particles such as talc or silica (Fig. 4) (J. T. Hoffeld, submitted for publication). Macrophages hyperactivated in vivo appear to suppress lymphocytes, in vitro, by both oxygen radicals and arachidonate derivatives (Fig. 5) (21). Furthermore, the prostaglandins released by macrophages can elevate cyclic adenosine $3',5'$-monophosphate levels, inhibiting the early stages of activation of other macrophages (Z. Metzger, J. T. Hoffeld, and J. J. Oppenheim, J. Immunol., in press).

Chronic inflammation/periodontal diseases. The intimate interconnection of oxygen radicals with cyclic nucleotides, arachidonate derivatives, divalent cations, and lymphokines prevents attribution of damage from chronic inflammation solely to reactive oxygen species; however, several pieces of evidence suggest a central role for peroxidative processes in chronic inflammation. The most compelling data are those in which treatment with scavenger antioxidants such as α-tocopherol inhibited granuloma formation and hastened resolution of chronic inflammation (4). Supplementation with high doses of α-tocopherol has been reported to decrease severity of periodontal disease in humans (reviewed in 8), but a study of the serum levels of α-tocopherol in patients with and without periodontal disease showed no significant differences (30).

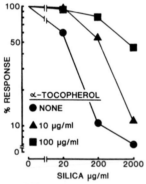

FIG. 4. *Effect of* α-*tocopherol on suppression by silica of lymphocyte proliferation. Normal murine spleen cells* (10^5) *were cultured in the presence of 10* μg *of lipopolysaccharide per ml, with or without graded doses of silica (particle size: 11 nm).* α-*Tocopherol was added in an ethanol/dimethyl sulfoxide carrier (0.1%, vol/vol, final concentration; this dose of carrier was also added to the "NONE" cultures and had no significant effect on the response). The responses are presented as percentage of response in cultures containing no silica particles. Standard error* $\leq$ *size of symbol.*

The efficacy of superoxide dismutase in decreasing tissue damage and swelling in patients with arthritis (19) suggested its possible therapeutic benefit in chronic destructive periodontal disease. Topical application of superoxide dismutase in the gingivae of beagle dogs had no measurable effect on the development or severity of their gingivitis (7). The lack of effect of that therapeutic regimen does not preclude a role for oxygen radicals at the inflammatory sites since topical application into the gingival sulcus has proved ineffective in the delivery of several types of drugs (reviewed in 9).

In contrast to the damaging and feedback-inhibitory effects of oxygen radicals, the presence of an intact intracellular oxidative metabolic capacity in phagocytic cells may well be a prerequisite to gingival health. A number of case reports of human or other species in which the bactericidal capacity of neutrophils was impaired have shown concomitant periodontopathies (22). This correlation suggests a "guardian" role for the crevicular neutrophil; that is, the oxidative bactericidal capabilities of neutrophils may be necessary for maintaining periodontal health.

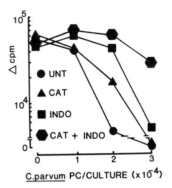

FIG. 5. *Effect of catalase and indomethacin on suppression of lymphocyte proliferation. Peritoneal cells (PC) from* Corynebacterium parvum-*treated mice were added to cultures of 10^5 normal murine spleen cells, either unstimulated or stimulated with 1 μg of concanavalin A per ml. Catalase (CAT), 10,000 U/ml, or indomethacin (INDO), 10 μg/ml, or both, were added to the cultures. Untreated (UNT) cultures received no chemical additives. Proliferation was measured for both stimulated and unstimulated cultures, and the differences are expressed as the change in counts per minute. Standard error ≤ 10%.*

SUMMARY

The production of reactive oxygen species by phagocytic cells has previously been considered primarily as a bactericidal mechanism. Evidence accumulating during the past few years has relegated this group of short-lived substances to the additional roles of inter- and intracellular mediators. In inflammation and immunity, wherein cellular interactions have been shown to depend not only on physical interactions, but also on soluble mediators such as arachidonate derivatives, cyclic nucleotides, divalent cations, and lymphokines, the oxygen radicals produced by phagocytic cells intimately interconnect with those previously defined mediators. The role of oxygen radicals as phagocyte-derived mediators acting upon lymphocytes is defined primarily as a suppressive action. The effector functions attributed to phagocyte-derived oxygen radicals, in addition to bactericidal activity, include specific and nonspecific connective tissue damage. The implication of reactive oxygen species in the tissue damage and immunosuppression in several models of chronic inflammation suggests that they may also be involved in the chronic inflammatory lesions of periodontal disease.

LITERATURE CITED

1. **Baldridge, C. W., and R. W. Gerard.** 1933. The extra respiration of phagocytosis. Am. J. Physiol. **103:**235–236.
2. **Borregaard, N., and K. Kragballe.** 1980. Role of oxygen in antibody-dependent cytotoxicity mediated by monocytes and neutrophils. J. Clin. Invest. **66:**676–683.
3. **Boxer, L. A., J. M. Oliver, S. P. Spielberg, J. M. Allen, and J. D. Schulman.** 1979. Protection of granulocyes by vitamin E in glutathione synthetase deficiency. N. Engl. J. Med. **301:**901–905.
4. **Bragt, P. C., J. I. Bansberg, and I. L. Bonta.** 1980. Antiinflammatory effects of free radical scavengers and antioxidants. Inflammation 4:289–299.
5. **Clark, R. A., and S. Szot.** 1981. The myeloperoxiodase-hydrogen peroxide-halide system as effector of neutrophil tumor cell cytotoxicity. J. Immunol. **126:**1295–1301.
6. **Egan, R. W., J. Paxton, and F. A. Kuehl, Jr.** 1976. Mechanism for irreversible self-deactivation or prostaglandin synthetase. J. Biol. Chem. **251:**7329–7335.

7. **Gaffar, A., H. P. Niles, and W. J. King.** 1979. Effects of an anti-inflammatory drug Palosein on gingivitis in beagles. J. Dent. Res. **59:**1910.
8. **Goodson, J. M.** 1975. Vitamin E. therapy and periodontal disease, p. 53–66. *In* S. P. Hazen (ed.), Diet, nutrition and periodontal disease. American Society of Preventive Dentistry, Chicago.
9. **Goodson, J. M., A. Haffajee, and S. S. Socransky.** 1979. Periodontal therapy by local delivery of tetracycline. J. Clin. Periodontol. **6:**83–92.
10. **Green, T. R., R. E. Schaefer and M.T. Makler.** 1980. Orientation of the NADPH dependent superoxide generating oxidoreductase on the outer membrane of human PMN's. Biochem. Biophys. Res. Commun. **94:**262–269.
11. **Greenwald, R. A., and W. W. Moy.** 1980. Effect of oxygen-derived free radicals on hyaluronic acid. Arthritis Rheum. **23:**455–463.
12. **Halliwell, B.** 1978. Biochemical mechanisms accounting for the toxic action of oxygen on living organisms: the key role of superoxide dismutase. Cell Biol. Int. Rep. **2:**113–128.
13. **Harman, D., M. L. Heidrick, and D. E. Eddy.** 1977. Free radical theory of aging: effect of free-radical-reaction inhibitors on the immune response. J. Am. Geriatr. Soc. **25:**400–407.
13a. **Hoffeld, J. T.** 1981. Agents which block membrane lipid peroxidation enhance mouse spleen cell immune activities *in vitro:* relationship to the enhancing activity of 2-mercaptoethanol. Eur. J. Immunol. **11:**371–376.
14. **Hoffeld, J. T., Z. Metzger, and J. J. Oppenheim.** 1981. Oxygen-derived metabolites as suppressors of immune responses in vitro, p. 63–86. *In* E. Pick (ed.), Lymphokines, vol. 2. Academic Press, Inc., New York.
15. **Huber, W., K. B. Menander-Huber, M. G. P. Saifer, and P. H. C. Dang.** 1977. Studies on the clinical and laboratory pharmacology of drug formulations of bovine Cu-Zn superoxide dismutases (orgotein), p. 527–540. *In* D. A. Willoughby, J. P. Giroud, and G. P. Velo (ed.), Perspectives in inflammation: future trends and developments. University Park Press, Baltimore.
16. **Iyer, G. Y. N., M. F. Islam, and J. H. Quastel.** 1961. Biochemical aspects of phagocytosis. Nature (London) **192:**535–541.
17. **Johnston, R. B., Jr.** 1980. Biochemical defects of polymorphonuclear and mononuclear phagocytes associated with disease, p. 397–421. *In* A. J. Sbarra and R. R. Strauss (ed.), The reticuloendothelial system, a comprehensive treatise, vol. 2, Biochemistry and metabolism. Plenum Press, New York.
18. **Klebanoff, S. J.** 1967. Iodination of bacteria: a bactericidal mechanism. J. Exp. Med. **126:**1063–1078.
19. **Lund-Olesen, K., and K. B. Menander.** 1974. Orgotein: a new anti-inflammatory metalloprotein drug: preliminary evaluation of clinical efficacy and safety in degenerative joint disease. Curr. Ther. Res. **16:**706–717.
20. **Lunec, J., and T. L. Dormandy.** 1979. Fluorescent lipid-peroxidation products in synovial fluid. Clin. Sci. **56:**53–59.
21. **Metzger, F., J. T. Hoffeld, and J. J. Oppenheim.** 1980. Macrophage-mediated suppression. I. Evidence for participation of both hydrogen peroxide and prostaglandins in suppression of murine lymphocyte proliferation. J. Immunol. **124:**983–988.
22. **Mills, E. L., and P. G. Quie.** 1980. Congenital disorders of the functions of polymorphonuclear neutrophils. Rev. Infect. Dis. **2:**505–517.
23. **Mizel, S. B., J. J. Oppenheim, and D. L. Rosenstreich.** 1978. Characterization of lymphocyte-activating factor (LAF) produced by the macrophage cell line, P388D₁. I. Enhancement of LAF production by activated T lymphocytes. J. Immunol. **120:**1497–1503.
24. **Oppenheim, J. J., A. Shneyour, and A. I. Kook.** 1976. Enhancement of DNA synthesis and cAMP content of mouse thymocytes by mediator(s) derived from adherent cells. J. Immunol. **116:**1466–1472.
25. **Panganamala, R. V., H. M. Sharma, R. E. Heikkila, J. C. Geer, and D. G. Cornwell.** 1976. Role of hydroxyl radical scavengers dimethyl sulfoxide, alcohols and methional in the inhibition of prostaglandin biosynthesis. Prostaglandins **11:**599–607.
26. **Roos, D., R. S. Weening, and A. A. Voetman.** 1979. Host-defense by and self-defense of phagocytic leukocytes, p. 259–272. *In* J. G. Kaplan (ed.), The molecular basis of immune cell function. Elsevier/North-Holland Biomedical Press, Amsterdam.
27. **Rubin, R. P., and S. G. Laychock.** 1978. Prostaglandins, calcium and cyclic nucleotides in stimulus-response coupling, p. 133–155. *In* G. B. Weiss (ed.), Calcium in drug action. Plenum Press, New York.
28. **Sagai, M., and T. Ichinose.** 1980. Age-related changes in lipid peroxidation as measured by ethane, ethylene, butane and pentane in respired gases of rats. Life Sci. **27:**731–738.
29. **Sbarra, A. J., and M. L. Karnovsky.** 1959. The biochemical basis of phagocytosis. I. Metabolic changes during the ingestion of particles by polymorphonuclear leukocytes. J. Biol. Chem. **234:**1355–1362.
30. **Slade, E. W., Jr., D. Bartuska, L. F. Rose, and D. W. Cohen.** 1976. Vitamin E and periodontal disease. J. Periodontol. **47:**352–354.
31. **Tengerdy, R. P., R. H. Heinzerling, G. L. Brown, and M. M. Mathias.** 1973. Enhancement of the humoral immune response by vitamin E. Int. Arch. Allergy **44:**221–232.

32. **Thorne, K. J. I., R. J. Svvennsen, and D. Franks.** 1980. Role of hydrogen peroxide in the cytotoxic reaction of T lymphocytes. Clin. Exp. Immunol. **39:**486–495.
33. **Tsan, M. F.** 1980. Phorbol myristate acetate induced neutrophil autotoxicity. J. Cell Physiol. **105:**327–334.
34. **Tsan, M. F., and R. C. Denison.** 1981. Oxidation of n-formyl methionyl chemotactic peptide by human neutrophils. J. Immunol. **126:**1387–1389.
35. **Vanderhoek, J. Y., and W. E. M. Lands.** 1973. The inhibition of the fatty acid oxygenase of sheep vesicular gland by antioxidants. Biochim. Biophys. Acta **296:**382–385.
36. **Weiss, S. J., A. F. LoBuglio, and H. B. Kessler.** 1980. Oxidative mechanisms of monocyte-mediated cytotoxicity. Proc. Natl. Acad. Sci. U.S.A. **77:**584–587.
37. **Wolman, M.** 1975. Biological peroxidation of lipids and membranes. Israel J. Med. Sci. **11**(Suppl.):1–248.
38. **Yau, T. M.** 1979. Mutagenicity and cytotoxicty of malonaldehyde in mammalian cells. Mech. Ageing Dev. **11:**137–144.

CLINICAL IMPLICATIONS OF HOST–PARASITE INTERACTIONS

Analogous Mechanisms of Tissue Destruction in Rheumatoid Arthritis and Periodontal Disease

RALPH SNYDERMAN AND GALE A. McCARTY

Division of Rheumatic and Genetic Diseases and
Laboratory of Immune Effector Function of the Howard Hughes Medical Institute,
Department of Medicine, Duke University Medical Center, Durham, North Carolina 27710

Immunological processes mediate the localization and rapid destruction of substances such as microbial agents which, if disseminated, could disrupt the host's complex internal milieu. The immune system, unlike other organs, consists not only of fixed structures, but also of motile cells which transit through the circulation then wander throughout the body, performing surveillance. It is also the only tissue which is able to react against, and in some cases destroy, other components of the host. Both the protective and destructive abilities of immunological processes relate largely to their inflammatory potential (25).

The accumulation of granulocytes and macrophages at sites of inflammation can result in the phagocytosis and degradation of the agent which initiated the inflammatory event. The factors which determine whether a given inflammatory response will be protective or destructive to the host, however, are complex and poorly understood. They depend in part upon the nature and location of the inciting agent as well as its quantity and digestibility. The

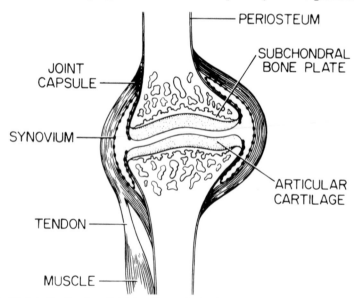

FIG. 1. *Model of a diarthrodial joint. From the Syllabus on Rheumatic Diseases prepared by the Public Education Committee of the Arthritis Foundation with their kind permission (J. Am. Phys. Ther. Assoc., **44**:574–583, 1964).*

354

genetic make-up and the immunoregulatory competency of the host are also important. In general, when the antigen or other inciting agent is rapidly disposed of, the inflammatory process is protective and self-limited. When the antigenic stimulus is excessive in amount or persists as plaque does in progressive periodontal disease, the inflammatory response results in a clinically apparent disorder.

Chronic periodontal disease (5) and rheumatoid synovitis (8) are two examples of human inflammatory diseases. The inflammation in periodontitis likely represents the reaction of the host's immune system to products or mediators released from plaque. In rheumatoid arthritis, the inciting antigen(s) is unknown.

RHEUMATOID SYNOVITIS AS A MODEL OF INFLAMMATION-MEDIATED TISSUE DESTRUCTION

A chronic, locally destructive inflammatory reaction in humans is exemplified by the synovitis present in some connective tissue disorders. The prototype disease in this category is rheumatoid arthritis. Certain structural features of the joint may influence the inflammatory processes which occur in this location (Fig. 1). The synovial membrane is highly vascular and lines all intra-articular structures except for cartilage. The synovial lining is devoid of a basement membrane and thus permits relatively free diffusion of soluble substances. Moreover, the synovial membrane lines a closed cavity, the joint space; therefore, any reactive materials gaining entrance to this space are difficult to remove (10).

Normal synovium is a thin layer of tissue whose lining is composed of two principal cell types supported by a loose connective tissue stroma (Fig. 2A). The type A synovial cell is rich in surface pseudopodia, and its cytoplasm has many lysosomes. Type A synovial cells have many characteristics of macrophages and are phagocytic, but ultrastructural studies have implied a secretory role for these cells as well. The type B synovial cell contains prominent rough endoplasmic reticulum, but few vacuoles or lysosomes. This cell is primarily a secretory cell, hyaluronic acid being an important product. Beneath the synovial membrane there are collagen fibrils, fatty tissue, and an extensive capillary network. Fibroblasts in the synovium produce type I and III collagen. Lastly, the dense fibrous joint capsule provides a support for the synovial lining membrane and separates the articular space from surrounding structures.

Rheumatoid synovitis exhibits three main features: inflammation, proliferation, and infiltration (9). In early stages, lining cells of both type A and type B proliferate and increase in size. Fibrin deposits are frequently present on the inner synovial lining. Polymorphonuclear leukocytes predominate in the synovial fluid exudate, but these cells are seen as infiltrates only in the superficial synovial layer. The supporting stroma beneath the lining cell layer becomes edematous, and the number of small blood vessels increases. Concurrently, there are focal accumulations of inflammatory cells consisting of lymphocytes, plasma cells, macrophages, and occasionally mast cells. If the inflammatory synovitis persists, a proliferative lesion develops, characterized by synovial membrane thickening and projection of villous formations into the articular cavity (Fig. 2B). There is a concomitant increase in supporting connective tissue, small blood vessels, mononuclear cell infiltrates, and occasional multinucleated giant cells, as well as increased numbers of

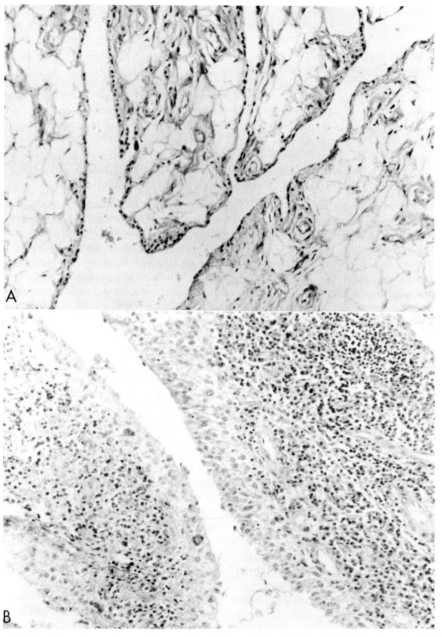

FIG. 2. *Normal synovium and synovitis of rheumatoid arthritis. (A) A delicate network of connective tissue supports a thin layer of synoviocytes. (B) The thickened rheumatoid synovium with villous projections is composed of hyperplastic, hypertrophic synoviocytes and is infiltrated with lymphocytes, plasma cells, macrophages, and occasional multinucleated giant cells. (C) Rheumatoid synovium invading articular cartilage and subchondral bone. From the Syllabus on Rheumatic Disease prepared by the Public Education Committee of the Arthritis Foundation with their kind permission.*

undifferentiated mesenchyme-like cells which have both phagocytic and synthetic potential. As the proliferative lesions progress, infiltration of surrounding structures develops as the fibrous mesenchymal tissue (pannus) begins to invade and to replace cartilage and bone at the periphery of the synovial reflection (Fig. 2C). The invasion of cartilage, subchondral bone, and tendon by inflammatory synovial tissue results in collagen destruction, degradation of proteoglycans in the cartilage matrix, and eventual bony resorption.

SIMILARITIES BETWEEN RHEUMATOID SYNOVITIS AND PERIODONTITIS

The mechanism by which inflammatory reactions result in the destruction of soft tissue and bone in the joint in rheumatoid arthritis bears a striking resemblance to the mechanisms which mediate tissue destruction in periodontal disease. Indeed, a great deal of our knowledge concerning the pathogenetic mechanisms of the collagen vascular diseases has been derived directly from research related to the pathogenesis of periodontal disease. In both conditions, a persistent inflammatory reaction occurs in specialized areas composed of connective tissue and bone. Activation of complement, production of cytokines, and release of other inflammatory cell products results in the destruction of connective tissue and the erosion of bone (5, 12, 17–19, 23, 24). The following discussion reviews current concepts concerning the mechanisms of tissue destruction in rheumatoid arthritis. Although a number of features of this condition differ from periodontal disease, the similarities of actual tissue destruction in both processes should be readily apparent.

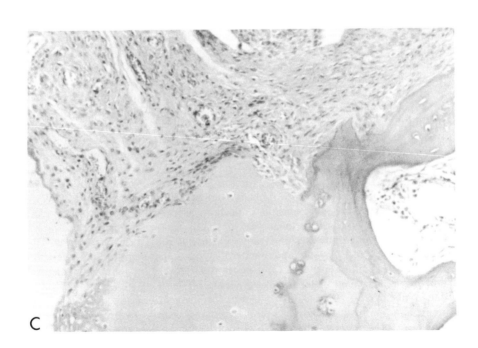

C

MECHANISMS OF TISSUE DESTRUCTION
IN RHEUMATOID ARTHRITIS

The characteristic tissue reaction in rheumatoid arthritis is the development of synovitis, in which the normally thin, loose connective tissue is replaced by a rich infiltrate of lymphocytes, macrophages, and plasma cells (Fig. 2B) (9, 10). In the synovial fluid, the predominant inflammatory cells are the polymorphonuclear leukocytes. The cells which have infiltrated the synovia are metabolically active; the plasma cells produce immunoglobulins, some of which are rheumatoid factors, and the mononuclear cells produce cytokines (26). Rheumatoid factors are immunoglobulin M, G, or rarely A. These factors bind to the Fc portion of immunoglobulin G antibodies which have either combined with antigen or have been aggregated or denatured. Polymorphonuclear leukocytes isolated from synovial fluids contain inclusions of immune complexes, which frequently contain rheumatoid factors (8, 31). Synovial fluid complement levels, particularly the components of the classical pathway, are markedly reduced in rheumatoid synovial fluid (8). Complement cleavage products such as C5a (8) are present in rheumatoid synovial fluid, as are hydrolytic enzymes derived from inflammatory cells, kinins, and 5,12-hydroxyeicosatetraenoic acid (16).

The sequence of events leading to the development of synovitis and destruction of surrounding structures in rheumatoid arthritis can be envisioned as follows. Some as yet undefined antigen localizes in synovium and is phagocytized by the type A synovial cells. One can assume that the antigen persists in, or diffuses into, the synovial fluid. Binding of the processed antigen to B lymphocytes induces their differentiation into plasma cells, which then produce antibodies and rheumatoid factors upon chronic stimulation. Antigen activation of T lymphocytes triggers lymphokine synthesis followed by blastogenesis. Macrophages in the synovium produce cytokines. Regardless of the initiating agent, combination of antibody with antigen, as well as combination of antigen–antibody complexes with rheumatoid factors, or self-association of rheumatoid factors, activates complement as well as the kinin-forming system by activation of Hageman factor (14). This results in the production of inflammatory products such as C5a, arachidonic acid metabolites (27), kinins, and fibrinopeptides (14), which diffuse into the synovial fluid and into synovial blood vessels. These phlogistic agents enhance vascular permeability and attract polymorphonuclear leukocytes and macrophages. Polymorphonuclear leukocytes ingest the abundant immune complexes in the fluid, release lysosomal enzymes (29), and generate superoxide anions (15). This causes destruction of hyaluronate polymers in the joint fluid, as well as injury to cartilage (9). Cytokine production in the synovium leads to the further accumulation of macrophages, fibroblasts, and additional lymphocytes (26). The unique structure of the joint space is important, as enzymes present in synovial fluid or released/synthesized locally by the cells comprising the proliferative synovial lesion contribute to the pathology evident in articular structures. The cartilage-degrading lysosomal enzymes, collagenase and elastase, are primarily derived from inflammatory cells (3). Proteinases released by dying cells may aid in superficial cartilage destruction by virtue of their role in uncross-linking collagen fibrils, thus increasing their susceptibility to enzymatic degradation. Macrophages in the synovium produce prostaglandins, hydrolytic enzymes, collagenase, plasminogen activator, and interleukin 1 (mononuclear cell factor).

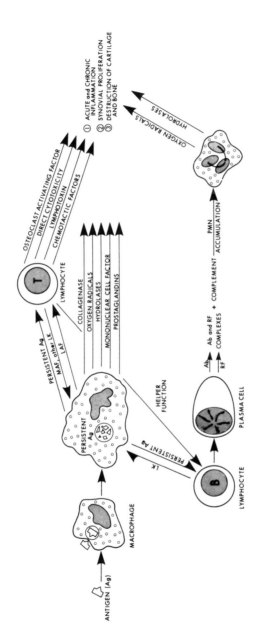

FIG. 3. *Model for the pathogenesis of articular inflammation in rheumatoid arthritis. Ab, Antibody; LAF, lymphocyte-activating factor; LK, lymphokines; MAF, macrophage-activating factor; RF, rheumatoid factor.*

The synovial cell which is the most abundant source of collagenase in the rheumatoid synovium is one which has an unusual dendritic appearance and is adherent to glass, but is nonphagocytic (30). Collagenase synthesis by this cell is greatly enhanced in the presence of interleukin 1 (20). With ongoing synovitis, early changes in cartilage involve the loss of proteoglycan content, often manifested microscopically as diminished metachromatic staining. In addition to collagenase, lysosomal proteinases can degrade aggregates of proteoglycans, and once released from cartilage, these solubilized components are then sensitive to further enzymatic attack (3). The final stage of the destructive process, demineralization of bone, may result from combined elements present initially in the inflammatory and later in the proliferative responses. Demineralization must occur in bone before this tissue is susceptible to collagenolytic enzymes. In rheumatoid synovitis, prostaglandins stimulate calcium release from bone matrix, and other arachidonic acid metabolites are responsible for long-term leaching of mineral from bony matrix (27). In addition, bone demineralization is enhanced by heparin which is released upon the degranulation of mast cells (7). Cellular mechanisms may also be operative in demineralization in that lymphocytes produce an osteoclast-activating factor (12). In addition, connective tissue activating peptides (1) and specific lymphokines such as lymphocyte-derived chemotactic factor for fibroblasts (22) attract and stimulate fibroblasts to produce collagen and may contribute to the ultimate fibrosis evident in the destroyed ankylosed joint (Fig. 3).

The net effect, either due to persistence of antigen or to disordered regulation of T- and B-cell activation, is a chronic inflammatory response in the synovium (Fig. 2B and C). Continued cellular proliferation and influx leads to synovial proliferation and its invasion into surrounding structures. Diffusion of collagenase, prostaglandin E, hydrolytic enzymes, and lymphokines into cartilage and bone results in erosion of these tissues. Rheumatoid arthritis thus illustrates the devastating local tissue destruction which results from chronic inflammatory reactions produced by the immune complex and delayed hypersensitivity types of immune responses.

SUMMARY

It should be readily apparent that the foregoing model for tissue destruction in rheumatoid arthritis, with minor modification, describes well what is known about the mechanisms of tissue destruction in periodontal disease.

As in rheumatoid arthritis, humoral and cellular inflammatory responses have been considered to be important in the pathogenesis of chronic periodontitis. Activation of complement occurs in the gingival sulcus and presumably leads to the production of chemotactic factors (H. A. Schenkein, this volume). The T and B lymphocytes from the blood of patients with periodontitis proliferate and produce lymphokines in response to antigens isolated from dental plaque (11, 13, 17, 18). When severe periodontal lesions are examined histologically, B lymphocytes and plasma cells are the predominant cell types present in the gingivae (17, 18). Recently, the B lymphocytes of adult patients with severe periodontitis were shown to exhibit hyperresponsiveness to staphylococcal protein A, a specific polyclonal B-cell activator (23). Interestingly, the existence of impaired neutrophil chemotaxis in some patients with juvenile periodontitis has been established by several investigators (2, 4,

28). Some patients with rheumatoid arthritis have depressed neutrophil chemotaxis, but the pathogenetic significance of these findings remains unclear (6, 21).

In the periodontium, the tooth articulates with alveolar bone and requires the support of a specialized network of collagenous ligaments. Bacterial plaque appears to initiate inflammatory events, which lead to the accumulation of polymorphonuclear leukocytes in the gingival sulcus. In the gingivae itself, mononuclear infiltrates in close proximity to the periodontal ligaments and alveolar bone produce soft tissue destruction and alveolar bone loss. Although the inciting agents in periodontal disease and rheumatoid arthritis may differ, persistent inflammation with the production of humoral and cellular inflammatory mediators appears to cause the destruction of the supportive tissues required for the normal function of the periodontium.

LITERATURE CITED

1. **Castor, C. W., J. C. Ritchie, M. S. Scott, and S. Whitney.** 1977. Connective tissue activation. X. Current studies of mediators and the process. Scand. J. Rheum. **5:**41–46.
2. **Clark, R. A., R. C. Page, and G. Wilde.** 1977. Defective neutrophil chemotaxis in juvenile periodontitis. Infect. Immun. **18:**694–700.
3. **Dayer, J. M., and S. M. Krane.** 1978. The interaction of immunocompetent cells and chronic inflammation as exemplified by rheumatoid arthritis. Clin. Rheum. Dis. **4:**517–524.
4. **Genco, R. J., T. Van Dyke, B. Park, M. Ciminelli, and H. Horoszewicz.** 1980. Neutrophil chemotaxis impairment in juvenile periodontitis. RES J. Reticuloendothel. Soc. **28**(Suppl.):815–915.
5. **Glickman, I.** 1971. Periodontal disease. N. Engl. J. Med. **284:**1071–1077.
6. **Goetzl, E. J.** 1976. Defective responsiveness to ascorbic acid of neutrophil random and chemotactic migration in Felty's syndrome and systemic lupus erythematosus. Ann. Rheum. Dis. **38:**510–515.
7. **Goldhaber, P.** 1965. Heparin enhancement of factors stimulating bone resorption in tissue cultures. Science **147:**407–409.
8. **Greenberg, P., and N. J. Zvaifler.** 1976. Immunobiology of rheumatoid arthritis. Pathobiol. Annu. **6:**279–297.
9. **Harris, E. D., Jr.** 1976. Insights into the pathogenesis of the proliferative lesion in rheumatoid arthritis. Arthritis Rheum. **19:**68–72.
10. **Harris, E. D., Jr.** 1981. Biology of the joint, p. 255–276. *In* W. N. Kelley, E. D. Harris, Jr., S. Ruddy, and C. B. Sledge (ed.), Textbook of rheumatology. W. B. Saunders Co., Philadelphia.
11. **Horton, J. E., J. J. Oppenheim, and S. E. Mergenhagen.** 1973. Elaboration of lymphotoxin by cultures of human peripheral blood leukocytes stimulated with dental plaque deposits. Clin. Exp. Immunol. **13:**383–393.
12. **Horton, J. E., L. G. Raisz, H. A. Simmons, J. J. Oppenheim, and S. E. Mergenhagen.** 1972. Bone-resorbing activity in supernatant fluid from cultured human peripheral blood leukocytes. Science **177:**793–795.
13. **Ivnayi, L., and T. Lehner.** 1970. Stimulation of lymphocyte transformation by bacterial antigens in patients with periodontal disease. Arch. Oral Biol. **15:**1089–1093.
14. **Kaplan, A. P., M. S. Meier, and R. Mandle, Jr.** 1976. The Hageman factor dependent pathways of coagulation, fibrinolysis, and kinin generation. Semin. Thrombosis Hemostasis **3**(1):1–26.
15. **Klebanoff, S. J.** 1980. Oxygen metabolism and the toxic properties of phagocytes. Ann. Intern. Med. **93:**480–489.
16. **Klickstein, L. B., C. Shapleigh, and E. J. Goetzl.** 1980. Lipoxygenation of arachidonic acid as a source of polymorphonuclear leukocyte chemotactic factors in synovial fluid and tissue in rheumatoid arthritis and spondyloarthritis. J. Clin. Invest. **66:**1166–1170.
17. **Mackler, B. F., L. C. Altman, S. Wahl, D. L. Rosenstreich, J. J. Oppenheim, and S. E. Mergenhagen.** 1974. Blastogenesis and lymphokine synthesis by T and B lymphocytes from patients with periodontal disease. Infect. Immun. **10:**844–850.
18. **Mackler, B. F., K. B. Frostad, P. Robertson, and B. M. Levy.** 1977. Immunoglobulin-bearing lymphocytes and plasma cells in human periodontal disease. J. Periodontal Res. **12:**37–45.
19. **Mergenhagen, S. E., T. R. Tempel, and R. Snyderman.** 1970. Immunologic reactions and periodontal inflammation. J. Dent. Res. **49:**256–261.
20. **Mizell, S. B., J. M. Dayer, S. M. Krane, and S. E. Mergenhagen.** 1981. Stimulation of rheumatoid synovial cell collagenase and prostaglandin production by partially purified lymphocyte activating factor (interleukin-1). Proc. Natl. Acad. Sci. U.S.A. **78:**2474–2477.
21. **Mowat, A. G., and J. Baum.** 1971. Chemotaxis of polymorphonuclear leukocytes from patients with rheumatoid arthritis. J. Clin. Invest. **50:**2541–2549.

22. **Postlethwaite, A., R. Snyderman, and A. Kang.** 1976. The chemotactic attraction of human fibroblasts to a lymphocyte-derived factor. J. Exp. Med. **144:**1118–1203.
23. **Smith, S., P. H. Beck, G. A. Miller, R. R. Ranney, P. L. Rice, J. H. Lalos, and J. G. Tew.** 1980. Polyclonal B cell activation: severe periodontal disease in young adults. Clin. Immunol. Immunopathol. **16:**354–366.
24. **Snyderman, R.** 1972. Role for endotoxin and complement in periodontal tissue destruction. J. Dent. Res. **51:**356–363.
25. **Snyderman, R.** 1980. Inflammation and autodestructive reactions initiated by antibody, p. 342–353. *In* W. K. Joklik, H. P. Willett, and D. B. Amos (ed.), Zinsser microbiology, 17th ed. Appleton-Century-Crofts, New York.
26. **Snyderman, R., and G. A. McCarty.** 1978. The role of macrophages in the rheumatic diseases. Clin. Rheum. Dis. **4:**499–515.
27. **Trang, L. E.** 1980. Prostaglandins and inflammation. Semin. Arthritis Rheum. **9:**153–190.
28. **Van Dyke, T. E., H. U. Horoszewicz, L. J. Cianciola, and R. J. Genco.** 1980. Neutrophil chemotaxis dysfunction in human periodontitis. Infect. Immun. **27:**124–132.
29. **Weissman, G.** 1977. Lysosomes and rheumatoid joint inflammation. Arthritis Rheum. **20:**S193–S204.
30. **Wooley, D. E., E. D. Harris, Jr., C. L. Mainardi, and C. E. Brinckerhoff.** 1978. Collagenase immunolocalization in cultures of rheumatoid synovial cells. Science **200:**773–775.
31. **Ziff, M.** 1973. Pathophysiology of rheumatoid arthritis. Symposium: models for the study and therapy of rheumatoid arthritis. Fed. Proc. **32:**131–133.

Influence of Pharmacological Agents
on Bone Resorption

PAUL GOLDHABER AND LUKA RABADJIJA

Harvard School of Dental Medicine, Boston, Massachusetts 02115

The opportunity for a rational pharmacological approach to the treatment of disease depends in large measure on the state of knowledge concerning its etiology and pathogenesis and the ability to insert effective blocking agents at different points along the pathophysiological pathway. In general, it is preferable to block the disease process at the point closest to its initiation. When possible, elimination of the initiating factor(s) is the ideal solution. However, when the initiating factors are unknown or too complex, therapeutic interventions may be introduced at subsequent stages of the disease mechanism.

If this analysis is applicable, in part, to chronic destructive periodontal disease, it should be possible to block the progress of this disease by interfering with the bone-resorption process. Indeed, this assumption has been at the core of our laboratory's efforts over the past two decades. During this same period, the studies of many laboratories throughout the world have yielded new basic knowledge about bone physiology and pathology that should eventually have a clinical "spin-off" with regard to the prevention and treatment of chronic destructive periodontal disease. This paper will review some of the factors and biological mechanisms that influence bone resorption in tissue culture with particular emphasis on certain pharmacological agents that interfere with bone resorption and might be useful in treating chronic destructive periodontal disease in humans.

PARATHYROID HORMONE AND PROSTAGLANDIN E

Parathyroid hormone and the prostaglandins of the E series (PGE) are two examples of factors that stimulate bone resorption directly in culture. Despite the fact that their origin and chemical structure are completely different, their mechanisms of action appear to have a common final pathway. Figure 1 shows the relationship between parathyroid hormone, prostaglandin, and the adenyl cyclase-cyclic adenosine 3',5'-monophosphate (cAMP) system. Both parathyroid hormone and prostaglandin stimulate adenyl cyclase in the cell membrane of the target bone cell. Adenosine triphosphate is converted to cAMP, and the elevated concentration of this "second messenger" gives rise to a chain of intracellular reactions within the effector cell that results in bone resorption. The presence of a methylxanthine, such as theophylline, prevents the cyclic nucleotide phosphodiesterase from degrading cAMP, thereby causing its elevation within the cell. Prostaglandin formation from fatty acid precursors, such as arachidonic acid, is controlled by cyclooxygenase (prostaglandin synthetase), which converts the fatty acid prostaglandin precursors to cyclic endoperoxides. The enzyme responsible for the formation of PGE is endo-peroxide-PGE isomerase. Indomethacin reduces prostaglandin concentrations by selective inhibition of cyclooxygenase. The fatty acid precursors are provided as a result of tissue damage due to trauma, infection, or inflammation, which

363

makes membrane phospholipids available as substrate for phospholipase A_2 released from lysosomes. The action of this enzyme results in the release of arachidonic acid from the phospholipid complex. Corticosteroids, such as dexamethasone, prevent the release of fatty acids from phospholipids by inhibiting phospholipase A_2 activity, thereby reducing prostaglandin concentrations (17).

The probability that the adenyl cyclase-cAMP system is involved in the action of parathyroid hormone received its initial stimulus from an observation made by Wells and Lloyd (68). These investigators reported that a single injection of theophylline in chronically parathyroidectomized rats simulated parathyroid hormone by bringing about a rapid, marked, and relatively long-lasting elevation in serum calcium, presumably by allowing cAMP to accumulate through inhibition of the phosphodiesterase that degrades cAMP. Bilateral nephrectomy did not alter the theophylline effect, suggesting that the drug did not depend on renal action for its hypercalcemic effect. Administration of an agent that *activates* phosphodiesterase, such as imidizole, produces a hypocalcemia in intact rats and negates the action of parathyroid extract in parathyroidectomized rats, as predicted from the hypothesis (69). Soon after, Chase and Aurbach (8) reported a rapid rise in the excretion of cAMP in the urine of parathyroidectomized rats after the administration of parathyroid hormone. Subsequently, this group demonstrated that parathyroid hormone stimulates adenyl cyclase activity and the accumulation of cAMP in bone homogenates (9, 10). Within a short period, several laboratories reported that the addition of dibutyryl-cAMP, a cAMP analog which penetrates cell membranes readily, mimics the action of parathyroid hormone by directly stimulating bone resorption in tissue culture at low concentrations (34, 59, 64). Apparently, the aciton of dibutyryl-cAMP on bone is due to the inhibition of cyclic nucleotide phosphodiesterase in the tissue, causing an accumulaton of endogenous cAMP (2).

In a recent critical review (57) of the hypothesis that cAMP functions as a "second messenger" with regard to the skeletal actions of parathyroid, it was pointed out that, although there are many persuasive arguments for the hypothesis, the case has not yet been proved. A frequent argument used against

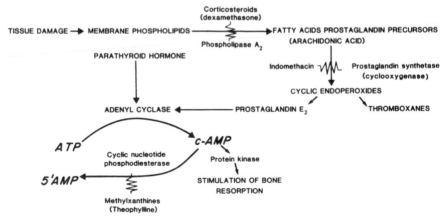

Fig. 1. *Diagram of the relationship between parathyroid hormone, prostaglandins of the E series, the adenyl cyclase–cAMP system, and bone resorption.*

the hypothesis is that, although calcitonin antagonizes parathyroid hormone-mediated bone resorption, it, too, activates adenyl cyclase and increases cAMP formation in bone cultures (2, 55), as does parathyroid hormone. This reasoning assumes that both hormones are stimulating the *same* target cell. Since the bone tissue tested contains many different cell types, one cannot make that assumption. Similarly, the stimulation of cAMP in *isolated bone cell populatons* by parathyroid and calcitonin assumes that the separation procedures used have resulted in two pure and different cell types (11). Such an assumption is unwarranted. Another argument against the hypothesis is that treatment of bone cultures with known phosphodiesterase inhibitors does not stimulate bone resorption (34, 46, 64). This is not the case, since theophylline has been reported to stimulate bone resorption in culture to the same extent as parathyroid extract (P. Goldhaber and L. Rabadjija, J. Dent. Res., abstr. 593, 1975). Furthermore, the more potent phosphodiesterase inhibitors, such as isobutylmethylxanthine, are also excellent stimulators of bone resorption (40; P. Goldhaber and L. Rabadjija, J. Dent. Res., abstr. 220, 1976). Although it may be "premature to regard cAMP as the second messenger for any of the diverse skeletal effects of parathyroid," it is still the best hypothesis we have. The problem is not so much with the hypothesis as with the crude techniques and methods available for testing the hypothesis.

In 1967 and 1968, Sutherland's group demonstated the involvement of prostaglandins in cAMP metabolism (6, 7). Chase and Aurbach's (9) report that prostaglandins increase cAMP in bone tissue in vitro led to the discovery by Klein and Raisz (45) that prostaglandins, primarily PGE, can stimulate bone resorption in tissue culture.

These findings spurred other studies concerning the possible involvement of prostaglandins in the bone-resorbing properties of a variety of human and animal tissues, including inflamed human gingival tissue (23, 41, 42), dental cysts (29), squamous cell carcinoma (26), and transplantable animal tumors (21; P. Goldhaber, Proc. Am. Assoc. Cancer Res., abstr. 90, 1960). The observation that indomethacin, an aspirin-like drug known to block prostaglandin synthetase, inhibited the stimulation of bone resorption by media from cultured human gingival fragments suggested the presence of a prostaglandin synthetase *in mouse calvaria* that plays a role in bone resorption (24). Figure 2 shows that indomethacin, at concentrations ranging from 1 to 100 ng/ml, has no effect on parathyroid extract-stimulated bone resorption, although at 1,000 ng/ml there is some inhibition. Figure 3 shows that media from human gingival fragments caused a substantial stimulation of bone resorption compared with untreated control cultures. In contrast to the parathyroid extract-stimulated resorption

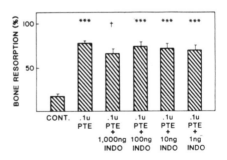

FIG. 2. *Lack of effect of different concentrations of indomethacin (INDO) on parathyroid extract (PTE)-stimulated bone resorption. Asterisks indicate differences from negative controls that are statistically significant, as follows: ***, P < 0.001. Daggers indicate differences from positive controls that are statistically significant, as follows: †, P < 0.05. Cont., Control.*

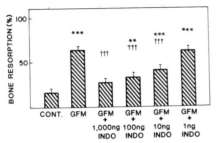

FIG. 3. *Inhibition of human gingival fragment medium (GFM)-stimulated bone resorption by various concentrations of indomethacin (INDO). Asterisks indicate differences from negative controls that are statistically significant, as follows: **, P < 0.01; ***, P < 0.001. Daggers indicate differences from positive controls that are statistically significant, as follows: †††, P < 0.001. Cont., Controls.*

stimulated by gingival fragment media was significantly inhibited at all concentrations of indomethacin, except 1 ng/ml. Although J. M. Goodson, F. Dewhirst, and A. Brunetti (J. Dent. Res., abstr. 496, 1973) showed that PGE_2 levels in inflamed gingival tissue are twice those seen in normal gingiva, preformed prostaglandins present initially in the gingival fragment media could not account for the results, since indomethacin blocks only the synthesis of *new* prostaglandins and cannot inhibit bone resorption by prostaglandins already present in the medium or in the bone. Figures 4 and 5 present some unpublished data obtained in collaboration with the laboratories of Armen H. Tashjian, Jr., and Lawrence Levine, corroborating the hypothesis that prostaglandin synthesis is not involved in parathyroid extract-stimulated bone resorption, but is involved in the bone resorption stimulated by gingival fragment media. Figure 5 shows that, at 100 ng/ml, indomethacin significantly inhibits resorption stimulated by gingival fragment media, and this is accompanied by a decreased level of prostaglandin in the media. One interpretation of these results is that the gingival fragment medium provides a prostaglandin *precursor(s)* which is converted to sufficient PGE_2 by the bone prostaglandin synthetase to result in bone resorption. That such a sequence is possible has been shown in our laboratory by a series of reports demonstrating that potential prostaglandin precursors (such as arachidonic acid) or their providers (such as phospholipase A_2) cause marked bone resorption when introduced into the culture medium and that this resorption is inhibited in the presence of indomethacin (L. Rabadjija and P. Goldhaber, J. Dent. Res., abstr. 342, 1974; W. Beyer, L. Rabadjija, and P. Goldhaber, J. Dent. Res., abstr. 222, 1976). These relationships and the connection between parathyroid hormone, prostaglandin, and the adenyl cyclase-cAMP system are shown diagramatically in Fig. 1.

OSTEOCLAST-ACTIVATING FACTOR

Immunological phenomena were linked to the process of bone resorption when it was shown that supernatant fluids from cultures of human leukocytes could be activated by phytohemagglutinin or antigenic materials in dental plaque of patients with periodontal disease to release osteoclast-activating factor (OAF), which causes osteoclasts to resorb bone in culture (38). OAF production requires cellular interaction between macrophages and lymphocytes, but it is believed that lymphocytes actually produce the factor (37). Since indomethacin does not inhibit the stimulation of bone resorption by OAF, it appears that prostaglandin synthesis is not involved in the function of this mediator (50). The production of collagenase by endotoxin-stimulated macrophages, however, is mediated by PGE (67). OAF has been implicated in the bone-resorbing capacity of human and mouse myeloma, as well as in the resorbing activity of supernatants from lymphoid cell tumors (53, 54; M. E. Neiders, J. E. Horton, J. Kim, and R. Asofsky, J. Dent. Res., abstr. 282, 1978). Recently, Horton et al. (39) reported that a cartilage-derived collagenolytic inhibitor, termed "anti-invasion factor," has the ability to completely block OAF-stimulated resorption by a direct, but reversible, action on the osteoclasts that is more potent than that obtained with calcitonin.

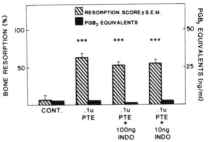

FIG. 4. *Lack of prostaglandin E involvement (as measured in PGB_2 equivalents) in parathyroid extract (PTE)-stimulated bone resorption, with or without indomethacin (INDO). Asterisks indicate differences from negative controls that are statistically significant, as follows: ***, P < 0.001. They apply only to "resorption score" bars. Prostaglandin data were obtained by analysis of pooled media. Cont., Controls.*

ENDOTOXIN

The finding by Hausmann et al. (31) that endotoxins from *Bacteroides melaninogenicus*, *Escherichia coli*, and *Salmonella typhi* stimulate bone resorption in tissue culture suggested that endotoxins released by gingival crevice organisms might be important with regard to the bone resorption observed in chronic destructive periodontal disease. Hausmann and Weinfeld (32) subsequently showed that crude dental plaque extracts from adults with periodontitis and children without periodontitis were each as effective as purified endotoxin in stimulating bone resorption in culture. Reasons given for the lack of clinical evidence of alveolar bone destruction in the children included a possible permeability barrier preventing the soluble resorptive factors from reaching the bone, effective reparative mechanisms, and the possibility that resorption was, indeed, taking place, but was undetectable by current diagnostic techniques. In futher studies (30), it was concluded that the lipid A portion of the lipopolysaccharide molecule is primarily responsible for its bone resorption activity. Since indomethacin in concentra-

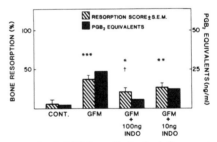

FIG. 5. *Inhibition of gingival fragment media (GFM)-stimulated bone resorption by indomethacin (INDO) and the correlation with prostaglandin E levels (as measured in PGB_2 equivalents) found in the bone culture media. Asterisks indicate differences from negative controls that are statistically significant, as follows: *, P < 0.05; **, P < 0.01; ***, P < 0.001. They apply only to the "resorption score" bars. Prostaglandin data were obtained by analysis of pooled media. Daggers indicate differences from positive controls that are statistically significant, as follows: †, P < 0.05. They apply only to the "resorption score" bars. Prostaglandin data were obtained by analysis of pooled media. Cont., Control.*

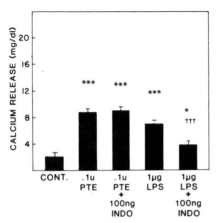

FIG. 6. *Inhibition of lipopolysaccharide (LPS; 1 μg/ml)-stimulated resorption (as measured by calcium release) by 100 ng of indomethacin (INDO) per ml. Asterisks indicate differences from negative controls that are statistically significant, as follows: *, P < 0.05; ***, P < 0.001. Daggers indicate differences from positive controls that are statistically significant, as follows: †††, P < 0.001. Bone cultures were prepared with the use of calvaria from 5-day-old mice mounted on stainless-steel grids in plastic petri dishes (no. 3001, Falcon Plastics) and maintained for 7 days in 2 ml of Dulbecco's modified Eagle medium, which was supplemented with 200 mM glutamine (2 ml/100 ml), bovine serum albumin, fraction V (5 mg/ml), penicillin (100 U/ml), streptomycin (100 μg/ml), and heparin (10 U/ml). Used media were removed and fresh media were added every 2 to 3 days. Used media were analyzed for calcium content with a calcium analyzer (model 940, Corning Glass Co.). Values of total calcium released from the bone into the medium during the 7-day period were subjected to an analysis of variance. LPS from S. typhosa 0901 was purchased from Difco Laboratories, Detroit, Mich. CONT, Control; PTE, parathyroid extract; INDO, indomethacin.*

tions ranging from 0.1 to 10.0 μg/ml did not inhibit lipopolysaccharide-stimulated bone resorption, it was concluded that agents such as lipopolysaccharide probably do not act by stimulating the synthesis of prostaglandin in embryonic bones and must have a different mechanism of action. This conclusion was apparently supported when it was found that lipopolysaccharides and lipid A, in contrast to PGE_1, PGE_2, and parathyroid hormone, failed to increase cAMP when added to the media of bone cell cultures (16). However, Meryon and Perris (51) recently reported that in a neonatal mouse calvaria culture system indomethacin significantly inhibits bone resorption stimulated by an *E. coli*-derived lipopolysaccharide. These latter findings are similar to our own unpublished results, wherein we observed that indomethacin (100 ng/ml) significantly inhibited the resorption stimulated by 1 μg of endotoxin from *S. typhi* per ml but was not consistently effective against endotoxin at a concentration of 10 μg/ml (Fig 6.) It should be noted that Hausmann et al. (30) did not test the effect of indomethacin on concentrations of lipopolysaccharide below 10 μg/ml, thereby possibly missing the inhibitory effect of indomethacin on lipopolysaccharide-stimulated bone resorption. If lipopolysaccharides do, indeed, act via the prostaglandin synthesis pathway, their failure to stimulate cAMP in bone cell cultures suggests that the bone *cell* culture system, unlike the bone *organ* culture system, does not contain all the cells necessary to form prostaglandins. In this regard, the presence of macrophages would be particularly important since Wahl et al. (67) have shown that macrophages produce prostaglandins in response to lipopolysaccharide. As reported by our laboratory in the past (21) and reiterated more recently (25), macrophages are prominent in neonatal mouse calvaria and have been shown by time-lapse microcinematography to participate directly in bone resorption.

BONE RESORPTION INHIBITORS

The difficulty in using bone tissue cultures to study potential bone resorption inhibitors is that a decrease in bone resorption may be brought about by any substance in toxic concentrations. Therefore, to rule out a "general toxic effect," it is important that the compound in question be tested in a bone-*forming* system as well as a bone-*resorbing* system to demonstrate a *differential* inhibitory effect on resorption versus formation. Ultimately, however, the compound must be effective in vivo to have potential therapeutic value to patients. To date, most of the compounds commonly used to treat various osteolytic diseases, such as fluoride, calcitonin, diphosphonates, inorganic phosphate, glucocorticoids, estrogens, and androgens, have been shown in tissue culture to inhibit resorption rather than stimulate new bone formation (1, 18, 22, 52, 60–63).

CALCITONIN

Copp et al. (12) reported that an unrecognized hormone, which they named "calcitonin," able to regulate the level of calcium in body fluids, was released from the isolated thyroparathyroid gland complex of the dog after its perfusion with high calcium. During the next two years, Hirsch and co-workers (35, 36) reported the discovery of a potent hypocalcemia and hypophosphatemic principle in extracts from rat and hog thyroid which they called "thyrocalcitonin" because it was derived from the thyroid and had a physiological action similar to that of calcitonin. It was subsequently determined that calcitonin is not derived from the colloid-containing thyroid cells, but comes from the thyroid's parafollicular "C" cells, which are of ultimobranchial origin (5, 13, 14). The finding that calcitonin inhibits parathyroid-stimulated bone resorption in tissue culture (1, 18) and that, ultrastructurally, calcitonin rapidly transforms the ruffled border area of osteoclasts to resemble inactive "clear zones" (44) provided an explanation for the hormone's hypocalcemic action in vivo. A number of studies

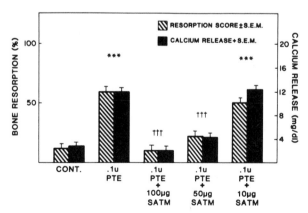

FIG. 7. *Inhibition of parathyroid extract (PTE)-stimulated resorption (as measured microscopically and by calcium release) by sodium aurothiomalate (SATM). Asterisks indicate differences from negative controls that are statistically significant, as follows:* ***, P < 0.001. Daggers indicate differences from positive controls that are statistically significant, as follows: †††, P < 0.001. Both asterisks and daggers apply to both sets of bars. Cont., Control.*

have called attention to the apparent dual action of parathyroid hormone on bone, causing a stimulation of resorption and an inhibition of formation (19, 33, 47, 39, 65, 70). On the basis of morphological findings, Gaillard (20) reported that thyrocalcitonin caused a shift in the balance between resorption and formation in favor of formation when added to parathyroid extract-containing bone cultures. He suggested that these changes were brought about by stimulating the modulation of inactive progenitor cells into osteoblasts. This hypothesis was not substantiated by morphological and biochemical criteria, which showed that thyrocalcitonin did not stimulate new bone formation with or without parathyroid extract in the medium (27).

Despite the drawbacks to calcitonin therapy (it must be injected subcutaneously or intramuscularly), it has become a key drug for long-term treatment of Paget's disease of bone. However, its use in the treatment of other bone diseases thought to be due to excessive bone resorption is still experimental and controversial (3).

INHIBITION OF BONE RESORPTION
BY SODIUM AUROTHIOMALATE

On the basis of the observation that in our bone cultures both indomethacin and aspirin inhibit bone resorption stimulated by gingival fragment media, other compounds used in the treatment of rheumatoid arthritis were tested. Penicillamine and phenylbutazone were ineffective at nontoxic concentrations in our parathyroid extract-stimulated bone resorption system. However, sodium aurothiomalate (SATM) significantly inhibits bone resorption induced by parathyroid extract or by an unknown factor in our bone remodeling system at concentrations that do not prevent good new osteoid formation (25). From Fig. 7, it may be seen that SATM at 100 μg/ml reduced the parathyroid extract-stimulated resorption to untreated control values. At 50 μg/ml, SATM is still a potent inhibitor of resorption. However, at 10 μg/ml SATM is ineffective. Histological examination revealed a striking correlation between the concentration of SATM tested, the number of macrophages filled with ingested gold particles, and the inhibition of resorption. In view of the report by Persellin and Ziff (58) that SATM inhibits the lysosomal acid phosphatase of guinea pig macrophages, representative histological sections were stained for acid phosphatase by the histochemical method of Barka and Anderson (4). Acid phosphatase staining of osteoclasts and the margins of the resorbed or resorbing bone was severely depressed in those cultures treated with the highest concentration of SATM as compared with the untreated, actively resorbing control bones. SATM could have affected the bone cells in several possible ways. Jessop et al. (43), using a "skin-window" technique, reported that the phagocytic activity of macrophages and neutral polymorphonuclear leukocytes is elevated in rheumatoid arthritis and progressively suppressed during treatment with gold salts. They ascribed these findings to a "progressive saturating effect on these cells." Viken and Lamvik (66) exposed human monocytic phagocytes to SATM at various stages of differentiation in vitro and observed a marked depression in differentiation of monocytes to macrophages. If monocytes or macrophages differentiate further by fusion to become osteoclasts (28), it is conceivable that high concentrations of SATM in precursor cells within the bone cultures could block osteoclast formation and function, thereby explaining the inhibition of resorption. Lipsky and Ziff (48) suggested that gold prevents T-lymphocyte activation by interfering with the ability of monocytes to serve as effective accessory cells in the initiation of the lymphoproliferative response. They concluded that the efficacy of gold compounds in reducing the immunologically mediated chronic inflammation of rheumatoid arthritis is due to their interference with mononuclear phagocytes in the induction of both cellular and humoral immune responses. A similar interaction or "teamwork" between macrophages and osteoclasts has been suggested as a requirement for active bone resorption (25). According to this hypothesis, osteoclasts could provide the organic acid (citric?) to demineralize the bone, and activated macrophages could provide the collagenase to help destroy the collagen matrix. Alternatively, either the osteoclast or the macrophage could resorb bone independently.

INHIBITION OF BONE RESORPTION
BY PROMETHAZINE HYDROCHLORIDE

To test the hypothesis that the inhibition of bone resorption by sodium aurothiomalate was due to impaired function of macrophages in our bone culture system, we studied the effect of promethazine hydrochloride, a phenothiazine compound reported to be a potent in vivo and in vitro macrophage inhibitor (15). As can be seen from Fig. 8, promethazine hydrochloride significantly inhibited parathyroid extract-stimulated bone resorption during the 7-day culture period, as measured morphologically and by calcium release into the medium. It should be noted that the untreated control cultures had a low basal resorption, and the addition of 0.1 U of parathyroid extract per ml resulted in a fourfold increase in the amount of calcium released into the medium. The morphological data, estimated microscopically in the living cultures as the percentage of the total calvarium resorbed, closely parallel the calcium release data. The various concentrations of promethazine hydrochloride tested inhibited parathyroid extract-stimulated bone resorption in a dose-response fashion. At a promethazine hydrochloride concentration of 5 μg/ml,

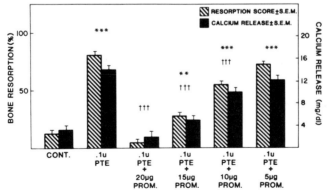

FIG. 8. *Inhibition of parathyroid extract (PTE)-stimulated resorption (as measured microscopically and by calcium release) by promethazine hydrochloride (PROM). Asterisks indicate differences from negative controls that are statistically significant, as follows: ***, P < 0.001. Daggers indicate differences from positive controls that are statistically significant, as follows: †††, P < 0.001. Both asterisks and daggers apply to both sets of bars. Cont., Control.*

there was no significant inhibition of resorption in this system. Similar effects were obtained in the bone remodeling system as well. The results of these experiments clearly indicate that promethazine hydrochloride, like sodium aurothiomalate, can significantly inhibit bone resorption in both our parathyroid extract-containing system and our bone-remodeling system at concentrations that do not prevent new osteoid formation. At present, we have no explanation for the inhibitory effect of promethazine hydrochloride on bone resorption. However, evidence available suggests that this effect, particularly at high concentrations of promethazine hydrochloride, may be related in part to the damaging of macrophages in cultured bones.

Since promethazine hydrochloride is a potent antihistamine, studies have been initiated to determine whether other antihistamines are capable of inhibiting bone resorption in tissue culture. Results of these studies, to be presented in detail elsewhere, indicate that a number of H_1-receptor antagonists are effective bone-resorption inhibitors, whereas H_2-receptor antagonists are without effect.

PHARMACOLOGICAL AGENTS AND
CHRONIC DESTRUCTIVE PERIODONTAL DISEASE

From the above review, it is clear that a number of local bone resorption-stimulating factors have the potential of playing a role in chronic destructive periodontal disease. They include (i) prostaglandins of the E series present in inflamed gingivae, (ii) PGE precursors present in gingivae, (iii) OAF present in inflamed gingivae, and (iv) endotoxins present in gingival crevice bacteria. Of interest is the fact that three of these four local factors involve the synthesis of prostaglandins. It may be recalled that in 1973, when we first demonstrated the inhibition by indomethacin of bone resorption stimulated by gingival fragment media in tissue culture, we suggested that indomethacin or aspirin should be tested further in long-term animal and human studies (24). Some progress has been made along these lines. Nyman et al. (56), using the experimental ligature-induced periodontitis model in three beagle dogs, observed that the administration of high doses of indomethacin during the 28-day test period led to a diminished inflammatory response, delayed onset of osteoclastic resorption, and reduced alveolar bone loss. It remains to be seen whether similar benefits of indomethacin treatment are possible in long-term studies on beagles who develop chronic destructive periodontal disease from natural causes. Of interest, too, is the retrospective epidemiological study of R. S. Feldman, J. E. House, H. H. Chauncey, and P. Goldhaber (J. Dent. Res., abstr. 115, 1980), wherein it was reported that alveolar bone loss was reduced in arthritis patients with a history of long-term ingestion of aspirin or indomethacin, or both, as compared with a group of healthy volunteers matched for age and number of teeth present. Although this study is encouraging, what is truly needed is a long-term *prospective* study, wherein the variables can be better controlled and the progress of the disease can be followed over time.

Our tissue culture findings with sodium aurothiomalate, promethazine hydrochloride, and other H_1-receptor blocking agents are intriguing. They provide new insight into the mechanisms of bone resorption as well as offer new approaches to the treatment of osteolytic diseases, including chronic destructive periodontal disease.

SUMMARY

With increasing knowledge concerning bone resorption, it should be possible to utilize effective pharmacological blocking agents at different points along the pathophysiological pathway to control osteolytic diseases. Among the important bone resorption-stimulating factors thought to be involved in the pathogenesis of chronic destructive periodontal disease are prostaglandins of the E series present in inflamed gingiva, PGE precursors present in gingiva, and endotoxins present in gingival crevice bacteria. Since each of these factors depends on prostaglandin synthesis for its formation or eventual bone resorption-stimulating effect, pharmacological blocking agents, such as indomethacin or aspirin, should be able to inhibit their bone-resorption effect. Other pharmacological agents such as sodium aurothiomalate and promethazine hydrochloride are effective in inhibiting parathyroid extract-stimulated bone resorption as well, which does not involve prostaglandin synthesis. These two more "general" bone resorption-inhibiting agents seem to act on macrophages, presumable interfering with their direct and indirect functions in the bone-resorption process.

ACKNOWLEDGMENTS

We express our deep appreciation to Joan Jennings, Lorraine Stevens, and Olita Treimanis for outstanding technical assistance.

This work was supported in part by Public Health Service grant DE-02849 from the National Institute of Dental Research.

LITERATURE CITED

1. **Aliapoulios, M. A., P. Goldhaber, and P. L. Munson.** 1966. Thyrocalcitonin inhibition of bone resorption induced by parathyroid hormone in tissue culture. Science **151:**330–331.
2. **Aurbach, G. D., R. Marcus, J. N. M. Heersche, R. N. Winickoff, and S. J. Marx.** 1972. Cyclic nucleotides in the action of native and synthetic parathyroid and calcitonin peptides, p. 502–510. *In* R. V. Talmage and P. L. Munson (ed.), Calcium, parathyroid hormone and the calcitonins. Excerpta Medica, Amsterdam.
3. **Austin, L. A., and H. Heath III.** 1981. Calcitonin: physiology and pathophysiology. N. Engl. J. Med. **304:**269–278.
4. **Barka, T., and P. J. Anderson.** 1962. Histochemical methods for acid phosphatase using hexazonium pararosanilin as coupler. J. Histochem. Cytochem. **10:**741–753.
5. **Bussolati, G., and A. G. E. Pearse.** 1967. Immunofluorescent localization of calcitonin in the 'C' cells of pig and dog thyroid. J. Endocrinol. **37:**205–209.
6. **Butcher, R. W., and C. E. Baird.** 1968. Effects of prostaglandins on adenosine 3',5'-monophosphate levels in fat and other tissues. J. Biol. Chem. **243:**1713–1717.
7. **Butcher, R. W., and E. W. Sutherland.** 1967. The effects of the catecholamines, adrenergic blocking agents, prostaglandin E$_1$, and insulin on cyclic AMP levels in the rat epididymal fat pad *in vitro.* Ann. N.Y. Acad. Sci. **139:**849–859.
8. **Chase, L. R., and G. D. Aurbach.** 1967. Parathyroid function and the renal excretion of 3'5'-adenylic acid. Proc. Natl. Acad. Sci. U.S.A. **58:**518–525.
9. **Chase, L. R., and G. D. Aurbach.** 1970. The effect of parathyroid hormone on the concentration of adenosine 3',5'-monophosphate in skeletal tissue *in vitro.* J. Biol. Chem. **245:**1520–1526.
10. **Chase, L. R., S. A. Fedak, and G. D. Aurbach.** 1969. Activation of skeletal adenyl cyclase by parathyroid hormone *in vitro.* Endocrinology **84:**761–768.
11. **Cohn, D. V., and G. L. Wong.** 1979. Isolated bone cells, p. 3–20. *In* D. J. Simmons and A. S. Kunin (ed.), Skeletal research: an experimental approach. Academic Press, Inc., New York.
12. **Copp, D. H., E. C. Cameron, B. A. Cheney, A. G. F. Davidson, and K. G. Henze.** 1962. Evidence for calcitonin—a new hormone from the parathyroid that lowers blood calcium. Endocrinology **70:**638–649.
13. **Copp, D. H., D. W. Cockcroft, and Y. Kueh.** 1967. Calcitonin from ultimo-branchial glands of dogfish and chickens. Science **158:**924–925.
14. **Copp, D. H., D. W. Cockcroft, and Y. Kueh.** 1967. Ultimobranchial origin of calcitonin. Hypocalcemic effect of extracts from chicken glands. Can. J. Physiol. Pharmacol. **45:**1095–1099.
15. **DeChatelet, L. R., P. S. Shirley, P. Wang, L. C. McPhail, and J. P. Gusdon, Jr.** 1976. Effects of promethazine hydrochloride on the metabolism of rabbit alveolar macrophages (39553). Proc. Soc. Exp. Biol. Med. **153:**392–395.

16. **Dziak, R., E. Hausmann, and Y. W. Chang.** 1979. Effects of lipopolysaccharides and prostaglandins on rat bone cell calcium and cyclic AMP. Arch. Oral Biol. **24**:347–353.
17. **Flower, R. J., and G. J. Blackwell.** 1979. Anti-inflammatory steroids induce biosynthesis of a phospholipase A_2 inhibitor which prevents prostaglandin generation. Nature (London) **279**:456–459.
18. **Friedman, J., and L. G. Raisz.** 1965. Thyrocalcitonin: inhibitor of bone resorption in tissue culture. Science **150**:1465–1467.
19. **Gaillard, P. J.** 1961. Parathyroid and bone in tissue culture, p. 20–45. *In* R. O. Greep and R. V. Talmage (ed.), The parathyroids. Charles C Thomas, Publisher, Springfield, Ill.
20. **Gaillard, P. J.** 1967. Bone culture studies with thyrocalcitonin. Proc. K. Ned. Akad. Wet. Ser. C **70**:309–320.
21. **Goldhaber, P.** 1961. Oxygen-dependent bone resorption in tissue culture, p. 243–254. *In* R. O. Greep and R. V. Talmage (ed.), The parathyroids. Charles C Thomas, Publisher, Springfield, Ill.
22. **Goldhaber, P.** 1967. The inhibition of bone resorption in tissue culture by nontoxic concentrations of sodium fluoride. Isr. J. Med. Sci. **3**:617–626.
23. **Goldhaber, P.** 1971. Tissue culture studies of bone as a model system for periodontal research. J. Dent. Res. **50**:278–285.
24. **Goldhaber, P., L. Rabadjija, W. R. Beyer, and A. Kornhauser.** 1973. Bone resorption in tissue culture and its relevance to periodontal disease. J. Am. Dent. Assoc. **87**(Spec. Issue):1027–1033.
25. **Goldhaber, P., L. Rabadjija, and G. Szabo.** 1978. Degradative processes of bone, p. 313–331. *In* R. D. Berlin, H. Herrmann, I. H. Lepow, and J. M. Tanzer (ed.), Molecular basis of biological degradative processes. Academic Press, Inc., New York.
26. **Goldhaber, P., S. I. Roth, and G. Cirulis.** 1964. The effect of parathyroid and other human tumors and tissues on bone resorption in tissue culture. Cancer Res. **24**:254–259.
27. **Goldhaber, P., B. D. Stern, M. J. Glimcher, and J. Chao.** 1968. The effects of parathyroid extract and thyrocalcitonin on bone remodeling in tissue culture, p. 182–195. *In* R. V. Talmage and L. F. Belanger (ed.), Parathyroid hormone and thyrocalcitonin (calcitonin). Excerpta Medica Foundation, New York.
28. **Hancox, N. M.** 1972. The osteoclast, p. 45–67. *In* G. H. Bourne (ed.), The biochemistry and physiology of bone, 2nd ed., vol 1. Structure. Academic Press, Inc., New York.
29. **Harris, M., and P. Goldhaber.** 1973. The production of a bone resorbing factor by dental cysts *in vitro*. Br. J. Oral Surg. **10**:334–338.
30. **Hausmann, E., O. Lüderitz, K. Knox, and N. Weinfeld.** 1975. Structural requirements for bone resorption by endotoxin and lipoteichoic acid. J. Dent. Res. **54**(Spec. Issue B):B94–B99.
31. **Hausmann, E., L. G. Raisz, and W. A. Miller.** 1970. Endotoxin: stimulation of bone resorption in tissue culture. Science **168**:862–864.
32. **Hausmann, E., and N. Weinfeld.** 1973. Human dental plaque: stimulation of bone resorption in tissue culture. Arch. Oral Biol. **18**:1509–1515.
33. **Heller, M., F. C. McLean, and W. Bloom.** 1950. Cellular transformations in mammalian bones induced by parathyroid extract. Am. J. Anat. **87**:315–339.
34. **Herrmann-Erlee, M. P. M.** 1970. A parathyroid hormone-like action of dibutyryl cyclic adenosine-3′,5′ monophosphate on the explanted embryonic mouse radius. Calcif. Tissue Res. **4**(Suppl.):70–72.
35. **Hirsch, P. F., G. F. Gauthier, and P. L. Munson.** 1963. Thyroid hypocalcemic principle and recurrent laryngeal nerve injury as factors affecting the response to parathyroidectomy in rats. Endocrinology **73**:244–252.
36. **Hirsch, P. F., E. F. Voelkel, and P. L. Munson.** 1964. Thyrocalcitonin: hypocalcemic hypophosphatemic principle of the thyroid gland. Science **146**:412–413.
37. **Horton, J. E., J. J. Oppenheim, S. E. Mergenhagen, and L. G. Raisz.** 1974. Macrophage-lymphocyte synergy in the production of osteoclast activating factor. J. Immunol. **113**:1278–1287.
38. **Horton, J. E., L. G. Raisz, H. A. Simmons, J. J. Oppenheim, and S. E. Mergenhagen.** 1972. Bone resorbing activity in supernatant fluid from cultured human peripheral blood leukocytes. Science **177**:793–795.
39. **Horton, J. E., F. H. Wezeman, and K. E. Keuttner.** 1978. Regulation of osteoclast-activating factor (OAF)-stimulated bone resorption *in vitro* with an inhibitor of collagenase, p. 127–150. *In* J. E. Horton, T. M. Tarpley, and W. F. Davis (ed.), Proceedings, Mechanisms of Localized Bone Loss (a special supplement to Calcified Tissue Abstracts). Information Retrieval, Arlington, Va.
40. **Ivey, J. L., D. R. Wright, and A. H. Tashjian, Jr.** 1976. Bone resorption in organ culture: inhibition by the divalent cation ionophores A23187 and X-537A. J. Clin. Invest. **58**:1327–1338.
41. **Jacobsen, N., and P. Goldhaber.** 1972. Bone resorption induced by epithelial and connective tissue from human gingiva *in vitro*. J. Dent. Res. **51**:1682.
42. **Jacobsen, N., and P. Goldhaber.** 1973. Bone resorption *in vitro* induced by products of human gingival cells in culture. J. Periodontal Res. **8**:171–178.
43. **Jessop, J. D., B. Vernon-Roberts, and J. Harris.** 1973. Effects of gold salts and prednisolone on inflammatory cells. I. Phagocytic activity of macrophages and polymorphs in inflammatory exudates studied by a 'skin-window' technique in rheumatoid and control patients. Ann. Rheum. Dis. **32**:294–300.

44. **Kallio, D. M., P. R. Garant, and C. Minkin.** 1972. Evidence for an ultrastructural effect of calcitonin on osteoclasts in tissue culture, p. 383–385. *In* R. V. Talmage and P. L. Munson (ed.), Calcium, parathyroid hormone and the calcitonins. Excerpta Medica, Amsterdam.
45. **Klein, D. C., and L. G. Raisz.** 1970. Prostaglandins: stimulation of bone resorption in tissue culture. Endocrinology 86:1436–1440.
46. **Klein, D. C., and L. G. Raisz.** 1971. Role of adenosine-3', 5'-monophosphate in the hormonal regulation of bone resorption: studies with cultured fetal bone. Endocrinology 89:818–826.
47. **Kroon, D. B.** 1958. Effect of parathyroid extract on osteogenic tissue. Acta Morphol. Neerl. Scand. 2:38–58.
48. **Lipsky, P. E., and M. Ziff.** 1977. Inhibition of antigen- and mitogen-induced human lymphocyte proliferation by gold compounds. J. Clin. Invest. 59:455–466.
49. **Martin, G. R., C. E. Mecca, E. Schiffmann, and P. Goldhaber.** 1965. Alterations in bone metabolism induced by parathyroid extract, p. 261–272. *In* P. J. Gaillard, R. V. Talmage, and A. M. Budy (ed.), The parathyroid glands: ultrastructure, secretion, and function. University of Chicago Press, Chicago.
50. **Mergenhagen, S. E., S. M. Wahl, L. M. Wahl, J. E. Horton, and L. G. Raisz.** 1975. The role of lymphocytes and macrophages in the destruction of bone and collagen. Ann. N.Y. Acad. Sci. 256:132–139.
51. **Meryon, S. D., and A. D. Perris.** 1981. Lipopolysaccharide-induced bone resorption is mediated by prostaglandins. Life Sci. 28:1061–1065.
52. **Minkin, C., L. Rabadjija, and P. Goldhaber.** 1974. Bone remodeling *in vitro:* the effects of two diphosphonates on osteoid synthesis and bone resorption in mouse calvaria. Calcif. Tissue Res. 14:161–168.
53. **Mundy, G. R., R. A. Luben, L. G. Raisz, J. J. Oppenheim, and D. N. Buell.** 1974. Bone-resorbing activity in supernatants from lymphoid cell lines. N. Engl. J. Med. 290:867–871.
54. **Mundy, G. R., L. G. Raisz, R. A. Cooper, G. P. Schechter, and S. E. Salmon.** 1974. Evidence for the secretion of an osteoclast-stimulating factor in myeloma. N. Engl. J. Med. 291:1041–1046.
55. **Murad, F., H. B. Brewer, Jr., and M. Vaughan.** 1970. Effect of thyrocalcitonin on adenosine 3',5'-cyclic phosphate formation by rat kidney and bone. Proc. Natl. Acad. Sci. U.S.A. 65:446–453.
56. **Nyman, S., H. E. Schroeder, and J. Lindhe.** 1979. Suppression of inflammation and bone resorption by indomethacin during experimental periodontitis in dogs. J. Periodontol. 50:450–461.
57. **Peck, W. A.** 1979. Cyclic AMP as a second messenger in the skeletal actions of parathyroid hormone: a decade-old hypothesis. Calcif. Tissue Int. 29:1–4.
58. **Persellin, R. H., and M. Ziff.** 1966. The effect of gold salt on lysosomal enzymes of the periotoneal macrophage. Arthritis Rheum. 9:57–65.
59. **Raisz, L. G., J. S. Brand, D. C. Klein, and W. Y. W. Au.** 1969. Hormonal regulation of bone resorption, p. 696–703. *In* C. Gual (ed.), Progress in endocrinology. Excerpta Medica Foundation, Amsterdam.
60. **Raisz, L. G., and I. Niemann.** 1969. Effect of phosphate, calcium and magnesium on bone resorption and hormonal responses in tissue culture. Endocrinology 85:446–452.
61. **Raisz, L. G., C. L. Trummel, J. A. Wener, and H. A. Simmons.** 1972. Effect of glucocorticoids on bone resorption in tissue culture. Endocrinology 90:961–967.
62. **Russell, R. G. G., R. C. Mühlbauer, S. Bisaz, D. A. Williams, and H. Fleisch.** 1970. The influence of pyrophosphate, condensed phosphates, phosphonates and other phosphate compounds on the dissolution of hydroxyapatite *in vitro* and on bone resorption induced by parathyroid hormone in tissue culture and in thryoparathyroidectomised rats. Calcif. Tissue Res. 6:183–196.
63. **Stern, P. H.** 1969. Inhibition by steroids of parathyroid hormone-induced Ca^{45} release from embryonic rat bone *in vitro.* J. Pharmacol. Exp. Ther. 168:211–217.
64. **Vaes, G.** 1968. Parathyroid hormone-like action of N^6-2'-O-dibutyryl-adenosine-3'5' (cyclic)-monophosphate on bone explants in tissue culture. Nature (London) 219:939–940.
65. **Vaes, G. M., and G. Nichols, Jr.** 1962. Effect of a massive dose of parathyroid extract on bone metabolic pathways. Endocrinology 70:546–55.
66. **Viken, K. E., and J. O. Lamvik.** 1976. Effect of aurothiomalate on human mononuclear blood cells cultured *in vitro.* Acta Pathol. Microbiol. Scand. Sect. C 84:419–424.
67. **Wahl, L. M., C. E. Olsen, A. L. Sandberg, and S. E. Mergenhagen.** 1977. Prostaglandin regulation of macrophage collagenase production. Proc. Natl. Acad. Sci. U.S.A. 74:4955–4958.
68. **Wells, H., and W. Lloyd.** 1967. Effects of theophylline on the serum calcium of rats after parathyroidectomy and administration of parathyroid hormone. Endocrinology 81:139–144.
69. **Wells, H., and W. Lloyd.** 1968. Possible involvement of cyclic AMP in the actions of thyrocalcitonin and parathyroid hormone, p. 332–333. *In* R. V. Talmage and L. F. Belanger (ed.), Parathyroid hormone and thyrocalcitonin (calcitonin). Excerpta Medica Foundation, New York.
70. **Young, R. W.** 1963. Histophysical studies on bone cells and bone resorption, p. 471–496. *In* R. F. Sognnaes (ed.), Mechanisms of hard tissue destruction. Publication no. 75. American Association for the Advancement of Science, Washington, D.C.

Strategies in the Use of Antibacterial Agents in Periodontal Disease

HARALD LÖE AND KENNETH KORNMAN

University of Connecticut School of Dental Medicine, Farmington, Connecticut 06032

The development of effective strategies for the use of antibacterial agents in bacterial disease requires knowledge of the bacteria involved, knowledge of the nature of the host and tissue responses to these bacteria, and knowledge of the host–bacterium response to treatment. Chemotherapeutic treatment, without due regard for these basic parameters, usually turns into a superficial preoccupation with the isolation of supposed pathogens and the dispensing of antibacterial agents. Therapy often focuses on the identification of bacteria with pathogenic potential and the determination of the susceptibility of these organisms to antimicrobial agents of one kind or another. This "magic bullet" approach ignores the fact that these agents do not completely eliminate bacteria but merely give the host an opportunity to remove the microorganisms or to reestablish a balance which is compatible with health.

During our early experimental gingivitis studies, it was noted that the microbial flora of the accumulating supragingival plaque changed from a relatively simple gram-positive coccal flora to a complex composition including gram-positive and gram-negative rods and spirochetes (11). It was also noticed that the development of clinical inflammation coincided with the final state of completion of this complexity (20). However, in a more refined assessment, it was evident that inflammatory changes at the subclinical level started several days before the full development of the complex flora (8), indicating that the initial tissue responses were more a function of the increase in mass of the resident flora than a result of drastic changes in composition of the plaque.

By the use of antibiotic mouth rinses which affected either the gram-positive or the gram-negative bacteria, or both, it was subsequently shown that rinses with vancomycin (active against gram-positive organisms) resulted in a gram-negative plaque and the development of gingivitis and that rinsings with tetracycline (active against most oral bacteria) essentially prevented all growth of bacteria on the teeth and the devlopment of gingivitis. Rinsings with polymyxin B (active against gram-negative bacteria) left the question as to the role of gram-positive organisms unanswered (2, 12).

Studies of plaque during the development of gingivitis have suggested that, among the different species constituting supragingival plaque, the greatest relative increase occurred in *Actinomyces* species (13, 18). Other organisms encountered regularly were *Fusobacterium nucleatum* and various species of *Bacteriodes, Veillonella*, and *Streptococcus*.

In advanced periodontitis in adults, the predominant bacteria of the subgingival plaque are gram-negative rods, including *B. asaccharolyticus* and *B. melaninogenicus* subsp. *intermedius, F. nucleatum*, and various anaerobic motile rods and spirochetes (15).

Monitoring of the cultivable flora during progression of naturally occurring gingivitis to periodontitis in monkeys has shown that increased pocket depth and evidence of active alveolar bone loss coincide with increased numbers of gram-negative anaerobic organisms, with *B. asaccharolyticus* as the dominant cultivable organism. (4, 16).

As must be obvious to any spectator of the work in periodontal microbiology over the past 15 years, this field has witnessed tremendous dynamism and some substantial advances. However, so far, no study has clearly defined a group of bacteria, much less a specific organism, as being responsible for the development of chronic gingivitis, nor is it known whether all plaque of a certain quantity and age is able to elicit inflammatory reactions in the gingiva or if there is a characterizable plaque which does not produce gingivitis at all. Current microbiological data do not allow the designation of any single microorganism or definable groups of microorganisms as the distinct agent or agents in the development of advanced chronic periodontitis in the adult (19). Therefore, the only real guidance that can be derived from research to date is that bacterial plaque is the cause of chronic gingivitis and that elimination or suppression of plaque is consistent with gingival health.

Since the progressive destruction of connective tissue and bone only occurs in areas exhibiting gingivitis (5), it follows that prevention of gingivitis is also prevention of periodontitis, and the clinical goal must continue to be the control of supragingival plaque.

During the past decade, this strategy has been thoroughly tested by using chlorhexidine as well as other antibacterial substances in the form of frequent rinses, gel applications, irrigation devices, and so on. Many of the fundamental effects of the application of antiseptics to the oral cavity have been elucidated, and numerous short- and long-term studies of the clinical effects, toxicology, teratology, and metabolism of chlorhexidine (7, 10) have indicated the feasibility of effectively controlling supragingival bacterial colonization and gingivitis. It is apparent, however, that the effect of antimicrobial therapy is limited to the period of administration, and thus maintenance of plaque control would require administration of the antimicrobial agent on a regular, continuing basis (9). After more than 10 years of study as well as clinical experience with the use of chlorhexidine in various parts of the world, it is apparent that chlorhexidine is one of the safest antiseptics known and that the side effects are inconsequential. Still, we are reluctant to advocate an uncontrolled and indiscriminate use of this or other agents and believe that the selective use of oral antiseptics should be based on firm diagnostic criteria and should be appropriately monitored and that the frequency of application should be prescribed on the basis of disease characteristics. Given these circumstances, we believe that the topical use of a general antiseptic like chlorhexidine is entirely in order.

The issue of a specific chemotherapeutic approach to the treatment of moderate and severe periodontal disease seems conceptually more difficult at this time. The practical part of the problem is that an active agent administered by a rinse of any other local vehicle will not reach the depth of the periodontal pockets (9). There are probably situations where slow-release systems may be used to bring the antimicrobial agent into individual or isolated pockets (1). However, for all practical purposes the only effective approach to the delivery of antimicrobial agents into deep periodontal lesions seems to be by the systemic route.

In a more fundamental sense, however, for a true treatment of periodontal disease, it is essential to determine why a pathogenic flora persists in the subgingival area and what form of therapy would cause a reduction in the pathogenicity of the flora.

It has become evident in the past few years that the bacteria which dominate the subgingival flora in chronic advanced periodontitis are also present in health *and* in gingivitis, but in much lower numbers. The organisms which have been associated with the disease, therefore, can be classified as members of the commensal or normal microflora. These indigenous bacteria of the body are difficult to eradicate and are characteristically at well-defined levels, which are dictated by the local environment. In fact, it appears that the indigenous flora exists in specific sites because the organisms have adapted metabolically to the environment and have evolved mechanisms for evading host clearance of bacteria. These very properties, which allow the existence and persistence of a normal mucosal flora, appear to account for the success of antibiotic treatment of classic infections.

For example (Fig. 1), a sore throat caused by *S. pyogenes* involves infection by exogenous bacteria which become established among the organisms of the normal flora of the oropharynx. If this condition is treated with antibiotics, all susceptible bacteria are reduced in number, including *S. pyogenes* and most of the normal throat flora. The success of treatment depends entirely on which organisms regrow after treatment is stopped. Since the indigenous bacteria are favored in that environment, they will persist during the host clean-up procedure and will rapidly regrow to preinfection levels. The invading organisms will either be cleared by the host or pushed out by the reestablishment of the normal flora. This ability for indigenous organisms to persist is most dramatically evident during attempts at preoperative bowel sterilization. Patients hospitalized for bowel resection are given daily cathartics, nonabsorbable animoglycosides, and intravenous tetracycline. Prior to surgery the only organisms cultivable from the feces are fungi, but within 3 days of the discontinuation of antibiotic therapy the fecal flora returns to its pretreatment composition.

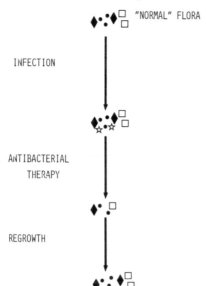

FIG. 1. *Diagrammatic representation of antimicrobial treatment of classical bacterial disease. Invading organisms are represented by stars.*

However, the stability of the indigenous microflora which allows success in the treatment of classic infections produces inherent limitations in the treatment of the so-called opportunistic bacterial diseases (Fig 2). Since periodontitis involves increased proportions of indigenous bacteria, regrowth of the flora after treatment may merely reestablish the disease-associated flora. The opportunistic nature of periodontitis, therefore, precludes the treatment of the disease as if it were a classic infection, and treatment strategies must acknowledge involvement of the indigenous flora. Based on these considerations, there are theoretically two approaches to making the subgingival flora compatible with periodontal health (Fig. 3). The first is to *reduce the total amount of plaque* such that the host is capable of detoxifying the pathogens. Lines A and B represent plaques with different levels of pathogens. If plaque mass is at level Z, where both A and B are beyond the disease threshold, reduction of plaque mass to point Y would bring it below the disease threshold for a low level of pathogens, as in line A, but not for a high level, as in line B. This is essentially the same as the principle currently used in the treatment of gingivitis, i.e., reducing the plaque to a level compatible with the individual patient's gingival health.

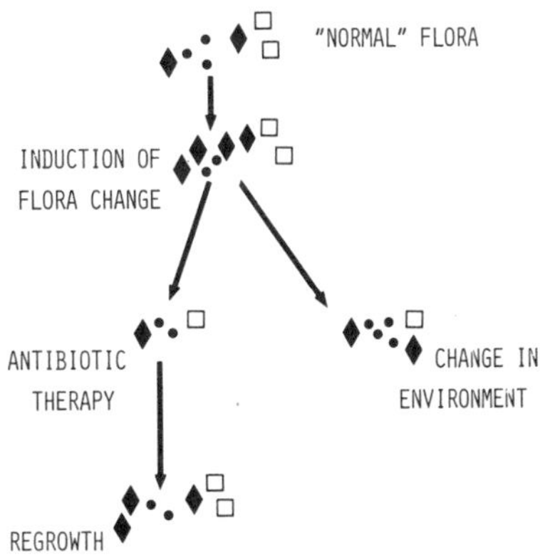

The other approach to making the flora compatible with health would be to *reduce the level of pathogens* in the plaque with or without decreasing the total plaque mass. This would be represented by shifting the flora from line B to line A, which, at a given plaque mass, e.g., point Y, would bring the flora below the disease threshold.

Past attempts at reducing the level of potential pathogens by suppressing specific organisms have not been successful in achieving a stable alteration of the microflora or a long-term resolution of clinical disease. In human periodontitis with pockets beyond 3 mm, Listgarten et al. (6) observed regrowth of the base-line subgingival flora 24 weeks after combined mechanical treatment and subgingival antibiotic therapy. Slots et al. (17), in a similar study in which six subjects with moderate to severe periodontitis received thorough subgingival scaling and root planing and adjunct systemic tetracycline therapy, noticed a return of the original flora beginning at 10 weeks after treatment. In both studies no real differences were found between mechanical therapy alone and with adjunctive antibiotic treatment. On the other hand, recent studies in monkeys have demonstrated that a combination of intensive local anti-

FIG. 2. *Diagrammatic representation of two approaches to treatment of opportunistic bacterial diseases: antibiotic therapy (left); change in environment (right).*

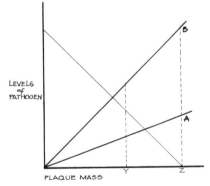

FIG. 3. *Diagrammatic representation of relationships between levels of pathogen and plaque mass. Line A represents low levels of pathogen; line B, high levels. Stippled vertical line at Z denotes a plaque mass which is incompatible with health. Stippled vertical line at Y shows a plaque mass which is compatible with health at low levels of pathogen (line A) but incompatible with health at high levels of pathogen (line B).*

bacterial treatment and systemic antibiotics administered for 40 days was capable of reducing subgingival levels of *B. asaccharolyticus* and *B. melaninogenicus* subsp. *intermedius* below detection for 72 days after all treatment was stopped (3). However, the sample sites in the monkeys had shallow probeable sulcus depths, so these findings may not be extrapolated to eliminating an organism found in a deep periodontal pocket.

Another problem with these studies is that in none of them was the principle of a reduced level of pathogens really tested, since both the local and the systemic agents used suppress the total flora and therefore reduced the total bacterial mass. This is also the most likely reason for the fact that in these studies no differences were seen between patients who received mechanical and antibacterial treatment.

Our conclusion is that so far, with the exception of juvenile periodontitis, the attempts to treat periodontitis by utilizing the concept of suppressing specific pathogens have clearly failed and that future progress in this area will rest both on the extent to which it is possible to demonstrate pathogenic characteristics of the subgingival flora and on the development of antibacterial compounds which are targeted to the elimination of such pathogens.

At present, the long-term resolution of moderate and advanced periodontal disease appears to be most predictable after surgical and nonsurgical change of the local environment and subsequent control of supragingival plaque.

LITERATURE CITED

1. **Goodson, J. M., A. Haffajee, and S. S. Socransky.** 1979. Periodontal therapy by local delivery and tetracycline. J. Clin. Periodontol. **6**:83–92.
2. **Jensen, S. B., H. Löe, and E. Theilade.** 1968. Experimental gingivitis in man. IV. Vanomycin induced changes in bacterial plaque composition as related to development of gingival inflammation. J. Periodontal Res. **3**:284–293.
3. **Kornman, K. S., R. G. Caffesse, and C. E. Nassjleti.** 1980. The effect of intensive antibacterial therapy on the sulcular environment in monkeys. Part I. Changes in the bacteriology of the gingival sulcus. J. Periodontol. **51**:34–38.
4. **Kornman, K. S., S. E. Holt, and P. B. Robertson.** 1981. The microbiology of ligature-induced periodontitis in the cynomolgus monkey. J. Periodontal Res. **16**:363–371.
5. **Lindhe, J., S.-E. Hamp, and H. Löe.** 1975. Plaque induced periodontal disease in beagle dogs. A 4 year clinical, roentgenological and histometric study. J. Periodontal Res. **10**:243–255.
6. **Listgarten, M. A., J. Lindhe, and L. Helden.** 1978. Effects of tetracycline and/or scaling on human periodontal disease. J. Clin. Periodontol. **5**:246–271.
7. **Löe, H.** 1973. Does chlorhexidine have a place in the prophylaxis of dental diseases. J. Periodontal Res. **12**(Suppl.):93–99.
8. **Löe, H., and P. Holm-Pedersen.** 1965. Absence and presence of fluid from normal and inflamed gingiva. Periodontics **3**:171–177.
9. **Löe, H., and C. R. Schiött.** 1970. The effect of suppression of the oral microflora upon the development of dental plaque and gingivitis, p. 247–255. *In* W. D. McHugh (ed.), Dental plaque. E. & S. Livingstone, Edinburgh.
10. **Löe, H., C. R. Schiött, L. Glavind, and T. Karring.** 1976. Two years oral use of chlorhexidine in humans. J. Periodontal Res. **11**:135–144.
11. **Löe, H., E. Theilade, and S. B. Jensen.** 1965. Experimental gingivitis in man. J. Periodontol. **36**:177–187.
12. **Löe, H., E. Theilade, S. B. Jensen, and C. R. Schiött.** 1967. Experimental gingivitis in man. III. The influence of antibiotics on gingival plaque development. J. Periodontal Res. **2**:282–289.
13. **Loesche, W. J., and S. A. Syed.** 1978. Bacteriology of human experimental gingivitis: effect of plaque and gingivitis score. Infect. Immun. **21**:830–839.
14. **Slots, J.** 1977. Microflora in the healthy gingival sulcus of man. Scand. J. Dent. Res. **85**:247–254.
15. **Slots, J.** 1977. The predominant cultivable microflora of advanced periodontitis. Scand. J. Dent. Res. **85**:114–121.

16. **Slots, J., and E. Hausmann.** 1979. Longitudinal study of experimentally induced periodontal disease in *Macaca arctoides*: relationship between microflora and alvoeolar bone loss. Infect. Immun. **23**:260–269.

17. **Slots, J., P. Mashimo, M. J. Levine, and R. J. Genco.** 1979. Periodontal therapy in humans. I. Microbiological and clinical effects of a single course of periodontal scaling and root planing, and of adjunctive tetracycline therapy. J. Periodontol. **50**:495–509.

18. **Slots, J., D. Möenbo, J. Langebalk, and A. Frandsen.** 1978. Microbiota of gingivitis in man. Scand. J. Dent. Res. **86**:174–181.

19. **Socransky, S. S.** 1977. Microbiology and periodontal disease—present status and future considerations. J. Periodontol. **48**:497–504.

20. **Theilade, E., W. H. Wright, S. B. Jensen, and H. Löe.** 1966. Experimental gingivitis in man. II. A longitudinal clinical and bacteriological investigation. J. Periodontal Res. **1**:1–13.

Treatment of Localized Juvenile Peridontitis

JAN LINDHE

Department of Periodontology, Faculty of Odontology,
University of Göteborg, S-400 33 Gothenburg, Sweden

INTRODUCTION

Localized juvenile periodontitits (LJP) is a disorder which involves only the periodontal tissues of the first molars and incisors (3) but which may develop into a generalized form of periodontitis and involve also other parts of the dentition (8). Clinically, LJP is characterized by deep periodontal pockets and angular bony defects adjacent to tooth surfaces showing an absence of gross accumulations of subgingival calculus (3, 11, 30).

Recent observations have revealed that LJP lesions harbor a subgingival plaque which is loosely attached to the tooth surface (12, 31) and which consists predominantly of gram-negative anaerobic and capnophilic rods (12, 15, 16, 25, 27). It has also been demonstrated that individuals suffering from this unusual (24), rapidly progressive form of periodontal disease, i.e., rapid down growth of subgingival plaque (29, 30) and rapid bone loss (3, 8), have not only an enhanced antibody titer against *Actinobacillus actinomycetemcomitans* (J. L. Ebersole, D. E. Frey, M. A. Taubman, D. J. Smith, and R. J. Genco, J. Dent. Res. Spec. Issue A, vol. 55, abstr. 249, 1980) but also an impaired function of their polymorpho-nuclear leukocytes (7, 10, 28).

Data regarding the effect of treatment of LJP are sparse. Waerhaug (30) reported from a retrospective study of 21 patients with LJP, monitored over a period of 8 to 34 years, that a treatment which involved excision of the deepened pocket, root curettage, and plaque control was effective in arresting the progression of the disorder. He stated, "the most important observation made in this material was that so-called periodontosis responds to total plaque control just as well as does ordinary advanced periodontitis." Baer and Socransky (4) presented a long term follow-up history of a patient with periodontosis and suggested that antibiotics such as tetracycline and penicillin can "be a helpful adjunct to patient management [including] full thickness flaps and curettage in affected areas."

The aim of the present study was to analyze the effect on LJP of a treatment program including (i) tetracycline administration, (ii) surgical elimination of inflamed tissues, (iii) root curettage, and (iv) professional tooth cleaning. Patients suffering from adult periodontitis (AP) served as controls.

MATERIALS AND METHODS

The study was comprised of 16 individuals aged 14 to 18 years (juvenile periodontitis [JP] group) and 12 individuals aged 39 to 48 years (adult periodontitis [AP] group) who were referred to the Department of Periodontology, University of Gothenburg, during the period February–November 1978 for treatment of periodontal disease. Full mouth radiographs were obtained from all patients, and the presence of angular bony defects adjacent to first molars and incisors was identified. In the JP group lesions in both upper and lower first molars were examined and treated, whereas in the AP group lesions in the upper molar regions were disregarded in the present trial. Some microbiological and histopathological characteristics of the diseased sites of 8 of the patients of the JP group have been reported previously (11).

An initial examination was carried out including assessments of:

1. *Oral hygiene status.* The teeth were stained with a disclosing solution to determine the presence or absence of a continuous layer of stained material in the cervical portion of each tooth surface adjacent to the angular bony defect in the molar and incisor tooth regions.

2. *Gingival conditions.* The presence or absence of signs of bleeding was assessed after gentle probing—to the bottom of the pocket—in the gingival unit adjacent to the angular bony defect.

3. *Probing depth.* The depth of the periodontal pocket was measured from the gingival margin with a graduated periodontal probe on the surfaces of the molar and incisor lesions.

4. *Attachment level.* The longest distance between the cemento–enamel junction and the bottom of the clinical pocket was assessed in the diseased molar–incisor sites by a technique described by Ramfjord et al. (20).

5. *Marginal alveolar bone level.* Periodic, reproducible radiographs were taken of first molar and incisor tooth regions showing the presence of angular bony defects. The radiographic examination, which was repeated 6, 12, 18, and 24 months after treatment, was carried out by a technique described by Rosling et al. (22). Alterations of the configuration of the marginal alveolar bone crest and alterations of the bone topography were assessed in the following manner. The radiograph was placed in a Diavisor (Esselte, Sweden) giving a magnification ($\times 10$) of the image on a glass screen. The outline of the angular osseous defect as well as the contour of the neighboring teeth was traced on transparent paper. After the tracing of the radiograph from the initial examination, a second radiograph representing 6 (or 12, 18, or 24) months of healing, was placed in the Diavisor in such a way that all fixed landmarks coincided. The outline of the "new" marginal alveolar bone was traced to determine alterations of the following linear distances: (i) CEJ to bone crest, (ii) CEJ to bottom of bony defect, (iii) bone crest to bottom of the bony defect.

Subgingival plaque. After the clinical examination, bacterial samples were obtained from each molar and incisor site showing the presence of an angular bony defect. The technique used to sample subgingival plaque was identical to the method originally described by Listgarten and Helldén (13). The bacterial sample was examined by dark-field microscopy ($\times 1,200$) in a Wild sampling microscope. The following morphological forms were enumerated, and the results are expressed as percentage distribution of the total sample: coccoid cells, straight rods, motile rods, filaments, fusiforms, and spirochetes.

Treatment. After bacterial sampling, all patients were subjected to a treatment program involving administration of tetracycline hydrochloride (250 mg four times per day for 2 weeks) and removal of granulation tissue after flap elevation (the modified Widman flap technique; 21). Surgery was performed 1 to 2 days after the start of the tetracycline regimen. A reverse bevel incision was made along the gingival margin on the buccal and lingual aspects of the diseased site, and full thickness muco–periosteal flaps were raised. The soft tissue of the defect area was excised, placed in a Karnovsky (9) fixative, and subsequently processed for histological examination (see below). A total of 64 biopsies were sampled from diseased sites of the JP group and 42 biopsies were sampled in the AP group. The walls of the bony defects and the root surfaces were carefully curetted. Under direct inspection, the anatomy of the dento–alveolar tissues was determined, and the number of two- and three-wall infrabony defects was recorded. No osseous surgery was performed. The flaps were repositioned with their margins at the presurgical level and sutured with interrupted proximal sutures. Complete coverage of the angular defects was always ensured. No surgical dressing was used, but the patients were instructed to rinse the mouth with 0.2% chlorhexidine digluconate for 2 min twice a day during the first 2 postsurgical weeks.

The patients of the AP group were, during several consecutive appointments, in addition subjected to careful full mouth scaling and root planing. During the first 6 months after surgery, all participants were recalled once every 4 weeks for professional tooth cleaning (1, 2). Subsequently, they were recalled once every 3 months to be checked regarding their oral hygiene and to receive prophylaxis.

At 6, 12, 18, and 24 months after the surgical treatment, the initially diseased molar and incisor sites of all patients were reexamined regarding oral hygiene, gingival conditions, pocket depths, attachment levels, and bone defect alterations.

Reentry operation. Immediately after the 18-month recall appointment, two radiographically "healed" areas were surgically reopened in three patients from the JP group and three from the AP group. Reentry operations were performed to evaluate grossly the alterations of the osseous defects. During surgery, the entire soft tissue portion of the interdental papilla covering the healed alveolar bone was excised, placed in a Karnovsky (9) fixative, and cut in a mesio–distal plane, parallel to the long axis of the tooth. Blocks 1 mm thick containing the pocket epithelium and the underlying connective tissue were prepared. From each of these six patients one biopsy of a nondiseased premolar or canine site, representing clinically healthy gingiva, was also obtained. For details regarding biopsy technique, tissue preparation, and histological and morphometric analysis, the reader is referred to a paper by Liljenberg and Lindhe (11).

RESULTS

The 28 patients included in the study showed all signs of advanced periodontal tissue destruction in the first molar or incisor regions, which in the

TABLE 1. *Frequency distribution of tooth surfaces harboring plaque and gingival units which bled upon probing* [a]

	Plaque (%)		Gingivitis (%)	
	JP group	AP group	JP group	AP group
Initial	67	100	100	100
Follow-up				
6 mo	19	14	9	5
12 mo	23	12	13	10
18 mo	17	10	3	7
24 mo	16	17	9	7

[a] Only measurements made at initially diseased sites have been included.

TABLE 2. *Number and depth of two-wall and three-wall angular bony defects in JP and AP patients and degree of bone fill 24 months after therapy* [a]

Classification of bony defect	No. of defects		24-mo follow-up examination					
			Initial depth of bony defect (mm)[b]		Resorption of bone crest (mm)[b]		% Bone fill	
	JP group	AP group	JP group	AP group	JP group	AP group	JP group	AP group
Molars								
Two-wall	13	3	6.2 ± 0.8	5.8 ± 1.4	0.4 ± 0.2	0.5 ± 0.25	61.3	72.4
Three-wall	25	21	6.9 ± 1.1	5.4 ± 0.6	0.3 ± 0.2	0.4 ± 0.2	75.4	90.7
Incisors								
Two-wall	19	9	5.3 ± 0.6	4.9 ± 1.1	0.6 ± 0.3	0.6 ± 0.7	58.5	63.2
Three-wall	7	9	5.1 ± 0.8	4.8 ± 0.4	0.5 ± 0.15	0.5 ± 0.6	64.7	85.4
Total	64	42	6.1 ± 0.7	5.2 ± 0.4				

[a] The measurements were made from drawings representing the defects before and 24 months after the start of therapy.
[b] Results show the mean ± the standard error of the mean.

radiographs had the character of angular bony defects. In addition, 3 of the patients of the JP group suffered alveolar bone loss in the upper premolar regions. All patients of the AP group showed signs of destructive periodontitis in most parts of the dentition. The 16 individuals of the JP group had, in all, 64 angular bony defects in the first molar and incisor parts of the dentition. The corresponding number of similar molar–incisor defects in the AP group was 42.

Supragingivally located plaque was found after staining on 67% (JP group) and 100% (AP group) of the proximal tooth surfaces adjacent to the lesions (Table 1). All gingival units of the diseased sites bled on gentle probing. The initial average probing depth of the diseased sites in the JP group was 8.1 ± 1.4 mm (standard error), with a range of 5 to 12 mm, and the average loss of attachment was 6.9 ± 1.2 mm (range, 4 to 10 mm). The corresponding figures for the AP group were 6.4 ± 1.7 mm (probing depth) and 5.8 ± 1.9 mm (attachment level).

The initial depth of the infrabony defects, measured in the radiographs as the vertical distance between the bone crest and the level of the bottom of the bony defect, is presented in Table 2 and Fig. 1. The overall average depths of the infrabony defects were 6.1 ± 0.7 mm (JP group) and 5.2 ± 0.4 mm (AP group). The angular defects were generally somewhat deeper adjacent to molars than incisors (Fig. 1). Of the 64 angular defects examined in the JP group, 38 were located adjacent to molars and 26 were in incisor tooth regions; the number of two-wall and three-wall defects was similar, i.e., 32. In the AP group, 24 defects were located on the mesial aspect of lower molars and 18 were in the incisor tooth region; 30 of the defects were three-wall and 12 were two-wall or a combination of two- and three-wall defects.

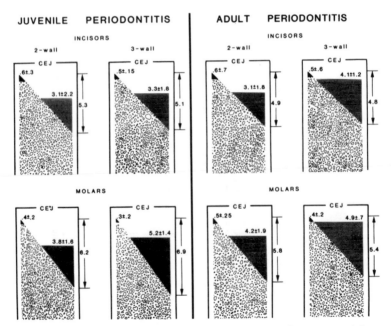

FIG. 1. *Diagrammatic presentation of alterations of various dimensions of the angular bony defects between the initial examination and the reexamination 24 months after active therapy.*

After treatment, there was, in both groups, a general reduction to about 10 to 20% in the frequency of tooth surfaces harboring plaque (Table 1). The frequency of bleeding gingival units declined from 100% prior to therapy to 3 to 13% at the various reexaminations (Table 1).

The average probing depths of the initially diseased sites calculated from measurements made at the initial and the follow-up examinations are presented in Table 3. It is evident that treatment in both groups resulted in a marked reduction of the probing depth of all sites examined. At the different follow-up examinations, the average probing depths varied between 3 and 4.6 mm. Table 4 shows the gain of clinical attachment of the initially diseased sites between the initial and the follow-up examination. In the molar regions of the JP group, the average gain of clinical attachment varied between 5.1 and 4.7 mm. In the corresponding incisor region the gain of clinical attachment was less pronounced and varied between 2.0 and 2.6 mm at the follow-up examinations. There was no obvious difference between the attachment gain of two- and three-wall defects. In the AP group the gain of clinical attachment was, in comparison to the corresponding sites in the JP group, less pronounced and varied in molar sites between 2.9 and 3.4 mm and in incisors between 1.7 and 2.2 mm at the various follow-up examinations.

The average initial depth of the 64 angular defects in the JP group was 6.1 ± 0.7 mm (Table 2). At the termination of the observation period, the marginal bone crest was located 0.3 to 0.6 mm apical to the initial bone level (Table 2, Fig. 1). The crestal resorption tended to be somewhat larger in the incisor tooth region than in the molars. The refill of bone, assessed after 24 months of treatment, was between 3.1 and 5.2 mm (Fig. 1). The treatment program used resulted, in the JP group, in more bone fill in three-wall defects in molars than in the other three categories of defects analyzed (Table 2). On the average, 75.4% of the three-wall defects in molars were refilled with bone. The corresponding fill in the incisor tooth region was 64.7%. In the AP group the degree of crestal resorption as well as bone fill in the various angular defects was similar to that described for lesions of the JP group (Table 2 and Fig. 1). As a rule, the percentage of bone fill tended to be somewhat larger in the AP than in the JP lesions.

Figure 2 presents the results of assessments made in a dark-field microscope regarding the composition of the microflora of the initially diseased sites. The plaque samples obtained at the initial examination from the JP-group lesions were dominated by coccoid cells and straight rods which made up close to 70% of the total microbiota. Filaments and fusiforms accounted for 20% of the microbiota, whereas motile rods and spirochetes were present in relatively low numbers. The corresponding figures for the AP-group sites were 25% (coccoid cells and straight rods), 13% (filaments and fusiforms), and 62% (motile rods and spirochetes). Dark-field examinations carried out on subgingival plaque samples obtained from the same sites of the JP-group patients 6, 12, 18, and 24 months after initial treatment (Fig. 2) showed that only minor alterations of the composition of the microbiota had occurred. The frequency distribution of coccoid cells and straight rods tended to be somewhat increased, whereas the motile organisms had decreased in relative numbers. In the AP-group patients, however, marked alterations of the subgingival microbiota occurred after treatment. The average figures from the samplings at the reexaminations showed that coccoid cells and straight rods consistently made up between 66 and

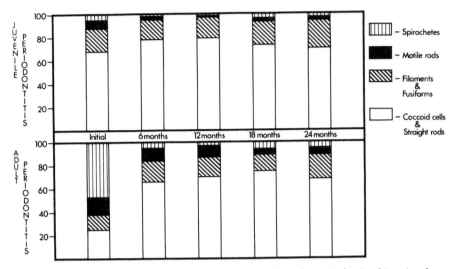

FIG. 2. *Histogram illustrating the composition of the subgingival microbiota in plaque samples from the initially diseased sites and from the same sites 6, 12, 18, and 24 months after active therapy. Dark-field examination of the plaque samples from patients in the JP group did not reveal any marked alterations between the various examination intervals. In the AP group, however, therapy resulted in a pronounced relative decrease in spirochetes and motile rods, whereas coccoid cells and straight, nonmotile rods increased.*

75% of the microbiota, whereas motile rods and spirochetes were absent or present in low numbers.

The biopsies from the initially diseased sites contained large areas of inflammatory cell infiltration (infiltrated connective tissue, ICT). In sections representing JP as well as AP lesion plasma cells dominated the infiltrates (Fig. 3). In the JP group plasma cells and blast cells together made up around 70% of

TABLE 3. *Average probing depth of the diseased sites calculated from measurements made at the initial and follow-up examinations*[a]

Treatment group	Anatomy of defect	Initial	Follow-up examinations			
			6 mo	12 mo	18 mo	24 mo
JP	Molars					
	Two-wall	8.2 ± 0.9	3.1 ± 0.4	3.0 ± 0.3	3.3 ± 0.6	3.1 ± 0.4
	Three-wall	8.6 ± 1.2	3.4 ± 0.5	3.1 ± 0.6	3.4 ± 0.4	3.3 ± 0.5
	Incisors					
	Two-wall	7.9 ± 0.6	4.3 ± 0.6	4.4 ± 0.5	4.6 ± 0.5	4.3 ± 0.3
	Three-wall	7.1 ± 0.8	3.4 ± 0.2	3.3 ± 0.4	3.4 ± 0.4	3.3 ± 0.4
AP	Molars					
	Two-wall	6.2 ± 2.1	3.4 ± 0.9	3.5 ± 1.1	3.3 ± 0.8	3.3 ± 0.9
	Three-wall	6.6 ± 0.8	3.1 ± 0.4	3.1 ± 0.4	3.1 ± 0.5	3.0 ± 0.3
	Incisors					
	Two-wall	5.4 ± 0.6	3.4 ± 0.2	3.6 ± 0.3	3.4 ± 0.2	3.3 ± 0.4
	Three-wall	5.8 ± 1.1	3.1 ± 0.15	3.3 ± 0.2	3.3 ± 0.4	3.1 ± 0.3

[a] Depths (in millimeters) are given as the mean ± the standard error of the mean.

TABLE 4. *Gain of clinical attachment of the diseased sites between the initial and the 6-, 12-, 18-, and 24-month follow-up examinations*[a]

Treatment group	Diseased site	Follow-up examinations			
		6 mo	12 mo	18 mo	24 mo
JP	Molars				
	Two-wall	4.8 ± 0.4	4.7 ± 0.6	4.9 ± 0.3	4.8 ± 0.5
	Three-wall	5.1 ± 0.6	5.0 ± 0.7	5.0 ± 0.6	5.1 ± 0.7
	Incisors				
	Two-wall	2.1 ± 0.3	2.2 ± 0.4	2.0 ± 0.2	2.1 ± 0.15
	Three-wall	2.6 ± 0.4	2.4 ± 0.6	2.4 ± 0.3	2.4 ± 0.6
AP	Molars				
	Two-wall	3.2 ± 1.2	3.0 ± 1.1	2.9 ± 1.1	3.2 ± 1
	Three-wall	3.3 ± 0.4	3.4 ± 0.3	3.3 ± 0.2	3.3 ± 0.2
	Incisors				
	Two-wall	1.8 ± 0.2	2.1 ± 0.3	1.7 ± 0.2	1.8 ± 0.4
	Three-wall	2.1 ± 0.4	2.1 ± 0.2	2.2 ± 0.2	2.1 ± 0.3

[a] Gains (in millimeters) are given as the mean ± the standard error of the mean.

the volume of the lesion. The corresponding figure for the AP group was only 35%. Another marked difference between the ICT composition of JP and AP lesions concerned the volume of noncellular structures (collagen and residual tissue). Thus, whereas in the AP group lesions noncellular structures occupied a volume of around 54% (collagen, 14%; residual tissue, 40%), in the JP lesion only around 20% of structures were noncellular.

All 18 biopsy units taken 18 months after initial treatment, from healed as

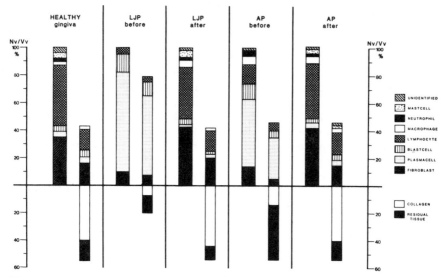

FIG. 3.   *Average numerical (N_v) and volumetirc (V_v) densities of tissue components (%) of ICT in gingival tissue of JP and AP sites as well as normal sites and healed sites in the same patients.*

well as healthy sites, contained small but definite areas of inflammatory cell infiltration. The infiltrates (ICT) were located immediately below the dento-gingival epithelium. Figure 3 shows the numerical (N_v) and volumetric (V_v) densities of various structures within the ICT portion. The small ICT of the healed JP sites was comprised of 44% (V_v) collagen, 10% (V_v) residual tissue, and 46% (V_v) cellular structures. The corresponding figures for healed AP sites were similar, i.e., 40% collagen, 14% residual tissue, and 46% cell structures. Clinically healthy gingival units in JP and AP patients contained 42% collagen, 14% residual tissue, and 44% cellular structures.

The cell population of the ICT in the healed JP sites was dominated by fibroblasts (N_v, 43%; V_v, 19%) and lymphocytes (N_v, 38%; V_v, 14%). Neutrophils and monocytes/macrophages occupied 1.2% (V_v) and 2.3% (V_v), respectively, of the ICT volume, and plasma cells and blast cells accounted for 1.2% (N_v) and 3.9 (N_v) of the cell population. The cell population of the healed AP sites had many features in common with the healed JP sites. Thus, fibroblasts made up 42% (N_v) and lymphocytes made up 40% (N_v) of all cells present. Also, the cell population of the ICT of healthy sites in juvenile and adult periodontitis patients (Fig. 3) was dominated by fibroblasts and lymphocytes (N_v, 36% and 46%), with plasma cells (N_v, 3%), blast cells (N_v, 2%), and mast cells (N_v, 3%) present in low numbers.

The reentry operations consistently revealed a degree of bone fill which was similar to that observed in the radiographs.

During the 2 years of observation, no patient in the AP group showed signs of recurrence of disease, whereas four patients in the JP group displayed recurrent disease in a total of six sites (one site in three patients and three sites in one patient).

DISCUSSION

The present investigation demonstrated that treatment of LJP lesions involving removal of subgingival plaque and inflamed periodontal tissues resulted in resolution of gingival inflammation, gain of clinical attachment, and refill of bone in angular bony defects. The clinical pattern of healing of this JP patient sample was similar to that observed in patients with AP. If anything, attachment gain and bone fill appeared to occur somewhat faster in young patients with localized lesions than in older individuals. Thus, there are reasons to assume that LJP lesions respond to treatment as well as do AP lesions. However, although no patient in the AP group showed signs of recurrent disease during the 2 years of observation, four individuals (a total of six sites) in the JP group had to be retreated because of recurrence of inflammation, increasing probing depth, and alveolar bone loss.

All initially diseased sites in the patients of the JP group showed an absence of gross deposits of subgingival calculus but harbored subgingival plaques in which coccoid cells and straight rods predominated. This finding is in close agreement with observations reported by Listgarten (12) and Westergaard et al. (31). They examined the structure of subgingival plaque in periodontosis sites and noted that the microbiota was dominated by gram-negative coccoid cells, rods, and filaments. Waerhaug (30) examined 27 teeth extracted from individuals aged 12 to 22 years. All teeth had deep periodontal pockets and advanced loss of bone but no detectable subgingival calculus. Waerhaug (30) stated, "The most significant observation made was that loss of attachment had never occurred unless subgingival plaque was found at a distance of 1.5 mm or less from the nearest attachment fibres." Thus, loss of attachment and also alveolar bone in cases of JP seems to be associated with the presence of a subgingival plaque.

Listgarten and Helldén (13) and J. Lindhe, B. Liljenberg, and M. Listgarten (submitted for publication) studied the subgingival microbiota from adult periodontitis lesions by dark-field microscopy and demonstrated significantly elevated percentages of spirochetes and motile rods in diseased sites in comparison with healthy sites in the same individuals. Similar findings were observed in samples obtained at the initial examination from the patients of the AP group. M. A. Listgarten and S. Levin (submitted for publication), during a 12-month period, monitored 20 subjects with adult periodontitis by clinical examination and dark-field analyses of subgingival plaque samples. All patients had been subjected to periodontal therapy, and the levels of spirochetes and motile rods were assessed as possible predictors of recurrence of periodontitis. They reported that the proportions of spirochetes were positively correlated with probing depths and suggested that the proportion of spirochetes could be used as a predictor for disease progression in this previously treated population. In the present study it was observed that spirochetes and motile rods were not always present in the subgingival microbiota from JP sites and, when present, they appeared in comparatively low numbers. Furthermore, in six lesions which relapsed during the observation period in the JP group, there was no increase in proportions of motile microorganisms. Hence, in JP, in contrast to AP, spirochetes cannot be used as a predictor of disease progress.

All diseased sites examined in the present groups of patients displayed signs of bleeding after gentle probing. After treatment, gingival bleeding was a rare finding in both groups (3 to 13%; Table 1). In addition, the degree of probing depth reduction, clinical attachment gain, and bone fill in infrabony lesions observed in the present JP group after therapy was similar to effects obtained in the AP group and also comparable to results of periodontal therapy performed in adults with advanced periodontal disease as reported by, for example, Ramfjord et al. (19), Nyman et al. (17), Rosling et al. (23), P. Axelsson (Thesis, University of Gothenburg, Gothenburg, Sweden, 1978), and Polson and Heijl (18). This suggests that the gingival part of the JP lesion responds to debridement and plaque control measures in a manner similar to AP lesions.

At the 12-month examination it was observed that six sites in four patients of the JP group, of the 64 initially treated sites, showed recurrence of disease. One of the sites was located in the incisor, and five were in the first molar regions. All six sites showed signs of bleeding on probing, the probing depth had increased >3 mm between the 6- and 12-month examinations, and in the radiographs an angular bony defect could be identified anew. Biopsies were harvested from the recurrent LJP lesions and analyzed in light and electron microscopes. The six gingival biopsies contained an ICT area which was occupied by large numbers of plasma cells and blast cells, i.e., had a cellular composition similar to that of the ICT in untreated LJP lesions (11). The sites of recurrent disease were retreated in a manner identical to that described for the initial treatment, and by the time of the 18-month examination they had healed, with bone fill and gain of clinical attachment. In the AP group none of the initially diseased molar–incisor sites showed signs of recurrent disease. The reason for recurrence of destructive lesions in the JP group is presently not understood. All patients were maintained in a meticulous plaque-control program, and only two sites of the six that showed recurrent disease at 12 months had detectable supragingival plaque deposits (after staining) at the 6- and 12-month examinations. Studies aimed at assessing the microbiology of the subgingival plaque and local defense mechanisms (14) of sites that, despite careful supragingival plaque control, develop inflammatory lesions are presently being carried out in my laboratory.

The initial treatment of the LJP and AP lesions resulted in gain of clinical attachment, as assessed by probing, in 60 of 64 sites (JP group) and 36 of 42 sites (AP group) examined. In addition, reentry operations performed in radiographically healed sites revealed that the earlier angular bony defects had been filled with bone. It should be emphasized, however, that measurements such as clinical probing and bone fill determinations, performed in radiographs or in conjunction with reentry operations, do not reveal the quality of the new attachment that was formed during healing. Recent observations by Caton and co-workers (6, 7; J. Caton and S. Nyman, submitted for publication) from experiments in the monkey have shown that surgical treatment of infrabony lesions almost always results in the establishment of a long junctional epithelium facing the exposed root surface. There are reasons to assume that LJP lesions also heal with a new epithelial rather than a new connective tissue attachment. Whether such an attachment is more susceptible to recurrence of disease than a connective tissue attachment remains to be assessed.

In the present study the subgingival microbiota of the LJP lesions was subjected to mechanical and chemical antimicrobial therapy. Identical therapy was used in the control group of AP patients. Thus, tetracycline was administered (via the sytemic route) before and after surgical exposure of the diseased sites, the root surfaces were carefully scaled and planed after the excision of the granulation tissue in the bony defects, and chlorhexidine mouth rinsing was performed daily (for 2 weeks) after surgery. Obviously, the rationale behind this combined treatment program of LJP lesions was based more on empiric than on scientific evidence. However, tetracycline was administered because microorganisms which have been associated with LJP lesions (e.g., *A. actinomycetemcomitans* and *Capnocytophaga)* are sensitive to this drug (26). Root planing was performed because it has been demonstrated that the root surface of LJP lesions harbors a subgingival plaque (12, 29, 30) which might be altered by mechanical debridement. Finally, the soft tissue of the bony defects was excised because it contains an inflammatory cell infiltrate with large numbers of plasma cells and blast cells (11) which might interfere with bone regeneration and healing. The findings reported in this study unequivocally demonstrate that this combined treatment approach was effective. This does not necessarily mean, however, that each single procedure used must be regarded as an obligatory component of therapy of LJP lesions. Studies are presently being performed in my department in which some LJP lesions are not subjected to (i) scaling and root planing or (ii) elimination of granulation tissue from the infrabony defect. In some LJP patients antibiotics are not being used; only mechanical root debridement and soft tissue curettage are being performed.

SUMMARY

The present investigation was performed to study the effect on LJP lesions of a treatment program which included tetracycline administration, surgical elimination of inflamed tissues, scaling and root planing, and careful plaque control during healing. Treatment of LJP lesions was carried out in 16 individuals aged 14 to 18 years (JP group). Lesions in first molars and incisors in an AP group were treated in an identical manner and served as controls. The presence of angular bony defects adjacent to first molars and incisors was first documented in all patients. Thereafter, a clinical examination was carried out, including assessments of oral hygiene status, gingival conditions, probing depths, and attachment levels. In addition, periodic reproducible radiographs were taken from first molars and incisors to study alterations of the bony defects after treatment. Bacterial samples were obtained from each molar and incisor site showing the presence of an angular bony defect. The bacterial sample was examined by dark-field microscopy to assess the relative distribution of different morphological forms. The patients were subjected to a treatment program involving administration of tetracycline (250 mg four times per day for 2 weeks), removal of granulation tissue after flap elevation, and root curettage. After surgery, the patients were instructed to rinse the mouth with 0.2% chlorhexidine for 2 min twice a day during the first 2 postsurgical weeks. Professional tooth cleaning was carried out once every 3 months during a 2-year period. At 6, 12, 18 and 24 months after surgical treatment, the patients were reexamined regarding oral hygiene, gingival conditions, depths, attachment levels, and bone defect alterations. After the 18-month recall appointment, six radiographically healed areas were surgically reopened in three patients from the JP group. A corresponding number of healed areas were reopened in the AP group. Treatment of LJP lesions involving removal of subgingival plaque and inflamed periodontal tissues resulted in resolution of gingival inflammation, gain of clinical attachment, and refill of bone in angular bony defects. The healing of the lesions of this patient sample was comparable to healing observed in patients with AP.

ACKNOWLEDGMENT

This work was supported by Public Health Service grant DE04890 from the National Institute of Dental Research.

LITERATURE CITED

1. **Axelsson, P., and J. Lindhe.** 1974. The effect of a preventive programme on dental plaque, gingivitis and caries in schoolchildren. Results after one and two years. J. Clin. Periodontol. 1:126–138.
2. **Axelsson, P., and J. Lindhe.** 1978. Effect of controlled oral hygiene procedures on caries and periodontal disease in adults. J. Clin. Periodontol. 5:133–151.
3. **Baer, P. N.** 1971. The case for periodontosis as a clinical entity. J. Periodontol. 42:516–520.
4. **Baer, P. N., and S. S. Socransky.** 1979. Periodontosis: case report with long-term follow-up. Periodontal Case Rep. 1:1–6.
5. **Caton, J., S. Nyman, and H. Zander.** 1980. Histometric evaluation of periodontal surgery II. Connective tissue attachment levels after four regenerative procedures. J. Clin. Periodontol. 7:244–231.
6. **Caton, J. G., and H. A. Zander.** 1979. The attachment between the root and gingival tissues after periodic root planing and soft tissue curettage. J. Periodontol. 50:462–466.
7. **Clark, R. A., R. C. Page, and G. Wilde.** 1977. Defective neutrophil chemotaxis in juvenile periodontitis. Infect. Immun. 18:694–700.
8. **Hörmand, J., and A. Frandsen.** 1979. Juvenile periodontitis. Localization of bone loss in relation to age, sex, and teeth. J. Clin. Periodontol. 6:407–416.
9. **Karnovsky, M. J.** 1965. A formaldehyde-glutaraldehyde fixation of high osmolarity for use in electron microscopy. J. Cell Biol. 27:137A–138A.
10. **Lavine, W. S., E. G. Maderazo, J. Stolman, P. A. Ward, R. B. Cogen, I. Greenblatt, and P. B. Robertsson.** 1979. Impaired neutrophil chemotaxis in patients with juvenile and rapidly progressing periodontitis. J. Periodontal Res. 14:10–19.

11. **Liljenberg, B., and J. Lindhe**. 1980. Juvenile periodontitis. Some microbiological, histopathological and clinical characteristics. J. Clin. Periodontol. **7:**48–61.
12. **Listgarten, M. A.** 1976. Structure of the microbial flora associated with periodontal health and disease in man. A light and electron microscopic study. J. Periodontol. **47:**1–18.
13. **Listgarten, M. A., and L. Helldén.** 1978. Relative distribution of bacteria at clinically healthy and periodontally diseased sites in humans. J. Clin. Periodontol. **5:**115–132.
14. **Murray, P., and M. Patters.** 1980. Gingival crevice neutrophil function in periodontal lesions. J. Periodontal Res. **15:**463–469.
15. **Newman, M. G., and S. S. Socransky.** 1977. Predominant cultivable microbiota in periodontosis. J. Periodontal Res. **12:**120–128.
16. **Newman, M. G., S. S. Socransky, E. D. Savitt, D. A. Propas, and A. Crawford.** 1976. Studies of the microbiology of periodontosis. J. Periodontol. **47:**373–379.
17. **Nyman, S., B. Rosling, and J. Lindhe.** 1975. Effect of professional tooth cleaning on healing after periodontal surgery. J. Clin. Periodontol. **2:**80–86.
18. **Polson, A. M., and L. Heijl.** 1978. Osseous repair in infrabony periodontal defects. J. Clin. Periodontol. **5:**13–23.
19. **Ramfjord, S. P., J. W. Knowles, R. R. Nissle, F. G. Burgett, and R. A. Shick.** 1975. Results following three modalities of periodontal therapy. J. Periodontol. **46:**522–526.
20. **Ramfjord, S. P., J. W. Knowles, R. R. Nissle, R. A. Shick, and F. G. Burgett.** 1973. Longitudinal study of periodontal therapy. J. Periodontol. **44:**66–77.
21. **Ramfjord, S. P., and R. R. Nissle.** 1974. The modified Widman flap. J. Periodontol. **45:**601–607.
22. **Rosling, B., L. Hollender, S. Nyman, and G. Olsson.** 1975. A radiographic method for assessing changes in alveolar bone height following periodontal therapy. J. Clin. Periodontol. **2:**211–217.
23. **Rosling, B., S. Nyman, and J. Lindhe.** 1976. The effect of systematic plaque control on bone regeneration in infrabony pockets. J. Clin. Periodontol. **3:**38–53.
24. **Saxén, L.** 1980. Juvenile periodontitis. Review article. J. Clin. Periodontol. **7:**1–19.
25. **Slots, J.** 1976. The predominant cultivable organisms in juvenile periodontitis. Scand. J. Dent. Res. **84:**1–10.
26. **Socransky, S. S.** 1977. Microbiology of periodontal disease—present status and future considerations. J. Periodontol. **48:**497–504.
27. **Tanner, A. C. R., C. Haffer, G. Bratthall, R. A. Visconti, and S. S. Socransky.** 1979. A study of the bacteria associated with advancing periodontitis in man. J. Clin. Periodontol. **6:**278–307.
28. **Van Dyke, T. E., H. U. Horoszewicz, L. J. Cianciola, and R. J. Genco.** 1980. Neutrophil chemotaxis dysfunction in human periodontitis. Infect. Immun. **27:**124–132.
29. **Waerhaug, J.** 1976. Subgingival plaque and loss of attachment in periodontosis as observed in autopsy material. J. Periodontol. **47:**636–642.
30. **Waerhaug, J.** 1977. Plaque control in the treatment of juvenile periodontitis. J. Clin. Periodontol. **4:**29–40.
31. **Westergaard, J., A. Frandsen, and J. Slots.** 1978. Ultrastructure of the subgingival microflora in juvenile periodontitis. Scand. J. Dent. Res. **86:**421–429.

Diagnosis of Creviculoradicular Infections: Disease-Associated Bacterial Patterns in Periodontal Lesions

PAUL H. KEYES, MORRISON ROGOSA, THOMAS E. RAMS,
AND DAVID E. SARFATTI

National Institute of Dental Research,
National Institutes of Health, Bethesda, Maryland 20205

Before 1960, the microbiota associated with dental caries was thought to include almost all of the nonspecific acidogenic bacteria indigenous to the oral cavity. This view changed with the identification of *Streptococcus mutans* as a microorganism with an especially high caries-conducive potential (2). In fact, the odontopathic potential of *S. mutans* is so well established that efforts are now underway to prepare vaccines against this microorganism as a means of controlling carious lesions.

In 1964, a pleomorphic gram-positive rod, now known as *Actinomyces viscosus*, was identified as a microorganism with a high periodontopathic potential in hamsters whose alimentary canals and oral cavities did not contain this bacterium; i.e., periodontal lesions developed only in hamsters infected with *A. viscosus* (6). It was of interest to find that other microorganisms indigenous to the alimentary canals of hamsters and rats did not colonize surfaces of the molar teeth, did not invade gingival crevices, and did not induce destructive periodontitis (7).

The observations mentioned above provided insights for induction of the hypothesis that bacterial factors associated with periodontal diseases might differ qualitatively from those associated with health. Indeed, if the hard surfaces of the teeth are comparable to other hard surfaces in aquatic environments throughout nature, they would provide an ecological niche for life (bacteria) specifically adapted for attachment to and proliferation upon such surfaces. Furthermore, the colonized surfaces would provide other types of aquatic microlife with a favorable environment for survival.

These findings and others have led Loesche (9) to offer the specific-plaque hypothesis with respect to the pathogenesis of periodontal lesions. Other investigators have offered the nonspecific-plaque hypothesis and propose that periodontal lesions are associated with an overgrowth of "normal" indigenous residents in the oral cavity; i.e., the microbiological differences between health and disease are quantitative, not qualitative. Implicit in the nonspecific-plaque hypothesis is the assertion that all dentobacterial plaques have an equal periodontopathic potential.

If the specific-plaque hypothesis is correct, this means that clinicians treating creviculoradicular infections and the periodontal lesions associated with them will need to: (i) determine (diagnose) the prevalence of specific microorganisms on creviculoradicular surfaces of the teeth, (ii) direct therapy towards the elimination of bacteria not associated with periodontal health (correct bacterial defects), (iii) monitor the microbiological changes induced by the therapeutic measures used, and (iv) be prepared to adjust therapeutic regimens to avoid

395

leaving patients at risk of bacteria associated with disease (BAD). By using this system of monitored and modulated therapy, clinicians and investigators will judge success in the management of creviculoradicular infections more on the basis of correction of microbiological defects than by assessments of morphological and anatomical features of cases.

This study was undertaken to determine whether examination of creviculoradicular plaque specimens with a phase-constant microscope would disclose any qualitative differences between disease-associated samples and health-associated specimens, i.e., whether the bacterial populations recovered from root surfaces adjacent to inflamed periodontal tissues would show characteristic differences from those adjacent to healthy tissues.

From our findings we propose: (i) that the hard outer surfaces of the teeth provide an ecological niche for primary bacterial colonizers, i.e., microorganisms specifically adapted for attachment to hard surfaces, (ii) that primary colonizers provide surfaces for localization of secondary stationary forms, (iii) that proliferation of static forms helps to create the spaces and surfaces that allow

TABLE 1. *Bacterial forms and configurations found[a]*
in subgingival plaque samples examined by phase-contrast microscopy:
frequency of appearance in patients

Bacterial forms	No detectable disease 12 patients		Marginal gingivitis 12 patients		Destructive periodontitis 30 patients	
	No.	%	No.	%	No.	%
Filaments and cocci						
Loose networks	12	100	0	0	0	0
Dense masses	0	0	12	100	30	100
Spirochetes						
Isolated clusters	0	0	12	100	0	0
Brushes–masses	0	0	0	0	30	100
Rods—spinning[b]						
2 by 3 to 5 μm	0	0	9	75	28	93
6+ μm long	0	0	2	17	1	3
Spirals, 2 by 20 to 50 μm	0	0	4	33	0	0
Rods—gliders[c]	0	0	0	0	29	97
5 to 9 by 2.5 μm	0	0	0	0	24	80
10 to 10+ by 2.5 μm	0	0	0	0	16	53
Rods—thin flexers						
"Arm clocks"	0	0	8	75	1	3
Looping, 50 to 100 μm	0	0	0	0	1	3
"Cocci"—spinning	4	33	3	25	0	0
Amoebae	0	0	0	0	30	100
Trichomonads	0	0	0	0	1	3
Leukocytes						
0 to 5 per field	12	100	0	0	0	0
5 to 10 per field	0	0	10	83	0	0
10 to 100 per field	0	0	2	17	0	0
Too numerous to count	0	0	0	0	30	100

[a]0 indicates none observed.
[b]Rods with end-over-end rotary motion.
[c]Rods with movements by flexing and not spinning.

the establishment of motile populations, (iv) that the bacterial organizations associated with health differ markedly from those associated with disease, (v) that prudent therapy should aim to eliminate or suppress bacterial populations that are not associated with health, and (vi) that periodontal therapy should be monitored and modulated with respect to specific subgingival bacterial complexes, i.e., BAD.

METHODS

A phase-contrast microscope was used to examine the microbiotas present in plaque samples removed from the crevicular surfaces of 12 persons with no evidence of periodontal inflammation (5 males and 7 females between 10 and 55 years of age). Examinations were also made of samples removed from radicular surfaces of 4 females and 8 males between 50 and 95 years of age who had marginal gingivitis, but no clinical or radiographic evidence of destructive periodontitis, and more than 30 patients who presented with typical signs of destructive periodontitis. Samples were usually taken from the proximal surfaces of maxillary and mandibular molars. If supragingival deposits were present, they were removed before the samples were taken from the root surfaces. Samples were removed with a curette and quickly transferred to either a drop of tap water or physiological saline on clean microscope slides. The specimens were then quickly covered with a cover slip and only lightly compressed to spread them for satisfactory examinations at ×600 and ×1,000 with a phase-contrast microscope. Attempts to disperse, dilute, or stain the samples were not made. Every effort was made to examine the bacterial complexes "intact" after removal from the circumradicular spaces. When needed to prevent evaporation and streaming of the fluid beneath the cover slip, a small amount of petrolatum was smeared along the edges of the cover slip. Ten or more fields of outer surface aggregates were examined, notations were recorded, and video tape recordings were made of representative fields to permit a review of findings, independent evaluations by other observers, and education of patients.

FINDINGS

Figure 1 diagramatically shows specific patterns of organization seen in the circumradicular spaces which are characteristic of healthy and diseased subjects. Because recognition of many of these specific patterns involves identification and observation of a dynamic environment in motion, a motionless representation, such as Fig. 1, inadequately displays our findings. Some of the bacterial patterns, which are difficult to quantify conventionally, are described here for the first time. A gross distribution of various bacterial morphotypes present in samples taken from patients in each of the three groups is given in Table 1.

Bacterial patterns found in periodontal health. In persons with excellent periodontal health, very little bacterial plaque could be obtained from either the buccoproximal surface of maxillary molars or the linguoproximal surfaces of lower molars. In the samples obtained, a typical bacterial pattern could be identified consistently. The pattern consisted of a background of bacterial aggregations that appeared to be a loosely organized network of filamentous microorganisms, or "thread forms." Shapes typical of actinomycetes were predominant. The thread forms appeared to be partly colonized by coccoidal

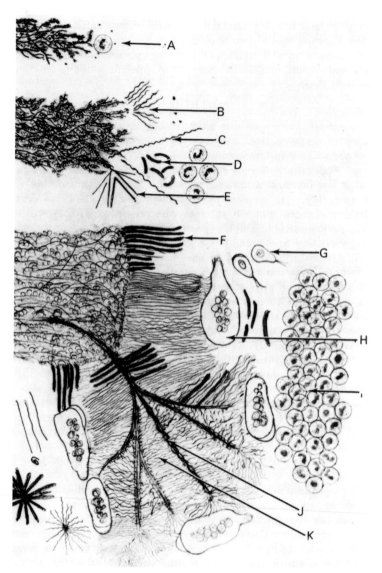

FIG. 1. *Composite drawing depicting the more typical bacterial configurations found in periodontal health, marginal gingivitis, and destructive periodontitis. (Top) Patterns associated with periodontal health show loose networks of thread forms colonized by cocci and other small stationary microorganisms; no larger motile forms are present, and leukocytes (A) are scarce. (Middle) Patterns associated with marginal gingivitis in older persons show static masses of thread and coccoidal forms that are colonized by a few isolated and loosely organized small spirochetes (B); clusters of long spiral rods (C), small spinning rods (D), and arm clocks (Cytophaga) (E) are present. (Bottom) Complex organizations associated with periodontal pockets show gliding rods assembled on the outer surface of a static mass (F), trichomonads (G), amoebae (H), an accumulation of leukocytes (I), a brush pattern formed by turbulent masses of spirochetes that attach themselves to branching chains of rods that are usually colonized by coccoidal forms (J), and organized masses of spirochetes.*

forms and other very small microorganisms. On occasion, a few very small and highly motile coccus-like cells could be seen darting around in erratic circles independent of the filamentous network. In one sample, we observed a few small (1.0 by 0.1 μm) rods that moved rapidly back and forth.

Spirochetes or other larger motile forms were not observed in any of the plaque samples taken from healthy mouths (Table 1), and no surface turbulence, as will be described later, was present. Overall, the bacterial pattern in periodontal health consisted of a static and stationary network of microorganisms where occasionally a few leukocytes could be found adjacent to the network. An appropriate description of these fields totally free of true motility would be tranquil or peaceful.

Bacterial patterns found in marginal gingivitis. In samples taken from older persons (50 years of age) with marginal gingivitis, the bacterial patterns were different from those seen in periodontal health (Fig. 1). Greater aggregations of bacteria and a wider variety of microbial types were seen; both motile and nonmotile forms were observed. The nonmotile microorganisms formed a static mass composed of complex networks of filamentous forms colonized by coccoidal and other small forms. The outer surface of this mass was not compactly organized. In fields adjacent to the static configurations, motile organisms were found in all cases except one, a finding that was significantly different from samples taken from healthy mouths.

Of the motile organisms observed in marginal gingivitis, the most common morphological types were rods. Smaller rods (2 by 3 to 5 μm) were seen that moved by a rapid rotary motion at one end, and in occasional fields these were too numerous to count. These cells showed little tendency to attach to the outer surfaces of the static microorganisms, but rather would spin rapidly in the outer interstices of the aggregated nonmotile forms. Thin flexing rods ("arm clocks") that glided slowly were found in eight patients (Table 1); after affixing one end of themselves to the glass surfaces, they would move rapidly in clockwise or counterclockwise arcs. These forms have been identified as strains of *Cytophaga* (1). Four specimens harbored long spiral rods (2.5 by 20 to 50 μm) that glided with a flexing and twirling motion and showed no tendency to attach to other cells. When one of these microorganisms encountered a cluster of static forms, it would continue to twirl on its long axis and would often bore its way through the bacterial cluster.

In 11 of 12 cases, spirochetes were seen. However, they formed a relatively minor part of the bacterial congregations; more than 50 spirochetes in a field were rarely seen, and many fields showed none. Leukocyte levels were not as high as expected from the appearance of the tissues. In some fields there were 5 to 10 leukocytes and in only a few fields were there 100 or more (Table 1).

Characteristically, the bacterial pattern present in marginal gingivitis was that of static or stationary masses of filaments and coccoidal forms associated with various types of motile forms, including rods and spirochetes. However, motile forms were neither highly organized in their relationships to one another nor in their patterns of activity (motion). This behavioral pattern differed from that observed in destructive periodontitis.

Bacterial patterns in periodontitis. Complex, highly organized aggregations of aquatic microlife were found in samples removed from root surfaces of pockets in patients with typical signs of chronic destructive periodontitis who had not received antibiotic therapy before their examination.

The bacterial patterns exhibited a degree of organization and behavior that is not seen in other states of periodontal health and disease, and, to the best of our knowledge, some of these have not been described heretofore.

In these microbial complexes both motile and nonmotile organisms were present. The stationary microorganisms formed a densely aggregated static mass that had associated with it long, branching, sometimes twisted, ropelike chains of rods colonized by layers of coccoidal forms (Fig. 1). These structures apparently extended into the circumradicular spaces, where they provided attractive surfaces for the motile forms to congregate and organize.

Motile microorganisms constituted the most outstanding and distinctive features of the subgingival complexes. Plaques from pockets showed motile bacteria that were highly organized in their collective behavior. In typical fields great numbers of long (10 to 15 μm) and thick spirochetes formed dense, highly turbulent, brushlike coatings on the static mass by affixing one end to the outer surface of the mass. These organized congregations of rods and spirochetes have been described as "brush patterns" and were seen only in persons with destructive periodontitis. The masses of spirochetes characteristically synchronized their movement and behavior so that their gyrations produced rippling waves of motion. These spirochetal masses beating in unison have been seen directly attached to pieces of calculus or so closely attached that any intermediate cells were not apparent.

In other fields we observed great numbers of thick flexing rods (2.5 by 5 to 15 μm) attached to the outer surfaces of the static mass or to the brush patterns. These flexing rods often appeared so closely assembled that no spirochetes could be detected among them. Clusters of similar-appearing cells attached to a central point were seen without spirochetes. In some fields groups of spirochetes seemed to be aggressively "attacking" small particles that appeared to be disintegrating erythrocytes or leukocytes. Figure 1 shows a diagrammatic example of turbulent populations attached to surfaces of static forms. These populations, composed largely of spirochetes or gliding rods or a combination of these, were able to translocate from one surface to another.

Only in this microbial complex were amoebae consistently observed. Numerous amoebae often were found in clustered positions around the gyrating ends of the spirochetes and flexing rods. These organisms were the only forms seen capable of moving through the waves of spriochetal turbulence. It would appear that this ecological environment is favorable and attractive to amoebae. Once, trichomonads were seen among the other motile forms (Table 1).

Another predominant feature found in destructive periodontitis was the vast accumulation of leukocytes in the too-numerous-to-count range (Table 1). The leukocytes appeared to be located in the outer regions of the congregations, away from the highly turbulent spirochetal configurations that covered the dense masses of static forms. At no time were leukocytes seen to migrate close to the turbulent surfaces. These findings suggest that leukocytes are forced to locate in fluids that circulate between turbulent populations and the epithelial cells of pocket walls, i.e., far from surfaces coated with aggressive bacteria.

Although other types of motile bacteria added to the complexity of the microbial organizational patterns, they were found with less frequency than those described.

DISCUSSION

We have found that bacterial plaque adjacent to inflamed periodontal tissues differs in five ways from aggregations associated with noninflamed (healthy) tissues: (i) in the types of bacteria present, (ii) ipso facto in the number of microorganisms, (iii) in the organization and interrelationship between cells, (iv) in the dynamic behavior of certain populations, and (v) in inflammatory potential, as indicated by populations of leukocytes. We refer to these patterns as BAD, bacteria associated with disease.

The implication of these observations is that one can monitor and modulate therapy designed to control BAD, i.e., (i) make a diagnosis, using either microscopic, cultural, or biochemical methods, (ii) develop therapeutic regimens to eliminate BAD, (iii) assess the level of control of BAD that patients attain, and (iv) modify treatment, as necessary, to eliminate and eradicate microorganisms not found in healthy dentitions.

Clearly, our observations do not support the hypothesis that periodontal lesions are caused by overall proliferation of the "normal indigenous flora." Rather, we postulate that the microbiotas associated with creviculoradicular infections and periodontal lesions differ qualitatively from those associated with health and that some of the clinical features of lesions are a reflection of these qualitative differences.

Many specific microorganisms have been implicated as important contributors to the periodontopathic potential of subgingival microbiotas, e.g., *Bacteroides melaninogenicus* subsp. *asaccharolyticus* (7), *Clostridium histolyticus* (10), *Bacillus cereus* (11), *Eikenella corrodens* (1, 4; J. Bockacz, J. Erbland, and T. R. Dirksen, J. Dent. Res. Spec. Issue A **59**:386, 1980), *Bacteriodes ochraceus* or *Capnocytophaga* (16; J. T. Irving, S. S. Socransky, M. G. Newman, and J. Savitt, J. Dent. Res. Spec. Issue B **55**:257, 1976), and *Actinobacillus actinomycetemcomitans* (J. Slots, H. S. Reynolds, P. M. Lobbins, and R. J. Genco, J. Dent. Res. Spec. Issue **59**:328, 1980; N. S. Taichman and J. M. A. Wilton, J. Dent. Res. Spec. Issue **59**:323, 1980). However, to fully understand the periodontopathic potential of the many individual organisms associated with periodontitis, it will be necessary to know whether they are primary or secondary invaders, whether they initiate, aggravate, or simply reside in the lesions, i.e., how they fit spacially and biochemically into organized bacterial complexes. It will be difficult to satisfy Koch's postulates if symbiotic bacterial relationships are necessary for establishment of populations conducive to destructive periodontitis. This does not mean, however, that clinicians should disregard either recognizable complexes or individual types of bacteria in directing therapy towards suppression of disease-associated microorganisms. Even before having specific knowledge on the etiological potential of members of the complexes, these complexes may be useful as "indicator" organisms of active disease. This is analogous to coliform counts used to detect fecal contamination in water or milk (3).

The findings reported in this paper are consistent with observations made on the specificity of bacterial attachment, colonization, and invasion found in other parts of the body (12, 13). Inflammatory disease of the periodontium appears to be associated with the presence and activity of specific microbial complexes that establish themselves in crevicular areas (9). Indeed, many of the disease-associated microorganisms found in circumradicular crevices are morphologically similar to pathogens associated with lesions in the intestinal and genitourinary tracts: actinomyces, spirochetes, amoebae, and trichomonads. Consequently, there is no reason to believe that the therapeutic rationale for control of crevicular infections in the mouth should differ from that for control of crevicular infections in other parts of the body, e.g., the genitourinary tract. That is, specific therapeutic targets are identified and selected in diagnosis; treatment is then target directed, with clinical success based upon an assessment of how well these targets have been controlled (5, 14, 15).

As soon as it is possible to identify any qualitative difference between the bacterial populations found in health and in disease, there is strong presumptive evidence that a bacterial infection must be treated to control or prevent the disease in question.

We are convinced that one needs to use appropriate diagnostic methods to assess the microbiological status of creviculoradicular areas as well as anatomical and morphological features of the periodontal tissues. This position is in full agreement with that of Listgarten and Levin (8), who studied spirochetal populations in periodontal lesions and concluded that plaque scores, gingival index scores, probing depths, or recession measurements "are not particularly useful in differentiating between . . . subjects . . . and confirmed the inability of most clinical parameters to identify disease susceptible subjects. By contrast to the clinical measurements, the microbial proportions appeared to provide much better discrimination between disease resistant subjects."

Therapy ought to be directed primarily towards the elimination of BAD and other ecological factors important for bacterial colonization. Success in treatment should be based on freedom from BAD as indicated by appropriate microbiological assessments, and not solely on symptomatic relief and improvement in the clinical appearance of the tissues.

Although it will take many years before the periodontopathic potential of BAD will be fully understood, clinicians should nonetheless consider using BAD as a diagnostic tool so as not to leave patients at risk of uncontrolled infections. Our observations also raise the possibility of clinicians using "pattern recognition" techniques in determining the presence of specific disease— associated bacterial complexes, as this offers the potential of a rapid and meaningful chairside assessment of the microbiological status of a patient.

CONCLUSIONS AND QUESTIONS

Before 1960, bacteria were not widely recognized as primary cofactors in the pathogenesis of periodontal lesions. Today, there is almost universal agreement that inflammatory reactions in the periodontal tissues are induced by bacteria and bacterial by-products associated with creviculoradicular infections adjacent to the periodontal tissues. There is substantial evidence that some microorganisms have a greater periodontopathic potential than others (4, 10, 16, 18; Bockacz et al., J. Dent. Res. Spec. Issue A 59:386, 1980; Irving et al., J. Dent. Res. Spec. Issue B 55:257, 1976; Slots et al., J. Dent. Res. Spec. Issue 59:328, 1980; Taichman and Wilton, J. Dent. Res. Spec. Issue 59:323, 1980). We have found that bacterial complexes associated with periodontal lesions differ morphologically, kinetically, and pyogenically from those associated with health. These findings lead us to pose several questions with respect to the rationale used to manage creviculoradicular infections.

What types of microbiological assessments need to be used to diagnose periodontopathic bacteria in the creviculoradicular milieu? How should clinicians and researchers quantify bacterial populations recovered from lesions? Do macroscopic examinations that score or quantify morphological characteristics of the teeth and anatomical features of periodontal tissues adequately reflect the microbiological features of a case? Is there a chance of spreading the infection (BAD) by conventional probings, i.e., passage of the probe through highly infected fields and inserting it deep into the periodontal tissues? Should one monitor success of therapy by the elimination of specific or nonspecific bacterial complexes? How will the clinician and patient recognize attainment of successful bacterial control, i.e., threshold levels for health and disease association? What procedures should be used in the management of a case when satisfactory bacterial control has not been attained? Finally, should one have concern about the use of *any* type of experimental treatment of periodontal disease that is not monitored microbiologically and modulated therapeutically?

LITERATURE CITED

1. **Celesk, R. A., R. M. McCabe, and J. London.** 1979. Colonization of the cementum surface of teeth by oral gram-negative bacteria. Infect. Immun. **26:**15–18.
2. **Fitzgerald, R. J., and P. H. Keyes.** 1960. Demonstration of the etiologic role of streptococci in experimental caries in the hamster. J. Am. Dent. Assoc. **61:**9–19.
3. **Frobisher, M.** 1968. Fundamentals of microbiology, 8th ed., p. 442. The W. B. Saunders Co., Philadelphia.
4. **Glassman, A. B., and J. S. Simpson.** 1975. *Eikenella corrodens*: a clinical problem. J. Am. Dent. Assoc. **91:**1237–1241.
5. **Hoeprich, P. D.** 1972. Infectious disease —a guide to the understanding and management of infectious processes. Harper & Row, Publishers, New York.
6. **Jordan, H. V., and P. H. Keyes.** 1964. Aerobic, gram-positive, filamentous bacteria and etiologic agents of experimental periodontal disease in hamsters. Arch. Oral Biol. **9:**401–414.
7. **Jordan, H. V., P. H. Keyes, and S. Bellack.** 1972. Peridontal lesions in hamsters and gnotobiotic rats infected with actinomyces of human origin. J. Periodontal Res. **7:**21–28.
8. **Listgarten, M. A., and S. Levin.** 1981. Positive correlation between the proportions of subgingival spirochetes and motile bacteria and susceptibility of human subjects to periodontal deterioration. J. Clin. Periodontol. **8:**122–138.
9. **Loesche, W. J.** 1976. Chemotherapy of dental plaque infections. Oral Sci. Rev. **9:**65–107.
10. **Loesche, W. J., R. N. Hockett, and S. A. Syed.** 1972. The predominant cultivable flora of tooth surface plaque removed from institutionalized subjects. Arch. Oral. Biol. **17:**1311–1325.
11. **Loesche, W. J., K. U. Paunio, M. P. Woolfolk, and R. N. Hockett.** 1974. Collagenolytic activity of dental plaque associated with periodontal pathology. Infect. Immun. **9:**329–336.
12. **Mims, C.** 1976. The pathogenesis of infectious disease, p. 18. Academic Press, London.
13. **Reed, W. P., and R. C. Williams.** 1978. Bacterial adherence: first step in pathogenesis of certain infections. J. Chronic Dis. **31:**67–72.
14. **Richards, P., and H. Mather.** 1977. Clinical medicine and therapeutics. Blackwell Scientific Publications, Ltd., London.
15. **Sleisenger, M. H., and J. S. Fordstrom.** 1978. Gastrointestinal disease: pathophysiology, diagnosis, management, 2nd ed. The W. B. Saunders Co., Philadelphia.
16. **Slots, J.** 1976. The predominant cultivable organisms in juvenile periodontitis. Scand. J. Dent. Res. **84:**1–10.
17. **Slots, J., and R. J. Gibbons.** 1978. Attachment of *Bacteroides melaninogenicus* subsp. *asaccharolyticus* to oral surfaces and its possible role in colonization of the mouth and of periodontal pockets. Infect. Immun. **19:**254–264.
18. **Socransky, S. S.** 1977. Microbiology of periodontal disease—present status and future considerations. J. Periodontol. **48:**497–504.

Summary of Conference and Perspectives for the Future

IRWIN D. MANDEL

School of Dental and Oral Surgery,
Columbia University, New York, New York 10027

Obviously, it is impossible to summarize 34 comprehensive papers in a 20-min discussion. I could hardly read the titles or splice bits and pieces together in so short a period. What I will do instead is to take an overview of the conference and try to place it in historical perspective, as least as I see it.

From 400 B.C. until 1955 A.D. (except for a few lapses), the prevailing view was that periodontal disease was caused by calculus, a word not ever mentioned at this symposium. According to Hippocrates (at a symposium in Athens, or perhaps Syracuse, certainly not Buffalo—I know it feels as if we've been here since 400 B.C. but it's really only 3 days), inflammation of the gums was produced by accumulations of pituita (calculus), and hemorrhage occurred when the disease was persistent (4). This was the beginning of the *Era of Calculus.* Prior to this period, B.C. really meant "before calculus." The major contribution of this era was the teachings of Albucasis (936–1013), an Arabian healer, who not only recognized the relationship between tartar and disease of the gums but also developed a system of treatment and designed a special set of instruments.

Sometimes on the surface of the teeth, both inside and outside, as well as under the gums, are deposited rough scales, of ugly appearance, and black green or yellow in colour; thus corruption is communicated to the gums, and the teeth are in the process of time denuded. It is necessary for thee to lay thy patient's head upon thy lap and to scrape the teeth and molars, on which are observed either true incrustations, or something similar to sand, and this until nothing more remains of such substance. If a first scraping is sufficient, so much the better, if not, thou shalt repeat it on the following day, or even on the third or fourth day, until the desired purpose is obtained. Thou must know however, that the teeth need scrapers of various shapes and figures, on account of the very nature of this operation. In fact the scalpel with which the teeth must be scraped on the inside, is unlike that with which thou shalt scrape the outside, and that with which thou shalt scrape the interstices between the teeth shall likewise have another shape. Therefore thou must have all this series of scalpels ready if so it pleases God. (4)

Although these recommendations were enunciated in the year 1000, Albucasis could have been chairman of most departments of periodontics until 1955, and probably later if he had tenure.

From 1955 to 1970, it became apparent that calculus was mineralized plaque, and plaque (rather than calculus) was the prime agent provocateur, giving rise to an array of toxic products that initiated and perpetuated periodontal disease. This was the *Era of Plaque* during which plaque not only dominated the periodontal literature but the tartar–plaque relationship began to infiltrate the popular literature as well. In the 1970 novel *Local Anaesthetic* by Günter Grass (2), much of the story takes place in a dental office, and the reconstruction of a prognathic jaw is the metaphor for the contemporary attempts at social engineering. Early in the reconstruction, the dentist cleans the teeth of the protagonist and muses:

Enemy number one is tartar. While we walk, yawn, tie our tie, digest and pray, our saliva never ceases to produce it. It forms a deposit that ensnares the tongue. Always looking for incrustations, the tongue is drawn to rough surfaces and provides nourishment that reinforces our enemy, tartar. It chokes our tooth necks with its crust. It is consumed with blind hatred for enamel—*your tartar is your calcified hate.* Not only the microflora in your oral cavity, but also your muddled thoughts, your obstinate squinting backward, the way you regress when you mean to progress, in other words, the tendency of your diseased gums to form germ catching pockets, all that, the sum of dental picture and psyche, betrays you; it is stored-up violence, full of murderous designs.

Periodontal research in the early 1970s moved quickly from the stored up violence of the plaque to the nature of the murderous designs: the impact on the tissues, the host response. It corresponded to the flowering of immunology and immunopathology and dominated our thinking. One of the most effective descriptions from this *Era of the Host Response* (1970–1975) was Lewis Thomas's essay on "Germs," from *Lives of a Cell* (3).

The microbes that seem to have it in for us in the worst way—the ones that really appear to wish us ill—turn out on close examination to be rather more like bystanders, strays, in from the cold. They will invade and duplicate if given a chance; but it is our response to their presence that makes the disease. Our arsenal for fighting off bacteria are so powerful, and involve so many different defense mechanisms, that we are in more danger from them than from the invaders. We live in the midst of explosive devices; we are mined.

The gram-negative bacteria are best examples of this. They display LPS endotoxin in their walls and when we sense LPS we are likely to turn on every defense at our disposal; we will bomb, defoliate, blockade, seal off and destroy all the tissue in the area. All of this seems unnecessary, panic driven. It is basically a response to propaganda. We tear ourselves to pieces because of symbols; we are more vulnerable to this than to our predators. We are in effect at the mercy of our own Pentagon.

Periodontal disease began to appear to many people as a metaphor for our own tendency to self destruction, an inexorable progressive annihilation of our supporting structures because we would not take the necessary steps to deal effectively with the microbial hordes that coexist with us.

The microbiologist, however, did not succumb to despair. He began to reexamine plaque, shifted focus from supragingival to subgingival areas, moved from the general to the specific, and by 1975 introduced the *Era of Bacterial Specificity,* so ably described at this symposium. The in-depth examination of the pocket flora has ushered in a new period of excitement and discovery, a new world deep in the gingival sea, populated by strange inhabitants whose cultural characteristics and life styles are being assessed. These studies have many of the characteristics of archeological and anthropological explorations. Assembling the shards and separating the artifacts has led to a steady succession of new finds, and a revisionist history is modifying our view of the older favorites of periodontal microbiology. On the basis of relative pathogenicity, *Actinomyces viscosus* is now thought of as a garden-variety minor offender, and the *Capnocytophaga* organisms are no longer considered to be of special significance. On the other hand, the evidence is mounting that the asaccharolytic *Bacteroides* species, specifically *B. gingivalis,* and *Actinobacillus actinomycetemcomitans* (Y4) are very specifically involved in aggressive disease. *Actinobacillus* appears to be especially significant in localized juvenile periodontitis (LPJ). Developing data suggest that *Eubacterium* species may also be important, and there is a revival of interest in the fusiform organisms and the spirochetes. If one takes a "deja vu," it is possible to hear the strains of the fuso–spirochetal quartet in the background.

Microbiologists do not live by taxonomy alone, and rapid strides are being made in bacterial sociology as well. We now hear fascinating stories of how the subgingival microbial societies colonize, recruit new members by providing free transportation and opportunities for cohabitation, forage for food, and survive in a hostile and competitive environment. Although it was tempting to become immersed in the intrigues of bacterial succession, there was immediate interest in environmental impact, in disease initiation and progression, and so the *Era of Bacterial Specificity* quickly became the *Era of Host-Bacterium Interactions*.

Despite the technical difficulties associated with harvesting, culturing, and identifying the very complex and fastidious subgingival flora, significant information has been generated, and very effective methods have been developed for making sense out of what could have been an overwhelming bacterial mass of data. The "modified Koch's postulates" provide a very reasonable framework for assigning specific pathogenicity to an organism. Several laboratories are showing statistical associations between a limited number of bacteria and disease in cross-sectional and short-term longitudinal studies. Animal models, especially ligature-accelerated monkey periodontal disease, and laboratory models for pathogenic potential and immunological response offer reasonable test systems. The examination of the response to antibacterial therapy provides a valuable clinical endpoint. We are still limited, however, by the very few "specific" therapeutic agents available.

Even in the face of the freneticism and disagreements that characterized periodontal microbiology during the past 5 years, there is increasing support for the concept of specificity—microorganisms that are disease specific, stage specific, and site specific. It does appear at times, however, that site specific means one set of pathogenic organisms at Forsyth, another at Buffalo, and at least a third set in Virginia. This is to be expected since the harvesting techniques are different, and despite the recent technical advances, at least 30% of the subgingival flora cannot be adequately cultured. It will still take a while to sort things out, but I think the direction is clear, at least for the aggressive, severe forms of periodontal disease. The area of greatest public health need, however, is in the earlier periods of the more common forms of periodontal disease, most importantly perhaps, in the transition from gingivitis to periodontitis. The importance of exploring this area has been repeatedly pointed out, especially so at the International Conference on Research in the Biology of Periodontal Disease in 1977. The specific flora of the deep pocket may be of major significance only at a late stage of periodontal disease. In caries research, for instance, the flora of deep dentinal caries is quite different from that of early caries. In a study by Edwardsson in 1974 (1), lactobacilli were found to be the organisms in greatest abundance, followed by gram-positive pleomorphic rods and filaments. The incidence of gram-positive cocci was low, in marked contrast to their presence in coronal plaque and in caries initiation. Initiation, early progression, and advanced progression may involve different organisms.

The next research period may well become the *Era of Transition*. A transition team should be established to explore fully the critical changes from an established gingivitis to a periodontitis. As frequently pointed out, this change could be due to alterations in ecological balance that cause a shift in local microflora or a change in host resistance (susceptibility), or a combination thereof. A variety of host mechanisms were explored at this symposium, mechanisms that have been or could be implicated in periodontal disease. This review of the host side of the interaction not only included the full complement of humoral and cellular immunological factors (except perhaps for platelets) but the non-immunological as well, a radical departure in periodontics. In the non-immunological area there was particular interest in the susceptibility of *A. actinomycetemcomitans* to lysozyme and the loss of this sensitivity after passage of the organism through media containing tetracycline. The role of salivary lysozyme, lactoperoxidase, and lactoferrin in the potentially cariogenic flora is an active area of research. It would seem appropriate to extend these studies to the periodontopathic flora as well. In multifactorial disease all aspects have to be explored until a reasonable determination can be made of which factors (host as well as bacterial) are most critical.

The exquisite complexity of the interaction of both endotoxin and leucotoxin with host cells was fully explored by a number of speakers. In the exploration process it became increasingly apparent from the evidence presented that, although the polymorphonuclear leukocytes (PMNs) and their interactions in the gingival crevice may be the focus of much of the current research, consideration has to be given as well to the lymphocytes and macrophages and the specifics of their role in repair as well as destruction of connective tissues. Indeed, indirect evidence of lymphocyte and macrophage contribution to repair and healing was given in a study of the results of treatment of LJP (J. Lindhe, this volume). From the active discussion that characterized the interaction between the immunologists and the microbiologists, it became evident that there is great need for bridging the gap between tissue and organ culture systems and clinical disease and the importance of appropriate animal model systems. Mice and rats with clearly defined genetic defects are especially valuable.

The PMN defect in LJP has become a veritable symbol for the role of host cell populations as a determinant of susceptibility to periodontal disease. Evidence was presented that the chemotactic defect involves specific cell wall receptors and may be genetically determined. There is increasing evidence for a defect in phagocytic capability and increased release of granules accompanying frustrated phagocytosis. It may be that the problem may not really be impotence but rather premature ejaculation. There seems to be considerable controversy (the usual clash when symbols are involved) as to just how the PMN defect manifests itself clinically. Despite what appear to be some inconsistencies at this time, the PMN in LJP is an important model for examining the role of host factors and for studying the association between in vitro systems and clinical disease.

The interaction of the PMN and the leukotoxin produced by the vesicles (blebs) of *A. actinomycetemcomitans* (Y4) is generating great interest. Recent demonstration of the sensitivity of monkey PMNs to the toxin should provide an interesting model system. Some of the questions on the specific role of leucotoxin antibody (as well as leucotoxin itself) will become amenable to study.

In a rare display of agreement, several laboratories reported high levels of specific antibody to *B. gingivalis* and *A. actinomycetemcomitans* (Y4) in LJP, generalized juvenile periodontis, and adult periodontitis. A relatively limited number of patients have been studied to date, and hence there is still a question of whether the "*n*" justifies the means. The need to standardize clinical criteria for adult periodontics is becoming obvious. Both "adult" and "periodontitis" mean different things to different people. The coexistence of increased antibody and increased disease and the time course of their developments require full elucidation, as does the relative importance of polyclonal versus specific antigen activation. There was a strong sense of the need to find ways to manipulate the host immune system to reduce its destructive capability. The plea was made that, rather than restricting efforts (conceptually at least) to a vaccine approach for the eventual control of periodontal disease, a long-term goal may well be induction of tolerance, a very reasonable appeal for tolerance.

With the growing appreciation of the importance of helper and suppressor cells and the complex interactions that occur, one may envision a new *Era of Regulation*. It is difficult to predict just how these immunoregulatory agencies may operate, but it would seem inevitable that they are important in periodontal disease (transition and progression)—as inevitable as cell death and chemotaxis.

I think it is very fitting that the concluding session of this symposium on host–bacterium interactions dealt with the overt trident response of the host to periodontal microflora—oral hygiene, surgery, and antibacterial agents. No matter how sophisticated the research, the major determinant of clinical success in the immediate and probably intermediate future will remain personal plaque control, supported by professional maintenance with augmentation by surgical therapy and antibacterial agents in advanced aggressive disease.

Does the fact that effective plaque control is still our basic strategy in the prevention and treatment of periodontal disease mean that we have made little progress in 2,000 years? The evidence from the presentations over the past 3 days strongly refutes this. We have an exquisitely detailed view of what is happening in the progression of this disease—the attacking forces, the potentially protective forces, the interaction, and the consequences. We can use our expanded surgical and antibacterial armamentarium to treat advanced disease very effectively. We know we can prevent initiation and can reverse gingivitis, and we can virtually stop the progression of most forms of chronic periodontitis by a variety of mechanical and surgical means. What we appear to be searching for is an easier way out, the secret that would enable us to swallow a magic bullet or rub on a magic lotion so that we would not have to be bound to a regimen of brushing, flossing, and squirting—surely a situation devoutly desired. It is not too different from Ponce de León's quest for the fountain of youth. His dream was to immerse himself in the magic waters and banish all wrinkles. As Art Ellison once pointed out to me, if Ponce de León actually found the fountain of youth and jumped in, the chances are he would have emerged with acne.

I'm not sure if the moral of the story is that there is no free lunch or that there is always an element of risk, even in panaceas. Regardless of which cliché we prefer, caution is always good exercise, but it should not inhibit vigorous pursuit of full knowledge. It is only when we have a true appreciation of the host-bacterium interactions in periodontal diseases that we will be able to devise more effective, widely acceptable strategies for the prevention and treatment of these diseases.

LITERATURE CITED

1. **Edwardsson, S.** 1974. Bacteriological studies on deep areas of carries dentin. Odontol. Revy **25**(Suppl. 32):100–103.
2. **Grass, G.** 1970. Local anesthetic. Harcourt Brace Jovanovich Inc., New York.
3. **Thomas, L.** 1974. The lives of a cell. The Viking Press, New York.
4. **Weinberger, B. W.** 1948. History of dentistry. C. V. Mosby Co., St. Louis.

Author Index

Baehni, P.C., 261
Baehni, Pierre, 179
Berthold, P., 261
Boldt, Paul R., 318
Brandtzaeg, Per, 270
Burton, James, 193

Celesk, Roger, 76
Cisar, John O., 121

Dziak, Rosemary, 151

Ebersole, J. L., 283
Ellen, Richard P., 98
Evian, C., 261

Genco, R. J., 235
Gilbert, Joanne V., 193
Goldhaber, Paul, 363
Goodson, J. Max, 1
Grossbard, Barbara L., 318

Haffajee, Anne D., 1
Hammond, B. F., 46
Hausmann, Ernest, 151
Hillman, Jeffrey D., 1
Hoffeld, J. Terrell, 343
Holdeman, L. V., 13
Holt, Stanley C., 139

Iacono, Vincent J., 318

Jordan, Harold V., 169

Keyes, Paul H., 395
Kolenbrander, Paul, 76
Kornman, Kenneth, 376
Kornman, Kenneth S., 132

Ladenheim, Steven, 318
Laughon, Barbara E., 62
Lehner, Thomas, 202
Levine, M. J., 235
Lindhe, Jan, 382
Listgarten, Max A., 112
Löe, Harald, 376
Loesche, Walter J., 62
London, Jack, 76

MacKay, Bruce J., 318
Mandel, Irwin D., 404
McArthur, W. P., 261
McArthur, William P., 179
McCarty, Gale A., 354
Mergenhagen, Stephan E., 160
Moore, W. E. C., 13

Nair, Bala Chandran, 151

Page, Roy C., 217
Plaut, Andrew G., 193
Pollock, Jerry J., 318

Rabadjija, Luka, 363
Rams, Thomas E., 395
Ranney, R. R., 13
Rochon, Mary L., 318
Rogosa, Morrison, 395

Sandberg, Ann L., 309
Sarfatti, David E., 395
Schenkein, Harvey A., 299
Shenker, B. J., 179, 261
Slots, Jørgen, 27
Smith, D. J., 283
Snyderman, Ralph, 354
Socransky, Sigmund S., 1
Stevens, R., 261
Stevens, R. H., 46

Taichman, N. S., 261
Taichman, Norton S., 179
Tanner, Anne C. R., 1
Taubman, M. A., 283
Tolo, Kåre, 270
Tsai, C.-C., 261
Tsai, Chi-Cheng, 179

Van Dyke, T. E., 235
van Houte, Johannes, 86
Vogel, Stefanie N., 160

Wahl, Sharon M., 225
Wilton, J. M. A., 246

Subject Index

Actinobacillus actinomycetemcomitans
juvenile periodontitis, 46
leukocidal mechanisms, 261
noncytolytic effects on leukocyte functions, 179
Actinomyces
oral colonization, 98
pathogenicity, 169
Adherence, cell
mediated by microbial lectins, 121
Age
effect on periodontal microflora, 132
Antibacterial agents
use in periodontal disease, 376
Antibody
sytemic and local, and peridontal disease, 283
titers to oral bacteria, 270

Bacterial patterns
disease-associated periodontal lesions, 395
Bacterial surface structures
role in periodontal disease, 139
Bacteroides, black-pigmented
importance in periodontal disease, 27
Bone loss
bacterial components resulting in, 151
Bone resorption
humoral and cellular mediation, 309
influence of pharmacological agents, 363

C3H/HeJ mice
endotoxin susceptibility, 160
Capnocytophaga
juvenile periodontitis, 46
Cellular
adherence mediated by microbial lectins, 121
aspects of host responses, 202
basis of endotoxin susceptibility, 160
immunity in periodontal disease, 202
mediation of bone resorption, 309
Chemotactic factor receptors, 235
Coaggregation reactions between oral bacteria, 121

Colonization
gram-positive bacteria significant to disease, 98
mechanisms in development of the oral microbiota, 86
patterns, clinical implications, 112
periodontopathic organisms, 86
Complement system in disease, 299
Connective tissue
mononuclear cell-mediated alterations, 225
Creviculoradicular infection
diagnosis, 395
Culture methods
periodontal flora, 13
Cytophaga sp.
new oral gliding gram-negative bacteria, 76

Effector systems
specific and nonspecific, 270
Endotoxin susceptibility
cellular basis, 160
Etiology of periodontal disease
studies, background and present status, 1

Gingival crevice
polymorphonuclear leukocytes in, 246
Gliding bacteria
hydroxyapatite-attaching, 76
Gram-negative bacteria
Cytophaga sp., 76
hydroxyapatite-attaching, 76
Gram-positive bacteria
oral colonization, 98

Host
interactions with bacteria, clinical implications, 354
response
cellular aspects, 202
lysozyme in, 318
Humoral mediation of bone resorption, 309
Hydroxyapatite
oral gram-negative bacteria attaching to, 76

412

Immunity
 mechanisms in periodontal disease, 202
 oxygen radicals in, 343
Immunoglobulin A proteases
 modification with synthetic peptide
  analogs, 193
Inflammation
 connective tissue alterations caused by,
  225
 oxygen radicals in, 343

Juvenile periodontitis
 Capnocytophaga and *A. actinomycetemcomitans*, 46
 treatment, 382

Lectins
 cell-to-cell adherence mediated by, 121
Leukocidal mechanisms of *Actinobacillus
  actinomycetemcomitans*, 261
Leukocyte functions
 noncytolytic effects of *A. actinomycetemcomitans*, 179
Lipopolysaccharide
 cellular basis of susceptibility to, 160
Localized juvenile periodontitis
 treatment, 382
Lymphoid cell responsiveness and periodontitis, 217
Lysozyme
 role in host response to periodontal
  pathogens, 318

Mononuclear cell-mediated alterations in
  connective tissue, 225
Motile rods
 colonization of subgingival areas, 112
Mucosal disease
 immunoglobulin A proteases, 193

Neutrophil abnormalities
 relationship to periodontal diseases, 235

Oral bacteria
 coaggregation reactions between, 121
 gram-positive, colonization, 98
 mechanisms in development of population, 86
Osteolytic diseases
 pharmacological agents, 363
Oxygen radicals
 inflammation and immunity, 343

Pathogenic and virulence factors in
  periodontal disease, 139
Peptide analogs
 modification of immunoglobulin A protease, 193
Periodontal disease
 analogy to rheumatoid arthritis, 354
 antibacterial agents, 376
 association of systemic and local antibody with, 283
 bacterial surface structures, 139
 black-pigmented *Bacteroides,* 27
 cellular immunity in, 202
 colonization by significant gram-negative bacteria, 98
 complement system, 299
 microbial ecology, studies, 1
 neutrophil abnormalities, 235
 pathogenic and virulence factors, 139
 prospects for future research, 404
 serum antibody titers to oral bacteria,
  270
 spirochetes, 62
Periodontal flora
 methods for sample and culture, 13
 species identification and significance,
  13
Periodontal lesions
 disease-associated bacterial patterns,
  395
 therapeutic rationale for prevention
  and control, 395
Periodontal microflora
 effect of host-derived factors, 132
Periodontal pathogens
 lysozyme in host response, 318
Periodontitis
 localized juvenile, treatment, 382
 lymphoid cell responsiveness, 217
Periodontopathic organisms
 colonization, 86
Pharmacological agents
 influence on bone resorption, 363
Polymorphonuclear leukocytes
 functions in human gingival crevice,
  246

Rheumatoid arthritis
 analogy to periodontal disease, 354

Sample methods
 periodontal flora, 13

Serum antibody titers to oral bacteria
relation to disease activity, 270
Species identification and significance of
periodontal flora, 13
Spirochetes
colonization of subgingival areas, 112
role in periodontal disease, 62
Steroid hormones
effect on periodontal microflora, 132
Subgingival areas
clinical implications of colonization
patterns, 112
Subgingival microflora
effect of host-derived factors, 132

Subgingival plaque
effect of host-derived factors, 132
Surface structure of bacteria
role in periodontal disease, 139

Therapeutics
prevention and control of periodontal
disease, 395
Tissue destruction
rheumatoid arthritis and periodontal
disease, 354

Virulence factors in periodontal disease,
139